ABSTRACT ALGEBRA

Academic Press
Textbooks in Mathematics

GEORGE BACHMAN and LAWRENCE NARICI. Functional Analysis
P. R. MASANI, R. C. PATEL, and D. J. PATIL. Elementary Calculus
WILLIAM PERVIN. Foundations of General Topology
ALBERT L. RABENSTEIN. Introduction to Ordinary Differential Equations
JAMES SINGER. Elements of Numerical Analysis
EDUARD L. STIEFEL. An Introduction to Numerical Mathematics
HOWARD G. TUCKER. An Introduction to Probability and Mathematical Statistics
CHIH-HAN SAH. Abstract Algebra

In preparation

LEOPOLDO V. TORALBALLA. Calculus with Analytic Geometry and Linear Algebra
DONALD W. BLACKETT. Elementary Topology: A Combinatorial and Algebraic Approach

CHIH-HAN SAH

University of Pennsylvania

ABSTRACT ALGEBRA

ACADEMIC PRESS

New York and London

ACADEMIC PRESS INC.
111 Fifth Avenue, New York, New York 10003

United Kingdom Edition published by
ACADEMIC PRESS INC. (LONDON) LTD.
Berkeley Square House, London W.1

Library of Congress Catalog Card Number: 66-29641

Second Printing, 1968

PRINTED IN THE UNITED STATES OF AMERICA

to

William L. Everitt

and

Dorothy W. Everitt

PREFACE

This book is intended for a one-year algebra course on the level of advanced undergraduate or beginning graduate work in mathematics.

Our viewpoint is to consider basic techniques and results in algebra from a position that can be easily generalized. In particular, concepts are introduced in a general setting; special cases that do not involve too many technical complications are considered in some detail. Exercises and excursions are inserted to give some indication of the possible generalizations that have been neglected in the main body of the text.

The exercises form an integral part of the book. Aside from those that have been mentioned in the preceding paragraph, they are designed to test the reader's understanding of the material presented, to show the strength as well as the limitations of some of the results, and to give the reader a chance to practice his skill in writing out complete proofs. Most of the harder exercises have hints supplied, and in a few cases the exercises have been worked out in detail. The reader is encouraged to ignore these hints and solutions. On first reading the various excursions may be bypassed. However, near the end of the book a few of the earlier excursions are used in the proofs.

Results are referred to as ...I.2.3; ... stands for Theorem, Lemma, Corollary, Exercise, and so on, I stands for chapter number, 2 stands for section number, and 3 stands for the number of the particular result. The chapter number is omitted when the reference is made in the same chapter; the section number is also omitted when the reference is made in the same section. Thus Theorem I.2.3 is labeled Theorem 2.3 in Chapter I and Theorem 3 in Chapter I, Section 2.

We now describe the organization of and the prerequisites for the text.

The reader should have some familiarity with set theory. Aside from this, he is assumed to have had only the standard beginning college-level mathematics courses.

The relevant concepts and results from set theory have been summarized in Chapter 0. A reader who has not studied set theory before should go through Chapter 0 and verify the elementary assertions stated there. The reader who has already studied set theory should only glance through Chapter 0 to make certain that he is familiar with our version of the required results. In any event, our summary is not intended to be a systematic treatment of set theory. This can be found in the references listed at the end of the chapter.

In Chapter I we review the basic properties of the natural numbers, the integers, and the rational numbers. The reader who has studied these concepts from only an "informal" or an "intuitive" viewpoint should go through Chapter I with some care. Otherwise, he need only glance through the chapter to make sure that he is familiar with the present development.

Chapter II summarizes rather quickly some of the basic algebraic concepts as well as a few of the examples of the objects to be considered later. The reader should come back and review Chapter II every so often. The basic thing to keep in mind is that Chapter II is a "dictionary." It formalizes the concepts of Chapter 0 and I; it also "classifies" some of the objects considered in Chapter 0 and I.

In any event, Chapters 0, I, and II are the introductory chapters. The reader who has already studied some abstract algebra should look only for things that do not appear to be familiar on the surface.

Chapter III is devoted to the study of groups. We deliberately go backward in time and look at groups from the viewpoint of transformation groups. Some indications are made regarding the connection of this viewpoint with geometry. The study of abstract groups is barely hinted at. A vast amount of literature exists on the subject of group theory. The interested reader should consult the references listed at the end of the chapter for more detailed study.

Chapter IV is devoted to a preliminary study of rings. In particular, it contains a generalization of the divisibility theory of the rational integers; it points out the connection between rings and commutative groups—namely, rings are viewed as rings of endomorphisms of commutative groups. The latter is analogous to our viewing groups as transformation groups.

Chapter V is fairly technical and quite important. The concepts introduced here are used in many parts of mathematics. This chapter is deliberately made quite abstract; its results are used and illustrated later.

Chapter VI presents an abbreviated treatment of vector spaces. It is not our intention to study vector spaces exhaustively. The basic concern is to make certain that the reader becomes familiar with the results of Chapter V in the special case of a vector space. Included in this chapter are standard results on the solutions of systems of linear equations and of systems of linear homogeneous differential equations with constant coefficients. The latter serve to illustrate the uses of algebra in another part of mathematics.

In Chapter VII we consider fields from the point of view of solving polynomial equations. Rather quickly, we convert them into the problem of forming field extensions and apply our earlier results to the study of this problem.

Chapter VIII deals with Galois theory. This is a continuation of Chapter VII, and most of its results involve putting together the relevant results of group theory, factorization theory, and field theory. As "applications," we indicate how some famous problems are solved by the methods of field theory and Galois theory.

The purpose of the rather short Chapter IX is to provide an almost completely algebraic proof of the fundamental theorem of algebra. Again, it illustrates the use of some of our earlier results.

Many interesting topics of algebra have been neglected in our treatment. Also unmentioned are many different and instructive approaches to the topics selected. In addition to the usual excuses of lack of time and space, I must plead my incompetence and my bias. It is my hope that the reader will find the references at the end of each chapter of sufficient use that he may discover the other possible approaches and explanations.

It is impossible for me to thank everyone who deserves credit for the preparation of this book. To Alfred Hales I owe a debt for his critical reading of the various drafts. To Herman Gluck and Academic Press I owe the debt of making the book possible. To my former students at Harvard University and the University of Pennsylvania, I owe the debt of their patience in sitting through incoherent lectures and in fighting through disorganized lecture notes. To my many friends and colleagues, especially Oscar Goldman, goes the credit for the encouragement and numerous useful critical comments I received. Last, but certainly not least, I must thank Mrs. Madge Goldman for her infinite patience in rectifying some of the atrocities I committed on the English language.

C.H.S.

Philadelphia, Penn.

CONTENTS

ABSTRACT ALGEBRA

CHAPTER 0 Preliminaries

In this chapter we review briefly some of the concepts and results from set theory that are used throughout the remainder of this book. The reader may consult the references at the end of the chapter for more detailed discussions of set theory.

The notions "A is a set" and "x is a member of the set A" are considered as "primitive" concepts.

» 0·1 SET THEORETIC NOTATIONS

Let P be a statement concerning a variable element x and let A be the set of all elements x for which the statement P holds; we then write $A = \{x \mid P\}$. This is to be read as "A is equal to the set of all elements x for which the statement P holds." The reader should take care that P is a "well-formed" statement in order to avoid logical difficulties. We write $x \in A$ to denote that x is a member of the set A.

When A and B are sets, then $A \subset B$ means that every member of the set A is also a member of the set B. This is to be read as "the set A is a subset of the set B." The reader should note that $A \subset B$ does not exclude the possibility that A and B are equal. Indeed, A and B are equal as sets if and only if $A \subset B$ and $B \subset A$. The equality of the sets A and B is denoted by $A = B$. If $A \subset B$ and $A \neq B$, we say that A is a proper subset of B.

The set with no elements is called the **empty set,** denoted by $\varnothing$. If A and B are sets, then $A - B = \{x \mid x \in A \text{ and } x \notin B\}$. Thus $A \subset B$ if and only if $A - B = \varnothing$.

Let A and B be sets and let $\{A_i \mid i \in I\}$ be a collection of sets indexed by the elements of the set I. Then $A \cup B = \{x \mid x \in A \text{ or } x \in B\}$ is called the **union** of A and B; $\bigcup_{i \in I} A_i = \{x \mid x \in A_i \text{ for some } i \in I\}$ is called the union of A_i, $i \in I$. Moreover, $A \cap B = \{x \mid x \in A \text{ and } x \in B\}$ is called the **intersection** of A and B; $\bigcap_{i \in I} A_i = \{x \mid x \in A_i \text{ for all } i \in I\}$ is called the intersection of A_i, $i \in I$.

The following "algebraic relations" hold among sets:

(a) $A \cup \varnothing = A$ and $A \cap \varnothing = \varnothing$.

(b) $A \cup A = A$ and $A \cap A = A$.

(c) $A \cup B = B \cup A$ and $A \cap B = B \cap A$.

(d) $(A \cup B) \cup C = A \cup (B \cup C)$ and $(A \cap B) \cap C = A \cap (B \cap C)$.

(e) De Morgan's Laws. $A \cup (\bigcap_{i \in I} B_i) = \bigcap_{i \in I}(A \cup B_i)$ and $A \cap (\bigcup_{i \in I} B_i) = \bigcup_{i \in I}(A \cap B_i)$.

(f) $A \subset B$ if and only if $A \cap B = A$ and $A \subset B$ if and only if $A \cup B = B$.

The reader who is not familiar with these relations should verify the assertions as an exercise. For example, a special case of De Morgan's law is $A \cap (B \cup C) = (A \cap B) \cup (A \cap C)$. The equality of these sets is nothing more than the logical equivalence of the following statements:

(a) x is a member of A and x is a member of $B \cup C$.

(b) x is a member of A and x is a member of B or C.

(c) x is a member of A and x is a member of B, or, x is a member of A and x is a member of C.

Often the symbol $\forall$ is used in place of the phrase "for each" or "for every." The choice is usually clear from context. Similarly, the symbol $\exists$ is used in place of the phrase "there exists" or "there is at least one." Finally, the set $\{x \mid P\} \cap B$ is often written as $\{x \in B \mid P\}$, and the set whose members are $x_1, \ldots$ is often written as $\{x_1, \ldots\}$; for example, $\{x\}$ is the set whose only member is the element x.

» 0 · 2 CORRESPONDENCES, MAPS, RELATIONS

If A and B are sets, the Cartesian product of A and B is denoted by $A \times B$; it is the set of all ordered pairs (a, b) in which $a \in A$ and $b \in B$. Often a is called the first, and b the second, component of (a, b).

If $C \subset A \times B$, then C defines a ***correspondence*** between the subsets of A and the subsets of B in the following sense:

(*) If $A' \subset A$, then C associates to A' the subset $C(A') \subset B$ defined by $C(A') = \{b \in B \mid \exists\, a \in A' \text{ with } (a, b) \in C\}$.

We note that $C(\varnothing) = \varnothing$. In the preceding definition we have given A a particular role in that we assign to each subset of A a subset of B, not the reverse. This is somewhat unfair. To make the situation symmetric we define the "inverse" of C to be the subset $C^{-1} \subset B \times A$ such that $C^{-1} = \{(b, a) | (a, b) \in C\}$. It is then possible to use C^{-1} to assign to each subset B' of B the subset $C^{-1}(B')$ of A given by $C^{-1}(B') = \{a \in A \mid \exists\, b \in B' \text{ with } (b, a) \in C^{-1}\} = \{a \in A \mid \exists\, b \in B' \text{ with } (a, b) \in C\}$.

CONVENTION 1 · When there is no possibility of confusion, a one-element subset of a set A is "identified" with the element itself. For example, if $C \subset A \times B$ and $a \in A$, we write $C(a)$ in place of $C(\{a\})$.

Exercise 1 · Let $A = B =$ the set of all "real numbers." Let $C = \{(x, y) \in A \times B \mid x^2 + y^2 = 1\}$. Find $C(1)$, $C(0)$, $C(-3)$, $C^{-1}(0)$, $C(\{x \in A \mid -2 \leqslant x < 0\})$. (We assume that the reader has a working knowledge of "real numbers." We shall develop them more systematically later.)

We are interested in only a few special cases of correspondence.

DEFINITION 1 · Let $F \subset A \times B$. F is said to be a ***map*** a ***function*** or a ***mapping*** from the set A to the set B if and only if the following condition holds:

(*) To each $a \in A$ there is a unique $b \in B$ such that $(a, b) \in F$. Equivalently, $F(a)$ is a one-element subset of B for every $a \in A$. A is called the ***domain*** of F, B is called the ***range*** of B, and $F(A)$ is called the ***image*** of A under F or simply the image of A.

As an example, we note that the correspondence of Exercise 1 is not a map. Since $\varnothing$ is the only subset of itself, we see that there is a unique map of the empty set into any set B, namely, $\varnothing = \varnothing \times B$. By the same reasoning we see that there is no map of a nonempty set A into the empty set. In any event, if F is a map from A to B, then $F = \{(a, F(a)) | \, a \in A\}$.

DEFINITION 2 · Let F be a map from A to B. We then write $F : A \to B$. F is said to be ***injective*** (or one-to-one into) if and only if $\forall\, a, a' \in A$, $F(a) = F(a')$ implies that $a = a'$. F is said to be ***surjective*** (or onto) if and only if $F(A) = B$, that is, $\forall\, b \in B$, $\exists\, a \in A$ such that $F(a) = b$. F is said to be ***bijective*** (or one-to-one onto) if and only if F is both injective and surjective.

Let $F : A \to B$ and $G : B \to C$ be maps. The ***composition*** of F and G is the map $H : A \to C$ such that $H(a) = G(F(a))\ \forall\, a \in A$. H is usually written as $G \circ F$.

CONVENTION 2 · On a few occasions, notably in Chapters I, II, and III, we use the "exponential" notation a^F in place of $F(a)$, in which case the composition of F and G is written as FG. It will be clear from the context which notation is in use.

Often it is convenient to draw a diagram in order to exhibit a collection of maps. For example, the following diagrams exhibit a collection of three and four maps, respectively.

$$\begin{array}{ccc} A & \xrightarrow{\alpha} & B \\ & {\scriptstyle\gamma}\searrow & \downarrow{\scriptstyle\beta} \\ & & C \end{array} \qquad\qquad \begin{array}{ccc} A & \xrightarrow{\alpha} & B \\ {\scriptstyle\gamma}\downarrow & & \downarrow{\scriptstyle\beta} \\ C & \xrightarrow{\delta} & D \end{array}$$

These diagrams are said to be ***commutative*** if and only if the composition of maps indicated in them depends on the initial point and the end point and not on the path chosen. Thus the first diagram is commutative if and only if $\gamma = \beta \circ \alpha$; the second diagram is commutative if and only if $\delta \circ \gamma = \beta \circ \alpha$.

In general, a map will not necessarily preserve the intersection of subsets. However, the following is true:

THEOREM 1 · Let $F : A \to B$ be a map. Then F^{-1} preserves both union and intersection; that is, $F^{-1}(\bigcup_{i\in I} B_i) = \bigcup_{i\in I} F^{-1}(B_i)$, $F^{-1}(\bigcap_{i\in I} B_i) = \bigcap_{i\in I} F^{-1}(B_i)$, where $B_i \subset B$, $\forall\, i \in I$.

The proof of Theorem 1 is straightforward and is left to the interested reader.

An immediate consequence of Theorem 1 is the following:

COROLLARY · Let $F : A \to B$ be a map. Let $b, b' \in B$ such that $b \neq b'$; then $F^{-1}(b) \cap F^{-1}(b') = \varnothing$. Moreover, $A = \bigcup_{b\in B} F^{-1}(b)$.

It is clear that in the formation of A as a union of $F^{-1}(b)$, $b \in B$, we may ignore those subsets $F^{-1}(b)$ that are equal to $\varnothing$; that is, we may ignore $F^{-1}(b)$ for $b \in B - F(A)$. This then leads to the following:

DEFINITION 3 · Let A be a nonempty set. A ***partition*** of A is a set $\{A_i \mid i \in I\}$ such that the following conditions are satisfied,

(a) A_i is a nonempty subset of A, $\forall\, i \in I$.

(b) $A = \bigcup_{i \in I} A_i$.

(c) $A_i \cap A_j = \varnothing \ \forall\, i, j \in I$ such that $i \neq j$.

From the foregoing corollary we easily see that every map $F : A \to B$ may be factored in the following sense:

THEOREM 2 · Let $F : A \to B$ be a map. Then there exist sets I and J and maps $\alpha : F \to I$, $\beta : I \to J$, and $\gamma : J \to B$ which satisfy the following conditions:

(a) $F = \gamma \circ \beta \circ \alpha$.

(b) α is surjective, β is bijective, and γ is injective.

(c) If α', β', γ', I', and J' satisfy (a) and (b), then there exist unique bijections $\delta : I \to I'$ and $\epsilon : J \to J'$ such that the following diagram is commutative:

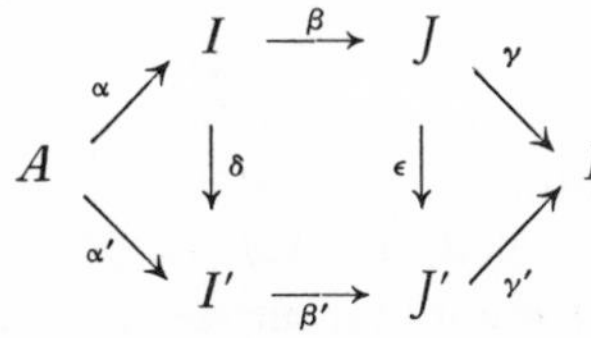

As far as the existence of I, J, α, β, and γ is concerned, we may take J to be $F(A)$ and I to be the partition $\{F^{-1}(j) \mid j \in J\}$ of A; α is defined by $\alpha(a) = F^{-1}(j)$ if and only if $F(a) = j$; β is defined by $\beta(F^{-1}(j)) = j$; and γ is defined by $\gamma(j) = j$. Conditions (a) and (b) are rather easy to check. Condition (c) requires the following exercises:

Exercise 2 · Show that the composition of surjective (respectively, bijective, injective) maps is surjective (respectively, bijective, injective).

Exercise 3 · Let $G : B \to C$ be a map. Show that the following assertions hold:

(a) G is injective if and only if for any set A and maps $F_1, F_2 : A \to B$ such that $G \circ F_1 = G \circ F_2$, we must have $F_1 = F_2$.

(b) G is surjective if and only if for any set D and maps $H_1, H_2 : C \to D$ such that $H_1 \circ G = H_2 \circ G$, we must have $H_1 = H_2$.

Granting Exercises 2 and 3 for the moment, we see that $\beta' \circ \alpha'$ is surjective. Since γ' is injective and $F = \gamma' \circ (\beta' \circ \alpha')$, we see that γ' is a bijection between J' and $J = F(A)$. It follows that we may select ϵ to be the inverse map to γ'. It is clear that $\gamma' \circ \epsilon = \gamma$. Since β, ϵ, and β' are all bijections, we may take δ to be $\beta'^{-1} \circ \epsilon \circ \beta$. It is clear that $\beta' \circ \delta = \epsilon \circ \beta$. Thus we have $F = \gamma \circ \beta \circ \alpha = \gamma' \circ \epsilon \circ \beta \circ \alpha = \gamma' \circ \beta' \circ \alpha'$. From Exercise 3(a) we conclude that $\epsilon \circ \beta \circ \alpha = \beta' \circ \alpha'$. Hence $\beta' \circ \delta \circ \alpha = \beta' \circ \alpha'$. Again from Exercise 3(a) we obtain $\delta \circ \alpha = \alpha'$. Thus we have shown that each of the three smaller cells of the diagram is commutative. We leave it up to the reader to convince himself that a diagram of maps is commutative if and only if each of its cells is commutative. The uniqueness of δ and ϵ follow easily from Theorem 2, Exercise 3(a), and various commutativity relations. We omit the details.

The reader should note that the burden of the proof lies in verifying Exercises 2 and 3. The first is rather easy. The second is a bit harder. Once these exercises have been done, the rest of the proof of Theorem 2 is nothing more than an amusing game of "chasing around a diagram." In order to do Exercise 3, we furnish the following hint:

Hint (a). Take A to be $G(B)$. Let $F_1, F_2 : G(B) \to B$ be maps such that $F_1(c)$ and $F_2(c)$ are randomly selected elements of $G^{-1}(c)$, where $c \in G(B)$. It follows that $G \circ F_1 = G \circ F_2 =$ identity map on $G(B)$. If G can be canceled, then $F_1 = F_2$. It would then follow that $G^{-1}(c)$ is a one-element subset of B, that is, G is injective. Conversely, if G is injective, then $G(F_1(a)) = G(F_2(a))$ implies that $F_1(a) = F_2(a)\ \forall\ a \in A$, that is, $F_1 = F_2$. We have concluded the proof of (a).

The concept of a partition is connected with another special case of a correspondence.

DEFINITION 4 · Let A be a set and $R \subset A \times A$. Then R is called a ***relation*** on the set A. We say that $a \in A$ is ***R-related*** to $a' \in A$ and write $a\,R\,a'$ if and only if $(a, a') \in R$.

The set $\Delta(A) = \{(a, a) | a \in A\}$ is called the ***diagonal,*** or the identity relation, of A. The relation R is said to be ***reflexive*** if and only if $\Delta(A) \subset R$; that is, every element of A is R-related to itself. R is ***antireflexive*** if and only if $R \cap \Delta(A) = \varnothing$. R is said to be ***symmetric*** if and only if $R = R^{-1}$; that is, a is R-related to b implies that b is R-related to a. R is ***antisymmetric*** if and only if $R \cap R^{-1} = \varnothing$. R is said to be ***transitive*** if and only if $a\,R\,b$ and $b\,R\,c$ imply $a\,R\,c$ $\forall\, a, b, c \in A$. (This may also be defined by way of "composition" of correspondences. However, we seldom if ever invoke this general notion, hence will content ourselves with the present definition of transitivity.)

A relation R is called a ***partial ordering*** on A if and only if R is transitive and $R \cap R^{-1} = \Delta(A)$.

A relation R is called a ***linear ordering*** on A if and only if R is transitive, $A \times A = R \cup \Delta(A) \cup R^{-1}$ and $R \cap R^{-1} = \varnothing$. Equivalently, a linear ordering on A is a transitive relation R such that exactly one of the three relations, $a\,R\,b$, $a = b$, and $b\,R\,a$ must hold for any pair of elements a and b of A.

Occasionally, we may use partial ordering to mean a transitive relation such that $R \cap R^{-1} = \varnothing$, and we may also use linear ordering to mean a transitive relation such that $A = R \cup R^{-1}$ and $R \cap R^{-1} = \Delta(A)$. These abuses of terminology are usually clear from the context.

DEFINITION 5 · A relation R on a set A is called an ***equivalence relation*** if and only if the following conditions are satisfied:

(a) R is reflexive; that is, $a\,R\,a$, $\forall\, a \in A$.

(b) R is symmetric; that is, $a\,R\,b$ implies $b\,R\,a$, $\forall\, a, b \in A$.

(c) R is transitive; that is, $a\,R\,b$, $b\,R\,c$ imply $a\,R\,c$, $\forall\, a, b, c \in A$.

If $a \in A$ and R is an equivalence relation on A, then $R(a)$ is called the ***R-equivalence class*** of a. A/R then denotes the set of R-equivalence classes on A.

THEOREM 3 · Let A be a set. There is a natural bijection between the set of equivalence relations on A and the set of all partitions of A as follows:

(a) Let R be an equivalence relation on A. The set of R-equivalence classes forms a partition of A.

(b) Let $\{A_i \mid i \in I\}$ be a partition of A. The relation R defined by letting $a\,R\,b$ if and only if there exists $i \in I$ (necessarily unique) such that $a, b \in A_i$, is an equivalence relation on A. Moreover, A_i, $i \in I$, are precisely the R-equivalence classes on A.

» 0 · 3 CARTESIAN PRODUCT AND UNIVERSAL MAPPING PROPERTIES

Let $\{A_i \mid i \in I\}$ be a collection of sets indexed by the set I. The ***Cartesian product*** of A_i, $i \in I$, is the set of all maps $F : I \to \bigcup_{i \in I} A_i$ which satisfy the condition that $F(i) \in A_i$ for each $i \in I$. Because a map is uniquely determined by the values it takes on each element of its domain of definition, we identify F with $(..., F(i),...)_{i \in I}$. We denote the Cartesian product by $\prod_{i \in I} A_i$. It is the set $\{(..., a_i,...)_{i \in I} \mid a_i \in A_i \forall i \in I\}$. For each $j \in I$, the map $\pi_j : \prod_{i \in I} A_i \to A_j$ given by $\pi_j(..., a_i,...)_{i \in I} = a_j$ is called the ***projection*** of the Cartesian product onto its jth component. The reader should note that the Cartesian product is the empty set whenever A_i is the empty set for some $i \in I$. Assuming prior knowledge of the integers, when $I = \{1,..., n\}$, we also use $A_1 \times \cdots \times A_n$ to denote the Cartesian product.

The Cartesian product of A_i, $i \in I$, can be characterized as follows:

THEOREM 1 · Let $\{A_i \mid i \in I\}$ be a collection of sets indexed by the set I. Then there exists a set B, together with a collection of maps $\pi_i : B \to A_i$, $i \in I$, which satisfies the following condition:

(*) Let C be any set and let $\rho_i : C \to A_i$, $i \in I$, be any collection of maps. There then exists a unique map $\rho : C \to B$ such that $\pi_i \circ \rho = \rho_i$ holds for each $i \in I$.

Moreover, the set B is unique up to a natural bijection. (The meaning of this assertion will be clear from the proof that follows.)

Proof · We let B be $\prod_{i \in I} A_i$ and let π_i be the projection map for each $i \in I$. When C and $\{\rho_i \mid i \in I\}$ are given, we define $\rho : C \to B$ by letting $\rho(c)$ be $(..., \rho_i(c),...)_{i \in I}$. It is then immediately clear that $\pi_i \circ \rho = \rho_i \; \forall i \in I$. It is also clear that ρ is uniquely determined by the condition that $\pi_i \circ \rho = \rho_i \; \forall i \in I$.

Suppose that B' and $\{\pi_i' \mid i \in I\}$ also satisfy (*). We may then use B' in place of C and π_i' in place of ρ_i, $i \in I$. Thus we can find a map $\sigma : B' \to B$ such that $\pi_i \circ \sigma = \pi_i' \; \forall i \in I$. Since the situation is symmetric, we can interchange the role of B and B'. Thus we can also find a map $\sigma' : B \to B'$ such that $\pi_i' \circ \sigma' = \pi_i \; \forall i \in I$. It follows that $\sigma \circ \sigma' : B \to B$ is a map that satisfies $\pi_i \circ \sigma \circ \sigma' = \pi_i' \circ \sigma' = \pi_i \; \forall i \in I$. Now, using B in the place of C and π_i in the place of ρ_i, $i \in I$, the condition (*) asserts that there is a unique map $\rho : B \to B$ such that $\pi_i \circ \rho = \pi_i$ for each $i \in I$. Since the identity map on B clearly has this property and we have just seen that $\sigma \circ \sigma'$ also has it, we may conclude from the uniqueness of ρ that $\sigma \circ \sigma'$ is the identity map on B. By interchanging the role of B and B' once more we may conclude that $\sigma' \circ \sigma$ is the identity map on B'. It now follows from Exercise 2.2 that σ and σ' are both bijections. «

The word "natural" in the statement of the theorem is used to indicate that the bijection σ can be found directly from the condition (*).

We observe that the verification of the uniqueness of B (up to a natural bijection) in the preceding theorem is a formal exercise in "chasing around a diagram." There will be many occasions when we shall characterize sets with prescribed maps by means of theorems that are similar to Theorem 1. Such characterizations are called characterizations by means of ***universal mapping properties.*** Roughly speaking, Theorem 1 tells us the relevant property of the Cartesian product with respect to maps. Exercise 2.3 may be considered as a characterization of an injective and a surjective map by means of cancellation laws.

It is possible to characterize the set of equivalence classes as follows:

THEOREM 2 · Let R be an equivalence relation on the set A. Then there exists a set B, together with a map $\pi : A \to B$, which satisfies the following conditions:

(*) If $a\,R\,a'$, then $\pi(a) = \pi(a')$, where $a, a' \in A$.

(**) Let C be any set and let $\rho : A \to C$ be any map such that $\rho(a) = \rho(a')$ holds whenever $a\,R\,a'$. Then there exists a unique map $\sigma : B \to C$ such that $\rho = \sigma \circ \pi$.

Moreover, the set B is unique up to a natural bijection and the map π is surjective.

We omit the details of the proof of Theorem 2. Instead, we supply the following hint:

Hint. Let B be the set of R-equivalence classes on A. Let $\pi : A \to A/R = B$ be given by $\pi(a) = R(a)\ \forall\, a \in A$.

At first glance the Cartesian product of sets has very little in common with equivalence relations on sets or, what is the same (according to Theorem 2.3), with partitions of sets. However, we have the following characterization of a partition of a set. We see rather quickly that it is the dual of Theorem 1 in the sense that the only difference is the reversal of the directions of all the maps.

THEOREM 3 · Let $\{A_i \mid i \in I\}$ be a collection of sets indexed by the set I. Then there exists a set B, together with a collection of maps $\eta_i : A_i \to B$, $i \in I$, which satisfies the following condition:

(*) Let C be any set and let $\sigma_i : A_i \to C$, $i \in I$, be any collection of maps. Then there exists a unique map $\tau : B \to C$ such that $\tau \circ \eta_i = \sigma_i$ holds for each $i \in I$.

Moreover, the set B is unique up to a natural bijection. Finally, each η_i is injective, and, if $A_i \neq \varnothing$ for each $i \in I$, then $\{\eta_i(A_i) \mid i \in I\}$ is a partition of the set B.

The last assertion of Theorem 3 tells us how to construct B; namely, we let B be the disjoint union of the sets A_i, $i \in I$. This is occasionally denoted by $\coprod_{i \in I} A_i$. It is the subset of $(\bigcup_{i \in I} A_i) \times I$ which consists of all pairs (a, i) such that $a \in A_i$. The map η_i then sends $a_i \in A_i$ onto the element (a_i, i).

The careful reader will have noticed that nothing was mentioned in Theorem 1 about the maps ρ_i, $i \in I$. In fact, if $A_i \neq \varnothing$, $\forall i \in I$, then *not* each ρ_i is surjective. This assertion is related to the "axiom of choice." *true* We discuss it in Section 5.

To be true change ρ_i to η_i

» 0·4 CARDINAL NUMBERS

In the preceding section we have seen that sets are often constructed in such a way that they are unique only up to a natural bijection. In some sense we should consider abstract sets A and B as indistinguishable if there is a bijection between them. More generally, if there is an injective map $\rho : A \to B$, then A may be "identified" with the subset $\rho(A)$ of B. In this sense we may then say that B is at least as large as A or the **cardinal number** of B is at least equal to the cardinal number of A. We also say that A and B have the same cardinal number if and only if there is a bijection between A and B. We use $|A|$ to denote the cardinal number of the set A. When the cardinal number of A is less than or equal to the cardinal number of B, we write $|A| \leqslant |B|$. The equality of cardinal numbers is denoted by $|A| = |B|$. Thus it may seem that we have a relation among cardinal numbers. Unfortunately, the collection of cardinal numbers is too large to be a set. Nevertheless, we have the following results:

THEOREM 1 (Schröder-Bernstein) · Let A and B be sets. If there exist injective maps $\rho : A \to B$ and $\sigma : B \to A$, then there exists a bijection between A and B. (In terms of cardinal numbers the assertion is merely that $|A| \leqslant |B|$ and $|B| \leqslant |A|$ imply $|A| = |B|$.)

THEOREM 2 · Let A and B be sets. Then, either there exists an injective map $\rho : A \to B$ or there exists an injective map $\sigma : B \to A$. (In terms of cardinal numbers the assertion is merely that either $|A| \leqslant |B|$ or $|B| \leqslant |A|$.)

We can summarize Theorems 1 and 2 into the single statement:

(*) Let Γ be a set of cardinal numbers. Let $<$ be defined for $\alpha, \beta \in \Gamma$ by $\alpha < \beta$ if and only if $\alpha \leqslant \beta$ and $\alpha \neq \beta$. Then $<$ is a linear ordering on the set Γ.

The reader should note that we have made no attempt to define a cardinal number. Formally, Γ should be viewed as a collection of sets A_i, i ranging over an index set I, such that when $i \neq j$ there is no bijection between A_i and A_j.

We now give a tentative definition of a finite set. It is intuitive; however, it is not easy to work with. In Chapter I we provide a more convenient definition.

DEFINITION 1 · Let A be a set. A is called a ***finite set*** if and only if every injective map of A into A is automatically surjective (therefore, automatically bijective). A is said to be ***infinite*** when it is not finite. Occasionally, we write $|A| < \infty$ to indicate that A is a finite set.

Under the definition just given the empty set $\varnothing$ is finite. (The condition is vacuously satisfied.) A set with a unique element is a finite set.

Exercise 1 · Show that a set A is finite if and only if every surjective map of A onto A is automatically injective (therefore, automatically bijective).

Hint. Let $\rho : A \to B$ be a map. Show that ρ is surjective if and only if there exists an injective map $\sigma : B \to A$ such that $\rho \circ \sigma$ is the identity map on B. Similarly, show that ρ is injective if and only if there exists a surjective map $\rho : B \to A$ such that $\sigma \circ \rho$ is the identity map on A.

Exercise 2 · Let A be a subset of the set B. Show that when B is a finite set A is also a finite set. Equivalently, show that when A is an infinite set B is also an infinite set.

Hint. The set A is infinite if and only if there exists a map $\rho : A \to A$ such that ρ is injective but not surjective. When A is infinite, we may extend ρ to a map $\sigma : B \to B$ such that $\sigma(a) = \rho(a)$ for $a \in A$ and $\sigma(b) = b$ for $b \in B - A$. If ρ is injective but not surjective, the same assertions hold for σ.

» 0·5 ZORN'S LEMMA, AXIOM OF CHOICE, WELL-ORDERING AXIOM

We avoid using Zorn's lemma as much as possible. However, there will be occasions when the use of this lemma is either convenient or unavoidable. Actually, Zorn's lemma or one of its many disguised forms will have been used implicitly during our investigations long before we use Zorn's lemma explicitly.

DEFINITION 1 · Let A be a set partially ordered by the relation $\leqslant$. Let B be a subset of A. An element $a \in A$ is called an ***upper bound*** of B if and only if $b \leqslant a$, $\forall\, b \in B$. The element $a \in A$ is called a ***least upper bound*** of B if and only if (1) a is an upper bound of B and (2) $a \leqslant c$ holds for each upper bound c of B.

An element $b \in B$ is called a ***maximal element*** of B if and only if $a \in B$ and $b \leqslant a$ imply that $a = b$.

In a similar manner we may define ***lower bounds, greatest lower bounds,*** and ***minimal elements*** of B.

The set A is said to be ***well-ordered*** under $\leqslant$ if and only if every nonempty subset B of A has a greatest lower bound that lies in B.

We note that an easy consequence of the definition of partial ordering (Definition 2.4) is that a subset B can have at most one least upper bound and at most one greatest lower bound in A.

We next note that when A is well-ordered under $\leqslant$ it is then linearly ordered under $<$, where we define $a < b$ to mean $a \leqslant b$ and $a \neq b$. To determine this, we let $B = \{a, b\}$. From the definition of well-ordering we see that either $a \leqslant b$ or $b \leqslant a$. Thus exactly one of the conditions $a < b$, $a = b$, or $b < a$ must hold for the elements $a, b \in A$.

ZORN'S LEMMA · Let A be a nonempty set partially ordered by $\leqslant$. Suppose that A is inductive in the following sense:

(*) Every subset B of A linearly ordered by $\leqslant$ has an upper bound in A.

Then A has at least one maximal element.

As we remarked at the end of Definition 2.4, there is a slight abuse of the phrase "linear ordering" in (*).

Of course, we can also phrase Zorn's lemma in terms of lower bounds and minimal elements. In any event, there may be several maximal or minimal elements.

We now describe two equivalent forms of Zorn's lemma.

By recalling the definition of the Cartesian product of sets A_i, $i \in I$ we see that an element of the Cartesian product is nothing more than a selection of one element from each of the sets A_i, $i \in I$. Often such a selection is called a ***choice function.*** We remarked at the end of Theorem 3.3 that when A_i is nonempty for each $i \in I$ the projection map of $\prod_{i \in I} A_i$ onto A_j is surjective for each $j \in I$. An immediate consequence of this assertion is that the Cartesian product is not the empty set. This is precisely the content of the following axiom.

AXIOM OF CHOICE · Let $\{A_i \mid i \in I\}$ be a collection of nonempty sets A_i indexed by the nonempty set I. Then $\prod_{i \in I} A_i$ is nonempty.

By using the axiom of choice we can now show that the projection maps are surjective, provided that A_i is nonempty for each $i \in I$. Let $j \in I$ and $a_j \in A_j$; we need to show that there exists an element x of the Cartesian product such that $\pi_j(x) = a_j$. If $I = \{j\}$, then π_j is the identity map of A_j and we may take x to be a_j. Thus we may assume that $J = I - \{j\}$ is nonempty. Hence from the axiom of choice $\prod_{i \in J} A_i$ is nonempty. We let y be an element of $\prod_{i \in J} A_i$. It follows that y corresponds to the selection of an element $a_i \in A_i$ for each $i \in J = I - \{j\}$. Since $a_j \in A_j$ has already been given, we see that there exists an element of $\prod_{i \in I} A_i$ whose jth component is a_j, namely, the element $(\ldots, a_i, \ldots)_{i \in I}$. It follows that π_j sends this element onto a_j and therefore π_j is surjective.

It is known that the axiom of choice is equivalent to Zorn's lemma. It is also known that the axiom of choice is equivalent to the following axiom:

WELL-ORDERING AXIOM · Every set may be well-ordered in at least one way.

Depending on our experience, one of these three axioms may be more obvious, or believable, to us than the others. We often invoke the axiom of choice without saying so explicitly, but the use of Zorn's lemma will usually be pointed out. The well-ordering axiom is seldom used. However, the concept of well-ordering is applied once or twice in the process of constructing "fields."

As an illustration of the various uses of Zorn's lemma, we give a proof of Theorem 4.2.

Let A and B be sets. We then let $\mathcal{F} = \{(U, V, \rho) | U \subset A, V \subset B$ and $\rho : U \to V$ is a bijection$\}$. If either A or B is the empty set, there is nothing to prove. Thus we may assume that both A and B are nonempty. If $a \in A$ and $b \in B$, then $(\{a\}, \{b\}, \rho) \in \mathcal{F}$, where $\rho(a) = b$. Thus $\mathcal{F}$ is nonempty.

We now introduce a relation $\leqslant$ on $\mathcal{F}$ as follows:

(*) If (U_1, V_1, ρ_1) and $(U_2, V_2, \rho_2) \in \mathcal{F}$, we write $(U_1, V_1, \rho_1) \leqslant (U_2, V_2, \rho_2)$ if and only if the following conditions hold:

(a) $U_1 \subset U_2$,

(b) $V_1 \subset V_2$,

(c) $\rho_2(x) = \rho_1(x) \ \forall\, x \in U_1$.

It is easy to see that $\leqslant$ is a partial ordering on $\mathcal{F}$. We assert that $\mathcal{F}$ is inductive with respect to $\leqslant$ in the sense of Zorn's lemma; namely, let $\mathcal{G} = \{(U_i, V_i, \rho_i) | i \in I\}$ be a linearly ordered subset of $\mathcal{F}$. Then let $U = \bigcup_{i \in I} U_i$, $V = \bigcup_{i \in I} V_i$, and define $\rho : U \to V$ by setting $\rho(x) = \rho_i(x)$ whenever $x \in U_i$. It is clear that $U \subset A$ and $V \subset B$. Since $\mathcal{G}$ is linearly ordered with respect to $\leqslant$, we see that for $i, j \in I$, we may assume that $(U_i, V_i, \rho_i) \leqslant (U_j, V_j, \rho_j)$. It follows from condition (c) that ρ is a well-defined map; that is to say, $\rho(x)$ is a well-defined element of V, independent of the index $i \in I$ such that $x \in U_i$. If $x, y \in U$ such that $\rho(x) = \rho(y)$, we may assume that $x \in U_j$ and $y \in U_j$. Since ρ_j is injective, it follows that $x = y$; that is to say, ρ is injective. Since $\rho(U_i) = \rho_i(U_i) = V_i \ \forall\, i \in I$, it is clear that ρ is also surjective. It now follows easily that (U, V, ρ) is an upper bound of $\mathcal{G}$ in $\mathcal{F}$. By Zorn's lemma we may conclude that $\mathcal{F}$ has a maximal element (S, T, σ). If $S = A$, then σ is an injection of A into B. If $T = B$, the inverse of σ is an injection of B into A. Thus we are finished in either of these two cases. The proof will be completed when we show that one of these two cases must occur.

Assume that neither of the two cases occurs. Thus $A - S$ and $B - T$ are both nonempty. Let $a \in A - S$ and $b \in B - T$. Take $U = S \cup \{a\}$ and $V = T \cup \{b\}$. Define $\sigma : U \to V$ by setting $\sigma(x) = \rho(x) \ \forall\, x \in S$ and $\sigma(a) = b$. It is immediately seen that σ is a bijection, and it is clear that $(U, V, \sigma) \in \mathcal{F}$ and $(S, T, \rho) \leqslant (U, V, \sigma)$. Since U is not a subset of S, we see that $(S, T, \rho) < (U, V, \sigma)$. This contradicts the maximality of (S, T, ρ) in $\mathcal{F}$. Thus one of the two cases mentioned must occur and the proof of Theorem 4.1 is complete.

This particular illustration is typical of the uses of Zorn's lemma in our later investigations.

References

The book by Halmos [2] will give an adequate working knowledge of set theory. For a more axiomatic development of set theory the reader may consult [3] and the bibliographies contained in it. The results of Section 3 are, in some sense, the starting points of "category and functor theory." Interested readers may consult [1].

1. P. Freyd, *Abelian Categories*, Harper and Row, New York, 1964.
2. P. R. Halmos, *Naive Set Theory*, Van Nostrand, Princeton, N. J., 1958.
3. C. T. Yang, *Axiomatic Set Theory and Number Systems*, Academic Press, New York (in press).

CHAPTER I Natural Numbers, Integers, and Rational Numbers

In this chapter we summarize briefly the construction and some of the pertinent properties of the natural numbers, of the integers, and of the rational numbers. Many of the more complicated systems that occur later are in some way generalizations of these systems. Consequently, the reader may consider this chapter as a collection of the simplest examples of the objects that will interest us.

From the point of view of set theory natural numbers are the cardinal numbers of finite sets. From the point of view of everyday experience natural numbers are the counting numbers. The integers and the rational numbers are objects that arise from the natural numbers to answer some elementary arithmetical questions. In order to avoid a detailed discussion of set theory, we adopt the axiomatic approach and will try to achieve our goals as quickly as possible. A reader who is interested in a development of the natural numbers based on cardinal numbers may consult the references listed at the end of this chapter.

» I · 1 PEANO'S AXIOMS

We *postulate* the existence of a set P together with a map $+ : P \to P$, which sends $x \in P$ onto $x^+ \in P$ and which satisfies the following axioms of Peano:

P_1 (axiom of infinity) · The map $+$ is injective but not surjective. Thus $+$ leads to a bijection between P and a proper subset P^+ of P, where $P^+ = \{x^+ \mid x \in P\}$.

As examples, the reader may verify that $\{0_P\}$, $\{0_P, 0_P^+\}$, and P are all segments of P.

In order to facilitate our arguments, we collect several results concerning segments into the following exercise.

Exercise 5 · Let P and $+ : P \to P$ satisfy the Peano axioms. If $x \in P$, then $S(x)$ denotes the intersection of all the segments T of P such that $x \in T$.

(a) Let $\{S_i \mid i \in I\}$ be a set of segments of P indexed by the set I. Show that $\bigcap_{i \in I} S_i$ and $\bigcup_{i \in I} S_i$ are segments of P. Thus $S(x)$ is the least segment of P that contains x.

(b) Show that for each segment S of P such that $S \neq P$, there exists at least one element $x \in S$ such that $x^+ \notin S$. *Hint.* Use P_2' of Exercise 2.

(c) Show that $x \neq x^+$ for each element x of P. *Hint.* Both P_1 and P_2 are needed to show that $S = \{x \in P \mid x \neq x^+\}$ is the set P.

(d) Let S be a proper segment of P and $x \in S$, but $x^+ \notin S$. Show that $S \cup \{x^+\} = T$ is a proper segment of P. *Hint.* Show that $(x^+)^+ \notin T$ by using (c).

(e) Show that P is the union of all its *proper* segments. *Hint.* (d) is needed to show that every element of P lies in at least one proper segment.

(f) Let S be a proper segment of P and $x \in S$, but $x^+ \notin S$. Show that $S - \{x\}$ is either the empty set or again a proper segment of P. Combine this with (a) and (e) to show that $x^+ \notin S(x)\ \forall\, x \in P$.

(g) Show that $S(x^+) = S(x) \cup \{x^+\}\ \forall\, x \in P$. *Hint.* If a segment T contains the element y, then T contains $S(y)$.

(h) Show that every segment T of P is equal to $\bigcup_{x \in T} S(x)$.

We remark that although it is true it is difficult to verify at this stage that every proper segment of P has the form $S(x)$ for some $x \in P$. This is equivalent to the uniqueness of the element x described in (d).

DEFINITION 2 · Let P and $+ : P \to P$ satisfy the Peano axioms. Let Q be a set with a distinguished element q and let $F : Q \to Q$ be a map. Let S be a segment of P. A map $\rho : S \to Q$ such that (a) $\rho(0_P) = q$ and (b) $\rho(x^+) = F(\rho(x))$ when $x^+ \in S$ (therefore, $x \in S$) is called a ***partial map*** with domain S (and relative to F and q).

We are now in a position to verify the following:

DEFINITION BY INDUCTION · We use the notation of Definition 2; then there exists a unique map $\sigma : P \to Q$ which satisfies the following conditions,

(a) $\sigma(0_P) = q$.

(b) $\sigma(x^+) = F(\sigma(x)) \; \forall \, x \in P$.

Exercise 4 shows that σ is unique (if it exists at all). We need only to show the existence of σ. We establish the existence and the uniqueness of a partial map on each segment $S(x)$. Let $T = \{x \in P \mid$ there exists a unique partial map with domain $S(x)\}$.

Because $S(0_P) = \{0_P\}$, condition (a), together with the specification of $q \in Q$, implies that $0_P \in T$. Suppose that $y \in T$. From Exercise 5, (f) and (g) we deduce that $S(y^+) = S(y) \cup \{y^+\}$ and that $y^+ \notin S(y)$. Because $y \in T$, there is a unique partial map ρ with domain $S(y)$. Let $\tau : S(y^+) \to Q$ be defined by setting $\tau(z) = \rho(z)$ for $z \in S(y)$ and $\tau(y^+) = F(\rho(y))$. Because $y \in S(y)$ and ρ, F are maps, we conclude that τ is a map. It is easy to see that τ is a partial map with domain $S(y^+)$. Suppose that τ' is another partial map with domain $S(y^+)$. It is easy to see that the restriction of τ' to the segment $S(y)$ is a partial map on $S(y)$. Since $y \in T$, we conclude that $\tau'(z) = \rho(z) = \tau(z)$ for $z \in S(y)$; and since τ' is a partial map on $S(y^+)$ we find that $\tau'(y^+) = F(\tau'(y)) = F(\rho(y)) = \tau(y^+)$. Thus $\tau' = \tau$ and $y^+ \in T$.

It follows from the axiom of induction that $T = P$. Now, by using Exercise 5 (h) we define $\sigma : P \to Q$ by setting $\sigma(x)$ as the value of the partial map with domain $S(x)$ on the element x. The arguments we carried out show that σ is indeed a map. It is easy to see that this map σ satisfies (a) and (b).

We can now derive as a corollary the assertion that for any two sets P and Q with maps $+ : P \to P$, $* : Q \to Q$, both of which satisfy the axioms of Peano, there is a unique map $\sigma : P \to Q$ which satisfies the following conditions:

(a) $\sigma(0_P) = 0_Q$.

(b) $\sigma(x^+) = (\sigma(x))^* \; \forall \, x \in P$.

This map σ is a bijection.

The uniqueness of σ follows from Exercise 4. We simply take 0_Q for q and $*$ for F. Similarly, the existence of σ is a consequence of definition by induction. We need only verify that σ is a bijection. To show this we interchange the role of P and Q. Thus we can find a map $\sigma' : Q \to P$ such that (a) $\sigma'(0_Q) = 0_P$ and (b) $\sigma'(y^*) = (\sigma'(y))^+ \; \forall \, y \in Q$. Consequently $\sigma' \circ \sigma : P \to P$ satisfies (a) $(\sigma' \circ \sigma)(0_P) = 0_P$ and (b)

$(\sigma' \circ \sigma)(x^+) = ((\sigma' \circ \sigma)(x))^+ \ \forall\, x \in P$. Since the identity map on P has the same properties as $\sigma' \circ \sigma$, we conclude from the uniqueness of such maps that $\sigma' \circ \sigma$ is the identity map on P. Interchanging the roles of P and Q once again, we see that $\sigma \circ \sigma'$ is the identity map on Q. Thus σ must be a bijection with σ' as its inverse.

From the preceding discussion we see that all sets P and maps $+ : P \to P$ which satisfy the axioms of Peano may be considered the same, except for names and notations. We usually phrase this in the form: "If P, $+ : P \to P$ and Q, $* : Q \to Q$ are two systems that satisfy the axioms of Peano, they are ***isomorphic***". Axioms which imply that any two systems satisfying them are isomorphic are said to be ***categorical***. When we attempt to axiomatize a preconceived system, such as the natural numbers, we check first that the axioms are satisfied by the preconceived prototype and then that the axioms are categorical. When both have been done, we then say that we have axiomatically characterized the preconceived system. We now collect all our remarks to make the following definition:

DEFINITION 3 · Among all sets and maps that satisfy the Peano axioms, we select one such pair and fix it once for all. The set chosen is denoted by $\mathbf{P}$; the successor map associated with it is denoted by $+$. $\mathbf{P}$ is called *the* set of all natural numbers; $\mathbf{P}^+$ is the set of ***positive integers***. As a matter of convenience, we now assume that the reader is familiar with the decimal system and denote the nonsuccessor of $\mathbf{P}$ by 0, the successor of 0 by 1, the successor of 1 by 2, and so on.

We conclude this section with two more exercises that will be useful later.

Exercise 6 · (complete induction). Let S be a subset of $\mathbf{P}$ such that (a) $0 \in S$ and (b) if $S(x) \subset S$, then $x^+ \in S$, where x is any element of $\mathbf{P}$. Show that $S = P$. *Hint.* Use (h) of Exercise 5.

Exercise 7 · Let A, B, and C be sets. Let U^V denote the set of all maps from the set V to the set U. Show that there is a natural bijection $\sigma : C^{A \times B} \to (C^B)^A$. *Hint.* Let $f : A \times B \to C$ and define $\sigma(f) : A \to C^B$ by setting $(\sigma(f)(a))(b) = f(a, b) \ \forall\, a \in A$ and $b \in B$; namely, if f is a function of two variables, then for each fixed value of the first variable f may be considered as a function of the second variable.

The chief application of Exercise 7 is in the definition of maps by induction; namely, A will often be the set $\mathbf{P}$. The set C^B then plays the role of Q in definition by induction.

» I · 2 ADDITION IN **P**

DEFINITION 1 · Addition in $\mathbf{P}$ is a map $+ : \mathbf{P} \times \mathbf{P} \to \mathbf{P}$ (not to be confused with the successor map), which satisfies the following conditions [where we write $a + b$ for $+(a, b)$]:

(a) $0 + a = a \ \forall\, a \in \mathbf{P}$.

(b) $x^+ + a = (x + a)^+ \ \forall\, x, a \in \mathbf{P}$.

The existence and the uniqueness of the addition map may be verified by the definition by induction. Roughly, (a) tells us that $x + a$ is defined when $x = 0$ and a is arbitrary in $\mathbf{P}$; (b) tells us that $x^+ + a$ can be found whenever $x + a$ is defined. In this second step we note that x is uniquely determined by x^+. To make this rough argument more precise we may proceed as follows:

(1) From Exercise 1.7, a map from $\mathbf{P} \times \mathbf{P}$ to $\mathbf{P}$ is uniquely determined by a map from $\mathbf{P}$ to $\mathbf{P}^{\mathbf{P}}$. Equivalently, for each $a \in \mathbf{P}$ we must have a map $\rho(a) : \mathbf{P} \to \mathbf{P}$. The corresponding map from $\mathbf{P} \times \mathbf{P}$ to $\mathbf{P}$ is then the map that sends (x, a) onto $(\rho(a))(x)$. (The careful reader should realize that A and B in Exercise 1.7 can be interchanged.)

(2) Let $a \in \mathbf{P}$ be an arbitrarily chosen element. The map $\rho(a) : \mathbf{P} \to \mathbf{P}$ is defined by induction so that:

$$(*) \quad (\rho(a))(0) = a$$

and

$$(**) \quad (\rho(a))(x^+) = ((\rho(a))(x))^+ \ \forall\, x \in \mathbf{P}.$$

(We take Q to be $\mathbf{P}$, $q \in Q$ to be $a \in \mathbf{P}$, and $F : Q \to Q$ to be the successor map.)

The net result of (1) and (2) is that $x + a = +(x, a) = (\rho(a))(x)$; namely, $\rho(a)$ is the map that tells us how to add a to x from the right.

In the future proofs of this sort will be assumed to have been carried out by the reader.

From the definition and from repeated applications of Peano axioms the following result may be obtained:

THEOREM 1 · Addition in $\mathbf{P}$ has the following properties:

A_0 (existence of an additive identity). There exists an element $e \in \mathbf{P}$ such that $e + x = x = x + e \ \forall\, x \in \mathbf{P}$. Indeed, $e = 0$ is the unique additive identity of $\mathbf{P}$.

A_1 (associative law). $x + (y + z) = (x + y) + z$.

A_2 (commutative law). $x + y = y + x$.

A_3 (cancellation law). $x + y = x + z$ implies that $y = z$; x, y, and z denote arbitrary elements of **P**.

We give a proof of A_1 and leave the remaining proofs to the reader. The careful reader should observe that A_0 appears to be a consequence of A_2 and the definition that included $0 + a = a \ \forall \ a \in \mathbf{P}$. However, in order to verify A_2, we must first verify that $0 + y = y + 0 \ \forall \ y \in \mathbf{P}$; then we may proceed by induction on x. Thus we should verify A_0 for the element $e = 0$.

We now let $S = \{x \in \mathbf{P} \mid x + (y + z) = (x + y) + z \ \forall \ y, z \in \mathbf{P}\}$. A_1 is verified by showing that $S = \mathbf{P}$.

Since $0 + (y + z) = y + z = (0 + y) + z$ by the definition of addition, we see that $0 \in S$. If $x \in S$, then $x + (y + z) = (x + y) + z$ holds. Therefore, by using the definition of addition several times we have $x^+ + (y + z) = [x + (y + z)]^+ = [(x + y) + z]^+ = (x + y)^+ + z = (x^+ + y) + z \ \forall \ y, z \in P$. Thus $x^+ \in S$ whenever $x \in S$. It follows that $S = \mathbf{P}$ by the axiom of induction.

» 1 · 3 ORDERING IN *P*: A SECOND DEFINITION OF FINITENESS

In the preceding section we defined addition by using the presence of the successor map. We now define a linear ordering of **P** by means of addition in **P**.

DEFINITION 1 · Let $a, b \in \mathbf{P}$. We write $a \leqslant b$ (respectively, $a < b$) if and only if there is an x in **P** (respectively, in $\mathbf{P}^+$) such that $a + x = b$. We say that a is ***less than or equal to*** b (respectively, a is ***less than*** b). (The reader should note that the element x, if it exists, must be unique. This is a consequence of A_3 in Theorem 2.1.)

Exercise 1 · Show that $a < b$ if and only if $a \leqslant b$ and $a \neq b$, $\forall \ a, b \in \mathbf{P}$. Show that $a \leqslant a$ and $a < a^+ \ \forall \ a \in \mathbf{P}$.

Exercise 2 · Show that for all a, b, $c \in \mathbf{P}$, $a \leqslant b$ implies that $a + c \leqslant b + c$ and that $a \leqslant b, b \leqslant c$ imply that $a \leqslant c$.

Exercise 3 · Show that $<$ is a linear ordering on **P**.

Hint. For each $n \in \mathbf{P}$ let $T_n = \{x \in \mathbf{P} \mid x < n \text{ or } x = n \text{ or } n < x\}$. Show that $T_n = \mathbf{P}$; then show that the three possibilities mentioned in the definition of T_n are mutually exclusive. (For the last part it is necessary to verify that $x + y = 0$ has the unique solution $x = 0 = y$, where $x, y \in \mathbf{P}$.)

We are now in a position to identify the segments of $\mathbf{P}$.

THEOREM 1 · The proper segments of $\mathbf{P}$ may be described as follows:

(a) If $n \in \mathbf{P}$, then $S(n) = \{x \in \mathbf{P} \mid x \leqslant n\}$.

(b) If S is a proper segment of $\mathbf{P}$, there exists a unique $n \in \mathbf{P}$ such that $n \in S$ and $n^+ \notin S$; moreover, $S = S(n)$.

(c) If $m, n \in \mathbf{P}$, then $m \leqslant n$ if and only if $S(m) \subset S(n)$. Thus the proper segments of $\mathbf{P}$ are linearly ordered by (strict) inclusion.

(a) is proved by induction on n; namely, let $T = \{n \in \mathbf{P} \mid S(n) = \{x \in \mathbf{P} \mid x \leqslant n\}\}$. It is clear that $0 \in T$. (Again, we invoke the fact that $x + y = 0$, $x, y \in \mathbf{P}$ imply $x = 0 = y$.) By using (g) of Exercise 1.5, we find it rather easy to verify that $x \in T$ implies that $x^+ \in T$. Thus $T = \mathbf{P}$ by induction.

In (b) let S be a proper segment of $\mathbf{P}$. We have already remarked in (b) of Exercise 1.5 that there exists an $n \in S$ such that $n^+ \notin S$. Since S is a segment, we know that $S(n) \subset S$. From (a), preceding, and Exercise 3 we see that $z \in S - S(n)$ implies that $n < z$. It would then follow that $n^+ \leqslant z$ (for if $z < n^+$, then $z + a^+ = n^+$ for some $a \in \mathbf{P}$ and therefore $z + a = n$ for the same $a \in \mathbf{P}$. It would then follow that $z \leqslant n$ and $n < n$, an impossibility.) However, $z \in S$ implies that $S(z) \subset S$. From (a) we would obtain the contradiction that $n^+ \in S$. Thus $S - S(n) = \varnothing$ and therefore $S = S(n)$. The uniqueness of n follows quickly from (a) and the fact that $<$ is a linear ordering on $\mathbf{P}$. (c) follows easily from (a) and (b). «

THEOREM 2 (Greatest lower bound property) · Let S be a non-empty subset of $\mathbf{P}$. Then S has a greatest lower bound in $\mathbf{P}$ with respect to the partial ordering $\leqslant$. This greatest lower bound is a uniquely determined element of S.

We have already remarked in Chapter O that the greatest lower bound, when it exists, must be unique. To show the existence we consider the set $T = \{x \in \mathbf{P} \mid x \text{ is a lower bound of } S\}$. T is clearly a segment of $\mathbf{P}$. If $n \in S$, then $n^+ \notin T$. Thus T is a proper segment of $\mathbf{P}$

From Theorem 1 we see that T has a uniquely determined maximal element n; namely, $n \in \mathbf{P}$ is such that $T = S(n)$. It follows that n is the greatest lower bound of S. If $n \notin S$, then $n < x \ \forall\, x \in S$. Thus, when $x \in S$, $n + y^+ = x$ may be solved for $y \in \mathbf{P}$. It follows that $n^+ \leqslant x$ holds $\forall\, x \in S$ or $n^+ \in T$. This is a contradiction. Hence $n \in S$ as desired. «

We can now give a more convenient definition of a finite set. For this we need the following results:

THEOREM 3 · Let Q be a set. Then Q is infinite if and only if there exists an injective map $\sigma : \mathbf{P} \to Q$.

From Exercise O.2.3 it follows easily that under a bijection the notion of finiteness of a set does not change; namely, if ρ is a bijection between the sets A and B, then A is finite if and only if B is finite. Consequently, if $\sigma : \mathbf{P} \to Q$ is an injection, then Q contains an infinite subset $\sigma(\mathbf{P})$. From Exercise O.4.2 we conclude that Q must itself be infinite.

Conversely, suppose that Q is an infinite set. Then there exists a map $F : Q \to Q$ which is injective but not surjective. Thus $Q - F(Q)$ is nonempty, and we may select an element $q \in Q - F(Q)$. Using definition by induction, we can find a map $\sigma : \mathbf{P} \to Q$ such that (*) $\sigma(0) = q$ and (**) $\sigma(x^+) = F(\sigma(x)) \ \forall\, x \in \mathbf{P}$. We assert that σ is injective. To determine this we let

$$T = \{x \in \mathbf{P} \mid \text{if } y \in \mathbf{P} \text{ and } \sigma(x) = \sigma(y), \text{ then } y = x\}.$$

From (**) we see that $\sigma(\mathbf{P}^+) \subset F(Q)$. Since $\mathbf{P} - \mathbf{P}^+ = \{0\}$ and $q \in Q - F(Q)$, it is immediately clear that $0 \in T$. We now proceed by complete induction. Let $x \in \mathbf{P}$ such that $S(x) \subset T$. We must show that $x^+ \in T$. Thus let $\sigma(x^+) = \sigma(y)$, $y \in \mathbf{P}$. Since $x^+ \neq 0$ and $0 \in S(x) \subset T$, we see that $y \neq 0$. It follows that $y = z^+$ for some $z \in \mathbf{P}$; but, from (**), $\sigma(z^+) = F(\sigma(z))$ and $\sigma(x^+) = F(\sigma(x))$. Since F is injective and $\sigma(x^+) = \sigma(y) = \sigma(z^+)$, we see that $\sigma(x) = \sigma(z)$. Since $x \in S(x) \subset T$, we see that $x = z$, hence $x^+ = z^+ = y$. We have therefore proved that $x^+ \in T$ and that $T = \mathbf{P}$ by induction. This concludes the proof of Theorem 3. «

Exercise 4 · Show that every proper segment of **P** is a finite set. *Hint*. Let T be a set and $x \in T$. Let $S = T - \{x\}$. Show that S is finite implies that T is finite. (To accomplish this use the fact that $+$ is a bijection between **P** and $\mathbf{P}^+$ and that $\{0\} = \mathbf{P} - \mathbf{P}^+$.) Use it with (g) of Exercise 1.5 to complete the present exercise.

THEOREM 4 · Let Q be a set. Then Q is a finite nonempty set if and only if there is a bijection between Q and a proper segment $S(n)$ of **P**. The integer n is then uniquely determined.

We have already remarked in Exercise 4 that every proper segment of **P** is a finite nonempty set. Thus, if there is a bijection between Q and a proper segment of **P**, Q is also a finite nonempty set.

Conversely, suppose that Q is a finite nonempty set. We must show that a bijection between Q and some proper segment $S(n)$ of **P** does exist. To accomplish this, we consider the set $\mathcal{F}$ of all injective maps F such that F is defined on a segment of **P** and takes on values in Q. Since Q is nonempty, we can find $q \in Q$. Thus the map which sends 0 onto q is an injection with domain $S(0) = \{0\}$. Hence $\mathcal{F}$ is nonempty. We now define a partial ordering on $\mathcal{F}$.

(*) If F and $G \in \mathcal{F}$ such that they are defined on the segments S and T of **P**, we write $F \leqslant G$ if and only if the following conditions hold:

(a) $S \subset T$,

(b) $F(x) = G(x) \; \forall \, x \in S$.

It is immediate that $\leqslant$ is a partial ordering on $\mathcal{F}$. We now assert that $\mathcal{F}$ is inductive under $\leqslant$ in the sense of Zorn's lemma. To determine this we let $\{F_i \mid i \in I\}$ be a linearly ordered subset of $\mathcal{F}$. From Exercise 1.5(a) we see that $S = \bigcup_{i \in I} S_i$ is a segment and that S_i is the segment on which F_i is defined. We define $F : S \to Q$ by setting $F(x) = F_i(x)$ when $x \in S_i$. From the definition (*) and the hypothesis that $\{F_i \mid i \in I\}$ is linearly ordered we may deduce that F is a well-defined map. Since S_i, $i \in I$, are linearly ordered by inclusion, we see that x, $y \in S$ imply that there exists an $i \in I$ such that $x, y \in S_i$. Thus $F_i(x) = F(x) = F(y) = F_i(y)$ implies that $x = y$. It follows that F is injection; hence $F \in \mathcal{F}$. It is also clear that F is an upper bound of $\{F_i \mid i \in I\}$ in $\mathcal{F}$. From Zorn's lemma we see that $\mathcal{F}$ contains a maximal element G. Let T be the segment on which G is defined. Since G is an injection, we see that G is a bijection between the segment T and the subset $G(T)$ of Q. Since Q is finite, it follows from Theorem 3 that $T \neq$ **P**. Thus from Exercise 4 and Theorem 1 we see that $T = S(n)$ for some $n \in$ **P**. We now assert that $G(T) = Q$, that is to say, G is a bijection between and T and Q. If this were not the case, then $Q - G(T)$ would be nonempty. Let $q \in Q - G(T)$ and define $H : S(n^+) \to Q$ by setting $H(x) = G(x) \; \forall \, x \in S(n)$ and $H(n^+) = q$. It is then immediate that H is injective and is defined on the segment $S(n^+)$. It is now clear that $H \in \mathcal{F}$ and $G < H$. This contradicts the maximality of G in $\mathcal{F}$. We may now conclude that G is a bijection between $S(n)$ and Q.

Finally, we show that the integer n is uniquely determined by Q. Let $\sigma : S(n) \to Q$ and $\rho : S(m) \to Q$ be bijections. From Theorem 1(c) we may assume that $S(n) \subset S(m)$. Thus $\sigma^{-1} \circ \rho$ is a bijection between $S(m)$ and $S(n)$, where σ^{-1} is the inverse of σ. Since $S(m)$ is a finite set, we see that $S(n) = S(m)$. It follows from (b) of Theorem 1 that $n = m$. This completes the proof of Theorem 4.

DEFINITION 2 · Let Q be a finite set. If Q is the empty set, the cardinal number $|Q|$ of Q is defined to be $0 \in \mathbf{P}$. If Q is nonempty and n is the integer determined in Theorem 4, the cardinal number $|Q|$ of Q is defined as $n^+ \in \mathbf{P}$.

Exercise 5 · Let S and T be finite sets. Show that $|S \cup T| + |S \cap T| = |S| + |T|$. *Hint.* First consider the special case in which $S \cap T = \varnothing$. A map from $S \cup T$ to $\mathbf{P}$ can be constructed out of any two maps from S to $\mathbf{P}$ and from T to $\mathbf{P}$. Assume that ρ is a bijection from S to the segment $S(m)$ and that σ is a bijection from T to the segment $S(n)$. (The case in which S or T is empty is trivial and is omitted.) Let $\tau : \mathbf{P} \to \mathbf{P}$ be the map defined by $\tau(x) = x + m^+$. Show that $\alpha : S \cup T \to \mathbf{P}$ given by $\alpha(x) = \rho(x)\ \forall\, x \in S$ and $\alpha(y) = \tau(\sigma(y))\ \forall\, y \in T$ is a bijection between $S \cup T$ and the segment $S(m^+ + n)$.

» 1 · 4 MULTIPLICATION IN P

DEFINITION 1 · Multiplication in $\mathbf{P}$ is a map $\cdot : \mathbf{P} \times \mathbf{P} \to \mathbf{P}$ which satisfies the following conditions [where we write ab for $\cdot(a, b)$]:

(a) $0a = 0\ \forall\, a \in \mathbf{P}$.

(b) $x^+a = xa + a\ \forall\, x, a \in \mathbf{P}$.

Exercise 1 · Show that multiplication in $\mathbf{P}$ exists and is unique.

Exercise 2 · Show that $1a = a = a1\ \forall\, a \in \mathbf{P}$.

Exercise 3 · Show that if $a, b \in \mathbf{P}^+$, then $ab \in \mathbf{P}^+$.

Exercise 4 · Show that if a, b, and $c \in \mathbf{P}$ and $a \leqslant b$, then $ac \leqslant bc$.

THEOREM 1 · Multiplication in **P** has the following properties:

M_0 (existence of a multiplicative identity). There exists an element $f \in \mathbf{P}$ such that $fa = a = af \; \forall \; a \in \mathbf{P}$. Indeed, f must be 1.

M_1 (associative law). $a(bc) = (ab)c$.

M_2 (commutative law). $ab = ba$.

M_3 (cancellation law). If $a \neq 0$ and $ab = ac$, then $b = c$.

D (distributive laws). $a(b + c) = ab + ac$ and $(b + c)a = ba + ca$; a, b and c denote arbitrary elements of **P**.

M_0 follows from Exercise 1. The remaining properties should be verified in the order of D, M_1, M_2 then M_3. The verifications involve repeated applications of the axioms of Peano. In M_3 Exercise 3 and Exercise 3.3 are useful. We note that each of the two distributive laws follows from the other and the commutative law of multiplication.

Somewhat more difficult is the following:

Exercise 5 · Let S and T be finite sets and show that $|S \times T| = |S||T|$.

» I·5 CONSTRUCTION OF THE INTEGERS *Z*

We have already noted that for an arbitrary pair of elements a and b of **P** the equation $a + x = b$ may not necessarily have a solution for x in **P**. Indeed, the existence of such a solution had been used to define an ordering on **P**. We now wish to enlarge **P** so that a solution always exists in the larger system. To this end we introduce a relation $\sim$ on $\mathbf{P} \times \mathbf{P}$; namely, $(a, b) \sim (c, d)$ if and only if $a + d = b + c$. We see quickly that this is in fact an equivalence relation on $\mathbf{P} \times \mathbf{P}$. (Geometrically, each equivalence class consists of those points in the first quadrant that have integer coordinates and that lie on a line with slope 1. If we identify the integers with points on the horizontal axis which have integers as coordinates, we see that these lines with slope 1 meet the horizontal axis exactly at these integer points. Thus we can identify each equivalence class with an integer.) Formally, we let $\mathbf{Z} = (\mathbf{P} \times \mathbf{P})/\sim$ be the set of all equivalence classes. The equivalence class of (a, b) is denoted temporarily by $\overline{(a, b)}$. We define $+$ and $\cdot : \mathbf{Z} \times \mathbf{Z} \to \mathbf{Z}$ (called addition and multiplication, respectively) as follows:

$$\overline{(a, b)} + \overline{(c, d)} = \overline{(a + c, b + d)},$$

$$\overline{(a, b)} \cdot \overline{(c, d)} = \overline{(ac + bd, ad + bc)}.$$

It should be noted that (a, b) is but one of the many elements that form the equivalence class $\overline{(a, b)}$. In these definitions it is necessary to check that $+$ and $\cdot$ are indeed maps. For example, let $(a', b') \sim (a, b)$ and $(c', d') \sim (c, d)$. It follows that $a' + b = a + b'$ and $c' + d = c + d'$. Using Theorem 2.1, we may conclude that $(a' + c') + (b + d) = (a + c) + (b' + d')$ or $(a' + c', b' + d') \sim (a + c, b + d)$. Thus we can say that addition is well-defined. Similarly, it is possible to verify that multiplication is well-defined. In the future we shall leave the task of checking maps to be well-defined to the careful reader.

It will be convenient for the reader to refer to $\overline{(a, b)}$ as "a minus b." Indeed, the definitions given will then conform with rules that are familiar to the reader.

THEOREM 1 · Addition and multiplication in **Z** have the following properties:

A_0. Existence of an additive identity. Here $\overline{(0, 0)}$ is the unique element such that $\overline{(0, 0)} + x = x = x + \overline{(0, 0)}, \forall x \in \mathbf{Z}$.

A_1. Associative law for $+$.

A_2. Commutative law for $+$.

A_3. Existence of an additive inverse. Indeed, $\overline{(b, a)}$ is the unique element $z \in \mathbf{Z}$ such that $z + \overline{(a, b)} = \overline{(0, 0)} = \overline{(a, b)} + z$. If $x \in \mathbf{Z}$, the additive inverse of x will be denoted by $-x$.

M_0. Existence of a multiplicative identity. Here $\overline{(1, 0)}$ is the unique element $e \in \mathbf{Z}$ such that $ex = x = xe\ \forall x \in \mathbf{Z}$.

M_1. Associative law for $\cdot$.

M_2. Commutative law for $\cdot$.

M_3. Cancellation law for $\cdot$. If $x \neq \overline{(0, 0)}$ and $xy = xz$, then $y = z$, where x, y, and $z \in \mathbf{Z}$.

D. Distributive laws of $\cdot$ with respect to $+$.

Finally, the map that sends $a \in \mathbf{P}$ onto $\overline{(a, 0)} \in \mathbf{Z}$ is an injection of **P** into **Z** which preserves $+$ and $\cdot$. If we identify **P** and a subset of **Z** through this injection, then $\overline{(a, b)} = a + -b$ holds for all $a, b \in \mathbf{P}$.

The proof of Theorem 1 is straightforward. Each item can be verified by using the corresponding property of **P**. In view of the last assertion, we simplify the notation and make the following definition.

DEFINITION 1 · In **Z** let $\overline{(a, 0)}$ be denoted by a and let $\overline{(0, b)}$ be denoted by $-b$. Thus $-0 = 0$, $-b$ is the additive inverse of b, where $b \in \mathbf{P}$. In general, if $z \in \mathbf{Z}$, then $-z$ will denote the additive inverse of z.

Exercise 1 · Show that the existence of an additive inverse in $\mathbf{Z}$ implies that the cancellation law holds for $+$. Show that if $x \in \mathbf{Z}$ then $-(-x) = x$ and $-x = (-1)x$. Show that $\mathbf{Z}$ is the disjoint union of $\mathbf{P}^+$, $\{0\}$, and $-\mathbf{P}^+ = \{-x \mid x \in \mathbf{P}^+\}$. ($-\mathbf{P}^+$ is called the set of ***negative integers.***) Show that $-\mathbf{P}^+$ is closed with respect to addition. Show that $u, v \in -\mathbf{P}^+$ implies that $uv \in \mathbf{P}^+$.

DEFINITION 2 · In $\mathbf{Z}$ let $y - x$ denote $y + (-x)$ and write $x < y$ if and only if $y - x \in \mathbf{P}^+$. If $x \in \mathbf{Z}$, then $|x|$, the ***absolute value*** of x, is defined as follows:

$$|x| = x \quad \text{if} \quad x \in \mathbf{P} \quad \text{and} \quad |x| = -x \quad \text{if} \quad x \in -\mathbf{P}^+.$$

We note that $\mathbf{P}$ is the set of all absolute values.

THEOREM 2 · $\mathbf{Z}$ has the following properties:

O. $<$ is a linear ordering on $\mathbf{Z}$. If $a, b \in \mathbf{P}$, then $a < b$ in $\mathbf{Z}$ if and only if $a < b$ in $\mathbf{P}$.

OA. If $a < b$, then $a + c < b + c \; \forall \, a, b, c \in \mathbf{Z}$.

OM. If $0 < c$ and $a < b$, then $ac < bc$ and $b(-c) < a(-c)$, $\forall \, a, b, c \in \mathbf{Z}$.

AV. $|ab| = |a|\,|b|$ and $|a + b| \leqslant |a| + |b| \; \forall \, a, b \in \mathbf{Z}$.

GLB. Let S be a nonempty subset of $\mathbf{Z}$. Suppose that S has a lower bound with respect to $\leqslant$ ($a \leqslant b$ is defined by $a < b$ or $a = b$). S then has a unique greatest lower bound. This greatest lower bound lies in S.

The properties *O*, *OA*, and *OM* follow rather easily from the ordering properties of $\mathbf{P}$ and Theorem 1. *GLB* follows easily from the greatest lower bound property of $\mathbf{P}$ and the definition of $\leqslant$. We leave the details of these properties as well as the verification of *AV* to the reader. We note that by using the map sending x onto $-x$ it is possible to verify the least upper bound property in $\mathbf{Z}$ and $\mathbf{P}$.

» I · 6 DIVISIBILITY THEORY IN *Z*

Sections 3 and 5 were devoted to the study of an equation of the form $a + x = b$. When we insisted that a, b, and x all lie in $\mathbf{P}$, we were led to a linear ordering on **P**. By allowing a, b, and x to lie in **Z** we were able to solve all such equations. Indeed, x is uniquely determined by a and b. By insisting that x should lie in **P** we were able to obtain a linear ordering on **Z** that extends the linear ordering on **P**.

We can now carry out an analogous investigation for equations of the form $ax = b$. To be consistent we should first consider the set **P**, then the set **Z**. However, by using the property AV stated in Theorem 5.2 the investigation on **P** may be obtained from the investigation on **Z** by taking absolute values. Thus we go directly to the set **Z**.

DEFINITION 1 · Let $a, b \in \mathbf{Z}$. We say that a ***divides*** b, a is a ***factor*** of b, or b is a ***multiple*** of a if and only if the equation $ax = b$ has at least one solution for $x \in \mathbf{Z}$. When this is the case, we write $a \mid b$; otherwise we write $a \nmid b$. If $a \mid 1$, we say that a is a ***unit*** in **Z**. If $a \mid b$ and $b \mid a$, we say that a and b are ***associates***. Thus a unit is precisely an associate of 1.

Exercise 1 · Show that $\mid$ is a transitive and reflexive relation on **Z**. Show that $0 \mid a$ if and only if $a = 0$. (We note that $0 \mid a$ is more conveniently read as "a is a multiple of 0.") Show that $\pm 1 \mid a$ and $a \mid 0 \; \forall \, a \in \mathbf{Z}$. Show that $a \mid b$ and $a \mid c$ imply that $a \mid (b + c)$.

Exercise 2 · Show that $a, b \in \mathbf{Z}$ are associates if and only if $|a| = |b|$. Conclude that the relation "a is an associate of b" is an equivalence relation on **Z**. Show that $\mid$ is a partial ordering on **P**.

Exercise 3 · Show that $x \mid y$ in **Z** implies that either $y = 0$ or $|x| \leqslant |y|$.

The relation $\mid$ is not a partial ordering on **Z** because $-1 \mid 1$ and $1 \mid -1$ but $1 \neq -1$. The relation $\mid$ is a partial ordering on **P**, but it is not a linear ordering on **P**. In any event, some of the elements of **Z** might be termed "minimal." To be more precise we state the following:

DEFINITION 2 · An element $z \in \mathbf{Z}$ is said to be ***nonfactorizable*** (or ***irreducible***) if and only if the following conditions are satisfied:

(a) z is not a unit.

(b) If $z = xy$ in **Z**, either x or y must be a unit in **Z**.

DEFINITION 3 · An element $z \in \mathbf{Z}$ is called a ***prime*** in $\mathbf{Z}$ if and only if the following conditions are satisfied:

(a) z is not a unit.

(b) If $z \mid xy$ in $\mathbf{Z}$, either $z \mid x$ or $z \mid y$ in $\mathbf{Z}$.

We note that 0, 1, -1 are not nonfactorizable, 0 is a prime, and 1, -1 are not primes in $\mathbf{Z}$.

LEMMA 1 · Let $x \in \mathbf{Z}$ with $|x| > 1$. Then x is a product of a finite number of nonfactorizable integers.

Proof · It is easy to see that nonfactorizability is a property of the equivalence class determined by the relation of being associates. Thus we may assume that $x > 1$.

From Exercise 3 we see that 2 is nonfactorizable. By induction we assume that for $y \in \mathbf{P}^+$, $2 \leqslant y < x$, y is a product of a finite number of nonfactorizable integers. Now either x is nonfactorizable or $x = ab$, where $|a|$ and $|b|$ are both greater than 1. In the first case we are done. In the second case, by replacing a by $-a$ if necessary, we may assume that a and b both lie in $\mathbf{P}^+$. Thus $2 \leqslant a, b < x$. By the induction hypothesis both a and b are products of some finite number of nonfactorizable integers. Hence so is x.

THEOREM 1 (Euclid's division algorithm) · Let $a, b \in \mathbf{Z}$ with $b \neq 0$. Then there exist unique integers q and r which satisfy the following conditions:

(a) $a = qb + r$,

(b) $0 \leqslant r < |b|$.

The element r is called the ***remainder.***

Proof · We first show the uniqueness of q and r.

Let $q_1 b + r_1 = a = q_2 b + r_2$ and $0 \leqslant r_1 \leqslant r_2 < |b|$. We note that because $<$ is a linear ordering on $\mathbf{Z}$ the assumption that $r_1 \leqslant r_2$ may be made. Hence we obtain $r_2 - r_1 = b(q_1 - q_2)$. It follows that $|b|$ divides $r_2 - r_1$ and that $0 \leqslant r_2 - r_1 < |b|$. From Exercise 3 we conclude that $r_2 = r_1$. Using the cancellation law, we conclude that $q_2 = q_1$.

We now show the existence of q and r.

Since $b \neq 0$, we have to consider the two cases $b < 0$ and $0 < b$. We leave the first to the reader as an exercise and carry out the second.

Let $b > 0$ and let $T = \{x \in \mathbf{Z} \mid xb \leqslant a\}$. Since $b > 0$, we see that $-|a|b \leqslant a$ and $-|a| \in T$. Since $b > 0$, it is easy to see that T is bounded from above by $|a|$. From the remark after Theorem 5.2 T has a least upper bound q in T. Thus $r = a - qb \geqslant 0$. Since $q + 1 \notin T$, it follows that $a < (q + 1)b$. Thus $r = a - qb < b$. It follows that $0 \leqslant r < |b| = b$. «

We shall now construct systems with a finite number of elements that resemble the integers in the sense that they have almost all of the properties stated in Theorem 5.1.

DEFINITION 4 · Let $m \in \mathbf{Z}$. We say that ***a is congruent to b mod m*** if and only if $m \mid (a - b)$. In such cases we write $a \equiv b \pmod{m}$.

It follows from Exercises 1 and 2 that congruence mod m is an equivalence relation on $\mathbf{Z}$. The set of such equivalence classes is denoted by $\mathbf{Z}/(m)$.

On the set $\mathbf{Z}/(m)$ we may define $+$ and $\cdot$ as follows:

$\bar{a} + \bar{b} = \overline{(a + b)}$ and $\bar{a} \cdot \bar{b} = \overline{ab}$, where $\bar{a}$ denotes the congruence class of integers mod m determined by the integer a.

The reader should convince himself that $+$ and $\cdot$ are well-defined.

Exercise 4 · Show that with the possible exception of M_3 all assertions of Theorem 5.1 hold for $\mathbf{Z}/(m)$, $+$ and $\cdot$. Show that M_3 fails when $m = 4$. Show that when $m \neq 0$, $\mathbf{Z}/(m)$ has $|m|$ elements. Show that when $m = 4$, and $x = a^2$, $a \in \mathbf{Z}$, then $\bar{x} = \bar{0}$ or $\bar{1}$; use this to show that $4k + 3 = x^2 + y^2$ has no solutions for $k, x, y \in \mathbf{Z}$.

DEFINITION 5 · Let $a, b \in \mathbf{Z}$. An element $d \in \mathbf{Z}$ is called a ***greatest common divisor*** (to be abbreviated to g.c.d.) of a and b if and only if the following conditions hold:

(a) $d \mid a$ and $d \mid b$.

(b) If $z \in \mathbf{Z}$ is such that $z \mid a$ and $z \mid b$, then $z \mid d$.

The word "greatest" refers to the divisibility relation $\mid$ and not to the order relation $\leqslant$ in $\mathbf{Z}$. However, if we restrict ourselves to $\mathbf{P}$, it will make no difference whether we work with $\mid$ or with $\leqslant$ in the usage of the word "greatest."

THEOREM 2 (g.c.d.) · Let a, $b \in \mathbf{Z}$. Then a g.c.d. of a and b exists and is unique up to associates; it may be written as $af + bg$ for some elements $f, g \in \mathbf{Z}$.

Proof · The uniqueness of a g.c.d. up to associates follows directly from the definition.

Let $D = \{ax + by \mid x, y \in \mathbf{Z}\}$. It is clear that $D = \{0\}$ if and only if $a = 0 = b$. From the definition we see that 0 is a g.c.d. of a and b if and only if $a = 0 = b$. Thus we may assume that $D \neq \{0\}$. Since $|a|$ and $|b|$ both lie in D and at least one of them is in $\mathbf{P}^+$, we see that $D \cap \mathbf{P}^+ \neq \varnothing$. Let $d \in D \cap \mathbf{P}^+$ be the greatest lower bound of $D \cap \mathbf{P}^+$. Thus $d = af + bg$ for some $f, g \in \mathbf{Z}$. From Theorem 1 we see that $a = qd + r$, $0 \leqslant r < d$, for some q, $r \in \mathbf{Z}$. Thus $r = a - qd = a - q(af + bg) = a(1 - qf) + b(-qg) \in D$. By the minimality of d we see that $r = 0$; hence $d \mid a$. Similarly, $d \mid b$. Since $d = af + bg$, it is clear that $z \mid a$ and $z \mid b$ would imply that $z \mid d$. Thus d is a g.c.d. of a and b in $\mathbf{Z}$. «

The reader should note that the coefficients f and g are not uniquely determined. For example, 1 is a g.c.d. of 2 and 3; we may represent 1 as $3 - 2$ or as $2.2 - 3$ and so on.

Exercise 5 · Let $a_1, \dots, a_n \in \mathbf{Z}$, $n \in \mathbf{P}^+$. Generalize the definition of g.c.d. to n integers, $n > 0$. Prove the g.c.d. theorem for n integers. Show that d is a g.c.d. of $a_1, \dots, a_n$ if and only if $(d) = (a_1, \dots, a_n)$, where $(d) = \{dk \mid k \in \mathbf{Z}\}$ and (more generally) $(a_1, \dots, a_n) = \{a_1 f_1 + \cdots + a_n f_n \mid f_1, \dots, f_n \in \mathbf{Z}\}$. Show that, up to associates, g.c.d. is commutative and associative; that is to say, a g.c.d. of a and b is also a g.c.d. of b and a and so on. Show that $a \mid b$ in $\mathbf{Z}$ if and only if $(b) \subset (a)$.

We note that the ordering relation $\leqslant$ on $\mathbf{P}$ was translated into the inclusion relation among the segments of $\mathbf{P}$. In Chapter III we give a translation of the divisibility theory in $\mathbf{Z}$ in terms of an inclusion relation among "subgroups" of the "group" $\mathbf{Z}$, which is essentially based on the last assertion of Exercise 5.

Exercise 6 · Let a, $b \in \mathbf{P}^+$ such that $a \leqslant b$. Suppose that $r_i \in \mathbf{P}$ satisfy the following:

$$
\begin{aligned}
b &= q_1 a + r_1, & 0 < r_1 < a,\\
a &= q_2 r_1 + r_2, & 0 < r_2 < r_1,\\
&\dots\\
r_{n-1} &= q_{n+1} r_n .
\end{aligned}
$$

When $n = 0$, we agree to take $r_{-1} = b$ and $r_0 = a$. This occurs if and only if $a \mid b$.

Show that r_n is a g.c.d. of a and b, and use this procedure to find a g.c.d. of 105 and 135.

DEFINITION 6 · Let $a_1, \ldots, a_n \in \mathbf{Z}$, $n \in \mathbf{P}^+$ and let $(a_1, \ldots, a_n) = \{a_1f_1 + \cdots + a_nf_n \mid f_1, \ldots, f_n \in \mathbf{Z}\}$. We say that $a, b \in \mathbf{Z}$ are ***coprime***, or ***relatively prime***, to each other if and only if $(1) = (a, b)$.

We note that Exercise 5 asserts that we can always find an element $d \in \mathbf{Z}$ such that $(d) = (a_1, \ldots, a_n)$; namely, d is any g.c.d. of $a_1, \ldots, a_n$.

Exercise 7 · Show that if $a, b \in \mathbf{P}$ are coprime then there is an element N of $\mathbf{P}$ such that $m \in \mathbf{P}$ and $m > N$ imply that $m = ax + by$ for suitable x and y in $\mathbf{P}$. *Hint.* Select f and $g \in \mathbf{Z}$ such that $af + bg = 1$. Take M to be the least upper bound of the set $\{|fi|, |gi| \mid 1 \leqslant i \leqslant ab\}$. Then, with a bit of computation, the element N may be taken to be $2Mab$.

LEMMA 2 · Let p be a nonzero prime in $\mathbf{Z}$. Then p is nonfactorizable in $\mathbf{Z}$.

Proof · Suppose that $p = xy$, $x, y \in \mathbf{Z}$. Thus $p \cdot 1 = xy$ and $p \mid xy$. Because p is a prime, we may assume that $p \mid x$. Let $z \in \mathbf{Z}$ such that $pz = x$. On substitution, we see that $p \cdot 1 = pzy$. Since $p \neq 0$, it follows from the cancellation law for multiplication that $1 = zy$, or $y \mid 1$. Thus p is nonfactorizable. «

We observe that the proof of Lemma 2 is completely formal. It depends on the definitions and the cancellation law for multiplication.

LEMMA 3 · Let $a, b \in \mathbf{Z}$. Suppose that a and b are coprime; then $a \mid bc$ implies that $a \mid c$, where $c \in \mathbf{Z}$.

Proof · From Definition 6 and the hypothesis we can find f, $g \in \mathbf{Z}$ such that $1 = af + bg$. Thus $c = acf + bcg$. If $a \mid bc$, then it is clear that $a \mid c$. «

Again we observe that the proof of Lemma 3 is formal. The fact that a, b, c, f, and g are integers is not relevant.

Later, we shall generalize $\mathbf{Z}$ and verify similar generalizations of these lemmas. We now verify the converse of Lemma 2. This time the fact that p is an element of $\mathbf{Z}$ is relevant.

THEOREM 3 · Let $p \in \mathbf{Z}$. Then p is nonfactorizable if and only if p is a nonzero prime.

Proof · We need only to verify the converse of Lemma 2. Thus let p be nonfactorizable in $\mathbf{Z}$. By definition, $p \neq 0$. Suppose that $p \mid xy$, $x, y \in \mathbf{Z}$. We must show that either $p \mid x$ or $p \mid y$. Suppose that $p \nmid x$. Consider a g.c.d. d of p and x. Thus $d \mid p$. It follows that $p = dz$ for some $z \in \mathbf{Z}$. Since p is not factorizable, we see that either $z \mid 1$ or $d \mid 1$. If $z \mid 1$, then $p \mid d$. Since $d \mid x$, we would obtain the contradiction that $p \mid x$. Thus $d \mid 1$. From Exercise 5 we see that p and x are coprime. From Lemma 3 we conclude that $p \mid y$. Thus p is a prime. We have already remarked that $p \neq 0$. «

The reader may raise the question: "Why bother to separate out the notion of a prime and the notion of a nonfactorizable element?" The point will become clear when we come to the notion of an "ideal" in a "ring." At that point the theory of divisibility has another translation. In particular, the divisibility relation is translated into an inclusion relation among "principal ideals."

Exercise 8 · Show that $p \in \mathbf{Z}$ is a prime if and only if $\mathbf{Z}/(p)$ satisfies M_3 of Theorem 5.1. Show that if p is a nonzero prime, then every nonzero element of $\mathbf{Z}/(p)$ has a multiplicative inverse. [The zero element of $\mathbf{Z}/(p)$ is the congruence class of 0 mod p; the multiplicative identity of $\mathbf{Z}/(p)$ is the congruence class of 1 mod p.]

THEOREM 4 (Fundamental theorem of arithmetic or unique factorization theorem or UFT) · Let $a \in \mathbf{Z}$, $a \neq 0$. Then a is a finite product of primes and a unit. If $a = p_1 \cdots p_m = q_1 \cdots q_n$, where p_i and q_j are all primes, then $m = n$, and after a suitable reshuffling of the indices p_i and q_i are associates for $1 \leqslant i \leqslant m$.

(We use the convention that a is a unit if and only if $m = n = 0$.)

Proof · The case of units may be ignored by our convention. From Lemma 1 and Theorem 3 we conclude that a is a finite product of nonzero primes. Let $a = p_1 \cdots p_m = q_1 \cdots q_n$, where p_i and q_j are all nonzero primes. Since a is not a unit, both m and n are positive. From Theorem 3 we see that a is a prime if and only if $m = 1 = n$. In this case $p_1 = q_1 = a$ and we are done. We now carry out an induction on $m + n$. Since p_1 is a prime, an easy induction on the definition of a prime shows that $p_1 \mid q_i$ for some i. By shuffling the indices we may assume that $p_1 \mid q_1$. Thus $p_1 z = q_1$ for some $z \in \mathbf{Z}$. Since $p_1 \nmid 1$ and

q_1 is a nonzero prime, it follows from Theorem 3 that $z \mid 1$. Thus $p_1 p_2 \cdots p_m = p_1(zq_2) \cdots q_n$. By the cancellation law we have $p_2 \cdots p_m = (zq_2) \cdots q_n = b$. Since z is a unit and q_2 is a prime, we see that zq_2 is a prime that is an associate of q_2. Moreover, we have two factorizations of b into products of primes, and the total number of prime factors is $m + n - 2$. Thus, from induction, we may assume that $m - 1 = n - 1$ and that p_i is an associate of q_i for $i > 1$. Since p_1 and q_1 have been shown to be associates, we have proved the desired assertion. «

We observe that the uniqueness is a formal consequence of the existence of a prime factorization.

We conclude this section by showing the following:

THEOREM 5 (Euclid) · There exist an infinite number of primes in $\mathbf{P}^+$.

Proof · By way of contradiction, assume that only a finite number of primes occur in $\mathbf{P}^+$. Since 2 is a prime, as we have already seen, the set of primes in $\mathbf{P}^+$ is not empty. Let these primes be $p_1, p_2, \ldots, p_n$, where $p_i < p_{i+1}$. Let $N = \prod_{1 \leqslant i \leqslant n} p_i + 1$. From the unique factorization theorem we see that $N = \prod_i p_i^{a(i)}$, $a(i) \in \mathbf{P}$ and $1 \leqslant i \leqslant n$. Because $n \geqslant 1$, we see that $N > 1$. Thus $a(i) \in \mathbf{P}^+$ for some i. However, by definition, $p_i \nmid N \; \forall \, i$. Thus we must have $a(i) = 0 \; \forall \, i$. This contradiction establishes the theorem. «

Indeed, Theorem 5 gives us a crude procedure for finding primes in $\mathbf{P}$; namely, given primes p_i, $1 \leqslant i \leqslant n$, any prime divisor of N constructed in the proof must be distinct from each p_i.

For example, starting with prime 2, we can get prime $3 = 2 + 1$. Using 2 and 3, we find prime $7 = 2 \cdot 3 + 1$. Using 2, 3, and 7, we find prime $2 \cdot 3 \cdot 7 + 1 = 43$. Using 2, 3, 7, and 43, we find that $13 \cdot 139 = 2 \cdot 3 \cdot 7 \cdot 43 + 1$, that 13 and 139 are both primes, and so on.

» 1·7 CONSTRUCTION OF THE RATIONAL NUMBERS Q

We now imitate the procedure of constructing $\mathbf{Z}$ from $\mathbf{P}$ in order to make division possible. Thus we wish to enlarge $\mathbf{Z}$ to a system such that $ax = b$ has a solution in x whenever $a \neq 0$. We recall that when $a, b \in \mathbf{Z}$ the existence of a solution in $\mathbf{Z}$ had been used to define the notion of divisibility.

We now define a relation $\sim$ on $\mathbf{Z} \times \mathbf{Z}^\star$, where $\mathbf{Z}^\star = \mathbf{Z} - \{0\}$:

$(a, b) \sim (c, d)$ if and only if $ad = bc$, where $a, c \in \mathbf{Z}$ and $b, d \in \mathbf{Z}^\star$.

It is easy to see that $\sim$ is an equivalence relation. We let $\mathbf{Q} = (\mathbf{Z} \times \mathbf{Z}^\star)/\sim$ be the set of all such equivalence classes. Each equivalence class is called a ***rational number***. On the set $\mathbf{Q}$ we define addition and multiplication as follows:

$$\overline{(a, b)} + \overline{(c, d)} = \overline{(ad + bc, bd)},$$
$$\overline{(a, b)} \cdot \overline{(c, d)} = \overline{(ac, db)},$$

where $\overline{(a, b)}$ denotes the equivalence class of (a, b).

The reader should check to see that $+$ and $\cdot$ are well-defined. If we read $\overline{(a, b)}$ as "a divided by b," we quickly see that our definitions coincide with the usual rules for addition and multiplication of fractions.

The reader can verify the following as an exercise:

THEOREM 1 · Addition and multiplication in $\mathbf{Q}$ satisfy all the assertions of Theorem 5.1, where $\overline{(0, 1)}$ and $\overline{(1, 1)}$ are the additive and multiplicative identity elements, respectively. Moreover, every element of $\mathbf{Q}^\star = \mathbf{Q} - \{\overline{(0, 1)}\}$ has a multiplicative inverse.

The map that sends each element $a \in \mathbf{Z}$ onto the element $\overline{(a, 1)} \in \mathbf{Q}$ is an injection that preserves addition and multiplication.

Again, in order to simplify the notation, we state the following:

DEFINITION 1 · In $\mathbf{Q}$ let $a/b = \overline{(a, b)}$ and let $a/1 = a$, where $a, b \in \mathbf{Z}$. Thus we have identified $\mathbf{Z}$ with a subset of $\mathbf{Q}$ via the injection described in Theorem 1. The multiplicative inverse of the element $x \in \mathbf{Q}^\star$ is denoted by x^{-1}. In general, for $a \in \mathbf{Q}^\star$ and $n \in \mathbf{Z}$, we define a^n as follows:

$a^0 = 1$; if a^n has been defined for $n \geqslant 0$, then $a^{n+1} = a^n \cdot a$; and if a^n has been defined for $n \leqslant 0$, then $a^{n-1} = a^n \cdot a^{-1}$.

Thus a^n is the product of a with itself n times when $n \geqslant 1$ and the product of a^{-1} with itself $-n$ times when $n \leqslant -1$. As before, the empty product is taken to mean 1.

Exercise 1 · Let $a/b \in \mathbf{Q}^\star$, $a, b \in \mathbf{Z}$. Show that $(a/b)^{-1} = b/a$. Show that for $c \neq 0$, $c \in \mathbf{Z}$, $ac/bc = a/b$. Show that, if $x \in \mathbf{Q}$, there exists $d \in \mathbf{Z}$, $d \neq 0$, such that $dx \in \mathbf{Z}$. These elements are called ***denominators*** of x. Indeed, the denominators may be selected from $\mathbf{P}^+$.

From Exercise 1 we see that every element of $\mathbf{Q}$ is the solution of some equation of the form $dx = n$, where $d \neq 0$ and d, n are elements of $\mathbf{Z}$; namely, $x = n/d$.

Exercise 2 · Let $\mathcal{P} = \{p \in \mathbf{Z} \mid p \text{ is a prime and } p > 0.\}$. Show that every element of $\mathbf{Q}^{\star}$ admits a unique product representation:

$a = u \prod p^{\nu(p)}$, where u is a unit in $\mathbf{Z}$, $p \in \mathcal{P}$, $\nu(p) \in \mathbf{Z}$, and $\nu(p) = 0$ for all but a finite number of $p \in \mathcal{P}$. (Often we also say that $\nu(p) = 0$ for almost all $p \in \mathcal{P}$.)

Actually, we may replace $\mathcal{P}$ by any other set of primes, as long as the set selected satisfies the following conditions:

(a) The primes are all distinct from 0.

(b) Each nonzero prime of $\mathbf{Z}$ is an associate of exactly one prime in the set.

Such sets of primes are called ***complete sets of representatives*** of nonzero primes.

DEFINITION 2 · In $\mathbf{Q}$ let $\mathbf{Q}^{+} = \{a/b \mid a, b \in \mathbf{P}^{+}\}$. We write $x < y$ for $x, y \in \mathbf{Q}$ if and only if $y - x \in \mathbf{Q}^{+}$. Elements of $\mathbf{Q}^{+}$ are called ***positive rational numbers.*** If $x \in \mathbf{Q}$ is such that $-x \in \mathbf{Q}^{+}$, then x is called a ***negative rational number.***

Exercise 3 · Show that $<$ is a linear ordering on $\mathbf{Q}^{\#}$ and that it coincides with the ordering $<$ previously defined on $\mathbf{Z}$. Show that if $x, y \in \mathbf{Q}^{+}$ both $x + y$ and $xy \in \mathbf{Q}^{+}$. Define absolute value on $\mathbf{Q}$ and show that $|x + y| \leqslant |x| + |y|$ and that $|xy| = |x|\,|y|$ for x and y in $\mathbf{Q}$.

References

The reader may consult [2] for a systematic development of the natural numbers from set theory. However, he should bear in mind that the process of basing one theory on another cannot be carried out forever. Somewhere along the line one must select a theory or some concepts as primitive.

There is a detailed discussion of mathematical induction in [1].

1. L. Henkin, "On mathematical induction," *American Mathematical Monthly*, 323–338, (1960) 67.

2. C. T. Yang, *Axiomatic Set Theory and Number Systems.* Academic Press, New York (in press).

CHAPTER II — Groups, Rings, Integral Domains, Fields

In this chapter we formalize some of the concepts connected with the objects discussed in Chapters O and I. We discuss a few more important examples and collect some of the basic properties of these abstract "algebraic" objects. The reader may consider this chapter as a condensed dictionary.

» II·1 MULTIPLICATIVE SYSTEMS: GROUPS

One of the simplest, as well as the most important, objects in set theory is the set of all maps from a set A into a set B. For the moment let us denote this set by $\text{Map}(A, B)$. The composition of maps then defines a map $\circ : \text{Map}(A, B) \times \text{Map}(B, C) \to \text{Map}(A, C)$; namely, if $F \in \text{Map}(A, B)$ and $G \in \text{Map}(B, C)$, then $\circ(F, G) = G \circ F$. The analysis of this situation has mushroomed into the subject of "theory of categories and functors." The reader may consult the reference at the end of the chapter for more detailed discussions of this topic.

Instead of dealing with the general situation, we consider the set $\text{Map}(A, A)$. The reader can quickly verify that the associative law is satisfied by the composition product. Moreover, the identity map of A onto A is the identity element with respect to the composition product. We now formalize them into the following definition.

DEFINITION 1 · Let S be a nonempty set and let $\cdot : S \times S \to S$ be a map that satisfies the associative law; namely, if we write xy for $\cdot(x, y)$, then $x(yz) = (xy)z \ \forall\, x, y, z \in S$. We call the set S, together with the map $\cdot$, a ***multiplicative system***. It is also called a ***semigroup***. An element $e \in S$ is called an ***identity element*** if and only if $ex = x = xe \; \forall \, x \in S$. The multiplicative system, $S, \cdot$, is said to be ***commutative*** if and only if the commutative law also holds for $\cdot$; namely, $xy = yx \; \forall \, x, y \in S$. When there is no possibility of confusion, we simply speak of the multiplicative system S instead of $S, \cdot$. In any event, xy is called the ***product*** of x and y.

Aside from the example mentioned before the definition, it is easy to see that the following are multiplicative systems: $\mathbf{P}, +$; $\mathbf{P}^+, +$; $\mathbf{Z}, +$; $\mathbf{Q}, +$; $\mathbf{Z}/(m), +$; $\mathbf{P}, \cdot$; $\mathbf{P}^+, \cdot$; $\mathbf{Z}, \cdot$; $\mathbf{Q}, \cdot$; $\mathbf{Q} - \{0\}, \cdot$; $\mathbf{Z}/(m), \cdot$; $\mathbf{Z}/(p) - \{0\}, \cdot$, where p is a prime. (In the first two examples $+$ is used to denote the restriction of addition in $\mathbf{Z}$ to the subset $\mathbf{P}$ and $\mathbf{P}^+$; it is not the successor map.) Each of these examples is commutative; with the exception of $\mathbf{P}^+, +$, each of these examples has an identity element.

Exercise 1 · Show that a multiplicative system may have at most one identity element. Let $T = S \cup \{e\}$, $e \notin S$, and $S \neq \varnothing$. Assume that $S, \cdot$ form a multiplicative system. Define $* : T \times T \to T$ by setting $u * v = uv \; \forall \, u, v \in S$ and $u * e = u = e * u \; \forall \, u \in T$. Show that $T, *$ is a multiplicative system with the identity element e.

Exercise 2 · Let $S, \cdot$ be a multiplicative system with the identity element e. Consider the map $\rho : S \to \text{Map}(S, S)$ given by $\rho(s)(t) = st \; \forall \, s, t \in S$. Show that the following assertions hold:

(a) $\rho(e)$ is the identity map of S.

(b) ρ is injective. *Hint.* If $\rho(s) = \rho(t)$, then $\rho(s)(e) = \rho(t)(e)$.

(c) $\rho(uv) = \rho(u) \circ \rho(v) \; \forall \, u, v \in S$.

The reader should note that Exercise 1 shows that any multiplicative system may be "embedded" into a multiplicative system that has an identity element. Exercise 2 shows that any multiplicative system with an identity element may be viewed as a subset of $\text{Map}(A, A)$ for a suitable set A; moreover, when viewed in such a way, the product in the given multiplicative system may be taken to be the composition product defined in $\text{Map}(A, A)$. From these remarks we see that $\text{Map}(A, A), \circ$ and its subsets which are closed with respect to $\circ$ are the universal examples of multiplicative systems.

Exercise 3 · Let S be any nonempty set. Define $* : S \times S \to S$ by setting $x * y = x, \forall\, x, y \in S$. Show that $S, *$ is a multiplicative system and that the following assertions are equivalent:

(a) $S, *$ is commutative.

(b) $S, *$ has an identity element.

(c) S has exactly one element.

Exercise 4 · Define $* : \mathbf{Z} \times \mathbf{Z} \to \mathbf{Z}$ by setting $x * y = |xy|$. Show that $\mathbf{Z}, *$ is a commutative multiplicative system without an identity element.

Exercise 5 · Let $\# : \mathbf{P} \times \mathbf{P} \to \mathbf{P}$ be defined by setting $x \# y$ as the g.c.d. of x and y in $\mathbf{P}$. Show that $\mathbf{P}, \#$ is a commutative multiplicative system with an identity element.

We indicated in Chapter O that sets should be considered the "same" when there is a bijection between them. This led to the concept of cardinal numbers. It is natural to ask: "How many bijections are there between sets A and B?" In view of Exercises O.2.2 and O.2.3, it is easy to see that if ρ is a bijection from A to B, then the set of all bijections from A to B is the same as $\{\rho \circ \sigma \mid \sigma \text{ is a bijection of } A \text{ with } A\}$ and also the same as $\{\sigma \circ \rho \mid \sigma \text{ is a bijection of } B \text{ with } B\}$. Thus the question may be reduced to one of studying $Bij(A) = \{\sigma \in A \mid \sigma \text{ is bijection of } A \text{ with } A\}$.

Exercise 6 · Let $\rho : A \to B$ be a bijection between the set A and the set B. Let I_A and I_B be the identity map of A onto A and of B onto B, respectively. If σ is a bijection, let σ^{-1} be the inverse of the correspondence σ. In fact, σ^{-1} is a bijection. Show that the following assertions hold:

(a) $Bij(A)$ is a multiplicative system under composition.

(b) $Bij(A), \circ$ has the identity element I_A.

(c) If $\sigma \in Bij(A)$, then $\sigma^{-1} \in Bij(A)$ and $\sigma^{-1} \circ \sigma = I_A = \sigma \circ \sigma^{-1}$.

(d) Let $t : Bij(A) \to Bij(B)$ be defined by $t(\sigma) = \rho \circ \sigma \circ \rho^{-1}$. Then

(1) $t(I_A) = I_B$.

(2) $t(\sigma \circ \tau) = t(\sigma) \circ t(\tau)\ \forall\, \sigma, \tau \in Bij(A)$.

(3) $t(\sigma^{-1}) = (t(\sigma))^{-1}\ \forall\, \sigma \in Bij(A)$.

(4) t is a bijection.

We now formalize the assertions in Exercise 6 into the following definition:

DEFINITION 2 · Let G be a set and let $\cdot : G \times G \to G$ be a map. $G, \cdot$ (or simply G when there is no possibility of confusion) is called a ***group*** if and only if the following conditions hold:

G_1 (associative law). $x(yz) = (xy)z \ \forall\, x, y, z \in G$.

G_2 (existence of the identity element). $\exists\, e \in G$ such that $ex = x = xe \ \forall\, x \in G$.

G_3 (existence of the inverse). If $x \in G$, then there exists $x' \in G$ (x' depends on x, conceivably not unique) such that $x'x = e = xx'$.

A group G is called a ***commutative*** (or ***abelian***) group if and only if it also satisfies the following condition in addition to those above.

AG (commutative law). $xy = yx \ \forall\, x, y \in G$.

We note that a group G is automatically a multiplicative system with an identity element. Aside from the example mentioned before the definition, it is easy to see that the following are examples of groups,

$\mathbf{Z}, +$; $\mathbf{Q}, +$; $\mathbf{Z}/(m), +$; $\mathbf{Q} - \{0\}, \cdot$; $\mathbf{Z}/(p) - \{0\}, \cdot$, where p is a nonzero prime. Each of these examples is a commutative group.

Exercise 7 · (Cayley's theorem). Use Exercise 2 to show that for each group G there exists a set A and an injective map $\rho : G \to Bij(A)$ such that (a) $\rho(e) = I_A$, (b) $\rho(xy) = \rho(x) \circ \rho(y) \ \forall\, x, y \in G$.

Cayley's theorem shows that $Bij(A)$ and its subsets which are groups with respect to the composition product are universal examples of groups.

Exercise 8 · Show that every set with only one element can be turned into a multiplicative system in precisely one way; moreover, in this manner it becomes a group. Show that there exist precisely two ways to turn a set with two elements into a group. Write down the multiplication table for $Bij(\{1, 2, 3\})$; show that this is a noncommutative group with six elements.

Exercise 9 · Let G be a group. Verify the following assertions:

(a) The inverse x' of the element $x \in G$ is uniquely determined.

(b) Let x^{-1} denote the inverse of $x \in G$; then $(x^{-1})^{-1} = x$ and $(xy)^{-1} = y^{-1}x^{-1}$ hold $\forall\, x, y \in G$.

(c) If $xy = xz$, then $y = z$; similarly, if $yx = zx$, then $y = z$, where $x, y, z \in G$.

(d) $e \in G$ is the unique element that satisfies the equation $xx = x$.

✓ **Exercise 10** · Let G be a group. Show that the group axioms G_2 and G_3 may be replaced by the "weaker" axioms:

G_2^* (existence of left identity). $\exists\, e \in G$ such that $ex = x\ \forall\, x \in G$.

G_3^* (existence of left inverse). If $x \in G$, then $\exists\, x' \in G$ such that $x'x = e$. (Here e is the element named in G_2^*.)

Hint. First show that $xx' = e$ by computing $(x')'x'xx'$ in two ways. Next show that $xe = x$ by computing $xx'x$ in two ways.

$$\cancel{x}x' = e\,(xx') = ((x')'x')(xx') = (x')'((x'x)x) = (x')'(ex') = (x')'x' = e$$

» II · 2 HOMOMORPHISMS

In the preceding section we indicated that one of the most important things in set theory is the set $\text{Map}(A, B)$. As its stands, $\text{Map}(A, B)$ is uniquely determined by the cardinal numbers of A and B. However, the subsets of $\text{Map}(A, B)$ are not so easily determined. In particular, we may consider subsets of $\text{Map}(A, B)$ which "preserve" certain specified "structures" of the sets A and B. For example, if A and B are multiplicative systems, we may consider the subset of $\text{Map}(A, B)$ which preserves the product. Such maps are called **homomorphisms**. Condition (c) of Exercise 1.2 may be phrased into the statement, "ρ is a homomorphism of the multiplicative system S into the multiplicative system $\text{Map}(S, S)$." Conditions (1), (2) and (3) of Exercise 1.6(d) may be summarized into the statement, "t is a homomorphism of the group $Bij(A)$ into the group $Bij(B)$." Cayley's theorem may be stated as, "every group can be mapped injectively by a group homomorphism into a suitable group $Bij(A, A)$."

We now consider a slightly different problem; namely, how do we put a group structure on a set? Of course, the word "group" in the preceding sentence may be replaced by the word "semigroup." One procedure is as follows:

Let a group G, $*$ be given. Suppose that $\sigma : G \to H$ is a bijection of the set G with the set H. We define $\# : H \times H \to H$ by setting $x \,\#\, y = \sigma[\sigma^{-1}(x) * \sigma^{-1}(y)]$.

The reader may verify that H, $\#$ is a group. Indeed, $\sigma(e)$ is the identity element of H and $\sigma(x^{-1})$ is the inverse of $\sigma(x)$ in H. Moreover, σ is a homomorphism of the group $G, *$ into the group $H, \#$. The procedure just described is called "transporting the structure of G to H by means of the bijection σ." It should be clear to the reader that it is irrelevant whether G is a group or not. Had G been a multiplicative system, the end result would have been that $H, \#$ was a multiplicative system. The point is that the given procedure serves as a dictionary which gives the elements of G a different name. With this in mind, we see that one of the assertions in Section 1 of Chapter I can be stated as follows:

Let $P, +$ and $Q, *$ be two systems that satisfy the axioms of Peano; then there exists a unique bijection $\sigma : P \to Q$ such that $Q, *$ is the transported structure of $P, +$ according to σ.

As a further example, we assume for the moment that the reader is familiar with the real numbers. Let $\mathbf{R}, +$ be the group of real numbers under addition $+$. Let $\mathbf{R}^+, \cdot$ be the group of positive real numbers under multiplication. Let $\exp : \mathbf{R} \to \mathbf{R}^+$ be the map that sends $x \in \mathbf{R}$ onto $\exp(x) = e^x$. Then $\mathbf{R}^+, \cdot$ becomes the same group as that obtained from $\mathbf{R}, +$ by transporting the structure of $\mathbf{R}, +$ through the map exp.

The common feature of a "homomorphism" and a "transportation of structure" can be summarized most easily in a diagram; σ is a "homomorphism" of $G, *$ into $H, \#$ if and only if the following diagram is commutative,

$$\begin{array}{ccc} G \times G & \xrightarrow{\;*\;} & G \\ {\scriptstyle \sigma\times\sigma}\downarrow & & \downarrow{\scriptstyle \sigma} \\ H \times H & \xrightarrow{\;\#\;} & H \end{array},$$

where $\sigma \times \sigma$ is defined by $(\sigma \times \sigma)(x, y) = (\sigma(x), \sigma(y))\ \forall\, x, y \in G$. We recall that commutativity of the diagram asserts that $\sigma \circ * = \# \circ (\sigma \times \sigma)$; $\#$ is obtained from $*$ by transportation according to σ if and only if σ is a bijection in the commutative diagram.

With the various examples in mind, we now formalize them into the following definition.

DEFINITION 1 · Let G and H be sets with specified and corresponding operations. A map $\sigma : G \to H$ is called a ***homomorphism*** if and only if it preserves the corresponding operations. A homomor-

just define epis and monos. as given here, for time being ↓

phism which is injective as a map on the underlying sets is called a **monomorphism.** A homomorphism which is surjective as a map on the underlying sets is called an **epimorphism.** A homomorphism which is bijective as a map and such that its inverse is also a homomorphism is called an **isomorphism.** Thus the identity map is always an isomorphism.

Definition 1 is vague and imprecise. This is deliberate. In the "algebraic" situations that we encounter, operations mean maps and "identities" involving maps. For example, if G and H are multiplicative systems, then σ is a homomorphism if and only if $\sigma(xy) = \sigma(x)\sigma(y) \; \forall \; x, y \in G$. If G and H are both groups, then σ is a group homomorphism if and only if (a) $\sigma(xy) = \sigma(x)\sigma(y) \; \forall \; x, y \in G$, (b) $\sigma(1_G) = 1_H$, 1_G and 1_H are the identity elements of G and H, respectively, (c) $\sigma(x^{-1}) = (\sigma(x))^{-1} \; \forall \; x \in G$. However, from Exercise 1.9 the reader can verify rather easily that (b) and (c) are consequences of (a). As a result, if we consider G and H as multiplicative systems rather than groups, a homomorphism of G into H in the sense of multiplicative systems is already a group homomorphism. Thus a group homomorphism is frequently defined as a map that satisfies condition (a). More seriously, the definitions of a monomorphism and epimorphism are not quite correct. They are based on the properties of the associated maps on the underlying sets. The "correct" definitions should be based on Exercise O.2.3 or on the hint in Exercise O.4.1. The latter is a "stronger" definition.

The point is that the notion of a homomorphism depends on specified kind of objects; for example: sets; multiplicative systems; groups; sets and maps that satisfy Peano's axioms and so on. The important thing about homomorphisms is that their composition as set maps should again be a homomorphism. The critical property of injective and surjective maps between sets is the cancellation law indicated in Exercise O.2.3. Consequently, it should be the basis for the definition of monomorphism and epimorphism; namely, σ is a monomorphism if and only if $\sigma \circ \rho = \sigma \circ \tau$ implies that $\rho = \tau$ for any two homomorphisms ρ and τ. Similarly, σ is an epimorphism if and only if $\rho \circ \sigma = \tau \circ \sigma$ implies that $\rho = \tau$ for any two homomorphisms ρ and τ. The definition based on the hint in Exercise O.4.1 would be that σ is a monomorphism if and only if there exists a homomorphism $\eta : H \to G$ such that $\eta \circ \sigma$ is the identity homomorphism of G and that σ is an epimorphism if and only if there exists a homomorphism $\eta : H \to G$ such that $\sigma \circ \eta$ is the identity homomorphism of H. The reader can verify that these definitions are more restrictive. For example, if $P, +$ and $Q, *$ are systems satisfying the axioms of Peano, then

$\sigma : P \to Q$ is a homomorphism if and only if $\sigma(x^+) = (\sigma(x))^* \; \forall \, x \in P$. In this situation every homomorphism is injective, either as a map on the underlying sets or according to the cancellation-law definition. However, according to the last definition (existence of a left inverse), the only monomorphism is the homomorphism σ which also sends 0_P onto 0_Q. The reason for our choice of the definition of monomorphism and epimorphism is simply that the easiest way of checking the cancellation laws is as maps on the underlying sets. If the homomorphisms are injective and surjective, respectively, on the underlying sets, the appropriate cancellation laws must hold. Finally, the definition of an isomorphism is given in terms of the existence of an inverse homomorphism. In all the situations that we encounter the inverse map associated with a homomorphism that is bijective on the underlying sets is automatically a homomorphism. (This is false in "topology"; namely, the inverse of a continuous map that is bijective does not have to be continuous.) For a more detailed treatment of the cancellation-law definition of monomorphism and epimorphism, the reader should consult the reference to "category theory."

We now consider a few more examples. Let $\mathbf{P}, +$ be the multiplicative system of natural numbers under addition. Let $S, \cdot$ be any multiplicative system with the identity element 1. Suppose that $s \in S$. Then define $\rho_s : S \to S$ by setting $\rho_s(t) = st$. According to definition by induction in Section I.1, there is a unique homomorphism $\sigma : \mathbf{P} \to S$ such that (a) $\sigma(0) = 1$, (b) $\sigma(n + 1) = \rho_s(\sigma(n)) \; \forall \, n \in \mathbf{P}$. The reader can easily verify that $\sigma(n)$ is precisely the product of s with itself n times.

Let $\mathbf{Z}, +$ be the group of integers under addition. Then the map $- : \mathbf{Z} \to \mathbf{Z}$ which sends x onto $-x$ is an isomorphism of $\mathbf{Z}$ with itself. Let $G, \cdot$ be a group and let x be any randomly selected element of G. Combining this isomorphism and the result from the preceding paragraph, we easily determine that there is a unique map $\sigma : \mathbf{Z} \to G$ such that (a) $\sigma(0) = 1$, (b) $\sigma(n + 1) = \rho_x(\sigma(n)) \; \forall \, n \in \mathbf{P}$, and (c) $\sigma(-(n + 1)) = \rho_y(\sigma(-n)) \; \forall \, n \in \mathbf{P}$, where $y = x^{-1}$. The reader may check to see that σ is a group homomorphism.

DEFINITION 2 · Let $G, \cdot$ be a group and let $x \in G$. The image under σ of $m \in \mathbf{Z}$ is denoted by x^m. If the group is commutative and the group operation is written as $+$, the image under σ of $m \in \mathbf{Z}$ is denoted by mx. In either event, σ is the map described in the preceding paragraph. If $m \geqslant 0$, then x^m is the product of x with itself m times. (The empty product is agreed to be 1_G). If $m = -n < 0$, then $x^m = x^{-n}$ is the product of x^{-1} with itself n times.

Exercise 1 · Let S be the semigroup described in Exercise 1.3 and let R be the semigroup with one element. (There is a unique way of turning a set with one element into a semigroup.) Find all the homomorphisms of R into S and of S into R. *Map x in R to any ell of S*

Exercise 2 · Let $S, +$ be a commutative semigroup with identity element 0. Show that there is a unique group G (unique up to group isomorphism) which satisfies the following conditions:

(a) There is a semigroup homomorphism $\sigma : S \to G$.

(b) σ is *universal* with respect to semigroup homomorphisms of S into arbitrary groups.

The word "universal" means the following:

Let H be any group and $\rho : S \to H$ any semigroup homomorphism. Then there exists a unique group homomorphism $\varphi : G \to H$ such that $s^{\sigma\varphi} = s^{\rho}$ for all s in S. In terms of a diagram of maps we have the following commutative diagram:

$$G$$
$$\sigma \nearrow \quad \downarrow \varphi$$
$$S \xrightarrow{\rho} H$$

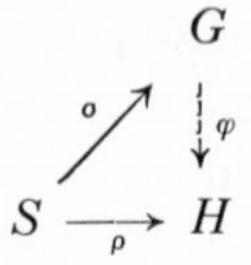

The dotted line means that φ is not given in advance.

Hint 1. We first prove the uniqueness of G. Let G and G' be two such groups with associated maps σ and σ'. Let G and G' play the role of H in succession in order to get group homomorphisms $\varphi : G \to G'$ and $\varphi' : G' \to G$ to satisfy the commutativity conditions. Thus $\varphi\varphi' : G \to G$ satisfies $s^{\sigma\varphi\varphi'} = s^{\sigma'\varphi'} = s^{\sigma}$ for all s in S. Because the identity map $\iota : G \to G$ satisfies, $s^{\sigma\iota} = s^{\sigma}$ for all s in S, the uniqueness of "φ" associated with G and $H = G$ shows that $\varphi\varphi' = \iota$. Similarly, $\varphi'\varphi = \iota'$, the identity map of G' onto itself. This shows that $\varphi : G \to G'$ is an isomorphism of groups.

Hint 2. The existence of G is a formalization of the construction of **Z** from **P**. We introduce the relation $\sim$ on $S \times S$ by letting $(a, b) \sim (c, d)$ if and only if there exists $t \in S$ such that $t + a + d = t + b + c$, where $a, b, c,$ and d lie in S. This may be seen to be an equivalence relation on $S \times S$ (notice that S does not have to satisfy the cancellation law). Let G be the set of equivalance classes $(S \times S)/\sim$ and define $+$ on G by $\overline{(a, b)} + \overline{(c, d)} = \overline{(a + c, b + d)}$, where $\overline{(a, b)}$ is the equivalence class of (a, b); $+$ may be seen to be well-defined; $G, +$ may be seen to be a group. Let $\sigma : S \to G$ be defined by $s^{\sigma} = \overline{(s, 0)}$; σ may be seen to be a semigroup homomorphism; G may be seen to be a commutative group.

 $-\overline{(a, b)} = \overline{(b, a)}$

phisms leads to a structure of a multiplicative system with an identity element on Hom(A, A). The obvious question is: "What are the connections between the group structure of Hom(A, A) under $+$ and the semigroup structure of Hom(A, A) under $\circ$?". The answer is that both the left and right distributive laws hold; namely, let f, g, $h \in$ Hom(A, A) and $a \in A$. Then $[(f + g) \circ h](a) = (f + g)(h(a)) = f(h(a)) + g(h(a)) = (f \circ h + g \circ h)(a)$ according to the definition of $+$ on Hom(A, A); $[h \circ (f + g)](a) = h(f(a) + g(a)) = h(f(a)) + h(g(a)) = (h \circ f + h \circ g)(a)$ according to the definition of $+$ on Hom(A, A) and the fact that h is a homomorphism of groups.

We now formalize these observations.

DEFINITION 1 · Let R be a set and let $+, \cdot : R \times R \to R$ be maps. Then $R, +, \cdot$ (or simply R when there is no possibility of confusion,) is called a ***ring*** if and only if the following conditions hold:

R_1. $R, +$ is a commutative group. The identity element is denoted by 0 and is called the zero element of R.

R_2. $R, \cdot$ is a multiplicative system; that is, multiplication is associative.

R_3. If $x, y, z \in R$, then $x(y + z) = xy + xz$ and $(y + z)x = yx + zx$.

R is called a ***ring with an identity element*** (or simply a ***ring with unit***) if and only if, in addition to the ring axioms, $R, \cdot$ has an identity element. This identity element is then denoted by 1. The possibility that 1 and 0 will coincide is not excluded.

R is called a ***commutative ring*** if and only if, in addition to the ring axioms, $R, \cdot$ is commutative.

The reader can easily check that $\mathbf{Z}$, $\mathbf{Z}/(m)$ and $\mathbf{Q}$ are all examples of rings. In each of these cases the ring is commutative and has an identity element. Moreover, in the ring $\mathbf{Z}/(1)$ the additive identity and the multiplicative identity coincide.

Exercise 1 · Let R be a ring. Verify the following assertions:

(a) $x0 = 0 = 0x \ \forall\, x \in R$. *Hint.* Use R_1 and R_3 with $y = z = 0$.

(b) $x(-y) = -(xy) = (-x)y \ \forall\, x, y \in R$, where $-x$ denotes the additive inverse of x in $R, +$.

(c) Suppose that R has the identity element 1 with respect to $\cdot$. Then $(-1)x = -x = x(-1) \ \forall\, x \in R$.

(d) Suppose that R has the identity element 1 with respect to $\cdot$. Then $1 = 0$ if and only if R has exactly one element. (When this is the case, R is called the ***zero ring***.)

In order to avoid possible misunderstanding, we state the definition of a homomorphism of rings as follows:

DEFINITION 2 · Let R, S be two rings. (We denote the ring operations by $+$ and $\cdot$ in both R and S.) A map $\sigma : R \to S$ is called a ***ring homomorphism*** if and only if the following conditions hold:

(a) $\sigma(x + y) = \sigma(x) + \sigma(y) \; \forall \; x, y \in R$.

(b) $\sigma(xy) = \sigma(x)\,\sigma(y) \; \forall \; x, y \in R$.

If R and S both have identity elements, then $\sigma : R \to S$ is called a homomorphism of rings with units if and only if, in addition to (a) and (b), $\sigma(1_R) = 1_S$.

The reader should verify that in either of the two cases given in Definition 2 a ring homomorphism always preserves the distributive laws. Indeed, this follows from (a) and (b). The reason for the restriction on identity elements is simply that ring homomorphisms in general do not send the multiplicative identity element onto the multiplicative identity element. (The reader should have observed an analogous situation in Exercise 2.1.) The situation that interests us is not the case of rings in general but rings with an identity element. In such a situation a ring homomorphism is to be understood in the sense of the second half of Definition 2.

Exercise 2 · Let $T = \mathbf{Z} \times R$. Suppose that R is a ring. Define $\#$, $* : T \times T \to T$ by setting $(m, x) \# (n, y)$ as $(m + n, x + y)$ and $(m, x) * (n, y)$ as $(mn, my + nx + xy) \; \forall \; m, n \in \mathbf{Z}$ and $x, y \in R$. Show that T is a ring with the identity element $(1, 0)$. Show that the map $\sigma : R \to T$ given by $\sigma(x) = (0, x) \; \forall \; x \in R$ is a monomorphism of the ring R into the ring T. (If R happens to have an identity element, then σ will not send it onto the identity element of T.)

Exercise 3 · Let R be a ring with the identity element 1. Let $\rho : R \to \text{Map}(R, R)$ be defined by $(\rho(x))(y) = xy \; \forall \; x, y \in R$. Show that ρ is a monomorphism of rings with identity elements from R to $\text{Hom}(R, R)$, where R is considered as a group under $+$ in defining $\text{Hom}(R, R)$.

Exercises 2 and 3 show that $\text{Hom}(A, A)$ (where A is a commutative group) and its subsets which are closed under $+$ and $\circ$ form the universal examples of rings. $\text{Hom}(A, A)$, $+$, $\circ$ is called the **endomorphism ring** of A, $+$.

DEFINITION 3 · A ring R with an identity element is called an **integral domain** if and only if $R - \{0\}$ is a commutative multiplicative system under the multiplication of R.

note $a, b \in R - \{0\} \Rightarrow ab \in R - \{0\}$
$\Rightarrow$ no nonzero division of zero

A ring R with an identity element is called a **field** if and only if $R - \{0\}$ is a commutative group under the multiplication of R.

The set $R - \{0\}$ is often denoted by $R^{\star}$.

Z; **Z**$/(p)$, p a prime; **Q** are examples of integral domains. **Z**$/(p)$, p a nonzero prime; **Q** are examples of fields. It is clear that every field is an integral domain. Occasionally the requirement of commutativity may be dropped in the consideration of a field, in which case we call the system a **division ring**.

Exercise 4 · Let R be a ring. An element $x \in R - \{0\}$ is called a **left zero divisor** if and only if $\exists y \in R - \{0\}$ such that $xy = 0$. Show that R is an integral domain if and only if the following conditions hold:

(a) R has a multiplicative identity element 1 distinct from 0.

(b) R has no left zero divisors.

(c) R is commutative.

DEFINITION 4 · Let $n, k \in \mathbf{P}$ such that $0 \leqslant k \leqslant n$. Then the binomial coefficients $\binom{n}{k}$ are defined by the formula

$$\binom{n}{k} = \frac{n!}{k! \cdot (n - k)!},$$

where $0! = 1$ and $(n + 1)! = n! \cdot (n + 1)$, $n \in \mathbf{P}$.

A priori we can say only that the binomial coefficients are elements of **Q**. However, we have the following:

THEOREM 1 (Binomial theorem) ·
(a) The binomial coefficients satisfy the following:

(1) $\binom{n}{k} = \binom{n}{n - k}$,

(2) $\binom{n}{k} < \binom{n}{k + 1}$ for $k + 1 \leqslant \dfrac{n}{2}$,

(3) $\binom{n}{k} + \binom{n}{k+1} = \binom{n+1}{k+1}$ for $k < n$,

(4) $\binom{n}{k} \in \mathbf{P}^+$.

(b) Let R be a commutative ring with unit 1. Let $a, b \in R$ and $n \in \mathbf{P}$. We then have the following:

$$(a+b)^n = \sum_{0 \leqslant k \leqslant n} \binom{n}{k} a^k b^{n-k}.$$

Indeed, (b) holds in an arbitrary ring R as long as $ab = ba$, $n \in \mathbf{P}^+$ and all occurrences of a^0 and b^0 are deleted.

Proof (a) · (1) is obvious. For (2) we use the definition to obtain

$$\binom{n}{k+1} = \binom{n}{k} \cdot \frac{n-k}{k+1};$$

if $k + 1 \leqslant n/2$, then $(n-k)/(k+1) \geqslant 1$; thus (2) follows. For (3) we see that

$$\binom{n}{k} + \binom{n}{k+1} = \binom{n}{k} \cdot \frac{k+1+n-k}{k+1} = \binom{n}{k} \cdot \frac{n+1}{k+1} = \binom{n+1}{k+1},$$

as desired. Using the fact that $\binom{m}{0} = \binom{m}{m} = 1$ and by induction on n in (3), we obtain (4). (b) follows from induction on n together with (3) of (a). To carry out the induction we need the distributive law and the commutative law of multiplication involving powers of a and b. The details are left to the reader. *(Student: Fill in details)*

$(a+b)^{n+1} = \sum_{0 \leqslant k \leqslant n} \binom{m}{h} a^{h+1} b^{m-h} + \sum_{0 \leqslant h \leqslant m} \binom{m}{h} a^k b^{m-k+1} = \left(\sum_{0 \leqslant k \leqslant m} \left[\binom{m}{h} + \binom{m}{h+1} \right] \right) a^{h+1} b^{(m+1)-(k+1)} + b^{m+1} + a$

THEOREM 2 (Frobenius) · Let R be a commutative ring. Suppose that $p \in \mathbf{P}^+$ is a prime such that $pa = 0$ for all $a \in R$. Then the map which sends x onto x^p is a ring homomorphism of R into R and is called the **Frobenius homomorphism**

Proof · Since R is commutative, it is clear that $(ab)^p = a^p b^p$. It remains for us to verify that $(a+b)^p = a^p + b^p$. From the binomial theorem and the hypothesis that $pa = 0$ for all $a \in R$, it suffices for us to show that $\binom{p}{k} \equiv 0 \pmod{p}$ where $0 < k < p$. Because $p \mid p!$, we see that $p \mid \binom{p}{k} \cdot k! \cdot (p-k)!$. Since p is a prime, $p \nmid k! \cdot (p-k)!$ when $0 < k < p$. Again, since p is a prime, we conclude that $p \mid \binom{p}{k}$ when $0 < k < p$. **«**

COROLLARY (Little Fermat theorem) · Let $p \in \mathbf{P}^+$ be a prime and $a \in \mathbf{Z}$. Then $a^p \equiv a \pmod{p}$.

Proof · The ring $\mathbf{Z}/(p)$ satisfies the hypothesis of Theorem 2. Since the Frobenius homomorphism of $\mathbf{Z}/(p)$ onto itself maps the congruence class of 1 mod p onto itself, it must map any finite sum of such classes onto the same finite sum (using the fact that the map is a ring homomorphism, hence preserves sums). But every element of $\mathbf{Z}/(p)$ is a finite sum of congruence classes of 1 mod p; thus we conclude that the Frobenius homomorphism on $\mathbf{Z}/(p)$ is the identity map. This is precisely the assertion we desired. «

Exercise 5 · Consider the map $\sigma : \mathbf{Z} \to \mathbf{Z}/(m)$ defined by sending each $n \in \mathbf{Z}$ onto the congruence class of n mod m. Show that σ is an epimorphism of rings with units.

Exercise 6 · Let E and F be fields. Let $\sigma : E \to F$ be a homomorphism of rings with units in which E and F are considered to be rings with units. Show that σ is a monomorphism. *Hint.* $\sigma(1_E) = 1_F . 1_F \neq 0_F$. Every nonzero element in a field has a multiplicative inverse. Finally, σ preserves sum and product.

Exercise 7 · Let R be an integral domain. Show that there exists a field F with the following properties:

(a) There is a ring monomorphism $\sigma : R \to F$ (σ automatically maps the identity of R onto the identity of F).

(b) σ is universal with respect to ring monomorphisms of R into fields; namely, for each ring monomorphism $\rho : R \to K$ of R into an arbitrary field K there is a unique field monomorphism $\tau : F \to K$ such that $\tau \circ \sigma = \rho$.

Moreover, F is unique up to a natural isomorphism of fields. F also enjoys the following property:

(c) For each $x \in F$ the set $\{d \in R \mid \sigma(d)x \in \sigma(R)\}$ contains nonzero elements which are called ***denominators*** of x. (If R is identified with a subset of F through the map σ, the preceding assertion is simply the statement that every element of G may be represented as ab^{-1} for some $a, b \in R$, $b \neq 0$. For this reason F is called the ***field of fractions*** of R.)

Hint. The uniqueness of F involves a diagram-chasing argument. The existence of F is completely analogous to the construction of $\mathbf{Q}$ from $\mathbf{Z}$. The reader should compare the universal property of F with Exercise 2.2.

Let $(c, d) \in R \times R$, $d \neq 0$
then $\exists \; x \ni (c, d) = (x, 1)$.
$\therefore F = R$.

Exercise 8 · Let R be a field. What is the field F associated to R
in Exercise 7. Suppose that R is **Z**. How many possibilities are there for σ where
$F = \mathbf{Q}$ and **Z** is not considered as a subset of **Q**?

$\sigma(1)\sigma(1) = \sigma(1) \neq 0$
since σ *is mono*,
$\therefore \sigma(1)[\sigma(1) \; \sigma(1)^{-1}] = 1_F$
so $\sigma(1) = 1 \cdot$

» II · 4 POLYNOMIAL RINGS

An important class of rings is the rings of polynomials. The
reader may have already encountered these objects. We now wish to
formalize the definition of a polynomial by observing that a polynomial
is uniquely determined by its coefficients and that there is only a finite
number of them. These coefficients are usually assumed to be "real"
or "complex" numbers. However, there is no particular reason to make
this assumption.

DEFINITION 1 · Let R be a ring with an identity element denoted
by 1. A map $f : \mathbf{P} \to R$ is called a **finite sequence** if and only if there
exists $N \in \mathbf{P}$ such that $f(n) = 0 \; \forall \, n \geqslant N$. As a matter of convenience, we
identify f with the set of values taken by f. Thus, if we denote by
$[a_0, ..., a_i, ...,]$, or even $[a_i]$, the ordered set of elements $a_i \in R$, $i \in \mathbf{P}$,
then $f = [f(i)]$.

Let S be the set of all finite sequences in R. Addition and
multiplication in S are defined as follows:

$$[a_i] + [b_i] = [c_i],$$

where $c_i = a_i + b_i \; \forall \, i \in \mathbf{P}$;

$$[a_i] \cdot [b_i] = [c_i],$$

where $c_i = a_0 b_i + a_1 b_{i-1} + \cdots + a_i b_0 \; \forall \, i \in \mathbf{P}$.

Exercise 1 · Show that $S, +, \cdot$ in Definition 1 is a ring with the
identity element $[1, 0, 0, ...]$. Show that the map which sends $c \in R$ onto $[c, 0, 0, ...]$
is a monomorphism of the ring R into the ring S and that this monomorphism
preserves the identity element.

Exercise 2 · Continuing with the notations of Exercise 1, let
$X = [0, 1, 0, 0, ...]$. Show that, for $n \geqslant 1$, X^n is the finite sequence $[a_i]$ such
that $a_n = 1$ and $a_i = 0 \; \forall \, i \in \mathbf{P}$ and $i \neq n$. Identify R with a subset of S through
the map in Exercise 1 and let X^0 denote 1; show that the finite sequence $[a_i]$ is
$\sum_i a_i X^i$ with the understanding that the sum stops with $a_N X^N$, where
$a_i = 0 \; \forall \, i > N$. Finally, show that $uX^n = X^n u \; \forall \, u \in R$ and $\forall \, n \in \mathbf{P}$.

DEFINITION 2 · The ring S constructed in Definition 1 is called the ***polynomial ring*** in one (commuting) ***indeterminate*** over the ring with identity element R. If X is the finite sequence described in Exercise 2, we write $S = R[X]$ and call S the polynomial ring in the (commuting) indeterminate X over R.

The word "commuting" in the preceding definition refers to the fact that $uX^n = X^n u \; \forall \, u \in R$.

We often identify $[a_i]$ with $\sum_i a_i X^i$. If $f : \mathbf{P} \to R$ is the finite sequence $[a_i]$, we often write $f(X) = \sum_i a_i X^i$. It is to be understood that $a_i X^i$ is to be left out whenever $a_i = 0$. If $f(X) \neq 0$, then $\max\{i \mid a_i \neq 0\}$ is called the ***degree*** of $f(X)$ and it is denoted by $\deg_X f(X)$ or simply $\deg f$. If $f(X) = 0$, the degree of $f(X)$ is $-\infty$. If $f(X) = \sum_i a_i X^i$, then a_i is called the ***coefficient*** of X^i in $f(X)$. If $\deg f = n$, $n \in \mathbf{P}$, then a_n is called the ***leading*** (or ***highest***) ***coefficient*** of $f(X)$. The leading coefficient of the zero polynomial is taken to be 0; $f(X)$ is called a ***monic polynomial*** if and only if $f(X)$ has leading coefficient 1.

Exercise 3 · Continuing with the notations of Definition 2, verify the following assertions:

(a) S is the zero ring if and only if R is the zero ring.

(b) S is a commutative ring if and only if R is a commutative ring.

(c) Let $f, g \in S$, then $\deg(f + g) \leqslant \max(\deg f, \deg g)$ and $\deg(fg) \leqslant \deg f + \deg g$, where $-\infty \leqslant n$ and $-\infty + n = -\infty \; \forall \, n \in \mathbf{P} \cup \{-\infty\}$.

(d) (division algorithm). Let $f \in S$ be a monic polynomial and $g \in S$, then there exist $q, r \in S$ such that $g = qf + r$ where $0 \leqslant \deg r < \deg f$. Also, there exist $q', r' \in S$ such that $g = fq' + r'$, where $0 \leqslant \deg r' < \deg f$. The elements q, r, q', and r' need not be unique; in fact, even when R is commutative they still need not be unique.

(e) S is an integral domain if and only if R is an integral domain. Moreover, if R is an integral domain, $\deg(fg) = \deg f + \deg g$ in (c), and q, r of (d) are uniquely determined.

One of the most important properties of the polynomial ring is the "substitution" property. We summarize it in the following exercise:

Exercise 4 · Let R and T be rings with identity elements. Let $\sigma : R \to T$ be a homomorphism of rings with identity elements; that is, σ is a ring homomorphism such that $\sigma(1_R) = 1_T$. Suppose that $a \in T$ satisfies the

∂ Identifying elements $[a_1, 0, 0 \cdots]$ in $R[X]$ with a_1 in R

condition, $a\,\sigma(r) = \sigma(r)a \;\forall\; r \in R$. Show that there is a unique homomorphism of rings with identity elements $\rho : R[X] \to T$ such that (a) $\rho(r) = \sigma(r)\;\forall\; r \in R$ and (b) $\rho(X) = a$; namely, $\rho(\sum_i a_i X^i) = \sum_i \sigma(a_i) a^i$.

Hint. First show the uniqueness of ρ by using the fact ρ is a ring homomorphism. Use the definition given for ρ and the commutativity condition to verify that the map ρ so defined is a ring homomorphism.

DEFINITION 3 · In the notation of Exercise 4, when $T = R$ and σ is the identity map, ρ is called the **substitution homomorphism.** In this case we use the notation $\rho : R[X] \to R[a]/R$. This is to be read as "ρ is the substitution homomorphism over R obtained by replacing X by a." The phrase "over R" is meant to indicate that ρ is the identity map on the set R. If $f(X) \in R[X]$, then the image of $f(X)$ under the substitution homomorphism is denoted by $f(a)$. In the general situation the image is denoted by $f^\sigma(a)$; f^σ is meant to indicate that σ is applied to the coefficients of $f(X)$. The kernel of ρ is called the **ideal of polynomial relations** satisfied by a over R.

Exercise 5 · (factor theorem). Let R be a ring with an identity element. Let $f(X) \in R[X]$ and let $a \in R$ with $ar = ra \;\forall\; r \in R$. Show that the following assertions are equivalent:

    (a) $f(a) = 0$.

    (b) $\exists\; q(X) \in R[X]$ such that $f(X) = (X - a)\,q(X)$.

    (c) $\exists\; r(X) \in R[X]$ such that $f(X) = r(X)(X - a)$.

Hint. Use Exercise 3(d).

In view of Exercise 1, it is clear that we can iterate the procedure of forming a polynomial ring. We formalize it in the following definition:

DEFINITION 4 · Let R be a ring with an identity element 1. Let $S_0 = R$. If $n \in P$ and S_n is a ring with an identity element 1, then S_{n+1} is defined as the polynomial ring in one indeterminate over S_n. We denote S_{n+1} by $S_n[X_{n+1}]$ and identify S_n with a subring of S_{n+1} by the monomorphism described in Exercise 2. Moreover, we write $S_n = R[X_1, ..., X_n]$ and call it the **polynomial ring over R in the** (commuting) **indeterminates** $X_1, ..., X_n$.

As it stands, the order of the indeterminates in Definition 4 appears to be important. However, from the assertion in Exercise 6 it follows that the order of the indeterminates is irrelevant.

make induction assumption that $\rho : S_k \longrightarrow T$ is unique homo (satisfying cond. given and $\ni \rho(c) t_\ell = t_\ell \rho(c)$ $\forall c \in S_k$ and $\ell = k+1, \ldots, n$

Exercise 6 · Show that the ring S_n, $n \in \mathbf{P}^+$, has the following property:

(*) Let $\sigma : R \to T$ be a homomorphism of rings with identity elements and let $t_1, \ldots, t_n \in T$ be arbitrary elements satisfying the condition

$$t_i \sigma(r) = \sigma(r) t_i, \qquad t_i t_j = t_j t_i \; \forall \, i, j \quad \text{and} \quad \forall \, r \in R$$

with $1 \leqslant i, j \leqslant n$. Then there exists a unique homomorphism of rings with identity elements $\rho : R \to T$ such that (a) $\rho(r) = \sigma(r) \, \forall \, r \in R$ and (b) $\rho(X_i) = t_i$, $1 \leqslant i \leqslant n$.

Like Exercise 1 using induction on n, i.e.

let $\rho : S_{n-1} \to T$ be unique homo. satisfying cond. Then define ρ^*/S_{n-1} as a homo $S_{n-1} \to T$ satisfying cond. of existence

$\rho^*(\sum c_i x_n^i) = \sum \rho(c_i) t_n$. *Ck this a homo. uniqueness follows*

THEOREM 1 · Let R be a ring with an identity element 1. Let S_n, $n \in \mathbf{P}^+$, be the polynomial ring over R in the commuting indeterminates $X_1, \ldots, X_n$. Let $\pi : \{1, \ldots, n\} \to \{1, \ldots, n\}$ be a bijection. Then there is a unique isomorphism of rings with identity element $\rho : S_n \to S_n$ such that (a) $\rho(r) = r \, \forall \, r \in R$ and (b) $\rho(X_i) = X_{\pi(i)}$, $1 \leqslant i \leqslant n$.

In order to prove Theorem 1, we note first that $X_i r = r X_i$ holds for every element r of S_n. Thus from Exercise 6 we can deduce the existence and uniqueness of ρ as a homomorphism of rings with identity elements. The fact that ρ is an isomorphism of rings with identity elements follows from constructing ρ' associated with the inverse of the bijection π and from the usual diagram-chasing argument involving the uniqueness of such maps ρ. We leave the details to the interested reader.

and $X_i X_j = X_j X_i \; \forall \, i, j$
by induction on n using Exercise 2.
For diagram chasing let
$$S_n \xrightarrow{\rho} S_n$$
$$\downarrow \rho'$$
$$S_n$$

holds and ρ' is unique map $\ni \rho'(r) = r \; \forall \, r \in R$ and $\rho'(X_{\pi(i)}) = X_i$. Then where ρ is unique map $\ni$ (a) and (b) of Exercise 6 ($\rho \circ \rho' = i$ (from the uniqueness). Also $\rho \circ \rho' = i$, so that ρ is 1-1 and an iso.

DEFINITION 5 · In the notation of Exercise 6 the map ρ is called the **substitution homomorphism extending** σ **and substituting** X_i **by** t_i, $1 \leqslant i \leqslant n$. If $f(X_1, \ldots, X_n) \in S_n$, then $\rho(f(X_1, \ldots, X_n))$ will be denoted by $f^\sigma(t_1, \ldots, t_n)$. When $R = T$ and σ is the identity map on R, we write $\rho : R[X_1, \ldots, X_n] \to R[t_1, \ldots, t_n]/R$; ρ is then called the **substitution homomorphism over** R **obtained by substituting** t_i **for** X_i, $1 \leqslant i \leqslant n$.

Theorem 1 could have been avoided; namely, we could have considered the set $\mathbf{P}^I$ of all maps from the set I into the set $\mathbf{P}$. We may define a polynomial as a map $f : \mathbf{P}^I \to R$ which has **finite support;** that is, $f(s) \neq 0$ for at most a finite number of elements $s \in \mathbf{P}^I$. Finally, we may define addition and multiplication of polynomials suitably to obtain a ring. This procedure is precisely what we used in Definition 1 when I consisted of a single element. In general, when I consists of n elements, $n \in \mathbf{P}^+$, we obtain a ring that is isomorphic to the ring S_n

If $I = \{1, 2, \ldots, n\}$
$f \to \sum f(s) X_1^{s(1)} X_2^{s(2)} \cdots$

$$f(s) = a_{m_1, m_2, \ldots, m_k} \quad \text{where } S : \begin{array}{c} 1 \to m_1 \\ 2 \to m_2 \\ \vdots \\ k \to m_k \end{array}$$

$$(f + g)(s) = f(s) + g(s)$$
$$(f \cdot g)(s) = \sum_{t, u} f(t) g(u) \quad \text{where } t(\ell) + u(\ell) = s(\ell) \text{ for each } \ell \in I$$

constructed in Exercise 6; the isomorphism depends on the order of the elements $X_1, \ldots, X_n$, and Theorem 1 follows immediately. The only advantage of the procedure mentioned is that the set I need not be a finite set.

In the following exercise we give an alternate description of a polynomial ring in an arbitrary set of (commuting) indeterminates.

Exercise 7 · Let R be a ring with an identity element 1. Let I be an arbitrary index set. For each finite subset J of I let S_J be the polynomial ring over R in the indeterminates X_j, $j \in J$. If $J \subset K$ and K is a finite subset of I, then S_J will be identified with a subring of S_K in the obvious way. Let $S = \bigcup_J S_J$, where J ranges over all the finite subsets of I. Show that the following assertions hold:

(a) S has a unique ring structure such that each S_J is a subring of S.

(b) If $\sigma : R \to T$ is a homomorphism of rings with identity elements, and if t_i, $i \in I$, are elements of T such that $t_i t_j = t_j t_i$, $t_i\,\sigma(r) = \sigma(r) t_i\ \forall\, i, j \in I$, and $r \in R$, then there exists a unique ring homomorphism $\rho : S \to T$ such that $\rho(r) = \sigma(r)\ \forall\, r \in R$ and $\rho(X_i) = t_i\ \forall\, i \in I$.

Hint. The ring axioms are of "finite character" in the sense that each axiom involves only a finite (but arbitrary) number of elements. Thus, given a finite set of elements of S, there is a sufficiently large finite subset J of I such that S_J contains these prescribed elements. From this remark it is then easy to verify (a) and (b).

THEOREM 2 · Let $p \in \mathbf{P}^+$ be a prime. Let $a \in \mathbf{P}$ and $m \in \mathbf{P}^+$. Then $\binom{p^a m}{p^a} \equiv m \pmod{p}$.

Proof · Let F be the field $\mathbf{Z}/(p)$ and form the polynomial ring $F[X]$ in the indeterminate X over F. $F[X]$ satisfies the theorem of Frobenius. From the binomial theorem the coefficient of X^{p^a} in $(1+X)^{p^a m}$ is $\binom{p^a m}{p^a}$. From the Frobenius theorem $(1+X)^{p^a m} = (1+X^{p^a})^m$. From the binomial theorem again we see that the coefficient of X^{p^a} is $\binom{m}{1} = m$. Because equality in $F = \mathbf{Z}/(p)$ is precisely congruence mod p, the desired conclusion follows. «

References

The concept of a commutative diagram is quite important. It is a shorthand notation for complicated equations involving many compositions of maps. Indeed, formal theories have been developed concerning these objects. The interested reader may consult [1] and [2].

The little Fermat theorem is quite important in elementary number theory. The interested reader may consult [3].

1. N. Bourbaki, *Eléments de mathématique, algèbre commutative*, Chapter 1, Hermann, Paris, 1961.

2. P. Freyd, *Abelian Categories*, Harper and Row, New York, 1964.

3. G. H. Hardy and E. M. Wright, *An Introduction to the Theory of Numbers*, 4th ed., Oxford University Press, London, 1960.

CHAPTER III Elementary Theory of Groups

We now take a more detailed look at some of the abstract mathematical objects encountered in Chapter II. One of the most important of these is a group. We mentioned earlier that the simplest way to obtain groups is to consider the set of all bijections of a set E onto itself. As it stands, E itself is devoid of any structure. We could have insisted that E be given some kind of structure and that the bijections considered be compatible with these structures. For example, we may give E the structure of a Euclidean space and insist on restricting ourselves to the collection of bijections of E which preserve the Euclidean distance in E. The group so obtained is usually called the group of ***Euclidean motions.*** In a sense, the study of geometric properties of Euclidean space may be considered as a study of those properties of E that are invariant under the action of the Euclidean group of motions. To push this point further, we may even say that the properties of the Euclidean space E are in essence the properties of the associated group of Euclidean motions.

In this chapter we have collected some properties of groups in general, and we shall study some special examples of groups. We also present some construction procedures for groups that imitate those for sets.

» III · 1 BASIC CONCEPTS

DEFINITION 1 · Let H be a subset of a group G. Then H is called a ***subgroup*** of G if and only if H forms a group under the group operation already present in G. If $S \subset G$, then $\langle S \rangle$ is the intersection of all subgroups H of G such that $S \subset H$; $\langle S \rangle$ is called the ***subgroup of G generated by S***. When S consists of a single element $s \in G$, we usually write $\langle s \rangle$ in place of $\langle \{s\} \rangle$; $\langle s \rangle$ is called the ***cyclic subgroup of G generated by s***. More generally, if $S = \{s, t, \ldots\}$, we often write $\langle s, t, \ldots \rangle$ for $\langle S \rangle$.

We use the notation $H \leqslant G$ to mean that H is a subgroup of G; $H < G$ then means that $H \leqslant G$ and $H \neq G$; that is, H is a ***proper subgroup of*** G.

When the group operation is $\cdot$, we usually denote the identity element of G by 1 and the subgroup $\langle 1 \rangle$ also by 1. When the group operation is $+$, we usually denote the identity element of G by 0 and the subgroup $\langle 0 \rangle$ also by 0.

As an illustration of subgroups, we consider the group $\mathbf{Z}, +$. The collection of all integral multiples of $m \in \mathbf{Z}$ is a subgroup; in fact, it is precisely $\langle m \rangle$.

Exercise 1 · In the group $\mathbf{Z}/(4), +$, find the elements of the cyclic subgroups generated by the congruence class of 2, of 3, and of -1.

Exercise 2 · Use the Euclidean division algorithm to show that every subgroup of $\mathbf{Z}, +$ has the form $< m >$ for some $m \in \mathbf{Z}$.

Exercise 3 · Let H be a subset of a group $G, \cdot$. Show that H is a subgroup of G if and only if the following conditions hold:

(a) $1 \in H$.

(b) If x and y are in H, then xy^{-1} is in H.

Exercise 4 · Let S be a subset of a group G. Let the group operation in G be $\cdot$ and let $S^{-1} = \{x^{-1} \mid x \in S\}$. Show that $\langle S \rangle$ consists of all finite products of elements of the set $S \cup S^{-1}$. As usual, the empty product is the element 1 of G. *Hint.* Use Exercise 3.

We now proceed with the study of subgroups of a group G. It turns out that there is an intimate relation between the subgroups of a group G and some of the equivalence relations on the group G. It would be too much to expect that we could study all possible equivalence relations because we would then be forgetting the group structure of the set G. The equivalence relations on a group G, which are of interest, should in some sense respect, or be compatible with the group structure. Keeping this in mind, we state the following:

DEFINITION 2 · Let $\sim$ be an equivalence relation on a group $G, \cdot$; $\sim$ is called a ***right (left) equivalence*** if and only if $x \sim y$ and $z \in G$ imply that $xz \sim yz (zx \sim zy)$; $\sim$ is called a ***normal equivalence*** if and only if it is both a right and a left equivalence.

As an example, we consider the group $\mathbf{Z}, +$ and let $m \in \mathbf{Z}$. The equivalence relation, congruence mod m, is a normal equivalence on $\mathbf{Z}, +$.

Of course, whenever a group is commutative, there is no difference between right equivalence, left equivalence and normal equivalence. In general, the following exercise shows that we may restrict ourselves to right equivalences.

Exercise 5 · Let $\sim$ be a left equivalence on a group $G, \cdot$. Define the relation $\sim'$ on G by the condition that $x \sim' y$ if and only if $x^{-1} \sim y^{-1}$. Show that $\sim'$ is a right equivalence on G. Show that the map that sends $\sim$ onto $\sim'$ is a bijection between the set of all left equivalences on G and the set of all right equivalences on G. Show that $\sim$ is a normal equivalence on G if and only if $\sim = \sim'$.

THEOREM 1 · Let G be a group under $\cdot$. Let $\sim$ be a right equivalence on G. Then $H = \{x \in G \mid x \sim 1\}$ is a subgroup of G. Moreover, the $\sim$ equivalence class of $g \in G$ is $\{xg \mid x \in H\}$.

Proof · Since $1 \sim 1$, we have $1 \in H$. Let $x, y \in H$. From $x \sim 1$, we obtain $xy^{-1} \sim y^{-1}$. From $y \sim 1$ we obtain $yy^{-1} \sim y^{-1}$. Since an equivalence relation is symmetric and transitive, we obtain $xy^{-1} \sim 1$. Thus $xy^{-1} \in H$. Exercise 3 then implies that H is a subgroup of G. Since $x \sim 1$ implies that $xg \sim g$, we see that each element of the form $xg, x \in H$, lies in the equivalence class of g. Conversely, suppose that $z \sim g$. It follows that $zg^{-1} \sim gg^{-1}$. Thus $zg^{-1} \in H$. If we let $x = zg^{-1}$, it would then follow that $z = xg, x \in H$. «

In view of Theorem 1, we state the following definition.

DEFINITION 3 · Let H be a subgroup of a group $G, \cdot$. If $x \in G$, then $Hx = \{hx \mid h \in H\}$ is called the ***right coset*** determined by x with respect to the subgroup H of G. The set of all right cosets of G with respect to H is denoted by $H \backslash G$. (The notation will remind us of the side of H and that right multiplication by elements of G will send right cosets onto right cosets.) Similarly, $xH = \{xh \mid h \in H\}$ is called the ***left coset*** determined by x with respect to the subgroup H of G.

The set of all left cosets of G with respect to H is denoted by G/H. The reader should be warned that "right" and "left" are sometimes interchanged in the literature.

THEOREM 2 · Let H be a subgroup of a group G. Define the relation $\sim_H$ by setting $x \sim_H y$ if and only if $xy^{-1} \in H$. The following assertions then hold:

(a) $\sim_H$ is a right equivalence on G.

(b) Hg is the $\sim_H$ equivalence class of $g \in G$. In particular, $H = \{x \in G \mid x \sim_H 1\}$.

(c) The distinct right cosets of G with respect to H form a partition of G.

Proof · (a) Since $1 \in H$, it follows that $x \sim_H x \; \forall \, x \in G$. If $xy^{-1} \in H$, then $(xy^{-1})^{-1} = yx^{-1} \in H$; thus $\sim_H$ is symmetric. If xy^{-1}, $yz^{-1} \in H$, then $xz^{-1} = (xy^{-1})(yz^{-1}) \in H$; thus $\sim_H$ is transitive. If $xy^{-1} \in H$ and $z \in G$, then $xy^{-1} = xzz^{-1}y^{-1} = xz(yz)^{-1} \in H$. Thus $\sim_H$ is a right equivalence on G.

(b) It is obvious that $H = \{x \mid x \sim_H 1\}$; (b) now follows from (a) and Theorem 1. (c) follows from (a), (b) and Theorem O.2.1. «

We may summarize Theorem 1 and Theorem 2 as follows:

THEOREM 3 · Let G be a group, let $\mathcal{H}$ be the set of subgroups of G, and let $\mathcal{S}$ be the set of all right (respectively, left) equivalences on G. A "natural" bijection between $\mathcal{H}$ and $\mathcal{S}$ is then described by Theorems 1 and 2.

We have seen that congruence mod m is a normal equivalence on the group $\mathbf{Z}, +$. Moreover, we have defined $+$ on $\mathbf{Z}/(m)$ in a natural way so that $\mathbf{Z}/(m), +$ becomes a group. We shall now see that this phenomenon occurs whenever we have a normal equivalence on a group G.

THEOREM 4 · Let $G, \cdot$ be a group and $H \leqslant G$. The following assertions hold:

(a) The right equivalence on G determined by H is a normal equivalence if and only if $Hx = xH$ for all $x \in G$.

(b) Let H determine a normal equivalence on G. Define $\# : H\backslash G \times H\backslash G \to H\backslash G$ by setting $(Hx) \# (Hy) = Hxy$. Then, $H\backslash G, \#$

is a group, and the "natural" map sending $g \in G$ onto $Hg \in H\backslash G$ is a surjective group homomorphism of $G, \cdot$ onto $H\backslash G, \#$.

Proof · (a) follows immediately from (b) of Theorem 2.

(b) First we must check that $\#$ is well-defined. The point is that the coset Hx does not determine x uniquely. If $Hx = Hs$, then $s = hx$ for some $h \in H$. Similarly, if $Hy = Ht$, then $t = ky$ for some $k \in H$. Since $Hx = xH$, we see that $xk = ux$ for some $u \in H$. Thus $st = hxky = huxy \in Hxy$ and $Hst = Hxy$. It follows that $\#$ is well-defined.

The interested reader can verify that $Hxy = \{st \mid s \in Hx \text{ and } t \in Hy\}$; this will give another proof of the fact that $\#$ is well-defined.

Each of the group axioms on $H\backslash G, \#$ is a consequence of the corresponding axiom on $G, \cdot$. For example, H is the identity element of $H\backslash G$ and $(Hx)^{-1} = Hx^{-1}$. It is clear from the definition that the "natural" map described is a surjective group homomorphism. «

DEFINITION 4 · Let H be a subgroup of a group $G, \cdot$. H is called a ***normal subgroup*** of G if and only if $Hx = xH$ for all x in G. When H is a normal subgroup, we write $H \lhd G$. The group $H\backslash G$ $(= G/H)$ defined in Theorem 4 is called the ***quotient group*** of G with respect to H. The group operation in $H\backslash G$ is often denoted by $\cdot$, the same symbol used for that in G.

Exercise 6 · Let $\sigma : G \to H$ be a homomorphism of groups. Show that σ is an isomorphism if and only if σ is bijective as a map of the set G into the set H. (The point is that when σ is bijective as a map, then the inverse of σ is automatically a group homomorphism.)

Exercise 7 · Let H be a subgroup of a group G and let $x \in G$. Show that $x^{-1}Hx = \{x^{-1}hx \mid h \in H\}$ is a subgroup of G; in fact, show that the map which sends $h \in H$ onto $x^{-1}hx$ is an isomorphism between H and $x^{-1}Hx$. Show that $H \lhd G$ if and only if $x^{-1}Hx \subset H$ for all $x \in G$.

DEFINITION 5 · Let S be a subset of a group G and let $x \in G$. Then $x^{-1}Sx = \{x^{-1}sx \mid s \in S\}$ is denoted by S^x and is called the ***conjugate of S by the element x***. If $S = \{y\}$, then we identify S with y and S^x with $y^x = x^{-1}yx$. The isomorphism of G onto G sending y onto y^x is called the ***conjugation by x***, or the ***inner automorphism*** of G ***induced by x***.

Exercise 8 · Let S be a subset of a group G. Show that the intersection of all normal subgroups of G containing S is the subgroup of G generated by $\bigcup_{x\in G} S^x$. This intersection is called the ***normal subgroup of G generated by S.***

DEFINITION 6 · Let H be a subgroup of a group G. $|G:H|$ will denote the number of right cosets of G with respect to H. It is called the ***index of H in G.*** In view of Exercise 5, $|G:H|$ is also the number of left cosets of G with respect to H. Moreover, $|G:H|$ is equal to the cardinality $|G/H|$ of G/H as well as equal to the cardinality $|H\backslash G|$ of $H\backslash G$. The **order** of the group G is defined as the cardinality of G; thus $|G| = |G:1|$.

Generally speaking, these quantitative descriptions of the relative sizes of subgroups of a given group G are useful only when they are finite.

Exercise 9 · Let H be a subgroup of a group G. Show that $|G:H| \leqslant 2$ implies that H is a normal subgroup. Show that $|G:H| = |G:H^x|\ \forall\, x \in G$.

THEOREM 5 (Lagrange) · Let H be a subgroup of a group G. Then $|G| = |G:H|\,|H|$.

Proof · The map that sends an element $h \in H$ onto the element $hx \in Hx$ is a bijection between H and Hx. Since G is the disjoint union of the distinct right cosets of G with respect to H, the assertion follows. «

DEFINITION 7 · Let G be a group and $g \in G$. The ***order of g*** is $\min\{n \in \mathbf{P}^+ \mid g^n = 1\}$ where we agree that the minimum of an empty set of natural numbers is ∞. The order of g is usually denoted by $|g|$.

Exercise 10 · Let g be an element of order d in a group G. Show that $d = |\langle g\rangle|$.

Exercise 11 · Let G be a group of finite order n. Show that $g^n = 1$ for all $g \in G$. Show that $g^t = 1$ if and only if $|\langle g\rangle| \mid t$.

Exercise 12 · Give a group-theoretic proof of the little Fermat theorem; that is, show that if $a \in \mathbf{Z}$ and p is a prime in $\mathbf{P}^+$ then $a^p \equiv a \pmod{p}$. *Hint.* Use the fact that $\mathbf{Z}/(p)$ is a field.

Exercise 13 · Let G be a group and let $g \in G$ be an element of finite order d. Let $e \in \mathbf{Z}$, $f \in \mathbf{P}^+$ such that $(e, d) = (f)$. Show that g^e has order d/f. *Hint.* Show that $\langle g^e \rangle = \langle g^f \rangle$; note that $\langle x \rangle = \langle y \rangle$ if and only if $x \in \langle y \rangle$ and $y \in \langle x \rangle$.

Exercise 14 · Let H and K be normal subgroups of a group G. Suppose that H and K have coprime orders m and n, respectively, where $m, n \in \mathbf{P}^+$. Verify the following assertions:

(a) $H \cap K = 1$ and $hk = kh$ holds $\forall\, h \in H, k \in K$.

(b) Each element of $\langle H, K \rangle$ has a unique representation as hk, where $h \in H, k \in K$.

» III · 2 HOMOMORPHISMS OF GROUPS

We now investigate in more detail the concept of a group homomorphism. We recall that $\sigma : G \to H$ is a group homomorphism from a group G into a group H if and only if $(xy)^\sigma = x^\sigma y^\sigma \;\forall\, x, y \in G$.

DEFINITION 1 · Let $\sigma : G \to H$ be a homomorphism from a group G into a group H: $\ker \sigma = \sigma^{-1}(1) = \{x \in G \mid x^\sigma = 1\}$ is called the ***kernel*** of the homomorphism σ; $\operatorname{im} \sigma = G^\sigma = \{x^\sigma \mid x \in G\}$ is called the ***image*** of the homomorphism σ. When σ is an isomorphism between G and H, we write $\sigma : G \cong H$ or simply $G \cong H$ when σ itself is not important. Properties of groups preserved under isomorphisms are often called ***group-theoretical properties.***

Exercise 1 · Let $\sigma : G \to H$ be a homomorphism from a group G to a group H. Let $K \leqslant G$; show that $K^\sigma \leqslant H$. Let S and T be conjugate subsets of G; show that S^σ and T^σ are conjugate subsets of H. Let S be any subset of G; show that $|S| \geqslant |S^\sigma|$.

Exercise 2 · Show that the order of a group, the order of an element in a group, and the index of a subgroup in a given group are preserved under isomorphisms between groups.

Exercise 3 · Consider the natural homomorphism of $\mathbf{Z}, +$ onto $\mathbf{Z}/(m), +$. Find the kernel and the image of the homomorphism.

Exercise 4 · Let $G, \cdot$ be a *commutative* group and $n \in \mathbf{Z}$. Show that the map which sends $g \in G$ onto g^n is a homomorphism. Describe the kernel of this homomorphism in terms of orders of elements in G. Usually the image is denoted by G^n, regardless of the hypothesis of commutativity of G; it is called the set of ***nth powers*** in G.

THEOREM 1 (First isomorphism theorem) · Let $\sigma : G \to H$ be a *surjective* homomorphism of a group G onto a group H. Let $K = \ker \sigma$. If $H' \leqslant H$, let $G' = \sigma^{-1}(H') = \{g \in G \mid g^\sigma \in H'\}$. The following assertions hold:

(a) $K \leqslant G' \leqslant G$, that is, the inverse image of a subgroup of H is a subgroup of G containing the kernel of σ.

(b) Let $\mathcal{G}$ be the set of all subgroups of G which contain K and let $\mathcal{H}$ be the set of all subgroups of H. The map $\rho : \mathcal{H} \to \mathcal{G}$ given by $\rho(H') = G'$ is a bijection; moreover, ρ preserves intersection and conjugation.

(c) $G' \lhd G$ if and only if $H' \lhd H$.

(d) The map $\tau : G'/K \to H'$ given by $\tau(Kx) = x^\sigma\ \forall\, x \in G'$ is an isomorphism between G'/K and H'.

(e) Let $H' \lhd H$. The map $\eta : G/G' \to H/H'$ given by $\eta(G'x) = H'x^\sigma\ \forall\, x \in G$ is an isomorphism between G/G' and H/H'.

Proof · (a) The inclusion relations among the sets are immediate. Since $K = \langle 1 \rangle'$; it suffices to show that G' is always a subgroup of G. Let $x, y \in G'$; then $(xy^{-1})^\sigma = x^\sigma(y^\sigma)^{-1} \in H'$. Thus $xy^{-1} \in G'$ and (a) holds.

(b) Since σ is surjective as a map of sets, it follows that $G'^\sigma = H'$. We first show that ρ is injective. Let $H', H'' \in \mathcal{H}$ such that $\rho(H') = \rho(H'')$. Thus $G' = \sigma^{-1}(H') = \sigma^{-1}(H'') = G''$. By applying σ to each side, we see that $H' = H''$. We now show that ρ is surjective. Let $T \in \mathcal{G}$. We assert that $T = \rho(T^\sigma)$. It is clear that $T \subset \rho(T^\sigma) = \sigma^{-1}(T^\sigma)$. Conversely, let $x \in \rho(T^\sigma) = \sigma^{-1}(T^\sigma)$. Thus $x^\sigma \in T^\sigma$. It follows that we can find $y \in T$ such that $y^\sigma = x^\sigma$, and hence $(xy^{-1})^\sigma = 1$. Therefore $xy^{-1} \in K \subset T$ and $x = (xy^{-1})y \in T$. Hence $\rho(T^\sigma) \subset T$ as desired. As in Exercise 1, T^σ is a subgroup of H; hence we see that ρ is surjective. Next, since ρ is the inverse image map, it preserves intersections. From Exercise 1 we already know that σ preserves conjugation. Since $G'^\sigma = H'$, we see that if $\sigma^{-1}(H')$ and $\sigma^{-1}(H'')$ are conjugate in G then H' and H'' are conjugate in H. Conversely, let $H'' = H'^h$ for some $h \in H$. Since σ is surjective, we can find $x \in G$ such that $x^\sigma = h$. It is easy to see that $G'^x = \sigma^{-1}(H'')$. This shows that ρ preserves conjugation.

(c) Since a subgroup is a normal subgroup if and only if it coincides with all its conjugates, we see that (c) is a consequence of (b).

(d) Since $K = \ker \sigma$, τ is well-defined. Because $G'^\sigma = H'$, τ is surjective. It is easy to see that τ is a homomorphism. Finally, since $Kx = \sigma^{-1}(x^\sigma)$, the map τ is also injective. Thus (d) holds.

(e) We compose the epimorphism (= surjective homomorphism) σ with the natural epimorphism from H onto H/H'. This is then an epimorphism from G onto H/H' with kernel $G' = \sigma^{-1}(H')$; (e) is now a consequence of (d). «

Exercise 5 · Consider the situation described in Theorem 1. Let $S \leqslant T \leqslant G$. Show that $| T : S | \geqslant | T^\sigma : S^\sigma |$. Show that equality holds when $K \leqslant S$.

COROLLARY (Factorization of homomorphisms) · Let $\sigma : G \to H$ be a homomorphism from a group G into a group H. Then there exist groups (unique up to isomorphism) G_1, G_2 and homomorphisms $\sigma_1 : G \to G_1$, $\sigma_2 : G_1 \to G_2$ and $\sigma_3 : G_2 \to G$ such that $\sigma = \sigma_1\sigma_2\sigma_3$, σ_1 is surjective, σ_2 is bijective, and σ_3 is injective.

Proof · We first show the uniqueness of G_1 and G_2. Because σ_2 and σ_3 are both injective, it follows easily that $\ker \sigma = \ker \sigma_1$. Thus, from Theorem 1(d), G_1 must be isomorphic to $G/\ker \sigma$. Because σ_1 and σ_2 are both surjective, it follows that $\operatorname{im} \sigma = \operatorname{im} \sigma_3$ and G_2 must be isomorphic to $\operatorname{im} \sigma$. Of course, since σ_2 is an isomorphism, G_2 is also isomorphic to G_1.

As for proof of the existence, we take $G_1 = G/\ker \sigma$, $G_2 = \operatorname{im} \sigma$, $\sigma_1 =$ the natural epimorphism from G to G_1, $\sigma_2 =$ the isomorphism described in Theorem 1(d) between G_1 and G_2, and $\sigma_3 =$ the inclusion map of G_2 into H. It is almost immediate that all the conditions are satisfied. «

The reader should note that the maps σ_1, σ_2, and σ_3 are not necessarily uniquely determined by G_1 and G_2. We could have modified each of them suitably by an isomorphism of the domain, or the image.

Exercise 6 · Let $G = \langle g \rangle$ be a cyclic group of order $n = st$, where $n, s, t \in \mathbf{P}^+$. Show that G has exactly one subgroup of index t, hence of order s.

Hint. Form the epimorphism from **Z**, + onto G, · which sends $m \in \mathbf{Z}$ onto g^m. Apply Theorem 1 together with the fact that $\langle t \rangle$ is the unique subgroup of index t in **Z**, where $t \in \mathbf{P}^+$.

Exercise 7 · Let H and K be subgroups of G. Show that $HK = \{hk \mid h \in H, k \in K\}$ is a subgroup if and only if $HK = KH$. Assuming that $HK \leqslant G$, show that $|HK : K| = |H : H \cap K|$. When HK is not a subgroup of G, the same equality holds, provided that we interpret $|HK : K|$ to mean the number of distinct left cosets of G/K contained in the subset HK. *Hint*. Consider the map that sends the left coset $h(H \cap K)$ onto the left coset hK for $h \in H$ and show that this is a bijection between the sets $H/H \cap K$ and HK/K.

DEFINITION 2 · Let S be a nonempty subset of a group G. Then $N_G(S) = \{x \in G \mid S^x = S\}$ is called the ***normalizer of S in G,*** and $C_G(S) = \{x \in G \mid s^x = s \ \forall\, s \in S\}$ is called the ***centralizer of S in G.***

Exercise 8 · Let S be a nonempty subset of a group G. Show that $C_G(S) \lhd N_G(S) \leqslant G$. Show that group isomorphisms preserve normalizers and centralizers of nonempty subsets which correspond to one another under the isomorphism.

Exercise 9 · Let G be a group. Verify the following assertions:

(a) If $H \leqslant G$, then $N_G(H)$ is the largest subgroup of G which contains H as a normal subgroup. In particular, $H \lhd G$ if and only if $G = N_G(H)$.

(b) If $H \lhd G$ and $K \leqslant G$, then $H \cap K \lhd K$.

(c) If $H \lhd G$ and $H \leqslant K \leqslant G$, then $N_{G/H}(K/H) = N_G(K)/H$.

(d) If $\sigma : G \to H$ is a group homomorphism and S is a nonempty subset of G, then $N_G(S)^\sigma \leqslant N_H(S^\sigma)$ and $C_G(S)^\sigma \leqslant C_H(S^\sigma)$.

THEOREM 2 (Second isomorphism theorem) · Let G, · be a group. Let $H, K \leqslant G$ such that $K \leqslant N_G(H)$. The following assertions hold:

(a) $HK \leqslant G$.

(b) $H \lhd HK$.

(c) $H \cap K \lhd K$.

(d) $K/(H \cap K) \cong HK/K$ under the map that sends $(H \cap K)k$ onto $Hk \ \forall \ k \in K$. *This follows easily from exercise 7 ... map ... a homo.*

or follows from Th.1 by mapping $HK \to K/H \cap K$ by

Proof · Use Exercises 7 and 9 and the first isomorphism theorem.

$hk \to (H \cap K)k$

noting ker of map

is H.

Excursion I

We now examine the divisibility theory in **Z** and the structure of the group $\mathbf{Z}/\langle m \rangle, +$. We first note that (m) and $\langle m \rangle$ are indistinguishable as sets. $\mathbf{Z}/\langle m \rangle, +$ is precisely the additive group of the ring $\mathbf{Z}/(m)$.

1. Using the Euclidean algorithm, we have $|\mathbf{Z} : \langle m \rangle| = |m|$ when $m \neq 0$. Using the Euclidean algorithm again, we find that every subgroup of **Z** has the form $\langle m \rangle$ for some $m \in \mathbf{P}$. Moreover, if $m \neq 0$, the map that sends $k \in \mathbf{Z}$ onto km is an isomorphism of **Z** onto $\langle m \rangle$.

2. $\langle m \rangle$ is a subgroup of $\langle n \rangle$ if and only if $n \mid m$. This should be remembered as "smaller integer generates larger subgroup."

3. A least common multiple of $m, n \in \mathbf{Z}$ generates the subgroup $\langle m \rangle \cap \langle n \rangle$. A greatest common divisor of $m, n \in \mathbf{Z}$ generates the subgroup $\langle m, n \rangle$. It happens that the subgroup $\langle m, n \rangle$ of $\mathbf{Z}, +$ consists of the same elements as (m, n). The difference in notation will become evident when we study "ideals" in "rings."

4. Consider the natural epimorphism of **Z** onto $\mathbf{Z}/\langle m \rangle$. From the first isomorphism theorem and item 2 each subgroup of $\mathbf{Z}/\langle m \rangle$ has the form $\langle n \rangle/\langle m \rangle$ with $n \mid m$. Thus subgroups of cyclic groups are cyclic. If $m \neq 0$, we may assume that $1 \leqslant n \leqslant m$. The number of distinct subgroups of $\mathbf{Z}/\langle m \rangle$, $m > 0$, is then equal to $d(m) =$ the number of distinct divisors of m between 1 and m. The calculation of $d(m)$ may be carried out by means of the unique factorization theorem. For example, if $m = \prod_i p_i^{a(i)}$, then $d(m) = \prod_i (a(i) + 1)$, where $p_i \in \mathbf{P}$ are distinct nonzero primes and $a(i) \in \mathbf{P}$.

5. Let $m \in \mathbf{P}^+$. Then $d + \langle m \rangle$ is a generator of $\mathbf{Z}/\langle m \rangle, +$ if and only if $(d, m) = (1)$. This may be seen from the g.c.d. theorem in **Z**. We let $\varphi(m)$ be the number of $d \in \mathbf{P}^+$ such that $d \leqslant m$ and $(d, m) = (1)$. It then follows that $\varphi(m)$ is the number of distinct generators of $\mathbf{Z}/\langle m \rangle$. This function φ is usually referred to as the **Euler φ-function**

Both the divisor function d in item 4 and the Euler φ-function in item 5 are of interest in number theory. Items 1, 2, and 3 should be

This follows by noting every finite cyclic group has ... to Z/⟨m⟩ ... and every infinite cyclic ... to Z.

considered as a translation between the divisibility theory in $\boldsymbol{P}$ and the subgroup structure in $\boldsymbol{Z}, +$.

» III · 3 TRANSFORMATION GROUPS: SYLOW'S THEOREM

We now describe a few specific methods for constructing groups. In view of our earlier discussions it is natural to state the following definition:

DEFINITION 1 · Let G be a group. A homomorphism of G into itself is called an ***endomorphism.*** An isomorphism of G onto itself is called an ***automorphism.*** Aut(G) denotes the set of all automorphisms of G. This is a group under the product defined by the composition of automorphisms as maps. The set of all inner automorphisms of G is denoted by Inn(G). Elements of Aut(G)-Inn(G) are called ***outer automorphisms.*** The subgroup $C_G(G)$ is called the ***center of*** G and is denoted by $\mathfrak{Z}(G)$.

Exercise 1 · Let G be a group. Show that Inn(G) is a group isomorphic to $G/\mathfrak{Z}(G)$. Show that Inn(G) $\lhd$ Aut(G). (The group Aut(G)/Inn(G) is sometimes called the ***group of outer automorphisms*** of G; the reader should realize that the elements of this group are *sets* of automorphisms.)

Exercise 2 · Let G be a group. Show that the following conditions are equivalent:

(a) G is commutative.

(b) $G = \mathfrak{Z}(G)$.

(c) The map that sends $g \in G$ onto $g^{-1} \in G$ is an endomorphism.

(d) The map that sends $g \in G$ onto $g^2 \in G$ is an endomorphism.

Exercise 3 · Let G and H be groups. A map $\sigma : G \to H$ is called an ***opposite homomorphism*** if and only if $(xy)^\sigma = y^\sigma x^\sigma$ for all $x, y \in G$. Show that there exists a bijection between the set of all homomorphisms of G into H and the set of all opposite homomorphisms of G into H. *Hint.* Show that the composition of two opposite homomorphisms is a homomorphism; then consider the map that sends $g \in G$ onto g^{-1} and its composition with an arbitrary homomorphism of G into H. Show that G is commutative if and only if the identity map is an opposite automorphism of G. Show that the set of all semiautomorphisms (that is, either automorphisms or opposite automorphisms) of G form a group under composition. This group contains $\mathrm{Aut}(G)$ as a normal subgroup of index 1 or 2. Show that the index is 2 if and only if G is not commutative.

Exercise 4 · Let $G = \mathbf{Z}/\langle m \rangle$, $m \in \mathbf{P}^+$. Find $\mathrm{Aut}(G)$. *Hint.* Excursion I. 5 shows that $|\mathrm{Aut}(G)| \leqslant \varphi(m)$. Consider G as the additive group of the ring $\mathbf{Z}/(m)$. Let U be the set of multiplicatively invertible elements of $\mathbf{Z}/(m)$. Show that under multiplication, elements of U induce automorphisms of G. Indeed, this defines a monomorphism of U into $\mathrm{Aut}(G)$. Show that $d + (m)$ is in U if and only if $(d, m) = 1$. Next show that U may be identified with $\mathrm{Aut}(G)$ and $|U| = \varphi(m)$. Show that if $(a, m) = (1)$, then $a^{\varphi(m)} \equiv 1 \pmod{m}$. This is the Euler-Fermat theorem; it generalizes the little Fermat theorem.

DEFINITION 2 · Let E be a set and let G be a group. Let $\sigma : E \times G \to E$ be a map and write $\sigma(s, g) = s^g \ \forall\, s \in E$ and $g \in G$. We say that G is a ***group of transformations*** (acting on the right) on E (through σ) if and only if the following conditions are satisfied:

(a) $s^1 = s \ \forall\, s \in E$.

(b) $s^{gh} = (s^g)^h \ \forall\, s \in E, g, h \in G$.

DEFINITION 3 · Let E be a set. We now use the exponential notation for maps. The set of all bijections of E with E, together with the operation of composition of maps, is a group. It is called the ***(unrestricted) symmetric group*** of E and is denoted by $\mathbf{S}_E$. If $|E| = n \in \mathbf{P}^+$, then we identify E with $\{1, \ldots, n\}$ and write $\mathbf{S}_n$ for $\mathbf{S}_E$. (In view of Exercise II.1.6, up to isomorphism, the group $\mathbf{S}_E$ is uniquely determined by the cardinal number of E.)

The reader should convince himself that the statement, "G is a group of transformations on the set E through σ," is equivalent to the statement, "the map sending $g \in G$ onto the map $\sigma(\ , g) : E \to E$ given by $\sigma(\ , g)(s) = s^g$ is a homomorphism of G into $\mathbf{S}_E$." In group theory it is sometimes more convenient to use exponential notation for maps. This is the main reason for our choice of notation in Definitions 2 and 3.

Let G act as a group of transformations on the set E. The elements $s, t \in E$ are said to be ***G-equivalent*** if and only if there is an element $g \in G$ such that $s^g = t$. The G-equivalence classes in E are called ***G-orbits*** on E. If F is the union of some of the G-orbits on E, then, by restricting our attention to F, G may also be considered as a group of transformations on F.

A transformation group G on a set E is said to be ***transitive*** if and only if E is the only G-orbit, that is, if and only if for any two elements $s, t \in E$, there exists $g \in G$ such that $s^g = t$.

Let G be a transformation group on a set E. Let S be a nonempty subset of G; $x \in E$ is called a ***fixed point*** of S if and only if $x^g = x \ \forall g \in S$. It is clear that x is a fixed point of S if and only if it is a fixed point of $\langle S \rangle$. Conversely, if F is a nonempty subset of E, the ***stabilizer*** of F in G is $\{g \in G \mid F^g = F\}$. The stabilizer is always a subgroup.

We now consider a few examples.

Example 1 · Let G be a group. Then, in analogy to Exercise II.1.7, G may act on the set G by right translation; namely, if $g, h \in G$, then $h^{\sigma(g)} = hg$. In this case an element $g \in G$ has a fixed point if and only if $g = 1$.

Example 2 · Let G be a group. Then G acts on the set G by conjugation; namely, if $g, h \in G$, then $h^g = g^{-1}hg$. The stabilizer of a nonempty subset S of G is $N_G(S)$. Indeed, $N_G(S)$ is the largest subgroup of G that may act as a group of transformations by conjugation on the subset S. The kernel of the homomorphism of $N_G(S)$ into $\mathbf{S}_S$ is precisely $C_G(S)$. It follows that $C_G(S) \lhd N_G(S)$.

Example 3 · Let $\mathbf{R}^2 = \{(a, b) \mid a, b$ are "real numbers"$\}$. Let d be the usual "Euclidean distance." Let G be the set of all distance preserving bijections of $\mathbf{R}^2$ with itself. Under the composition of maps G becomes a group—the Euclidean group of the plane.

If $g \in G$, $(1, 0)^g = (a, b)$, $(0, 1)^g = (c, d)$, and $(0, 0)^g = (x_0, y_0)$, it is easy to verify that $(a - x_0)(d - y_0) - (c - x_0)(b - y_0) = \pm 1$. When this number is 1, g is said to be ***orientation-preserving;*** otherwise, g is said to be ***orientation-reversing.*** The set G^+ of orientation-preserving elements of G forms a normal subgroup of index 2 in G.

If $g \in G^+$ such that either $g = 1$ or g has no fixed points on E, then g is called a ***translation*** on E. The set T of all translations is a normal subgroup of G^+; T is transitive on the set E. Indeed, for any given $P, Q \in \mathbf{R}^2$ there is a unique element $g \in T$ such that $P^g = Q$.

Let $P \in \mathbf{R}^2$ and let $I(P)$ be the stabilizer of P in G^+; $I(P)$ is called the group of **rotations** with **center** P. The reader can verify that $I(P) \cap T = 1$, $I(P)T = G^+$, and that $\{I(P) \mid P \in \mathbf{R}^2\}$ is the set of all G^+-conjugates of $I(P_0)$, $P_0 = (0, 0)$.

The reader can verify the following assertions as an exercise.

(a) $g \in G - G^+$ if and only if the fixed points of g form a straight line. Such an element g is called a ***reflection*** and the fixed line is called the ***axis of reflection.***

(b) $g \in G^+ - T$ if and only if g has exactly one fixed point. The fixed point of g is then the center of rotation of g.

(c) $g \in T - 1$ if and only if g has no fixed point. In such a case there exists a unique line L through (0, 0) such that $L^g = L$. This line L is called the ***direction of the translation*** g.

(d) $g = 1$ if and only if g fixes three points that do not lie on a straight line.

By now the reader should realize that the group G embodies a great deal of information concerning the "Euclidean plane" $\mathbf{R}^2$. Indeed, $\mathbf{R}^2$ may even be identified with the subgroup T.

THEOREM 1 (Fundamental theorem on transformation groups) • Let G be a transitive transformation group on a set E. Let s be an arbitrary (but fixed) point in E and let $I(s)$ be the stabilizer of s in G. The following assertions hold:

(a) $I(s)^g$ is the stabilizer of $s^g \in E \; \forall \, g \in G$.

(b) $K = \bigcap_{g \in G} I(s)^g$ is the kernel of the homomorphism of G into $\mathbf{S}_E$.

(c) Let $H \leqslant G$ and let $\rho : (H \backslash G) \times G \to H \backslash G$ be such that $\rho(Hx, g) = Hxg$. Then G is a transitive transformation group on the set $H \backslash G$ and $I(Hx) = H^x$.

(d) Let G act on E through σ. In the notation of (b) and (c) let $H = I(s)$ and take $\tau : I(s) \backslash G \to E$ to be the map that sends $I(s)x$ onto $s^x \; \forall \, x \in G$. Then τ is a bijection between $I(s) \backslash G$ and E; in particular, $|\, G : I(s)|$ is equal to the cardinality of E. Moreover, the following diagram is commutative,

$$\begin{array}{ccc} (I(s)\backslash G) \times G & \xrightarrow{\rho} & I(s)\backslash G \\ {\scriptstyle \tau \times \iota} \downarrow & & \downarrow {\scriptstyle \tau} \\ E \times G & \xrightarrow{\sigma} & E \end{array}$$

where $\tau \times \iota$ sends $(I(s)x, g)$ onto (s^x, g).

The proof of Theorem 1 is straightforward and the details are left as an exercise for the reader. The main point of Theorem 1 is that "representing a group G as a *transitive* group of transformations on a set E" is equivalent to "selecting a conjugate class of subgroups of G."

We observe that by using the identity subgroup 1 for H in the preceding theorem we would obtain Cayley's theorem in Exercise II.1.7.

The following exercises serve as illustrations of the uses of the preceding fundamental theorem.

Exercise 5 · Let G be a group and $H \leqslant G$. Suppose that $|G : H| = n \in \mathbf{P}^+$. Show that H contains a normal subgroup K of G such that $|G : K| \mid n!$.

Exercise 6 · Let G be a group of order $n \in \mathbf{P}^+$. Suppose that p is the smallest prime divisor of n. Show that every subgroup of index p in G must be a normal subgroup. We note that Exercise 1.9 is a special case of Exercises 5 and 6.

THEOREM 2 (Counting lemma for groups of prime-power order) Let G be a group of order p^a, p a prime in $\mathbf{P}^+$, and $a \in \mathbf{P}$. Suppose that G acts on a finite set E and that F is the set of all fixed points of G on E. Then $|E| \equiv |F| \pmod{p}$.

Proof · Theorem 1 is applicable to any G-orbit in E. By Lagrange's theorem and the unique factorization theorem in $\mathbf{Z}$ any G-orbit with more than one element must have a multiple of p elements. A G-orbit has one element if and only if that element is in F. Thus, since E is a disjoint union of the distinct G-orbits, we see that Theorem 2 follows by counting mod p. «

DEFINITION 4 · A finite group G of order a power of the prime p (zeroth power allowed) is called a ***p*-group**.

Exercise 7 · Let G be a finite p-group. Show that $G = 1$ if and only if $\mathfrak{Z}(G) = 1$. *Hint.* Let G act on itself by conjugation. What are the fixed points of this action of G on G?

Exercise 8 · Let G be a finite p-group and $p^b \mid |G|$. Show that G contains at least one normal subgroup of order p^b. *Hint.* Every subgroup of $\mathfrak{Z}(G)$ is normal in G; thus use induction, Exercise 2.6, Lagrange's theorem, and the first isomorphism theorem.

Exercise 9 · Let G be a finite p-group and $H < G$. Show that $H < N_G(H)$. Use this to show that every subgroup of index p in G is normal. (The second assertion also follows from Exercise 6.) *Hint.* Since $\mathfrak{Z}(G)$ is contained in every normalizer, the first assertion may be verified by using Exercise 7, induction, and Exercise 2.9.

Exercise 10 · Let G be a group. Show that G is commutative if and only if $G/\mathfrak{Z}(G)$ is cyclic.

Exercise 11 · Let p be as prime in $\mathbf{P}^+$ and let G be a group of order p^2. Show that G is commutative. Show that, up to isomorphism, there are only two such groups. *Hint.* G is cyclic if and only if G contains an element of order p^2.

Exercise 12 · Let G be a group of finite order and let H, K be subgroups of G. Show that $HK = \{hk \mid h \in H, k \in K\}$ contains $|H| \cdot |K| / |H \cap K|$ elements. Thus show that if HK is a subgroup of G, then HK is a p-group if and only if H and K are p-groups.

From Theorem 2 and the exercises following it it can be seen that p-groups are very interesting among groups of finite order. Lagrange's theorem tells us that p-groups may occur as subgroups of a finite group G only for prime divisors of $|G|$ (forgetting the trivial case that 1 is a p-subgroup for every prime). However, it is not clear that there is a nontrivial p-subgroup for each prime divisor of $|G|$. In fact, we shall soon see that this is actually the case.

LEMMA 1 · Let G be a finite group of order $p^a m$ where p is a prime in $\mathbf{P}^+$ and $p \nmid m$. Suppose that G contains a subgroup H of order p^a and that K is any p-subgroup of G. Then $\mathfrak{B} = \{H^x \mid x \in K\}$ consists of $|K : H \cap K|$ distinct subgroups of G, each conjugate to H.

Proof · K acts on $\mathfrak{B}$ by conjugation. It is clear from the definition that K is transitive on $\mathfrak{B}$. Thus, by Theorem 2, the number of elements in $\mathfrak{B}$ is $|K : N_G(H) \cap K|$. Since $H \leqslant N_G(H)$, we see that $H \cap K \leqslant N_G(H) \cap K$. From the second isomorphism theorem and Exercise 12 we see that $H(N_G(H) \cap K)$ is a p-subgroup of G containing H. From $p \nmid m$ and Lagrange's theorem we conclude that $H(N_G(H) \cap K) = H$. Hence $N_G(H) \cap K \leqslant H$ and therefore $N_G(H) \cap K = H \cap K$. «

DEFINITION 5 · Let p be a prime in $\mathbf{P}^+$ and let G be a finite group. Let $|G| = p^a m$, $a \in \mathbf{P}$, $m \in \mathbf{P}$ such that $p \nmid m$. A subgroup H of G of order p^a is called a ***Sylow p-subgroup*** of G.

It is clear from Lagrange's theorem that Sylow p-subgroups of a finite group are the maximal p-subgroups of G.

THEOREM 3 (Sylow) · Let p be a prime in $\mathbf{P}^+$ and let G be a finite group of order $p^a m$, $a, m \in \mathbf{P}$ such that $p \nmid m$. Let $\mathcal{A}$ be the set of all Sylow p-subgroups of G.

(a) $\mathcal{A}$ is nonempty.

(b) Let $S \in \mathcal{A}$ and T be any p-subgroup of G; then $\exists\, g \in G$ such that $T \leqslant S^g$.

(c) Under conjugation G is transitive on $\mathcal{A}$.

(d) $\mathcal{A}$ contains $|G : N_G(S)|$ distinct Sylow p-subgroups; this number is of the form $1 + kp$, $k \in \mathbf{P}$, and $(1 + kp) \mid m$.

Proof · (a) Let $\mathfrak{S}$ be the set of all p^a-element subsets of the set G. Let the group G act on $\mathfrak{S}$ by right multiplication, that is, for each $g \in G$ we associate the map that sends $A \in \mathfrak{S}$ onto $Ag \in \mathfrak{S}$, where $Ag = \{ag \mid a \in A\}$. The total number of elements in $\mathfrak{S}$ is precisely $\binom{p^a m}{p^a} \equiv m \pmod{p}$ by Theorem II.4.2. Since $p \nmid m$, at least one G-orbit in $\mathfrak{S}$ must have a number of elements prime to p. Let $\mathfrak{D}$ be this G-orbit and $A \in \mathfrak{D}$. Take H to be the stabilizer $I(A)$ in G. It follows that $Ah = A\ \forall\, h \in H$. Taking $a \in A$, we see that $aH \subset A$. It follows that $|H| \leqslant p^a$. However, from Theorem 2, $|G : H| = |\mathfrak{D}|$. From the choice of $\mathfrak{D}$ we see that $p \nmid |G : H|$. From Lagrange's theorem and the unique factorization theorem in $\mathbf{Z}$ we see that $p^a \mid |H|$, in particular, $p^a \leqslant |H|$. Thus $H \in \mathcal{A}$.

(b) Let $\mathcal{B}$ be the G-orbit of S under conjugation.

We first consider the action of S on $\mathcal{B}$ by conjugation. From Lemma 1 we see that each S-orbit in $\mathcal{B}$ distinct from $\{S\}$ has a cardinality equal to a multiple of p. Hence $|\mathcal{B}| = 1 + kp$, $k \in \mathbf{P}$.

We next consider the action of T on $\mathcal{B}$ by conjugation. Combining Lemma 1 and the result that $|\mathcal{B}| \equiv 1 \pmod{p}$, we see that at least one T-orbit in $\mathcal{B}$ must have exactly one element. Thus we can find some $g \in G$ such that $|T : S^g \cap T| = 1$. Hence $T \leqslant S^g$ as asserted; (c) follows from (b) by taking T to be an arbitrary element of $\mathcal{A}$, thus $\mathcal{A} = \mathcal{B}$; (d) now follows from (c), Theorem 1, and the fact that $S \leqslant N_G(S)$. «

Exercise 13 · Let $p < q$ be primes in $\mathbf{P}^+$. Show that all groups of order pq contain a normal subgroup of order q. Show that, up to isomorphism, there are only two groups of order $2p$.

DEFINITION 6 · Let G be a group and $x, y \in G$. Then $[x, y] = x^{-1}y^{-1}xy$ is called the **commutator** of x and y. If S and T are subsets of G, then $[S, T]$ is the subgroup of G generated by $\{[s, t] \mid s \in S, t \in T\}$; $[G, G]$ is called the **commutator** subgroup of G.

[margin: To show $[G,G] \lhd G$ by in $X^{-1}X$ between all commutators it is suff. to show $x^{-1}c^{-1}d^{-1}cd\,x \in [G,G]$. But $x^{-1}c^{-1}d^{-1}\,cx\,dd^{-1}x^{-1}dx = [(cx)^{-1}d^{-1}(cx)\,d]\,[d^{-1}x^{-1}dx]$]

Exercise 14 · Let G be a group. Show that $[G, G] \lhd G$. Show that $[G, G]$ is the intersection of all kernels of homomorphisms of G into arbitrary commutative groups. In other words, $G/[G, G]$ is the solution to the universal mapping problem of the group G into commutative groups.

[margin: For notation let $G' = [G$ and note $G'x)(G'y) = G'xy = G'yx = G'yx = (G'y)(G'x)$ so G/G' is comm. $\therefore G \to G/G'$ such a. Also if $\theta : G \to H$ a homo, H comm then $\theta(x^{-1}y^{-1}xy) \in \ker \theta$ or result, Finally $G \to G/G'$ Then $\phi(G'x) = (G'x)$ so ϕ]

Exercise 15 · Determine the commutator subgroup of the various groups associated to the group of the "Euclidean plane," as described in Example 3.

Exercise 16 · Let G be a group $\neq 1$. A proper subgroup M of G is said to be **maximal** if and only if $M < S \leqslant G$ implies that $S = G$. Suppose that G is a finite p-group; show that the following assertions hold:

(a) M is a maximal subgroup of G if and only if $|G : M| = p$.

(b) If M is a maximal subgroup of G, then $[G, G] \leqslant M \lhd G$.

(c) $\langle G^p \rangle \lhd G$ and G^p is contained in every maximal subgroup of G. In fact, $[G, G] \langle G^p \rangle$ is the intersection of all the maximal subgroups of G.

Exercise 17 · Let G be a group, finite or not. G is called a **p-group** if and only if every element of G has order a power of the prime p. Show that this definition is consistent with the earlier definition in the case of finite groups. Show that subgroups and quotient groups of p-groups are p-groups. Show that if $H \lhd G$, H and G/H are both p-groups, then G is a p-group.

» III · 4 THE FINITE SYMMETRIC GROUPS S_n

We now examine the finite symmetric groups S_n, $n \in P^+$, in some detail. First of all we note that Cayley's theorem asserts that every finite group may be considered as a subgroup of a suitable S_n. In this sense S_n is certainly of interest. However, for this same reason we should not expect to be able to say everything there is about S_n for every n, for saying everything would certainly include knowing all the subgroups, and thus we would then know everything about finite groups. This is too much to hope for.

S_n is usually called the **permutation group on n letters** or of **degree n;** and the elements of S_n are called **permutations.** If we let

E be the finite set $\{1, \ldots, n\}$, each permutation $g \in \mathbf{S}_n$ can be uniquely associated with a table $\begin{pmatrix} 1, & \cdots, & n \\ 1^g, & \cdots, & n^g \end{pmatrix}$ in the exponential notation, in which $i^g \in E$ and $i^g = j^g$ if and only if $i = j$. This tabular notation is rather cumbersome. Instead, we use the "cycle decomposition" for g; namely, if $g \in \mathbf{S}_n$, then E is decomposed into $\langle g \rangle$-orbits. Suppose that one of these $\langle g \rangle$-orbits consists of $i_1, \ldots, i_s$. Since any subgroup of a cyclic group is a normal subgroup, it follows from Theorem 3.1 that $\langle g^s \rangle$ is the stabilizer of any of the i_j's in the chosen $\langle g \rangle$-orbit and, moreover, $s \mid |g|$. By shuffling the indices we may assume that $i_{j+1} = i_j^g$, $1 \leqslant j \leqslant s - 1$ and $i_s^g = i_1$. We now use the notation $(i_1 i_2 \cdots i_s)$ to denote the action of g on this particular orbit. The action of g on E is uniquely determined by its actions on the various $\langle g \rangle$-orbits. We may arrange these "cycles" next to each other in any order we please Reading from left to right, the action of g is uniquely determined. The integer s is called the ***length*** of the cycle $(i_1 i_2 \cdots i_s)$. For convenience we omit all cycles of length one. As a result, unless n is specified, there is no way of telling where g lies.

Example 1 · Consider the permutation $\begin{pmatrix} 1, 2, 3, 4, 5, 6, 7, 8 \\ 2, 5, 4, 3, 1, 6, 8, 7 \end{pmatrix}$; its cycle decomposition is (125)(34)(87). We can also write the cycle decomposition as (43)(251)(78).

Under our convention the cycle $(i_1 \cdots i_s)$ is already an element of $\mathbf{S}_n$. Two such cycles are said to be ***disjoint*** if and only if they involve disjoint sets of letters. The identity element of $\mathbf{S}_n$ is simply denoted by 1.

Exercise 1 · Show that two disjoint cycles commute. (Exercise 1 justifies our convention in disregarding the orders of the cycles in the decomposition of the permutation g into the product of disjoint cycles.)

Exercise 2 · Show that $\mathbf{S}_n$ is not commutative when $n > 2$. Write down the table of multiplication for the group $\mathbf{S}_3$, using cycle decomposition for the elements of $\mathbf{S}_3$.

Exercise 3 · Let $g \in \mathbf{S}_n$: show that $g^{-1}(i_1 i_2 \cdots i_s) g = (i_1^g i_2^g \cdots i_s^g)$. Thus show that two elements of $\mathbf{S}_n$ are conjugate in $\mathbf{S}_n$ if and only if there is a bijection between the cycles of the decompositions such that corresponding cycles have the same length. Define a ***partition*** π of n as a sequence of integers $1 \leqslant j_1 \leqslant j_2 \leqslant \cdots \leqslant j_t \leqslant n$ such that $j_1 + j_2 + \cdots + j_t = n$. Show that the number of conjugate classes of elements in $\mathbf{S}_n$ is $\pi(n)$, the number of partitions of n. Thus $\pi(1) = 1$, $\pi(2) = 2$, $\pi(3) = 3$, $\pi(4) = 5$, $\pi(5) = 7$, and so on.

Exercise 4 · Let $j_1 < \cdots < j_t \in \mathbf{P}^+$ and $m_1, \ldots, m_t \in \mathbf{P}^+$ such that $m_1 j_1 + \cdots + m_t j_t = n$. Thus j_1 repeated m_1 times, j_2 repeated m_2 times,..., j_t repeated m_t times form a partition of n. Show that the number of elements in $\mathbf{S}_n$ whose cycle decompositions correspond to this partition is

$$\frac{n!}{j_1^{m_1} \cdots j_t^{m_t} \cdot m_1! \cdot \ldots \cdot m_t!};$$

show that the centralizer of such an element in $\mathbf{S}_n$ is a subgroup of order $j_1^{m_1} \cdots j_t^{m_t} \cdot m_1! \cdot \ldots \cdot m_t!$.

DEFINITION 1 · Cycles of length s are called ***s*-cycles;** 2-cycles are also called ***transpositions*** and are of the form (ij), $i \neq j$.

THEOREM 1 · $\mathbf{S}_n$ is generated by its transpositions.

Proof · We agree to use the convention that the empty product is the identity element. It now suffices to show that every cycle is the product of transpositions. The reader can show by induction that $(i_1 i_2 \cdots i_s) = (i_1 i_2)(i_1 i_3) \cdots (i_1 i_s)$. «

Because $1 = (12)(12) = (12)(12)(12)(12)$, it is clear that the number of transpositions needed in a decomposition of an element in $\mathbf{S}_n$, $n > 1$, is not unique. However, the "parity," or the congruence class mod 2, of this number is fixed. Granting this for the moment, we conclude that the assignment of the parity to each permutation is an epimorphism of $\mathbf{S}_n$, $n > 1$, onto $\mathbf{Z}/\langle 2 \rangle$. The immediate question we may raise is the following: how many such epimorphisms are there? As we shall see, the answer is *one*. Thus the notion of parity on $\mathbf{S}_n$, $n > 1$, is "intrinsically" associated to the group.

From the first isomorphism theorem, kernels of epimorphisms of a group onto $\mathbf{Z}/\langle 2 \rangle$ are subgroups of index 2. Since $\mathbf{Z}/\langle 2 \rangle$ has only the identity automorphism, we see that the number of distinct epimorphisms of a group onto $\mathbf{Z}/\langle 2 \rangle$ is equal to the number of normal subgroups of index 2 in the group given. Since every subgroup of index 2 is automatically normal, the problem is reduced to counting the number of subgroups of index 2 in $\mathbf{S}_n$, $n > 1$. We shall determine first that there is at most one such subgroup in $\mathbf{S}_n$.

LEMMA 1 · Let $n > 1$. Suppose that $H < \mathbf{S}_n$ with $|\mathbf{S}_n : H| = 2$. Then H is generated by all the 3-cycles in $\mathbf{S}_n$ and H consists of exactly all the permutations in $\mathbf{S}_n$ that may be decomposed into a product of an even number of transpositions.

Proof · We have already remarked that any subgroup of index 2 must be normal. Thus $\mathbf{S}_n/H$ is cyclic of order 2. When $n = 2$, $H = 1$, and there is nothing to prove. Let $n > 2$. Since $\mathbf{S}_n/H$ has order 2, we see that $H = H(ijk)^4 = H(ijk)$. Thus $(ijk) \in H$, and we see that H contains all the 3-cycles of $\mathbf{S}_n$. Now let K be the subgroup of $\mathbf{S}_n$ generated by all the 3-cycles in $\mathbf{S}_n$. Thus $K \leqslant H$. Using Lagranges theorem, we see that $| \mathbf{S}_n : K | \geqslant | \mathbf{S}_n : H | = 2$, in which equality holds if and only if $K = H$. We assert that $| \mathbf{S}_n : K | \leqslant 2$; hence $K = H$. For this we observe that $(ij)(ik) = 1$ or (ijk) and that $(ij)(st) = (ij)(js)(js)(st)$. Thus the product of an even number of transpositions lies in K. Hence, from Theorem 1, we conclude that $\mathbf{S}_n = K \cup K(12)$ or $| \mathbf{S}_n : K | \leqslant 2$. As we saw before, this implies that $K = H$ and that $K \cap K(12) = \varnothing$. The latter means that K consists of exactly all the elements of $\mathbf{S}_n$ that may be represented as a product of an even number of transpositions. «

LEMMA 2 · Let $n > 1$. Then $\mathbf{S}_n$ has a subgroup of index 2.

Proof · Let S be the polynomial ring $\mathbf{Z}[X_1, ..., X_n]$. If $g \in \mathbf{S}_n$, let g^ρ be the isomorphism of S with S described in Theorem II.4.1; namely, g^ρ permute the indices of X_i. It follows easily from Theorem II.4.1 that the map ρ is a homomorphism of $\mathbf{S}_n$ into the group of automorphisms of the ring S. (The automorphisms are written exponentially.) We now consider the polynomial $D = \prod_{1 \leqslant i < j \leqslant n} (X_i - X_j)$. Because $\mathbf{Z}$ is an integral domain, we see that S is also an integral domain. Thus $D \neq 0$. It follows from Theorem 1 that g^ρ sends D onto $\operatorname{sgn}(g)D$, where $\operatorname{sgn}(g) = \pm 1$. Since $D \neq 0$, $\operatorname{sgn}(g)$ is uniquely determined by g. It is called the ***sign*** of the permutation g. Since g^ρ is the identity map on $\mathbf{Z}$ and a ring automorphism of S, we see that $\operatorname{sgn}(gh) = \operatorname{sgn}(g) \cdot \operatorname{sgn}(h)$. Thus the map sending $g \in \mathbf{S}_n$ onto its sign, $\operatorname{sgn}(g)$, is a group homomorphism of $\mathbf{S}_n$ into the multiplicative group $\{1, -1\}, \cdot$. It is easy to see that $\operatorname{sgn}((12)) = -1$. Thus the map sgn is a surjective homomorphism of $\mathbf{S}_n$ onto $\{1, -1\}, \cdot$. It follows from the first isomorphism theorem that the kernel of sgn is a subgroup of index 2 in $\mathbf{S}_n$. «

COROLLARY · Under the notations of Lemma 2 and its proof the permutation g is a product of an even number of transpositions if and only if $\operatorname{sgn}(g) = 1$; g is a product of an odd number of transpositions if and only if $\operatorname{sgn}(g) = -1$.

We now summarize our results into the following theorem:

THEOREM 2 · Let $n > 1$ be an integer. Then $\boldsymbol{S}_n$ has a unique subgroup $\boldsymbol{A}_n$ of index 2. $\boldsymbol{A}_n$ is generated by all the 3-cycles in $\boldsymbol{S}_n$ and consists of all permutations of $\boldsymbol{S}_n$ that may be represented as a product of an even number of transpositions. The coset $\boldsymbol{S}_n - \boldsymbol{A}_n$ consists of all permutations of $\boldsymbol{S}_n$ that may be represented as a product of an odd number of transpositions. $\boldsymbol{A}_n$ is called the ***alternating group of degree n.***

Exercise 5 · Let G be a finite group of order $2(2n + 1)$, $n \in \boldsymbol{P}$. Show that G has a unique subgroup of index 2. *Hint.* Let G act on the *set* G by right translations. Use Sylow's theorem to conclude that there exists an element g of order 2 in G. Show that this element g is the product of $2n + 1$ transposition. Use the argument of Lemma 2 to conclude the existence of a subgroup of index 2. Finally, use Exercise 2.7 to conclude that G can have at most one subgroup of index 2 when $|G| = 2(2n + 1)$.

DEFINITION 2 · A group G is said to be ***simple*** if and only if $G \neq 1$ and the only normal subgroups of G are G and 1.

Exercise 6 · Show that a group G is commutative and simple if and only if $|G|$ is a prime.

Simple groups are the "building blocks" of groups in the sense that, given a normal subgroup H of G other than 1 and G, the group G may be broken down into the groups H and G/H. With some kind of finiteness conditions, the iteration of this process would eventually terminate and we would then obtain a collection of simple groups. Two problems arise immediately. First, to what extent are the simple groups obtained in this way from G unique (up to isomorphism, of course)? Second, given the collection of simple groups, in how many ways can we put them together to obtain groups that are different (nonisomorphic)? The answer to the first question is contained in the Jordan-Hölder-Schreier-Zassenhaus theorem. The answer to the second question is contained in the theory of group extensions. We make no attempt to treat either of these problems; the interested reader should refer to the literature. At the moment, we are content with some examples of noncommutative simple groups.

LEMMA 3 · If $n > 4$, all 3-cycles are conjugate under $\boldsymbol{A}_n$.

Proof · It suffices to show that all 3-cycles are conjugate to (123) in $\mathbf{A}_n$. From Exercise 3 we can find $g \in \mathbf{S}_n$ such that $(ijk)^g = (123)$. If g is an odd permutation, then $h = g(45)$ is an even permutation and $(ijk)^h = (123)$. Thus we can always find $x \in \mathbf{A}_n$ such that $(123) = (ijk)^x$. «

THEOREM 3 · If $n > 4$, then $\mathbf{A}_n$ is simple and nonabelian.

Proof · $\mathbf{A}_n$ has order $n!/2$ when $n > 1$. Thus, when $n > 4$, $\mathbf{A}_n$ is not of prime order. Hence the simplicity of $\mathbf{A}_n$, $n > 4$, would imply that it is nonabelian. Alternately, we could easily exhibit two 3-cycles which do not commute.

Let $n > 4$ and $1 < N \lhd \mathbf{A}_n$; we must show that $N = \mathbf{A}_n$. Since a cyclic group of order t contains a cyclic subgroup of order d for each $d \mid t$, $d \in \mathbf{P}^+$, we can find an element $x \in N$ of prime order p. (Indeed, using Sylow's theorem, p may be any prime divisor of the order of N.) Since p is a prime, x is a product of k disjoint p-cycles, $k \in \mathbf{P}^+$.

Case 1 · $p = 3$ and $k = 1$. Thus x is a 3-cycle. From Lemma 3 and $N \lhd \mathbf{A}_n$ we see that N contains all 3-cycles. Thus from Theorem 2 we conclude that $N = \mathbf{A}_n$.

Case 2 · $p > 3$. Let $x = (a_1a_2 \cdots a_p) \cdots$, and $y = (a_1a_2a_3) \in \mathbf{A}_n$. Since $N \lhd \mathbf{A}_n$, we see that $x^{-1}yx \cdot y^{-1} = x^{-1} \cdot yxy^{-1} \in N$. But $x^{-1}yx \cdot y^{-1} = (a_2a_3a_4)(a_3a_2a_1) = (a_1a_3a_4)$. Thus $N = \mathbf{A}_n$ by Case 1.

Case 3 · $p = 3$ and $k > 1$. Thus $x = (a_1a_2a_3)(a_4a_5a_6) \cdots (a_{3k-2}a_{3k-1}a_{3k})$. Let $y = (a_1a_2a_4) \in \mathbf{A}_n$; then, as in Case 2, we may conclude that $x^{-1}yx \cdot y^{-1} = (a_1a_4a_2a_3a_5) \in N$. From Case 2 we conclude that $N = \mathbf{A}_n$.

Case 4 · $p = 2$. From Theorem 2 it follows that $k \geqslant 2$ and k is even. Let $x = (a_1a_2)(a_3a_4) \cdots$, and let $y = (a_1a_2a_3) \in \mathbf{A}_n$. Using the reasoning of Case 2 again, we see that $x^{-1}yx \cdot y^{-1} = (a_2a_3)(a_1a_4) \in N$. Since $n > 4$, we may select $t \in \mathbf{P}^+$, $1 \leqslant t \leqslant n$ and t distinct from a_1, a_2, a_3, a_4. Let $z = (a_2a_3t)$ and $w = (a_2a_3)(a_1a_4)$. Thus, using the reasoning of Case 2 once more, we have $w^{-1}zw \cdot z^{-1} = (a_2a_3t) \in N$, and $N = \mathbf{A}_n$ by Case 1. «

Exercise 7 · Find all the normal subgroups of $\mathbf{S}_4$ and $\mathbf{A}_4$. Identify the commutator subgroup of each of the normal subgroups.

Exercise 8 · Let $\{G_i \mid i \in \mathbf{P}\}$ be a set of groups such that G_i is identified with a subgroup of G_{i+1}, $i \in \mathbf{P}$. Let $G = \bigcup_i G_i$ as a set. If $g, h \in G$, there is an index i such that $g, h \in G_i$. Define the product in G by taking gh to be the product in G_i. Show that this definition turns G into a group. This group G is often called the ***union of the increasing sequence of groups G_i***.

Exercise 9 · Show that the union of an increasing sequence of simple groups is again simple. Thus show that the union of $\mathbf{A}_n$, $n > 4$, is an infinite simple group. Instead of considering the union of $\mathbf{A}_n$, we may also consider elements of $\mathbf{A}_n$ as permutations of $\mathbf{P}^+$, leaving all integers greater than n fixed and permuting the integers between 1 and n according to its representation as a permutation in $\mathbf{A}_n$. The union is precisely the subgroup of $\mathbf{S}_{\mathbf{P}^+}$ generated by all $\mathbf{A}_n$, $n > 4$.

Exercise 10 · Show that there is no simple nonabelian group of order less than 60. *Hint.* Use Exercises 3.5, 3.6, 3.8, Sylow's theorem, and Exercise 5.

Exercise 11 · Exhibit one subgroup in each conjugate class of subgroups of $\mathbf{S}_4$ and $\mathbf{A}_4$. For each such subgroup find the centralizer, the normalizer, and the number of conjugates. Do the same thing for the elements of the groups.

Excursion II

In the following we shall study $\mathbf{A}_5$ and the automorphisms of $\mathbf{S}_n$ for $n \neq 6$.

THEOREM 1 · Let G be a simple group of order 60. Then G is isomorphic to $\mathbf{A}_5$.

Proof · Since G is simple, we see that the following assertions hold:

(a) If $1 < H < G$, then $H \leqslant N_G(H) < G$.

(b) If $H < G$, then $|G : H| \geqslant 5$. Moreover, if $|G : H| = 5$, then G is isomorphic to $\mathbf{A}_5$. To prove these assertions we let G act on $H\backslash G$ by right multiplication. Since G is simple and $H < G$, it follows that we have a monomorphism of G into $\mathbf{S}_{H\backslash G}$. Since $|G| = 60$ and $|\mathbf{S}_n| = n!$, we see that $|G : H| \geqslant 5$. Moreover, if $|G : H| = 5$, then

G is isomorphic to a subgroup of index 2 in $\mathbf{S}_5$. Thus, by Theorem 4.2, $G \cong \mathbf{A}_5$.

(c) Let S be a Sylow 2-subgroup of G and $N = N_G(S)$. By Sylow's theorem and (b) we see that $| G : N | = 5$ or 15. Similarly, let N_5 be the normalizer of a Sylow 5-subgroup of G; then $| G : N_5 | = 6$.

Now, proceeding by contradiction, we assume that G has no subgroup of index 5. Hence $N = S$, and there are 15 distinct subgroups of order 4. Let S_1 and S_2 be two distinct subgroups of order 4. Suppose that $1 < T = S_1 \cap S_2$. Thus $| T | = 2$; and, since $| S_i : T | = 2$, $T \lhd S_i$. It follows that $S_i \leqslant N_G(T) < G$. Since $S_1 \neq S_2$, we see that $S_i < N_G(T)$. Thus $| G : N_G(T)| = 3$ or 5. This contradicts (b) and the hypothesis that G has no subgroup of index 5. Hence any two distinct subgroups of order 4 have only the identity element in common. Because there are 15 such subgroups, we have accounted for 45 non-identity elements in G. Since $| G : N_5 | = 6$, there must be six distinct subgroups of order 5. Any two distinct subgroups of prime order could have only the identity element in common. Thus we have accounted for 24 elements of order 5, all of which must be distinct from the preceding 45 elements, for these 45 elements all have order dividing 4. But G has room for only 60 elements, and thus we have arrived at a contradiction. «

If we look at $\mathbf{A}_5$ in detail, it may be seen that $\mathbf{A}_4$ plays the role of N and has index 5.

The reader may be tempted to imitate the proof given and try to prove that a simple group of order 360 must be isomorphic to $\mathbf{A}_6$. The idea would be to find subgroups of index 6. However, the procedure that worked for $\mathbf{A}_5$ would not work for $\mathbf{A}_6$. The point is that in $\mathbf{A}_5$ the subgroups of index 5 all turned up as normalizers of Sylow 2-subgroups, but for $\mathbf{A}_6$ the subgroups of index 6 are isomorphic to $\mathbf{A}_5$. These are simple groups, hence are not found among the normalizers of smaller subgroups. A much more elaborate argument must be used to prove the corresponding theorem for $\mathbf{A}_6$. The reader should be warned that, although infrequent, there do exist nonisomorphic simple finite groups of the same order. The interested reader may consult the papers of Artin.

THEOREM 2 · Let $\sigma \in \mathrm{Aut}(\mathbf{S}_n)$. If σ sends some transposition onto a transposition, then $\sigma \in \mathrm{Inn}(\mathbf{S}_n)$.

Proof · We have already remarked that a homomorphism must preserve the notion of conjugates. Thus σ must permute the conjugacy classes (of elements) in $\mathbf{S}_n$. Since all transpositions form a single conjugacy class, we conclude that σ permutes the transpositions of $\mathbf{S}_n$ among themselves.

Since $(ij) = (1i)(1j)(1i)$ for $1 < i < j \leqslant n$, it follows from Theorem 4.1 that (12), (13),..., $(1n)$ generate $\mathbf{S}_n$. In order to show that $\sigma \in \mathrm{Inn}(\mathbf{S}_n)$, it is sufficient to show that the composition of σ with a finite sequence of inner automorphisms is the identity. This merely uses the fact that $\mathrm{Inn}(\mathbf{S}_n)$ is a subgroup of $\mathrm{Aut}(\mathbf{S}_n)$. It is then sufficient to show that σ composed with a finite sequence of inner automorphisms leaves (12), (13),..., $(1n)$ fixed.

Since any two transpositions are conjugate in $\mathbf{S}_n$, we can find $g \in \mathbf{S}_n$ such that $(12)^\sigma = (12)^g$. If we identify g with the inner automorphism on $\mathbf{S}_n$ induced by g, then σg^{-1} leaves (12) fixed. Thus we may replace σ by σg^{-1} and assume that σ leaves (12) fixed at the beginning.

If $(12)(ij) = (ij)(12)$, we can conclude that either $(ij) = (12)$ or (ij) is disjoint from (12). Since any automorphism of a group must preserve the relation $[x, y] \neq 1$, we see that σ must send (13) onto either $(1j)$ or $(2j)$ for some $j \neq 1$ or 2. In the second case we replace σ by $\sigma(12)$. Thus, we may assume that $(13)^\sigma = (1j)$, $j > 2$. If $j \neq 3$, we replace σ by $\sigma(3j)$; it follows that we may assume that σ fixes (12) and (13). Now let $i > 3$ and repeat the argument with the three pairs: (12), $(1i)$; (13), $(1i)$; and (23), $(1i)$. We see that $(1i)^\sigma = (1j)$ for some $j > 3$. Since σ is an automorphism, the map that sends i onto j must be a permutation of 4, 5,..., n. Let $h \in \mathbf{S}_n$ be the permutation that leaves 1, 2, and 3 fixed and permute 4, 5,..., n according to the map just defined from σ. It follows that σh^{-1} must leave (12), (13),..., $(1n)$ fixed. Thus $\sigma \in \mathrm{Inn}(\mathbf{S}_n)$. «

THEOREM 3 · If $n \neq 6$, then $\mathrm{Aut}(\mathbf{S}_n) = \mathrm{Inn}(\mathbf{S}_n)$.

Proof · Every element of order 2 in $\mathbf{S}_n$ has the form $(a_1a_2) \cdots (a_{2k-1}a_{2k})$, in which the a_i's are $2k$ distinct integers between 1 and n. Such an element is called a ***k*-transposition.** As we observed before in an exercise, the set C_k of all k-transpositions forms a single conjugate class of elements in $\mathbf{S}_n$. Moreover, C_k contains $\binom{2k}{n} \cdot (2k)!/2^k \cdot k!$ elements.

Let $\sigma \in \mathrm{Aut}(\mathbf{S}_n)$. Then $C_1^\sigma = C_k$ for some k with $2k \leqslant n$. If $k = 1$, Theorem 2 implies that $\sigma \in \mathrm{Inn}(\mathbf{S}_n)$. If $k \neq 1$, Theorem 4.2 shows that $k \geqslant 3$; hence $n \geqslant 6$.

We now assert that C_k has more elements than C_1 except when $k = 3$ and $n = 6$.

We first note that $\binom{n}{2} \leqslant \binom{n}{2k}$ for $2 \leqslant 2k \leqslant n - 2$ follows from the binomial theorem, whereas $(2k)!/2^k \cdot k! = 1 \cdot 3 \cdot \cdots \cdot (2k - 1) \geqslant (2k - 3)(2k - 1) > 1$ when $k \geqslant 3$. Thus we need only consider the cases $2k = n - 1$ or n.

If $2k = n - 1$, then $\binom{n}{2} = k \cdot \binom{n}{2k}$, whereas $(2k - 1)(2k - 3) > k$ for $k \geqslant 3$. Again, C_k has more elements than C_1.

If $2k = n$, then $\binom{n}{2} = k(2k - 1) \cdot \binom{n}{2k}$, whereas $(2k - 1)(2k - 3) > k(2k - 1)$ when $k > 3$. Thus, except when $k = 3$ and $n = 6$, C_k once again has more elements than C_1.

Our argument shows that $C_1^\sigma = C_1$ must hold unless $n = 6$. Thus Theorem 3 follows from Theorem 2 as observed. «

When $n = 6$, σ may interchange C_1 and C_3 and leave C_2 fixed. Indeed, this leads to a homomorphism of Aut($\boldsymbol{S}_6$) into $\boldsymbol{S}_{\{C_1, C_3\}}$ with kernel containing Inn($\boldsymbol{S}_6$). In fact, Theorem 2 implies that the kernel is exactly Inn($\boldsymbol{S}_6$). Thus we may conclude that $|\,\text{Aut}(\boldsymbol{S}_6) : \text{Inn}(\boldsymbol{S}_6)| = 1$ or 2. It turns out that the index is, in fact, equal to 2, but we make no attempt to prove it here. What happens is that $\boldsymbol{S}_6$ contains two conjugate classes of subgroups of index 6. If we represent $\boldsymbol{S}_6$ as a permutation group on the right cosets with respect to these subgroups, we obtain automorphisms of $\boldsymbol{S}_6$. One such family leads to inner automorphisms, whereas the other leads to outer automorphisms.

» III · 5 DIRECT PRODUCT OF GROUPS: FUNDAMENTAL THEOREM OF FINITE ABELIAN GROUPS

We now imitate the definition of Cartesian product of sets to obtain another procedure for building up groups. The reader who is familiar with "Euclidean geometry" from the point of view of vectors should be able to detect a similarity between the procedure to be described and the process of describing higher dimensional "Euclidean spaces."

DEFINITION 1 · Let $\{G_i \mid i \in I\}$ be a collection of groups indexed by the elements of the set I. A group G is called a ***direct product*** of G_i, $i \in I$, if and only if there exist group homomorphisms $\theta_i : G \to G_i$, $i \in I$, with the following universal mapping property.

(*) For any group H and any group homomorphisms $\varphi_i : H \to G_i$, $i \in I$, there exists a unique group homomorphism

$\varphi : H \to G$ such that $\theta_i \circ \varphi = \varphi_i \ \forall\, i \in I$; that is, the following diagram is commutative, $\forall\, i \in I$,

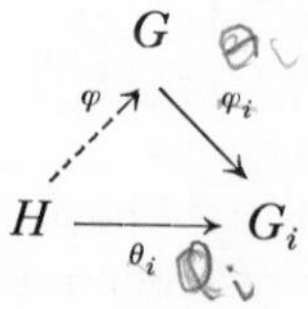

(The dotted arrow indicates that φ is not given in advance.)

Let Hom(A, B) denote the set of all homomorphisms of a group A into a group B. The definition of a direct product G of the groups G_i, $i \in I$, asserts that there is a bijection between the set Hom(H, G) and the Cartesian product $\prod_{i \in I}$ Hom(H, G_i) of the sets Hom(H, G_i), $i \in I$. The bijection is given by sending each $\varphi \in$ Hom(H, G) onto the element $(\theta_i \circ \varphi)_{i \in I}$ in the Cartesian product. We note that this bijection is given for all arbitrary groups H once we specify θ_i, $i \in I$.

THEOREM 1 · Let G_i, $i \in I$, be an indexed set of groups. Let G and G' be direct products of G_i, $i \in I$, with associated homomorphisms θ_i and θ_i'. Then θ_i and θ_i' are surjective, and there is a unique isomorphism $\varphi : G' \cong G$ such that $\theta_i' = \theta_i \circ \varphi \ \forall\, i \in I$.

Proof · Let H be G_i. Let $\varphi_i : H \to G_i$ be the identity and $\varphi_j : H \to G_j$, the "zero" homomorphism for $j \neq i$; that is, φ_j sends H onto 1. From the hypothesis that G is a direct product we see that there is a homomorphism $\varphi : G_i \to G$ such that $\theta_i \circ \varphi = \varphi_i$. Because φ_i is surjective by construction, we conclude that θ_i is surjective.

The second part is the uniqueness statement for direct products. It requires the usual diagram-chasing argument. We leave the details to the reader. «

THEOREM 2 · Let G_i, $i \in I$, be an indexed set of groups. Let G be the Cartesian product of the *sets* G_i, $i \in I$. Let $g = (g_i)_{i \in I}$ $h = (h_i)_{i \in I}$ be elements of G. Define $gh = (k_i)_{i \in I} \in G$, where $k_i = g_i h_i \ \forall\, i \in I$. Let $\theta_i : G \to G_i$ be the projection map, $i \in I$. Then G, together with θ_i, $i \in I$, is a direct product of G_i, $i \in I$.

Proof · It is easy to see that G is a group and $\theta_i : G \to G_i$ is an epimorphism $\forall\, i \in I$.

Let H be an arbitrary group and $\varphi_i : H \to G_i$, $i \in I$, be group homomorphisms. Let $\varphi : H \to G$ be given by $\varphi(h) = (\varphi_i(h))_{i \in I}$. It is easy to check that φ is the unique homomorphism such that $\theta_i \circ \varphi = \varphi_i \ \forall\, i \in I$. «

DEFINITION 2 · Let G_i, $i \in I$, be an indexed set of groups. The particular direct product constructed in Theorem 2 is denoted by $\prod_{i \in I} G_i$, the same notation as that used for the Cartesian product of the sets G_i, $i \in I$. Usually the meaning is clear from the context. When $I = \{1,..., n\}$, we often write $G_1 \times \cdots \times G_n$.

In any event, G_i is called a ***direct factor*** or simply a ***factor*** of the direct product; G_i is called ***trivial*** if and only if $|G_i| = 1$. By agreement, all trivial factors are ignored. A group $G \neq 1$ is called ***directly indecomposable*** or simply ***indecomposable;*** if and only if G admits no nontrivial direct decomposition.

Exercise 1 · Let G_i, $1 \leqslant i \leqslant n$, be a finite set of groups and $|G_i| = m_i$. Show that the direct product of G_i, $1 \leqslant i \leqslant n$, has order $m_1 \cdot ... \cdot m_n$.

Exercise 2 · Let $p \in \mathbf{P}$ be a prime (0 allowed) and $n \in \mathbf{P}^+$. Show that $\mathbf{Z}/\langle p^n \rangle$ is directly indecomposable.

Exercise 3 · Let $p \in \mathbf{P}^+$ be a prime. Identify all the groups of order p^2 with direct product of cyclic groups.

Exercise 4 · Let $p, n \in \mathbf{P}^+$, where p is a prime. Let $\pi = \{a(i) | 1 \leqslant a(1) \leqslant ... \leqslant a(t) \leqslant n\}$ be a partion of n. Let $G(p, \pi) = \prod_{1 \leqslant i \leqslant t} \mathbf{Z}/\langle p^{a(i)} \rangle$. Show that distinct partitions lead to nonisomorphic groups. *Hint.* Consider the subgroup G^{p^i} generated by p^ith powers of elements of G. Show that the partition may be recovered from the indices $|G^{p^i} : G^{p^{i+1}}|$, $i \in \mathbf{P}$.

THEOREM 3 · Let $I = \{1, 2,..., n\}$. Then a group G is a direct product of the groups G_i, $i \in I$, if and only if there exist $H_i \leqslant G$, $i \in I$ such that the following conditions hold:

(a) $H_i \lhd G \; \forall \, i \in I$,

(b) $H_i \cong G_i \; \forall \, i \in I$,

(c) Each element $g \in G$ has a unique representation as $g = g_1 \cdot \cdots \cdot g_n$ with $g_i \in H_i$, $i \in I$.

If we let H_i' be the subgroup of G generated by the H_j's with $j \neq i$, then (a) and (c) may be replaced by the following:

(a*) $H_i' \leqslant C_G(H_i) \; \forall \, i \in I$,

(c*) $G = H_i H_i'$ and $1 = H_i' \cap H_i \; \forall \, i \in I$.

Proof · If G is a direct product of G_i, $i \in I$, we may assume that G is the direct product of Theorem 2, in which case we may take $H_i = \{(1,..., 1, g_i, 1,..., 1) | g_i \in G_i\}$. It follows easily from the definition that (a), (b), and (c) hold, if we keep in mind that multiplication in G is done component by component.

Suppose that H_i, $i \in I$, are subgroups of G that satisfy (a), (b), and (c). We assert that (a*) and (c*) hold.

(a*) Let $i \neq j$, $h_i \in H_i$, and $h_j \in H_j$. Then, from (a), $h_i^{-1}h_j^{-1}h_i \cdot h_j = h_i^{-1} \cdot h_j^{-1}h_ih_j \in H_i \cap H_j$. We now assert that $H_i \cap H_j = 1$, for, if $x \in H_i \cap H_j$ and $x \neq 1$, viewing x as a product of 1's and x at the ith and at the jth position we would have two distinct product representations contradicting (c). Thus $h_i^{-1}h_j^{-1}h_ih_j = 1$ or $h_ih_j = h_jh_i$ and (a*) holds.

(c*) It follows from (c) and (a*) that $g_1 \cdots g_n = g_ig_1 \cdots g_{i-1}g_{i+1} \cdots g_n$. Thus $G = H_iH_i'$. Using (a*), we may repeat the preceding argument to show that $H_i \cap H_i' = 1$.

We now assume that (a*), (b), and (c*) hold for the subgroups H_i, $i \in I$, of G.

From (a*) it follows that $H_i' = H_1H_2 \cdots H_{i-1}H_{i+1}H_{i+2} \cdots H_n$. From (c*) it follows that $G = H_1H_2 \cdots H_n$, because the distinct factors commute. Thus each element $g \in G$ may be represented as $g = g_1g_2 \cdots g_n$, $g_i \in H_i$, in at least one way. If $g = g_1'g_2' \cdots g_n'$ is a second such representation, then $g_1^{-1}g_1' = g_2 \cdots g_n(g_n')^{-1} \cdots (g_2')^{-1}$ lies in $H_1 \cap H_1' = 1$. Thus $g_1 = g_1'$, and by induction we have $g_i = g_i' \ \forall\, i \in I$ and (c) holds. Let $\sigma_i : H_i \to G_i$, $i \in I$, be an isomorphism according to (b). It follows easily from (c) and (a*) that the map which sends $g = g_1 \cdots g_n$ onto $(g_1^{\sigma_1},..., g_n^{\sigma_n})$ is an isomorphism of G with the direct product of G_i, $i \in I$. «

DEFINITION 3 · When the group G contains a finite number of subgroups H_i that satisfy one of the two sets of conditions in Theorem 3, we often say that G is the ***direct product of the subgroups*** H_i, $i \in I$. This is also called the ***internal direct product*** to distinguish it from the "external" direct product of Theorem 2.

The important point to be noted is that the internal direct product is defined only for a finite number of factors, for the product of an infinite number of elements is not defined in a group.

Exercise 5 · Show that every finite commutative group G is the internal direct product of the uniquely determined Sylow p-subgroups, in which

p ranges over the set of prime divisors of $|G|$. Let $n = \prod_i p_i^{a(i)}$ be the unique factorization of $n \in \mathbf{P}^+$. Show that $\mathbf{Z}/\langle n\rangle$ is isomorphic to $\prod_i \mathbf{Z}/\langle p_i^{a(i)}\rangle$.

We note that Exercise 4 gives us a procedure for constructing nonisomorphic finite commutative p-groups; Exercise 5 tells us that a finite commutative group is determined (up to isomorphism) by its Sylow subgroups. The only missing piece is a theorem that tells us that all finite commutative groups can be constructed according to Exercises 4 and 5. The reader should observe that the direct product of groups satisfies the "associative law" and the "commutative law" for any number of factors in the sense of isomorphism; namely, $A \times B$ is isomorphic to $B \times A$; and $(A \times B) \times C$ is isomorphic to $A \times (B \times C)$.

THEOREM 4 (Fundamental theorem of finite abelian groups) · Let G be a finite commutative group. Then G is the direct product of a finite number of finite cyclic groups. We may select a direct product decomposition such that the factors have orders d_i, $1 \leqslant i \leqslant t$, $d_1 \neq 1$ and $d_i \mid d_{i+1}$, $1 \leqslant i \leqslant t-1$. When this choice is made, the d_i's are uniquely determined.

Proof · For the first assertion Exercise 5 allows us to make the assumption that G is a finite commutative p-group.

We now proceed by complete induction on $|G|$. If $|G| = 1$, there is nothing to prove. Thus we may assume that $|G| > 1$.

Let $g \in G$ be an element of maximal order, say $|g| = p^e$. Let $H = \langle g\rangle$. Thus $|G/H| < |G|$. By the induction hypothesis, G/H is isomorphic to a direct product of cyclic subgroups. Using the first isomorphism theorem and Theorem 3, we can find $H \leqslant H_i \leqslant G, 1 \leqslant i \leqslant s$, H_i/H is a cyclic group generated by Hh_i, such that $G/H = \prod_{1\leqslant i\leqslant s} H_i/H$.

Suppose for the moment that we can find $g_i \in H_i$ such that $H_i = \langle g\rangle \times \langle g_i\rangle$, $1 \leqslant i \leqslant s$. Then $G = H_1 \cdot \cdots \cdot H_s = \langle g, g_1, \ldots, g_s\rangle = \langle g\rangle \cdot \langle g_1\rangle \cdot \cdots \cdot \langle g_s\rangle$. The second equality uses the hypothesis that G is commutative. Thus every element of G has at least one representation as a product of elements out of $\langle g\rangle, \langle g_1\rangle, \ldots, \langle g_s\rangle$. If at least one element of G has two such representations, then $|G| < |g| \cdot |g_1| \cdot \cdots \cdot |g_s|$. However, $|G/H| = |H_1/H| \cdot \cdots \cdot |H_s/H| = |g_1| \cdot \cdots \cdot |g_s|$ and thus $|G| = |g| \cdot |g_1| \cdot \cdots \cdot |g_s|$. Hence we have verified (c) of Theorem 3. Since G is commutative, we see that $G = \langle g\rangle \times \langle g_1\rangle \times \cdots \times \langle g_s\rangle$. Thus we are reduced to proving the following,

(*) If G is a commutative p-group and $g \in G$ is an element of maximal order p^e such that $G/\langle g\rangle$ is cyclic, there is an element $h \in G$ such that $G = \langle g\rangle \times \langle h\rangle$.

To prove this we let $\langle g\rangle x$ be a generator of $G/\langle g\rangle$ and assume that $|G/\langle g\rangle| = p^c$. It follows that x^{p^c} is the least positive power of x which lies in $\langle g\rangle$. Suppose that x has order p^d; then by the choice of g we must have $c \leqslant d \leqslant e$; by using Exercise 1.13 $x^{p^c} = g^{mp^{e-(d-c)}}$, $p \nmid m$. Let $h = x(g^{-1})^{mp^{e-d}}$; then $\langle g\rangle h = \langle g\rangle x$ generates $G/\langle g\rangle$ and $h^{p^c} = 1$. Thus $G = \langle g, h\rangle = \langle g\rangle \cdot \langle h\rangle$. However, $|g| \cdot |h| = p^e |h| \leqslant p^{e+c} = |G|$. Repeating the earlier argument, we conclude that every element of G is uniquely representable as a product of an element from $\langle g\rangle$ and an element from $\langle h\rangle$. Thus $G = \langle g\rangle \times \langle h\rangle$ and (*) is proved.

For the second part of the theorem we proceed as follows:

G is the internal direct product of the uniquely determined Sylow p-subgroups of G, where p ranges over the prime divisors of $|G|$. Each Sylow p-subgroup is the internal direct product of some cyclic subgroups of order $p^{a(i)}$, $1 \leqslant a(1) \leqslant \cdots \leqslant a(s(p))$. Exercise 4 shows that for each prime p the integers $a(1),\ldots, a(s(p))$ are uniquely determined. The second half of Exercise 5 then shows us how to combine these cyclic p-groups to get a decomposition of G that satisfies the divisibility condition of the second assertion. The uniqueness of the integers d_i follows from the uniqueness of the integers $a(1),\ldots, a(s(p))$ associated to the various prime divisors of $|G|$ and the second half of Exercise 5. «

It is possible, in fact, to prove an analogous theorem for finitely generated commutative groups. However, we shall derive it much later as a special case of a more general theorem, namely, the fundamental theorem of modules of finite type over a principal ideal domain.

DEFINITION 4 · Let G be a finite commutative group; then the integers $d_1, \ldots, d_t$ of Theorem 4 are called the ***elementary divisors of G***.

Exercise 6 · Derive the following as a corollary to (*) in the proof of Theorem 4:

Let G be a finite commutative group and let $g \in G$ be an element of maximal order in G; then $\langle g\rangle$ is a direct factor of G.

Exercise 7 · Let p be a prime in $\mathbf{P}^+$ and $n \in \mathbf{P}$. Let G be a direct product of n cyclic groups of order p. Two decompositions of G as $G_1 \times \cdots \times G_n$ and $H_1 \times \cdots \times H_n$ into internal direct products of cyclic subgroups of order p are considered the same if and only if $G_i = H_i\ \forall\, i$. Show that the number of distinct direct decompositions of G is $\prod_{1\leqslant i\leqslant n}(p^n - p^{i-1})/(p-1)$. Show that

$|\operatorname{Aut}(G)| = \prod_{1 \leqslant i \leqslant n}(p^n - p^{i-1})$. *Hint.* A group of prime order p has $p - 1$ generators, namely, any of its nonidentity elements. As a generator of G_1, we may select any element of G distinct from 1; as a generator of G_2, we may select any element of G not in $G_1, \ldots$.

Exercise 8 · Let G be the direct product of n cyclic groups of prime order p. Let $G_{k,n}$ be the set of all subgroups of order p^k in G, $0 \leqslant k \leqslant n$. Show that $\operatorname{Aut}(G)$ is transitive on $G_{k,n}$. Show that $|G_{k,n}| = \prod_{1 \leqslant i \leqslant k}(p^n - p^{i-1})/\prod_{1 \leqslant i \leqslant k}(p^k - p^{i-1})$. *Hint.* Any subgroup of order p^k must be the direct product of k cyclic subgroups of prime order p. Thus the subgroup has the form $G_1 \times \cdots \times G_k$, and we may choose any element of G distinct from the identity to generate $G_1, \ldots$, and any element of G not in $G_1 \times \cdots \times G_{i-1}$ to generate $G_i, \ldots$. This gives the numerator of the order. The denominator arises from the fact that we are interested only in distinct subgroups. The number of distinct k-element subsets that generate the same subgroup of order p^k is precisely $|\operatorname{Aut}(H)|$, where H is a subgroup of order p^k. This order has been computed in Exercise 7. (Any k-element subset that generates the subgroup H of order p^k is called a ***minimal set of generators,*** or a ***basis*** of H.)

Exercise 9 · Let H and K be normal subgroups of G such that H and K have coprime finite orders. Show that the subgroup of G generated by H and K is the internal direct product of H and K.

Exercise 10 · Suppose that the finite group G is the internal direct product of the subgroups H and K. Suppose that H and K have coprime orders. Show that the group $\operatorname{Aut}(G)$ is naturally isomorphic to the direct product of $\operatorname{Aut}(H)$ and $\operatorname{Aut}(K)$.

Exercise 11 · Suppose that the group G is the internal direct product of simple nonabelian groups H and K. Verify the following assertions:

(a) If $\sigma \in \operatorname{Aut}(G)$, then σ maps H onto H, or onto K.

(b) If H is not isomorphic to K, then $\operatorname{Aut}(G)$ is naturally isomorphic to the direct product of $\operatorname{Aut}(H)$ and $\operatorname{Aut}(K)$.

(c) If H is isomorphic to K, then $\operatorname{Aut}(G) = NS$, where N is a normal subgroup of $\operatorname{Aut}(G)$ which is isomorphic to the direct product of $\operatorname{Aut}(H)$ and $\operatorname{Aut}(K)$, S is isomorphic to $\mathbf{S}_2$ and $N \cap S = 1$.

Generalize (c) to the case in which G is the direct product of n isomorphic nonabelian simple groups.

Excursion III

In Definition 1 of the direct product of groups we can "dualize" the concept by reversing all the arrows. The resulting group is then called the ***direct sum*** of G_i, $i \in I$. In the literature the direct sum is also called the ***free product*** of G_i, $i \in I$, and for it the corresponding Theorem 1 is very easy to prove. However, the corresponding Theorem 2 for the construction of a direct sum is much harder to prove. We are not concerned with the direct sum of groups. Instead, we give an example in the form of an exercise to illustrate the difficulties that are faced in dealing with it.

Exercise 1 · Let $G = \mathbf{Z} \times \{\pm 1\}$ as a *set*. Define multiplication on G by the equation $(m, \alpha)(n, \beta) = (m + \alpha n, \alpha\beta)$, where $\{\pm 1\}$ is considered as the multiplicative group of units in $\mathbf{Z}$. Show that G is a group under the multiplication just defined, with identity element $(0, 1)$. Show that $a = (1, -1)$ and $b = (0, -1)$ are elements of order 2 in G. Show that $ab = (1, 1)$ generates an infinite cyclic subgroup of index 2 in G. Show that $(ab)^{-1} = ba$ and that every element of G is *uniquely* represented as a finite string $b^s abab \cdots aba^t$, where $s, t \in \{0, 1\}$. Thus show that the *infinite* group G is the direct sum as groups of $H = \langle a \rangle$ and $K = \langle b \rangle$, two cyclic groups of order 2. Note that G is not a commutative group.

We next note that the definition of the direct product is completely formal. The essential materials are the following:

(a) Objects. In Definition 1 these are groups.

(b) Maps. In Definition 1 these are group homomorphisms.

In Chapter 0 we encountered a similar example; namely, the objects are sets and the maps are maps between sets. In this case the direct product is precisely the Cartesian product.

We can form a rather artificial example:

(a) The objects are groups of order 2.

(b) The maps are group homomorphisms.

In this example the reader can check to see that Hom(G, H) is always a set with two elements; namely, an isomorphism between the two groups of order 2 and the zero homomorphism which maps all of G onto the identity element of H. It is immediately apparent from the remark made after the definition of direct product that the direct product of two groups of order 2 does not exist in the present situation. The reason is simply that the direct product G of two such groups G_1 and G_2 must again be a group of order 2; moreover, Hom(H, G) must be a set with $2 \cdot 2 = 4$ elements, which is impossible.

We now combine the two remarks and consider the following situation:

(a) The objects are commutative groups.

(b) The maps are group homomorphisms.

We wish to consider the direct sums of commutative groups.

DEFINITION 1 · Let G_i, $i \in I$, be an indexed set of commutative groups. A commutative group G is called a ***direct sum*** of the commutative groups G_i, $i \in I$, if and only if there are homomorphisms $\theta_i : G_i \to G$, $i \in I$, with the following property:

(*) For any commutative group H and homomorphisms $\varphi_i : G_i \to H$, $i \in I$, there is a unique homomorphism $\varphi : G \to H$ such that $\varphi \circ \theta_i = \varphi_i \; \forall \, i \in I$.

Thus the map that sends $\varphi \in \text{Hom}(G, H)$ onto $(\varphi \circ \theta_i)_{i \in I}$ is a bijection between the set Hom(G, H) and the set $\prod_{i \in I} \text{Hom}(G_i, H)$.

The uniqueness of the direct sum is again a diagram-chasing argument. To prove its existence we take G to be the subgroup of the direct product $\prod_{i \in I} G_i$, constructed in Theorem 5.1, which consists of elements $(g_i)_{i \in I}$ such that $g_i \neq 1$ for at most a finite number of indices $i \in I$ (the finite number may vary from element to element). The map $\theta_i : G_i \to G$ is given by sending $g_i \in G_i$ onto the element $(..., 1,..., 1, g_i, 1,..., 1,...)$ of G. It is clear that every element of G may be uniquely represented as a *finite* product of elements of the form $\theta_i(g_i)$, $i \in I$. It is easy to see that G is indeed a direct sum. Again the point to be noted is that only the finite product of elements makes sense in a group.

We can restate the fundamental theorem of arithmetic as follows:

THEOREM 1 (Fundamental theorem of arithmetic) · Let $\mathbf{Q}^\star$ be the multiplicative group of rational numbers distinct from 0. Then $\mathbf{Q}^\star$ is the direct sum of a cyclic group of order 2 and a countable number of infinite cyclic groups.

Indeed, as an "internal" direct sum, the cyclic group of order 2 consists of ± 1, whereas the infinite cyclic groups are the subgroups generated by the positive primes (i.e., the powers, positive, negative and zero, of primes).

We shall return to the concept of direct sums later when we study "modules."

Exercise 2 · Let G_i, $i \in I$, be an indexed set of commutative groups. Show that the direct product of G_i, $i \in I$, as groups according to Definition 5.1 is the same (in the sense of isomorphism) as the direct product of G_i, $i \in I$, as commutative groups.

Exercise 3 · Let G_i, $i \in I$, be a *finite* indexed set of commutative groups. Show that the direct product and the direct sum of the commutative groups G_i, $i \in I$, are isomorphic.

Exercise 4 · Let G_1 and G_2 be two groups of order 2. Use Exercise 1 to show that the direct sum of G_1 and G_2 as groups is not isomorphic to the direct sum of G_1 and G_2 as commutative groups.

References

The importance of the role of group theory in geometry, as we indicated briefly in the introduction, was pointed out by Felix Klein in his Erlangen Program in 1872. The interested reader may consult the introduction of [13] for a description and development of some of the ideas.

Historically, a group always meant a group of transformations. Later it became necessary to introduce the notion of an abstract group. In the first case we are interested in the way a group acts on a set (possibly with some additional structures); in particular, we are interested in properties of the group and the set that are reflected in one another. In the second case we are interested in those properties of a group that are preserved under isomorphisms as well as those that are independent of the way the group may act on various sets. In some sense the fundamental theorem on transformations groups ties these two cases together. We have based the proof of Sylow's theorem on this fundamental theorem and the counting lemma. This proof is due essentially to G. A. Miller [12] and later rediscovered by H. Wielandt [14]. The reader interested in finite groups may consult [4], [5], [8], [15], and [16]. The reader interested in infinite groups may consult [10] and [11]. The reader interested in the connection between group theory and geometries of various kinds may consult [3], [6], and [13].

Theorem 3 of Excursion II is due to Hölder [9]. The concepts of the direct product and the direct sum of groups, or commutative groups, are given from the point of view of category theory. The interested reader may consult [7].

1. E. Artin, "The orders of the linear groups," *Communications of Pure and Applied Mathematics*, **8**, 355–366 (1955).
2. E. Artin, "The orders of the classical simple groups," *Communications of Pure and Applied Mathematics*, **8**, 455–472 (1955).
3. E. Artin, *Geometric Algebra*, Interscience, New York, 1957.
4. R. Brauer, "Representations of finite groups," *Lectures on Modern Mathematics*, Vol. 1, Wiley, New York, 1963, pp. 133–175.
5. W. Burnside, *Theory of Groups*, 2nd ed., Dover, New York, 1955.
6. R. H. Crowell and R. H. Fox, *Introduction to Knot Theory*, Ginn, New York, 1963.
7. P. Freyd, *Abelian Categories*, Harper and Row, New York, 1964.
8. M. Hall, *The Theory of Groups*, Macmillan, New York, 1959.
9. O. Hölder, "Bildung zusammengesetzter Gruppen," *Mathematisches Annalen*, **46**, 321–422 (1895).
10. I. J. Kaplansky, *Infinite Abelian Groups*, University of Michigan Press, Ann Arbor, Mich., 1954.
11. A. G. Kurosch, *The Theory of Groups*, Vols. 1 and 2, Chelsea, New York, 1955.
12. G. A. Miller, "A new proof of Sylow's theorem," *Annals of Mathematics*, **16**, 169–171 (1915).
13. H. Weyl, *The classical groups*, Princeton University Press, Princeton, N. J., 1946.
14. H. Wielandt, "Ein Beweis für die Existenz der Sylowgruppen." *Archiv der Mathematik*, **10**, 401–402 (1959).
15. H. Wielandt, *Finite Permutation Groups*, Academic Press, New York, 1964.
16. H. Zassenhaus, *The Theory of Groups*, Chelsea, New York, 1949.

CHAPTER IV Elementary Theory of Rings

In the preceding chapters we encountered some very useful rings; for example, the ring of integers, the ring of polynomials, and the ring of endomorphisms of a commutative group. Each of these rings has an identity element. Although rings without identity elements are quite interesting, notably in functional analysis, our attention is centered on rings with identity elements. The point is that our main interest is the study of the endomorphism ring of a given commutative group. Many of our results, in fact, hold for rings without identity elements; however, we are not concerned with these details. The interested reader can consider the possibility of generalizing the results to rings without identity elements as an exercise. In this setup it is then convenient to state the following blanket conventions:

CONVENTION 1 · Let R be a set and let $+, \cdot : R \times R \to R$ be maps; then R is called a ***ring*** if and only if the following conditions hold:

(a) $R, +$ is a commutative group. The additive identity element of R is denoted by 0.

(b) $R, \cdot$ is a multiplicative system with an identity element. The multiplicative identity element is denoted by 1_R or simply by 1. The possibility that $1 = 0$ is allowed.

(c) $x(y + z) = xy + xz$ and $(y + z)x = yx + zx$ hold $\forall\, x, y, z \in R$.

CONVENTION 2 · Let R and S be rings. A map $\sigma : R \to S$ is called a ***ring homomorphism*** if and only if the following conditions hold:

(a) $\sigma(x + y) = \sigma(x) + \sigma(y)\ \forall\, x, y \in R$.

(b) $\sigma(xy) = \sigma(x)\,\sigma(y)\ \forall\, x, y \in R$.

(c) $\sigma(1_R) = 1_S$.

σ is called a ring ***opposite-homomorphism*** if and only if conditions (a), (c), and (b′) hold:

(b′) $\sigma(xy) = \sigma(y)\,\sigma(x)\ \forall\, x, y \in R$.

We first remark that rings, unlike groups, are not in general oppositely isomorphic to themselves. However, if either R or S is a commutative ring, every opposite ring homomorphism of R into S is also a ring homomorphism. In particular, a commutative ring is oppositely isomorphic to itself under the identity map. We note that the composition of two opposite ring homomorphisms is a ring homomorphism and that the composition of an opposite ring homomorphism with a ring homomorphism is always an opposite ring homomorphism.

We next note that the subset R is said to be a ***subring*** of S if and only if the inclusion map of R into S is a ring homomorphism. Under our convention the subring R of the ring S must therefore contain the identity element of S. This requirement is not automatically satisfied when we do not impose the condition (c) of Convention 2.

Quite a few results in this chapter are direct generalizations of the results in Chapter III. In such cases the proof is usually left to the reader as an exercise.

» IV · 1 BASIC CONCEPTS

Nearly all the results and exercises in this section are direct imitations of the corresponding results and exercises in Chapter III. Our primary concern is that of notation.

DEFINITION 1 · Let $\sim$ be an equivalence relation on a ring R; $\sim$ is called a ***left equivalence*** if and only if the following conditions hold:

(a) If $x \sim y$, then $z + x \sim z + y\ \forall\, x, y, z \in R$.

(b) If $x \sim y$, then $zx \sim zy\ \forall\, x, y, z \in R$.

Right equivalence and ***two-sided equivalence*** are similarly defined.

The reader should observe that since $R, +$ is a commutative group, a left equivalence on the ring R is automatically a normal equivalence on the group $R, +$. It follows that the equivalence classes of R under $\sim$ form an additive group.

In anticipation of the exercises to come we introduce the following definition.

DEFINITION 2 · Let R be a ring. A subset I of R is called a ***left ideal*** of R if and only if the following conditions are satisfied:

(a) $I, +$ is a subgroup of $R, +$.
(b) If $r \in R$ and $i \in I$, then $ri \in I$.

When I is a left ideal of R, then R/I denotes the set of left cosets of R with respect to the subgroup I under addition.

Similarly, we may define a ***right ideal*** I by replacing condition (b) with the following:

(b′) If $r \in R$ and $i \in I$, then $ir \in I$.

I is said to be a ***two-sided ideal,*** or simply an ***ideal,*** of R if and only if it is both a left and a right ideal of R. If I is a right ideal of R, we will often use $I\backslash R$ to denote the set of right cosets of R with respect to the subgroup I under addition. As groups under addition there is no distinction between R/I and $I\backslash R$; however, when I is a left ideal, left multiplication by elements of R will carry a left coset of R with respect to I into another such coset. A similar statement holds when I is a right ideal. Our notations are designed to remind us of these facts.

Exercise 1 · If $\sim$ is a left equivalence on the ring R, show that $I = \{x \in R \mid x \sim 0\}$ is a left ideal of R and that the $\sim$ equivalence class of x in R is $x + I = \{x + i \mid i \in I\}$. Conversely, if I is a left ideal of the ring R, show that the relation $\sim$, defined by $x \sim y$ if and only if $x - y \in I$, is a left equivalence on the ring R and that under this definition $I = \{x \in R \mid x \sim 0\}$. Finally, show that there is a bijection between the set of left ideals of R and the set of left equivalences on the ring R.

A similar exercise may be carried out with "right" replacing "left" in Exercise 1. However, the reader should be aware that, unlike the situation for groups, there is in general no bijection between the set of left equivalences and the set of right equivalences on the ring R. Of course, when the ring R is commutative, the concept of left equivalence coincides with the concept of right equivalence.

As an example of an equivalence on a ring R we may recall the relation "congruence mod m" on the ring $\mathbf{Z}$. Furthermore, we saw that $\mathbf{Z}/(m)$ can be given the structure of a ring in a natural way. This phenomenon may be generalized to arbitrary rings.

Exercise 2 · Let I be a *two-sided* ideal in the ring R. On R/I, define $+$ and $\cdot$ by $(x + I) + (y + I) = (x + y) + I$ and by $(x + I) \cdot (y + I) = xy + I$. Show that these maps $+$, $\cdot$ are well-defined. Show that R/I, $+$, $\cdot$ is a ring. Show that the natural map which sends $x \in R$ onto $x + I \in R/I$ is a surjective ring homomorphism.

due for class

DEFINITION 3 · Let I be an ideal in the ring R. The ring R/I defined in Exercise 2 is called the ***quotient ring of R with respect to the ideal I.***

Although there is no natural bijection between the set of left equivalences and the set of right equivalences on a ring R, it is nevertheless possible for us to construct a second ring as a "mirror image" of the given ring.

DEFINITION 4 · Let R, $+$, $\cdot$ be a ring. Define $\circ : R \times R \to R$ by the equation $x \circ y = yx \; \forall \, x, y \in R$. R, $+$, $\circ$ can be easily seen to be a ring. It is called the ***opposite ring*** of R and is denoted by R°.

It is clear that $R = (R^\circ)^\circ$ and that the identity map of the set R onto itself is an opposite ring isomorphism between R and R°. R° is the mirror image of R in the sense that the statements valid for R remain valid for R°, provided that the words "left" and "right" are interchanged in these statements.

State one version for class

Exercise 3 · State and prove the first isomorphism theorem for rings. *Hint.* Normal subgroups should be translated into two-sided ideals. The kernel of a ring homomorphism is the inverse image of the zero element. Subgroups may be translated into additive subgroups, left, right, or two-sided ideals, subrings, or even multiplicative systems.

Part which says ℓ preserves composition omitted

DEFINITION 5 · Let R be a ring and let A, B be subsets of R. Then, AB denotes the *subgroup* of R, $+$, generated by $\{ab \mid a \in A, b \in B\}$. Again, a subset with only one element is identified with that element.

If S is a subset of R, the subring of R generated by S in R is the intersection of all subrings of R that contain S. Similarly, we define the **left** (or ***right*** or **two-sided**) ***ideal of R generated by S*** as the intersection of all left (or right, or two-sided) ideals of R that contain S.

The reader should note that the subring generated by S is the same as the subring generated by $S \cup \{1\}$. This is due to our convention on the words "subring" and "ring."

Exercise 4 · Let R be a ring. Show that the subring of R generated by the subset S is the subgroup of $R, +$ generated by the set of all finite product of elements of S. (The empty product is 1.)

Exercise 5 · Let S, I, J be a nonempty subset, a left ideal, and a right ideal of the ring R, respectively. Show that IS is a left ideal and SJ a right ideal of R. In particular, IJ is a two-sided ideal of R. Show that RS, SR, and RSR are, respectively, the left, the right, and the two-sided ideals of R generated by S in R. Let $S = \{s\}$ and show that Rs is precisely $\{rs \mid r \in R\}$. State an analogous statement for sR. (The analogous statement for RsR is false in general. Similarly, RS is strictly larger than $\{rs \mid r \in R, s \in S\}$ in general. Recall that RS is defined as a subgroup of $R, +$.)

In Exercise 5 the ideal RSR is sometimes denoted by (S). When R is commutative, we have $(S) = RSR = RS = SR$; we then select the most convenient notation for the particular situation. Following the notations of Chapter I, if $m \in \mathbf{Z}$, then (m) is the ideal generated by m in $\mathbf{Z}$. It happens that (m) coincides with the subgroup $\langle m \rangle$ of $\mathbf{Z}, +$ as a set.

Exercise 6 · Let I be a left ideal of the ring R. Verify the following assertions:

(a) Let $l : R \to \mathrm{Hom}(I, +; I; +)$ be given by $l(x)(i) = xi \; \forall \, x \in R$ and $i \in I$. Then l is a ring homomorphism of R into $\mathrm{Hom}(I, +; I, +), +, \circ$.

(b) Let $l : R \to \mathrm{Hom}(R/I, +; R/I, +)$ be given by $l(x)(y + I) = xy + I \; \forall \, x, y \in R$. Then l is a ring homomorphism of R into $\mathrm{Hom}(R/I, +; R/I, +), +, \circ$.

Exercise 6 shows that for each left ideal I of the ring R, we have two ring homomorphisms of R into rings of the form $\mathrm{Hom}(A, A)$, where A is an abelian group. The special case of $I = 0$ was considered in Exercise II.3.3.

» IV · 2 DIVISIBILITY THEORY IN INTEGRAL DOMAINS

We shall now study a family of commutative rings in some detail. In particular, we are interested in the possibility of generalizing the divisibility theory of **Z**, and we shall eventually see that the divisibility theory holds for a large family of integral domains, including all polynomial rings over fields.

DEFINITION 1 · Let R be an integral domain. Then R is called a ***Euclidean domain*** if and only if there exists a map $\theta : R \to \mathbf{Z}$ satisfying the following conditions:

(a) $\theta(x) > \theta(0)\ \forall\ x \in R - \{0\}$.

(b) If $a \in R$ and $d \in R - \{0\}$, then there exist $q,\ r \in R$ such that $a = qd + r$, and $\theta(r) < \theta(d)$.

Other definitions are given in the literature. The interested reader may consult [8] and [11; vol. 1]. The main point is to prove Theorem 1.

Example 1 · On the ring **Z** let $\theta(a) = |\,a\,|^n$, $n \in \mathbf{P}^+$. In this case q and r are not unique.

Example 2 · Let F be a field and define $\theta(0) = 0$, $\theta(x) = 1\ \forall\ x \in F - \{0\}$.

Example 3 · Let R be the polynomial ring in the indeterminate X over a field F. Define $\theta(f) = \deg f$ when $f \neq 0$ and $\theta(0) = -1$. In this case q and r are unique.

Exercise 1 · Let $R = \mathbf{Z}[X]/(X^2 + 1)$, where X is an indeterminate over **Z** and $(X^2 + 1)$ is the ideal generated by $X^2 + 1$ in $\mathbf{Z}[X]$. The coset of $a + bX$, $a, b \in \mathbf{Z}$, is denoted by $a + bi$. R is called the ***ring of Gaussian integers.*** Show that the map $\theta : R \to \mathbf{P}$ given by $\theta(a + bi) = a^2 + b^2$ turns R into a Euclidean domain.

In Exercise 1 the polynomial $X^2 + 1$ may be replaced by any polynomial $X^2 + n$, $n \in \mathbf{Z}$, $n \neq 0, 1$, and n has no square factors in **Z**. The question whether the corresponding integral domain is a Euclidean domain leads to some very interesting and deep questions in number theory. The reader may consult [4] for further discussions and references on this question.

Exercise 2 · Let R, θ be a Euclidean domain. Suppose that $a, b \in R - \{0\}$ such that $\theta(ab) < \theta(b)$. Show that $\exists\, u, v \in R$ such that $uv = 1$ and $\theta(ub) < \theta(b)$. *Hint.* Take $u \in R - \{0\}$ to minimize $\theta(ub)$ and apply (b) of Definition 1 to find v, r such that $b = vub + r$ with $\theta(r) < \theta(ub)$. Complete the proof by using the fact that R is an integral domain.

DEFINITION 2 · Let R be a commutative ring. An ideal of R which is generated by a single element is called a ***principal ideal*** of R. If R is an integral domain such that every ideal of R is principal, then R is called a ***principal ideal domain.*** We often abbreviate "principal ideal domain" to PID.

In this definition a principal ideal is simply an ideal of the form Rx, $x \in R$. It is clear the requirement that R be an integral domain is not needed in the second half of Definition 2. The interested reader may consult [11] for properties of principal ideal rings. Our main interests are centered around PID's.

From the preceding section we recall that the ideal in the commutative ring R generated by $a_1, \ldots, a_n$ is precisely $Ra_1 + Ra_2 + \cdots + Ra_n = \{r_1a_1 + \cdots + r_na_n \mid r_i \in R\ \forall\, i\}$. This ideal is often written as $(a_1, \ldots, a_n)$.

THEOREM 1 · Every Euclidean domain is a PID.

Proof · Let R be a Euclidean domain under the map θ. The zero ideal is $R0$; hence it is principal. Let I be a nonzero ideal of R. Thus $\{\theta(a) \mid a \in I - \{0\}\} = T$ is a nonempty set of integers bounded from below by $\theta(0) + 1$. Let $d \in I - \{0\}$ such that $\theta(d)$ is the greatest lower bound of T. It is clear that $Rd \subset I$. Conversely, if $a \in I$, then $a = qd + r$ with $q, r \in R$ and $\theta(0) \leqslant \theta(r) < \theta(d)$. Thus $r = a - qd \in I$. From the choice of d and the definition of θ it follows that $\theta(r) = \theta(0)$; hence $r = 0$ and $a \in Rd$. Therefore $I = Rd$ is a principal ideal. «

DEFINITION 3 · Let R be a commutative ring and let I be an ideal of R. I is called a ***prime ideal*** if and only if R/I is an integral domain. I is called a ***maximal*** ideal if and only if R/I is a field. I is called a ***maximal principal ideal*** if and only if I is maximal with respect to inclusion among the proper principal ideals of R.

Exercise 3 · Let R be a commutative ring and let I be an ideal of R.
Show that the following assertions are equivalent:

(a) I is a prime ideal.

(b) If $x, y \in R$, and $xy \in I$, then either $x \in I$ or $y \in I$. Moreover, $I \neq R$.

(c) $R - I$ is a multiplicative system.

(a) ⇒ (b) S. xy ∈ I ad x ∉ I, y ∉ I. Then x + I, y + I ≠ 0 with 0 = xy + I = (x+I)(y+I)

(b) ⇒ (c) clear

(c) ⇒ (a) x, y ∈ R - I ⇒ xy ∈ R - I or x + I, y + I ≠ 0 ⇒ xy + I ≠ 0.

Exercise 4 · Show that the ideal I of the commutative ring R is a
maximal ideal of R if and only if I is maximal with respect to inclusion among
the proper ideals of R. Show that a maximal ideal of the commutative ring R
is always a prime ideal. *1st part clear. Harder see p233 of Fraleigh*

Do for class

Example 4 · 0 is a prime ideal in the commutative ring R if and
only if R is an integral domain. 0 is a maximal ideal in the commutative
ring R if and only if R is a field. Thus 0 is a prime ideal but not a maximal
ideal in **Z**. However, every nonzero prime ideal of **Z** is a maximal ideal.
We shall soon see that this last assertion holds for any PID that is not
a field. Indeed, integral domains with the property that every nonzero
prime ideal is maximal are of great interest in number theory. Among
these domains are the so-called **Dedekind domains.** The interested
reader may consult [11; vol. 1].

To see the ... look at ... definition given below ...
Ex 10 in PID.
Then I a prime ideal ⇒ I = M₁ M₂ ... Mₖ with each Nᵢ maximal ... k > 1 and ... ∉ I. Then for ... x ∈ M, ... Mₖ we have x ∈ I (...) and ... continue this process k-1 times ⇒ M₁ ⊆ I ⇒ since M₁ maximal that M₁ = I (*) for uniqueness given in def.

We now restate the definition of divisibility for commutative
rings. However, the reader should bear in mind that our eventual goal
is to investigate the divisibility theory in integral domains. We shall
not consider the possibility of generalizing the results to noncommutative
rings.

DEFINITION 4 · Let R be a commutative ring with the identity
element denoted by 1.

Let $a, b \in R$. We write $a \mid b$ if and only if $\exists x \in R$ such that
$ax = b$. a, b are called **associates** in R if and only if $a \mid b$ and $b \mid a$.
If $u \mid 1$, then u is called a **unit** in R. $U(R)$ denotes the set of units in R.
It is a group under multiplication.

An element $p \in R$ is called a **prime** if and only if (1) $p \notin U(R)$
and (2) $p \mid xy$ implies $p \mid x$ or $p \mid y \ \forall \, x, y \in R$.

An element $c \in R$ is called **nonfactorizable** (or **irreducible**) if
and only if (1) $c \notin U(R)$ and (2) $c = xy$ implies $x \in U(R)$ or $y \in U(R)$.

Let $a_1, ..., a_n \in R$. Then $d \in R$ is called a **g.c.d.** of $a_1, ..., a_n$ in R
if and only if (1) $d \mid a_i \ \forall \, i$ and (2) $c \in R$ and $c \mid a_i \ \forall \, i$ imply that $c \mid d$.

Note in an integral domain this says 0 is a prime while 0 is not need since 0 = 0·0

Exercise 5 · Let R be a commutative ring. Show that $a \mid b$ if and only if $Rb \subset Ra$. Show that $a \in U(R)$ if and only if $Ra = R$ and that "a is an associate of b" is an equivalence relation on R.

Exercise 6 · Let R be a commutative ring. Show that $p \in R$ is a prime if and only if Rp is a prime ideal. Show that if $c \in R$ is nonfactorizable then Rc is a maximal principal ideal. Show that if $Ra_1 + \cdots + Ra_n = Rd$ then d is a g.c.d. of $a_1, \ldots, a_n$.

Exercise 7 · Let R be an integral domain. Show that $c \in R$ is nonfactorizable if and only if Rc is a maximal principal ideal. Let $U(R)$ act on R by multiplication and show that the $U(R)$-orbits in R are precisely the equivalence classes with respect to the relation of being associates. Show that every nonzero prime in R is nonfactorizable.

THEOREM 2 · Let R be a PID. Then any finite number of elements of R have g.c.d.'s. Indeed, d is a g.c.d. of $a_1, \ldots, a_n \in R$ if and only if $Rd = Ra_1 + \cdots + Ra_n$.

This follows immediately from hypothesis and Exercise 6. The reader should convince himself that the finiteness of the number of elements involved is not necessary; namely, in a PID, any number of elements have g.c.d's.

LEMMA 1 · Let R be an integral domain. Let $a \in R - \{0\}$ such that $a = up_1 \cdots p_m = vq_1 \cdots q_n$ with $u, v \in U(R)$ and p_i, q_j denote primes in R. Then $m = n$, and there exists a permutation π of the indices such that p_i and $q_{\pi(i)}$ are associates in R, $1 \leqslant i \leqslant m$.

Proof · a is a unit in R if and only if $m = 0$ or $n = 0$. In this case both m and n are 0 and there is nothing to prove. Thus we may proceed by induction on $m + n$ and assume that $m > 0$ and $n > 0$. By the definition of a prime we can deduce that $p_1 \mid q_i$ for at least one index i. Thus $q_i = p_1 x$ for some $x \in R$. From Exercise 7 we know that q_i is nonfactorizable. Thus, because p_1 is not a unit, we conclude that $x \mid 1$; that is, q_i and p_1 are associates. We now substitute $p_1 x$ for q_i in the factorization for a. It follows that $a = up_1 \cdots p_m = p_1(xv)q_1 \cdots q_{i-1}q_{i+1} \cdots q_n$. Since $p_1 \neq 0$ and R is an integral domain, it follows that $up_2 \cdots p_m = (xv)q_1 \cdots q_{i-1}q_{i+1} \cdots q_n = b$. The total number of primes in the two factorizations of b is $< m + n$. Since

$b \mid a$ and $a \neq 0$, it follows that $b \neq 0$. Thus by induction we see that $m - 1 = n - 1$ and that we can find a bijection

$$\pi : \{2, \dots, m\} \to \{1, \dots, i-1, i+1, \dots, m\}$$

such that p_j and $q_{\pi(j)}$ are associates when $j > 1$. If we let $\pi(1) = i$, the desired assertions follow immediately. «

DEFINITION 5 · Let R be an integral domain. Let $\mathcal{A}_i$, $i \in I$, be all the $U(R)$-orbits of nonzero primes in R. A subset $\{ p_i \in \mathcal{A}_i \mid i \in I\}$ is called a ***complete set of representatives of nonzero primes in R.***

Exercise 8 · Let K be the field of fractions of the integral domain R. Let $\mathcal{P}$ be a complete set of representatives of nonzero primes in R. Suppose that $d(K)$ is the subgroup of $K - \{0\}, \cdot$ generated by $U(R)$ and $\mathcal{P}$. Verify the following assertions (cf. Excursion III):

(a) $d(K)$ is independent of the choice of $\mathcal{P}$.

(b) $d(K)$ is the direct sum of $U(R)$ and the set of infinite cyclic groups C_p, $p \in \mathcal{P}$, where C_p is generated by p under multiplication.

(c) If $a \in d(K)$, there exist integers $\nu_i(a)$ and $u(a) \in U(R)$ such that the following conditions hold:

(1) $\nu_i(a) \neq 0$ for at most a finite number of $i \in I$.

(2) $a = u(a) \prod_{i \in I} p_i^{\nu_i(a)}$, where $\mathcal{P} = \{p_i \mid i \in I\}$.

(3) $\nu_i(a)$ and $u(a)$ are uniquely determined by (1) and (2).

(d) $R \cap d(K)$ is precisely the set of all elements of $R - \{0\}$ which admit factorizations into products of a unit with a finite number of nonzero primes.

(e) If $a \in R \cap d(K)$ and $b \in R$ such that $b \mid a$, then $b \in R \cap d(K)$ and $0 \leqslant \nu_i(b) \leqslant \nu_i(a)\ \forall\, i \in I$.

(f) Define $u(0) = 1$, $\nu_i(0) = \infty$, and $p_i^\infty = 0\ \forall\, i \in I$. If $a, b \in (R \cap d(K)) \cup \{0\}$, then $d = \prod_{i \in I} p_i^{\mu_i}$, $\mu_i = \min(\nu_i(a), \nu_i(b))\ \forall\, i \in I$, is a g.c.d. of a and b in R.

From the preceding exercise the reader should realize that the set $(R \cap d(K)) \cup \{0\}$ possesses a factorization theory similar to that of **Z**. If R is arbitrary, then we can only say that this set is a multiplicative system that is commutative and has an identity element $1 \neq 0$.

Exercise 9 · Let I be the principal ideal generated by $X^2 + 5$ in the polynomial ring $S = \mathbf{Z}[X]$. Let $\sqrt{-5}$ denote the coset of X in the ring $R = S/I$. Verify the following assertions:

(a) The map that sends $m \in \mathbf{Z}$ onto the coset of m in R is an injective ring homomorphism. Thus $\mathbf{Z}$ is identified with a subring of R.

(b) $R, +$ is a direct product (or direct sum) of the infinite cyclic groups generated by 1 and $\sqrt{-5}$ (under addition).

(c) Let $\theta : R \to \mathbf{P}$ be defined by $\theta(a + b\sqrt{-5}) = a^2 + 5b^2 \ \forall\, a, b \in \mathbf{Z}$. Then θ is a well-defined map such that (1) $\theta(x) = 0$ if and only if $x = 0$ and (2) $\theta(yz) = \theta(y)\,\theta(z), \forall\, x, y, z \in R$.

(d) R is an integral domain. $U(R) = \{1, -1\}$. *Hint.* Use (c).

(e) If $\mathbf{Z}$ is replaced by $\mathbf{Q}$, the resulting ring K may be identified with the field of fractions of R. In particular, each element of K is uniquely represented in the form $a + b\sqrt{-5}$ with $a, b \in \mathbf{Q}$. Moreover, the map θ of (c) may be extended to a map of K into $\mathbf{Q}^+ \cup \{0\}$ to satisfy the corresponding properties (1) and (2) of (c).

(f) If $x = a + b\sqrt{-5} \in R$ is such that $\theta(x)$ is a prime in $\mathbf{P}^+$, then x is nonfactorizable in R. *Hint.* Use (b).

(g) $3, 2 + \sqrt{-5}$ and $2 - \sqrt{-5}$ are nonfactorizable in R; $9 = 3 \cdot 3 = (2 + \sqrt{-5})(2 - \sqrt{-5})$ and the only associates of 3 in R are 3 and -3. Thus $3, 2 + \sqrt{-5}$ and $2 - \sqrt{-5}$ are not primes in R. *Hint.* Use (c) and (d).

(h) Let $x \in R$. If $\theta(x)$ is a nonzero prime in $\mathbf{P}$, then x is a prime in R. *Hint.* Let $x = a + b\sqrt{-5}$ and $p = \theta(x) = (a + b\sqrt{-5})(a - b\sqrt{-5})$. Show that R/Rp is a ring and that the order of $R/Rp, +$ is a divisor of p^2. Use (d) to show that R/Rx has order a proper divisor of p^2, therefore, R/Rx is a ring with p elements. Use Lagrange's theorem and the fact that R/Rx has an identity element to conclude that R/Rx is a field; hence Rx is a prime ideal and x is a prime.

(i) 11 is a prime in R and $\theta(11)=121$.

(j) Every nonzero element of R can be represented in at least one way as a product of a unit with a finite number of nonfactorizable elements.

The preceding exercise shows that the concepts of a nonfactorizable element and of a nonzero prime do not always coincide in an arbitrary integral domain. Indeed, it shows that there exist integral domains such that the nonzero elements can always be factored into a product of a unit with a finite number of nonfactorizable elements but that such a factorization is not unique in the sense that there may be a second factorization in which the nonfactorizable elements of the second factorization are not associates of any of the factors in the first.

DEFINITION 6 · Let R be an integral domain. Then R is called a *unique factorization domain* (abbreviated to UFD) if and only if the following conditions hold:

(a) Every nonzero element of R can be factored into a product of a unit with a finite number of nonfactorizable elements.

(b) Let $a = ux_1 \cdots x_m = vy_1 \cdots y_n$ be factorizations such that $u, v \in U(R)$ and x_i, y_j are nonfactorizable in R. Then $m = n$, and there exists a permutation π of the indices such that x_i and $y_{\pi(i)}$ are associates in R, $1 \leqslant i \leqslant m$.

If these do for claim

Exercise 10 · Let R be an integral domain. Show that R is an UFD if and only if every principal ideal I, distinct from R and 0, is the product of a finite number of maximal principal ideals and that these maximal principal ideals are unique to within a permutation of order.

Exercise 10 is the translation of Definition 5 in terms of ideals. This translation can be modified by putting "ideal" in place of "principal ideal" throughout; the end result is the concept of a "Dedekind domain." The example considered in Exercise 9 is a Dedekind domain that is not a UFD. It is known that a ring R is a PID if and only if R is both a UFD and a Dedekind domain. However, we shall not attempt to prove this fact. Instead, we shall be content with half of this theorem; namely, we shall show that every PID is a UFD as well as a Dedekind domain. The interested reader may consult [11, vol. 1] for more details.

Exercise 11 · Let R be an integral domain. Translate Lemma 1 into a statement concerning ideals of R. Verify that every PID is a Dedekind domain in the sense described in the preceding paragraph.

LEMMA 2 · Let R be an integral domain such that any two elements of R have a g.c.d. in R. Let $a \# b$ denote a g.c.d. of $a, b \in R$ and let $\sim$ denote the equivalence relation of being associates in R. The following assertions hold:

(a) Any finite number of elements of R have a g.c.d. in R.

(b) $(a \# (b \# c)) \sim ((a \# b) \# c) \sim d$, where d is a g.c.d. of a, b, and c in R.

(c) $a \# b \sim b \# a$ and $1 \sim 1 \# a$.

(d) $ac \# bc \sim (a \# b)c$. In particular, $c \# bc \sim c$.

(e) If $a \# b \sim 1$ and $a \# c \sim 1$, then $a \# bc \sim 1$.

$(\longrightarrow)$ Let Ra to R
Then $a = x_1 x_2 \cdots x_m$
x_i nonfact
$\Rightarrow Ra = Rx_1, Rx_2 \cdots$
result by Ex 7
uniqueness follows from Ex 7

Converse is similar.

give the definition

(Don't see how to show Ex 9 in 6 Dedekind domain)

I could only do this after doing Thm 3 and 4 on p. 113, 114
second part: Let $I \neq R$, $0 \neq I$ an ideal in R. Since PID, $I = Ra$. By Lemma 1, Thm 3, 4 & a $= Rp_1 Rp_2 \cdots Rp_m$, each Rp_i unique prime. By Ex 7 each p_i is nonfact $\Rightarrow$ by Ex 7 that each Rp is maximal prime ideal, hence max ideal, a PID D_i are Dedekind domain.

Student read on his own

Proof · (a) follows from the hypothesis by an easy induction; (b) and (c) can be checked from the definition of g.c.d.

(d) Because $(a \# b) | a$ and $(a \# b) | b$, it is clear that $(a \# b)c \,|(ac \# bc)$. Let $ac \# bc = u(a \# b)c$, $u \in R$. If $c = 0$, then $ac \# bc = 0 = (a \# b)c$. If $c \neq 0$, then $u(a \# b)c \mid ac$ implies that $u(a \# b) | a$ by using the cancellation law in the integral domain R. Similarly, $u(a \# b) | b$. Thus $u(a \# b) | (a \# b)$. Since $a \# b = 0$ if and only if $a = 0 = b$, we see that, except for $a = 0 = b$, $u \mid 1$ and $ac \# bc \sim (a \# b)c$. When $a = 0 = b$, again we have $ac \# bc = 0 = (a \# b)c$. Thus we have proved (d).

(e) From (c) and (d), we obtain $1 \sim a \# c \sim a \# ((a \# b)c) \sim a \# (ac \# bc) \sim (a \# ac) \# bc \sim a \# bc$. «

Before we proceed to the examination of some of the characterizations of a UFD, we present the following formal lemma. Its principal use is to facilitate some of our arguments in the proof.

LEMMA 3 · Let A be a set partially ordered by $\leqslant$. Then the following conditions are equivalent:

(a) ***Maximum condition.*** Any nonempty subset of A has maximal elements.

(b) ***Ascending chain condition.*** Any increasing sequence of elements of A has only a finite number of distinct elements.

Proof · Suppose that (a) holds and that $a_i \leqslant a_{i+1}$, $i \in \mathbf{P}$, is an increasing sequence of elements in A. Let $S = \{a_i \mid i \in \mathbf{P}\}$. Thus we may assume from (a) that $a_N \in S$ is a maximal element of S. It follows that $a_n = a_N \; \forall \, n > N$. Therefore S has only a finite number of distinct elements.

Conversely, assume that (b) holds and that $a \in S$. Let $\mathfrak{D}$ be the set of all increasing chains of elements of S starting from a; namely, $C \in \mathfrak{D}$ if and only if $C = \{s_i \in S \mid s_0 = a,\, s_i < s_{i+1}$ and $i \in I$, where I is a segment of $\mathbf{P}\}$. If $D = \{t_j \in S \mid t_0 = a,\, t_j < t_{j+1}$ and $j \in J$, where J is a segment of $\mathbf{P}\}$, we define $C \leqslant D$ to mean that $I \subset J$ and $s_i = t_i \; \forall \, i \in I$. From (b) we see that each $C \in \mathfrak{D}$ is a finite subset of S. If C_λ, $\lambda \in \Lambda$, is a linearly ordered subset of $\mathfrak{D}$, then $\{| C_\lambda | \mid \lambda \in \Lambda\} \subset \mathbf{P}^+$ and $C_\lambda \leqslant C_\mu$ if and only if $| C_\lambda | \leqslant | C_\mu |$, $\lambda, \mu \in \Lambda$. Thus we may as well assume that $\Lambda \subset \mathbf{P}^+$ and $| C_\lambda | = \lambda + 1$. It is clear that $C = \bigcup_{\lambda \in \Lambda} C_\lambda$ is an upper bound of $\{C_\lambda \mid \lambda \in \Lambda\}$. By Zorn's lemma, let $D = \{t_j \mid j \in J\}$ be a maximal element of $\mathfrak{D}$. Since D is a finite subset of S, the maximal element of D under the partial ordering $\leqslant$ is a maximal element of S. Thus (a) follows from (b). «

We now state several characterizations of a UFD.

THEOREM 3 · Let R be an integral domain. Then the following conditions are equivalent:

(a) R is a UFD.

(b) (1) (Divisor chain condition). There does not exist a subset $\{a_i \in R \mid i \in \mathbf{P}, a_{i+1} \mid a_i \text{ and } a_i \nmid a_{i+1}\ \forall\, i\}$;

(2) Any two elements of R have a g.c.d. in R.

(c) (1) (Ascending chain condition on principal ideals). Any increasing sequence of principal ideals under inclusion has only a finite number of distinct principal ideals;

(2) Every nonfactorizable element of R is a prime in R.

(d) (1) (Maximum conditions on principal ideals). Every nonempty set of principal ideals of R has a maximal element with respect to inclusion;

(2) Every maximal (proper) principal ideal of R is a prime ideal.

(e) Every nonzero element of R is a product of a unit in R with a finite number of primes in R. (In terms of Exercise 8, this condition is equivalent to $R \subset d(K) \cup \{0\}$.)

Proof · (a) implies (b). Let $a \in R - \{0\}$. If $b \mid a$ in R, then $b \neq 0$. Let $a = ux_1 \cdots x_m$ and $b = vy_1 \cdots y_n$ be factorizations of a and b in R according to (a), where $u, v \in U(R)$ and x_i, y_j are nonfactorizable. From (a), we see that $b \mid a$ if and only if there exist $wz_1 \cdots z_p \in R$ such that $ux_1 \cdots x_m = (vw)y_1 \cdots y_n z_1 \cdots z_p$, where $w \in U(R)$ and z_k's are nonfactorizable in R. From the uniqueness (up to order and associates) of such factorizations, we see that $b \mid a$ if and only if there exists an injective map $\pi : \{1,\dots, n\} \to \{1,\dots, m\}$ such that y_j is an associate of $x_{\pi(j)}$, $1 \leqslant j \leqslant n$. It follows that $a \in R - \{0\}$ may have only a finite number of nonassociate divisors. Thus (b)(1) holds. Similarly, it is easy to find the g.c.d. of a and b from the factorizations of a and b: d is a g.c.d. of a and b if and only if $d \mid a$, $d \mid b$ and a', b' have no common (up to associate) nonfactorizable factors in which $da' = a$, $db' = b$. Thus (b)(2) holds.

(b) implies (c). (c)(1) is the translation of (b)(1) in terms of ideals. Let p be nonfactorizable. Thus, in terms of the notations of Lemma 2, either $p \# x \sim p$ or $p \# x \sim 1\ \forall\, x \in R$. Since $p \# x \sim p$ if

← proper here means non-zero

and only if $p \mid x$, it follows from Lemma 2(e) that $p \nmid x$ and $p \nmid y$ imply that $p \nmid xy$; hence p is a prime. Thus (c)(2) holds.

(c) and (d) are equivalent. (c)(1) and (d)(1) are equivalent according to Lemma 3. (d)(2) is the translation of (c)(2) in terms of ideals.

(d) implies (e). The assertion (e) is equivalent to the statement that every principal ideal of R distinct from 0 and R is a product of a finite number of principal prime ideals of R. Let $\mathcal{F}$ be the set of principal ideals Rx of R such that $Rx \neq 0$ or R and such that Rx is not a product of a finite number of principal prime ideals in R. We must show that under the assumption of (d) $\mathcal{F}$ is empty. If $\mathcal{F}$ is not empty, then by (d)(1) we let Rx be a maximal element of $\mathcal{F}$. Let $\mathcal{G}$ be the set of all proper principal ideals of R that contain Rx. Thus $Rx \in \mathcal{G}$. Let Ry be a maximal element of $\mathcal{G}$. It follows from (d)(2) that Ry is a prime ideal of R. Since $Rx \subset Ry$, we see that $x = ya$ for some $a \in R$. Since $Rx \neq 0$, we see that $a \neq 0$. If $Ra = R$, then $a \mid 1$ and $Rx = Ry$ is a principal prime ideal. This contradicts the fact that $Rx \in \mathcal{F}$. Thus $Ra \neq R$. Because y is a prime, we see that $x \nmid a$. It follows that Ra is a principal ideal strictly between R and Rx. Because Rx is a maximal element of $\mathcal{F}$, we see that $Ra \notin \mathcal{F}$, and because $Ra \neq R$ we see that Ra is a product of a finite number of principal prime ideals of R. Finally, because $x = ay$, we see that $Rx = (Ry)(Ra)$ is also a product of a finite number of principal prime ideals of R. This contradicts the hypothesis that $Rx \in \mathcal{F}$. Thus $\mathcal{F}$ must be empty and (e) holds.

(e) implies (a). This follows from Exercise 7 and Lemma 1. «

THEOREM 4 · Every PID is a UFD.

Proof · It suffices to verify (c) of Theorem 3. We observed that (c)(2) is equivalent to (d)(2). Because every ideal in a PID is principal, we see that (d)(2) becomes the statement that every maximal ideal is a prime ideal. This statement is made obvious by Definition 3. Let I_i, $i \in \mathbf{P}$, be a sequence of ideals in the PID R such that $I_i \subset I_{i+1}\ \forall\, i$. Let $I = \bigcup_{i \in I} I_i$. It is easy to see that I must be an ideal of R. The point is that in order to verify that a subset of R is an ideal of R the checking procedure involves only a finite number of elements at a time. Since $I_i \subset I_{i+1}\ \forall\, i$, it follows that for any finite number of elements of I we can always find an integer N such that I_N contains all of these elements. Since I_N is an ideal of R, the same is also true for I. Since R is a PID, $I = Rx$ for some $x \in R$. Thus $x \in I_N$ for some $N \in \mathbf{P}$. It follows that $x \in I_n$ and $I = Rx \subset I_n \subset I\ \forall\, n > N$. Hence the sequence I_i, $i \in \mathbf{P}$, has at most $N + 1$ distinct ideals, namely, I_0, I_1,..., I_N. Thus (c)(1) holds.   «

stfd   **Exercise 12** · Show that a nonzero prime ideal of a PID is a maximal ideal. Generalize Lemma I.6.3 to a UFD. *Just use unique fact.*   *By Exercise 7.*

stfd   **Exercise 13** · Show that the integral domain given in Exercise 9 is not a PID. *Note by 9(g) that 9 has two factorization*

So far, all the examples of PID's are in fact Euclidean domains. The reader may consult [8] for an example of a PID that is not Euclidean. Thus the converse of Theorem 1 is false. We shall present a procedure for constructing many UFD's out of a given UFD. It will be seen that a UFD is, in general, not a PID. Thus the converse of Theorem 4 is also false.

Exercise 14 · Let X be an indeterminate over the ring R. Let I be a two-sided ideal of R. Let J denote the two-sided ideal of $R[X]$ generated by I. Show that the polynomial ring in the indeterminate Y over R/I is naturally isomorphic to $R[X]/J$, where the natural isomorphism σ has the property that $\sigma(Y) = X + J$ and $\sigma(r + I) = r + J \; \forall \, r \in R$. It is customary to identify these two rings under σ. The natural surjective ring homomorphism ρ from $R[X]$ to $(R/I)[Y]$ sending X onto Y and $r \in R$ onto $r + I$ is then called the **reduction homomorphism mod I** or the **reduction of the coefficients mod I**. *Hint.* Construct ρ as indicated. Show that $J = \ker \rho$. Let ρ' be the isomorphism induced by ρ from $R[X]/J$ to $(R/I)[Y]$. Show that σ is the inverse of ρ'.   *Follows Hint.*

DEFINITION 7 · Let X be an indeterminate over the UFD R. Let $f(X) = a_0 + a_1 X + \cdots + a_n X^n$, $a_i \in R$. Then $c(f)$ denotes the principal ideal of R generated by a g.c.d. of a_0,..., a_n in R. Since the g.c.d. is unique up to associates, $c(f)$ depends only on f: $c(f)$ is called the **content ideal** of f in R; f is said to be a **primitive polynomial** (in $R[X]$) if and only if $c(f) = R$.   *Same as gcd = 1*

Do for class

Exercise 15 · Let X be an indeterminate over the UFD R. Show that f is a primitive polynomial in $R[X]$ if and only if for each prime p in R the reduction of f mod Rp is a nonzero polynomial in R/Rp [X]. (We use X to denote the image of X under the reduction map.)

Prove the contrapositive. May use gcd of coef. instead of prim. ideal gen. by one.

THEOREM 5 (Gauss's lemma) · Let X be an indeterminate over the UFD R. If f, g are primitive polynomials in $R[X]$, then fg is also a primitive polynomial in $R[X]$.

Proof · Since R/Rp is an integral domain for each prime p in R, it follows that $R/Rp[X]$ is also an integral domain. Let $\bar{f}$ denote the reduction of f mod Rp. Because reduction is a ring homomorphism, we have $\overline{fg} = \bar{f} \cdot \bar{g}$. Thus our assertion follows from Exercise 15. «

Exercise 16 · Let X be an indeterminate over the UFD R. Let $f, g \in R[X]$. Show that $c(fg) = c(f)\,c(g)$ and that $c(af) = ac(f)$, where $a \in R$.

THEOREM 6 · Let F be the field of fractions of the UFD R. Let X be an indeterminate over F. Then the following assertions hold:

(a) If $f(X) \in F[X] - \{0\}$, then $\exists\, a, b \in R - \{0\}$ and $f_1(X) \in R[X]$ such that (1) $f(X) = ab^{-1}f_1(X)$, (2) 1 is a g.c.d. of a and b in R, and (3) $f_1(X)$ is a primitive polynomial in $R[X]$.

(b) In the representation of (*a*), a, b, and $f_1(X)$ are unique up to a unit factor in R.

Proof · Let $f(X) = a_0b_0^{-1} + \cdots + a_nb_n^{-1}X^n$, $\deg f = n$, a_i, $b_i \in R$, and $b_i \neq 0$. (Recall that every element of F may be represented as a fraction of an element of R divided by a nonzero element of R.) Let $d = b_0 \cdots b_n \in R$. Since $b_i \neq 0\ \forall\, i$, it follows that $d \neq 0$. Thus we may assume that $f(X) = d^{-1}f_2(X)$, $f_2(X) \in R[X]$. Let $c(f_2) = Rc$. Since $f \neq 0$, we see that $c \neq 0$. Thus from Exercise 16 we see that $f(X) = cd^{-1}f_1(X)$, where $f_1(X)$ is a primitive polynomial in $R[X]$. Finally, by the cancellation of a g.c.d. of c and d in R, we obtain the desired represention of $f(X)$ as exhibited in (*a*).

Suppose that $f(X) = ab^{-1}f_1(X) = cd^{-1}f_2(X)$ are two representations that satisfy the conditions in (a). Then $adf_1(X) = bcf_2(X)$. From Gauss's lemma and Exercise 16 we have $Rad = Rbc$. In the notation of Lemma 2 we have $a \# bc \sim a$ and $a \# b \sim 1$. From Exercise 12 and Lemma I.6.3 we get $a \mid c$. Similarly, using the fact that $c \# d \sim 1$, we have $c \mid a$. Thus a and c are associates. Since $a \neq 0 \neq c$, we see that $b \sim d$. Thus $ad \sim bc$, and we see that $f_1(X)$ and $f_2(X)$ differ by a unit factor in R. Hence (b) holds. «

DEFINITION 8 · Let F be the field of fractions of a UFD R. Then a representation of a nonzero polynomial in $F[X]$ given in Theorem 6 is called a ***reduced representation***.

Use that $K[X]$ is a Euclidean domain under 6 of Example 2

Let X be an indeterminate over the field K. Then the nonzero primes in the PID $K[X]$ are called **irreducible polynomials**. They are exactly the nonfactorizable polynomials in $K[X]$.

Recall primes and nonfact. elts same in UFD's (Thm 3)

THEOREM 7 · Let F be the field of fractions of the UFD R. Let X be an indeterminate over F. If $f(X) \in R[X] - \{0\}$, then $f(X)$ is a prime in $R[X]$ if and only if one of the following conditions holds:

(a) $\deg f = 0$ and $f(X)$ is a prime in R.

(b) $\deg f > 0$, $f(X)$ is primitive in $R[X]$ and $f(X)$ is irreducible in $F[X]$.

Proof · Throughout this proof we let $c(f) = R\,d(f)$. The element $d(f)$ is unique up to a unit factor in R.

Let $f(X)$ be a prime in $R[X]$. If $\deg f = 0$, then $f = a \in R$. Since R is a subset of $R[X]$, we conclude that f is a prime in R. Thus (a) holds. If $\deg f > 0$, then $f = d(f) \cdot f_1(X)$, where $f_1(X)$ is a primitive polynomial of $R[X]$. Since $f \neq 0$, we see that $\deg f_1 = \deg f > 0$. Thus f_1 is not a unit in $R[X]$. Since a nonzero prime is nonfactorizable in an integral domain, we see that $d(f)$ is a unit and f is primitive in $R[X]$. It remains for us to show that f is nonfactorizable in $F[X]$. Suppose that $f = gh$; g, h are polynomials of positive degrees in $F[X]$. Let $g = ab^{-1}g_1$ and $h = cd^{-1}h_1$ be reduced representations of g and h. Thus $bdf = ac(g_1h_1)$. From Gauss's lemma, g_1h_1 is primitive in $R[X]$. Thus, from Theorem 6, f and g_1h_1 differ by a unit factor in $R[X]$. Since $\deg g_1 = \deg g$, $\deg h_1 = \deg h$, and a unit in $R[X]$ must have degree 0, it follows that f is factorizable in $R[X]$. This contradiction shows that $f(X)$ is nonfactorizable in the PID $F[X]$; hence it is irreducible.

prime $(a,b) = (c,d) = 1$

Conversely, if $\deg f = 0$ and f is a prime in R, then $f \mid gh$ in $R[X]$ implies that the reduction of gh mod Rf is the zero polynomial. Since $(R/Rf)[X]$ is an integral domain, it follows that the reduction of g or h must be zero; namely, $f \mid g$ or $f \mid h$. Thus f is a prime in $R[X]$. Finally, suppose that $\deg f > 0$, f is primitive in $R[X]$, and f is irreducible in $F[X]$. If $f \mid gh$ in $R[X]$, then, by reading this as a divisibility in $F[X]$, we may assume that $f \mid g$ in $F[X]$. Let $fk = g$, $k \in F[X]$. We now show that k is already in $R[X]$. Let $k = ab^{-1}k_1$ be a reduced representation. Thus $bg = a(fk_1)$. From Gauss's lemma and the fact that both f and k_1 are primitive in $R[X]$, we see that fk_1 is primitive and we may take $d(afk_1) = a$. Since $g \in R[X]$, we see that $b \mid a$. However, by hypothesis a and b have g.c.d. 1; thus b is a unit in R and $k \in R[X]$. It follows that $f \mid g$ in $R[X]$ and that f is a prime in $R[X]$ as asserted. **«**

since $d(afk_1)$ = a: bl where $c(bg)$ = $b\,c(g)$ = Rbl.

THEOREM 8 · Let R be a UFD and let $X_1, \ldots, X_n$ be indeterminates over R. Then $R[X_1, \ldots, X_n]$ is a UFD.

Proof · By induction on n we may assume that $n = 1$ and $X_1 = X$.

We now verify (e) of Theorem 3. Let F be the field of fractions of R and suppose that $f(X)$ is a nonzero polynomial in $R[X]$. We first consider $f(X)$ as a nonzero element of the PID $F[X]$. Thus, in $F[X]$, $f(X)$ can be factored into a product of irreducible polynomials in $F[X]$. By applying Theorem 6 to each of these irreducible polynomials we may assume that $f(X) = \prod_i a_i b_i^{-1} f_i$, where $a_i b_i^{-1} f_i$ is a reduced representation of one of the irreducible polynomial factors of f in $F[X]$. Thus $(\prod_i a_i)(\prod_i f_i) = (\prod_i b_i) f$. From Gauss's lemma the content ideal of the left side is $R(\prod_i a_i)$ and the content ideal of the right side is $R(\prod_i b_i) \cdot c(f)$. Thus $(\prod_i b_i) | (\prod_i a_i)$ in R. By cancelling $\prod_i b_i$ on both sides we see that $f = d \prod_i f_i$, where $d \in R$ and f_i's are primitive polynomials of $R[X]$ such that $a_i b_i^{-1} f_i$ is irreducible in $F[X]$. Because $f \neq 0$, we see that $a_i b_i^{-1}$ are nonzero elements of the field F. It follows that f_i is irreducible in $F[X]$. From Theorem 7 we see that each f_i is a prime in $R[X]$. Similarly, by using the fact that R is a UFD and $d \in R$ we find from Theorem 7 that d is a finite product of primes with a unit in $R[X]$. Thus f is a finite product of primes in $R[X]$ with a unit in $R[X]$; hence we have verified condition (e) of Theorem 3. «

Exercise 17 · Let $X_i, i \in I$, be an arbitrary set of indeterminates over the UFD R. Show that $R[X_i]_{i \in I}$ is again a UFD. *Hint.* Use Theorem 8 and the fact that a factorization of a nonzero element can involve at most a finite number of indeterminates.

Exercise 18 · Let X be an indeterminate over the PID R. Show that the nonzero prime ideals of $R[X]$ are separated into the following two disjoint sets:

(a) A principal ideal generated by a nonzero prime in $R[X]$.

(b) An ideal generated by a nonzero prime p of R and a polynomial f which satisfies the condition that the image of f under the reduction homomorphism mod Rp is an irreducible polynomial in the PID $(R/Rp)[X]$.

Show that $R[X]$ is a PID if and only if R is a field.

Hint. Let I be a prime ideal of $R[X]$ distinct from 0. Show first that $R \cap I$ is a prime ideal of R. Then consider the following cases:

Case 1 · $R \cap I \neq 0$. Use Exercise 12 to conclude that $R \cap I = Rp$ is a maximal ideal of R. If $I = R[X]p$, then I belongs to (a). Otherwise, let J be the principal ideal generated by p in $R[X]$. Show that I/J is a nonzero prime ideal in the PID $R[X]/J$, which is isomorphic to $(R/Rp)[X]$. Use Exercise 12 to conclude that I belongs to (b).

Case 2 · $R \cap I = 0$. Since $I \neq 0$, we may select f as a polynomial of least positive degree in I. Use the fact that I is a prime ideal and use Theorem 7 to conclude that f is a prime in $R[X]$. Let F be the field of fractions of R. Use the division algorithm in $F[X]$ to show that, given any $g(X) \in I$, there exist $d \in R - \{0\}$, $q(X)$, $r(X) \in R[X]$ such that $dg(X) = q(X)f(X) + r(X)$ and $\deg r(X) < \deg f(X)$. Use the fact that I is an ideal and $\deg f(X)$ is minimal to conclude that $r(X) = 0$. Next, use the condition that I is a prime ideal and the hypothesis that $R \cap I = 0$ to conclude that $f(X) \mid g(X)$ in $R[X]$. Thus conclude that I is the principal ideal generated by $f(X)$; hence I falls in (a).

The converse as well as the last assertion are now easy to verify.

We conclude this section by proving the following useful result.

THEOREM 9 (Eisenstein's irreducibility criterion) · Let X be an indeterminate over the UFD R. Let $f(X) = X^n + a_{n-1}X^{n-1} + \cdots + a_0$, $a_i \in R$. Suppose that p is a prime in R such that $p \mid a_i \; \forall\, i$ and $p^2 \nmid a_0$. Then $f(X)$ is a prime in $R[X]$.

Proof · Since $R[X]$ is a UFD, it suffices to show that $f(X)$ is nonfactorizable in $R[X]$. Let $f = gh$, $g, h \in R[X]$. Since the leading coefficient of the product is the product of the leading coefficients, we may assume that g and h are both monic.

We now consider the reduction map mod Rp. The equality of the images of $a(X)$, $b(X)$ (both in $R[X]$) is denoted by $a(X) \equiv b(X) \bmod p$. Thus $f(X) \equiv X^n \bmod p$. In $(R/Rp)[X]$ the polynomial X generates a prime ideal J. The reason is simply that $(R/Rp)[X]/J$ is isomorphic to the integral domain R/Rp. Thus X is a prime in $(R/Rp)[X]$. Since $g(X)\,h(X) \equiv X^n \bmod p$, it follows from (e) of Exercise 8 or from direct observation that $g(X) \equiv X^s \bmod p$ and $h(X) \equiv X^{n-s} \bmod p$, $0 \leqslant s < n$, $\deg g = s$ and $\deg h = n - s$. If $0 < s < n$, the congruence equations imply that p divides the constant terms of g and of h. Thus p^2 would divide the product of the constant terms, that is, $p^2 \mid a_0$. This contradicts the hypothesis. Hence $s = 0$ or $s = n$. Equivalently, either $g = 1$ or $h = 1$ and f is nonfactorizable. «

Exercise 19 · Verify that the following polynomials are nonfactorizable in $\mathbf{Z}[X]$:

(a) $f(X) = X^{p-1} + \cdots + X + 1$, where p is a prime in $\mathbf{P}^+$.

(b) $f(X) = X^2 - X + 1$.

Hint. In (a) consider $g(X) = f(X + 1)$ and use the fact that $f(X) = g(X - 1) = (X^p - 1)/(X - 1)$ in the quotient field of $\mathbf{Z}[X]$. In (b) consider $f(-X)$ and apply (a).

» IV · 3 FIELDS OF RATIONAL FUNCTIONS: PARTIAL FRACTION DECOMPOSITION

We now give a rather elementary application of the divisibility theory.

DEFINITION 1 · Let X_i, $i \in I$, be a set of indeterminates over the field F: $F(X_i)_{i \in I}$ denotes the field of fractions of the polynomial ring $F[X_i]_{i \in I}$; $F(X_i)_{i \in I}$ is called the ***field of rational functions*** in X_i, $i \in I$, over the coefficient field F. We recall that each element of $F(X_i)_{i \in I}$ may be written as the quotient of elements of $F[X_i]_{i \in I}$.

In the case that interests us in the present section I has only one element. The reader should review Section II.4.

Exercise 1 · Let F be the field of fractions of an integral domain R. Suppose that X_i, $i \in I$, is a set of in determinates over F. Show that every element of $F(X_i)_{i \in I}$ may be written as a quotient of two elements of $R[X_i]_{i \in I}$.

DEFINITION 2 · Let X be an indeterminate over the field F. Let $f \in F(X)$ and p, $q \in F[X]$. If $f = p/q$, then p is called a ***numerator*** of f and q, a ***denominator*** of f; f is called a ***proper fraction*** if and only if $\deg p < \deg q$. The fraction p/q is said to be ***normalized*** if and only if q has leading coefficient 1 and 1 is a g.c.d. of p and q.

The following exercises all refer to the notation of Definition 2.

Exercise 2 · Show that the properness of a fraction is independent of its representation as a quotient of elements of $F[X]$. Show that the set $\{d(x) \in F[X] \mid d(X)f(X) \in F[X]\}$ is an ideal in $F[X]$; this ideal is called the

denominator ideal of the element. Show that each f has exactly one representation in the form of a normalized fraction p/q; p and q are then called *the* numerator and denominator of f, respectively. Show that *the* denominator is the monic polynomial that generates the denominator ideal.

Exercise 3 · Show that any finite sum of proper fractions is again a proper fraction.

Exercise 4 · Let p/q be a normalized fraction. Show that there exist unique $s, t \in F[X]$ such that $p/q = s + (t/q)$, where t/q is a normalized proper fraction.

Exercise 5 · Let p/q be a normalized proper fraction. Suppose that $m, n \in F[X]$ such that $q = mn$, m, n are monic and 1 is a g.c.d. of m and n in $F[X]$. Show that there exist unique polynomials $a, b \in F[X]$ such that $p/q = a/m + b/n$, where a/m, b/n are both normalized proper fractions.

Exercise 6 · Let q be an irreducible monic polynomial in $F[X]$ and $n \in \mathbf{P}^+$. Let p/q^n be a proper, normalized fraction. Show that there exist unique polynomials a_i, $i = 1,\ldots, n$ such that $a_n \neq 0$, $\deg a_i < q$, $i = 1,\ldots, n$ and $p/q^n = a_1/q + \cdots + a_n/q^n$.

Hints for Exercises 2–6: The Euclidean division algorithm holds with respect to the degree of a polynomial. The degree of the product is the sum of the factors. The degree of the sum is at most the maximum of the degrees of the summands.

THEOREM 1 (Partial fractions) · Let X be an indeterminate over the field F. Let p/q be a normalized fraction in $F(X)$ and let $q = \prod q_i^{n(i)}$ be the factorization of q in $F[X]$, in which q_i are monic irreducible polynomials, $q_i \neq q_j$ for $i \neq j$, $n(i) \in \mathbf{P}$, and $n(i) \neq 0$ for at most a finite number of i. (We assume that $n(i) > 0$ in the product.) Then there exist unique polynomials r, $a_{i,j}$ in $F[X]$, in which $i = 1,\ldots, t$, $j = 1,\ldots, n(i)$ such that $\deg a_{i,j} < \deg q_i$, $a_{i,n(i)} \neq 0$, and $p/q = r + \sum_{i,j} a_{i,j}/q_i^j$.

Proof · Combine Exercises 2–6.

Later, we give another proof of the partial fraction theorem. The main point in the present proof is that as long as a factorization of the denominator into irreducible factors is known the partial fraction decomposition reduces to the Euclidean division algorithm.

When F is the field of "real numbers," and we assume the

knowledge that every irreducible polynomial has a degree at most of two, the partial fraction theorem allows us to construct a procedure to evaluate the integral of any rational function in one indeterminate (or in one variable).

» IV · 4 MODULES AND THEIR ENDOMORPHISM RINGS. MATRICES

We now return to the study of rings from the point of view of rings of endomorphisms of commutative groups. Before we get started, we shall examine some of the formal properties of $\text{Hom}(A, B) = \{\sigma \mid \sigma \text{ is a group homomorphism from } A \text{ to } B\}$, in which A and B are commutative groups.

We again remind the reader that the conventions mentioned at the beginning of this chapter are still in force.

DEFINITION 1 · Let A, B, and C be commutative groups in which all group operations are denoted by $+$. A map $\cdot : A \times B \to C$ is called a ***bihomomorphism*** if and only if the following conditions hold (as usual, $\cdot(a, b)$ is denoted by $a \cdot b$):

(a) $(a + a') \cdot b = a \cdot b + a' \cdot b \ \forall\, a, a' \in A, b \in B$.

(b) $a \cdot (b + b') = a \cdot b + a \cdot b' \ \forall\, a \in A, b, b' \in B$.

If $A = B$, then $\cdot$ is said to be ***commutative*** (or ***symmetric***) if and only if $a \cdot b = b \cdot a \ \forall\, a, b \in A$.

If $A = B = C$, then $\cdot$ is said to be ***associative*** if and only if $a \cdot (b \cdot c) = (a \cdot b) \cdot c \ \forall\, a, b, c \in A$.

If $A = B = C$, then $\cdot$ is said to have an ***identity*** if and only if $\exists\, 1 \in A$ such that $a \cdot 1 = a = 1 \cdot a \ \forall\, a \in A$.

It is clear that $R, +, \cdot$ is a ring if and only if $R, +$ is a commutative group and $\cdot : R \times R \to R$ is an associative bihomomorphism with an identity element; $R, +, \cdot$ is a commutative ring if and only if $\cdot$ is commutative in addition to the preceding conditions.

DEFINITION 2 · Let A and B be commutative groups in which the group operations are denoted by $+$. Let $\text{Hom}(A, B)$ be the set of all group homomorphisms from A to B. If $a \in A$ and $f \in \text{Hom}(A, B)$, then the image of a under f is denoted by $f(a)$. If $f, g \in \text{Hom}(A, B)$, then $f + g$ is defined by the equation $(f + g)(a) = f(a) + g(a) \ \forall\, a \in A$.

As we observed in Section II.3, Hom(A, B) becomes a commutative group under this definition of "sum" of homomorphisms.

Exercise 1 · Let A, B, and C be commutative groups. Let $\circ : \text{Hom}(B, C) \times \text{Hom}(A, B) \rightarrow \text{Hom}(A, C)$ be defined as the composition of homomorphisms. Show that $\circ$ is a bihomomorphism. Suppose that $A = B = C$ show that Hom(A, A), $+$, $\circ$ is a ring.
Hint. Consult Section II. 3.

Exercise 2 · Let S be a nonempty subset of the ring T and let $C_T(S) = \{t \in T \mid ts = st \ \forall \ s \in S\}$. This is called the ***centralizer*** or ***commutant*** of S in T. Show that $C_T(S)$ is a subring of T. Show that $S_1 \subset S_2$ implies that $C_T(S_2) \subset C_T(S_1)$. Let S' be the subring of T generated by S; then show that $C_T(S) = C_T(S')$ and $S' \subset C_T(C_T(S))$. Finally, show that $C_T(S) = C_T(C_T(C_T(S)))$.

We now formalize Exercise 1.6 into the following definition:

DEFINITION 3 · Let I, J be left and right ideals, respectively, in the ring R. If $x \in R$, then we define $h_x \in \text{Hom}(R/I, R/I)$ by setting $h_x(r + I) = xr + I \ \forall \ r \in R$. When there is no confusion, we will also use $h_x \in \text{Hom}(I, I)$ to denote the map defined by $h_x(i) = xi \ \forall \ i \in I$. The element $h_x^\circ \in \text{Hom}(J\backslash R, J\backslash R)$ is defined by setting $h_x^\circ(J + r) = J + rx \ \forall \ r \in R$. Similarly, we define $h_x^\circ \in \text{Hom}(J, J)$ by setting $h_x^\circ(j) = jx \ \forall \ j \in J$. The reader should note that R/I, I, $J\backslash R$, and J are considered only as commutative groups under $+$ in the definition.

Exercise 3 · In the notation of Definition 3 verify the following assertions:

(a) The map that sends $x \in R$ onto h_x is a ring homomorphism of R into Hom(R/I, R/I) and Hom(I, I), respectively. In the first case the kernel is the largest two-sided ideal of R contained in I. In the second case the kernel is $\{x \in R \mid xI = 0\}$; this set is called the ***left annihilator*** of I in R.

(b) The map that sends $x \in R$ onto h_x° is an opposite ring homomorphism of R into Hom($J\backslash R$, $J\backslash R$) and Hom(J, J), respectively. In the first case, the kernel is the largest two-sided ideal of R contained in J. In the second case the kernel is the right annihilator of J in R.

Exercise 4 · Let I be a two-sided ideal in the ring R. In the notation of definition 3 verify the following assertions:

Let $f \in C_{\mathrm{Hom}(R/I, R/I)}(S)$ and let $f(1+I) = t+$ ... then $f(n+I) = f \cdot g_n (1+I)$ ... $g_n \in S$ ... $= nt$ ...

(a) $C_{\mathrm{Hom}(R/I,R/I)}(S) = T$ and $C_{\mathrm{Hom}(R/I,R/I)}(T) = S$; S is the image of R under the homomorphism described in (a) of Exercise 3 and T is the image of R under the opposite homomorphism described in (b) of Exercise 3. Morever, the kernel is I in either of these two cases.

(b) R/I is a commutative ring if and only $S = T$ in the preceding assertion. *Consider $f_x \in S$. $f_x(n+I) = x n + I = (x+I)(n+I) = (n+I)(x+I) = n x + I = n x + I \neq f_x$ ... $n + I \in R/I$ with R/I comm. ... Converse is similar*

Part (a) of Exercise 4 is best remembered as "the only endomorphisms of R/I, $+$ that commute with all left (or all right) multiplications are the right (or left) multiplications."

In the discussions on group theory we observed that transformation groups are the "universal" examples of groups. Later we observed that the rings of endomorphisms of commutative groups are the "universal" examples of rings. We now formalize the latter into a preliminary definition.

DEFINITION 4* · Let R be a ring. A commutative group, $M, +$, together with a map $\cdot : R \times M \to M$, is called a **left R-module** if and only if the following conditions are satisfied (as usual, we denote $\cdot(r, x)$ by rx):

(a) $r(x + y) = rx + ry$, $\forall\, r \in R$, $x, y \in M$.

(b) $(r + s)(x) = rx + sx$, $\forall\, r, s \in R$, $x \in M$.

(c) $(rs)(x) = r(sx)$, $\forall\, r, s \in R$, $x \in M$.

(d) $1x = x$, $\forall\, x \in M$.

In the notation of Definition 4* we let $\theta : R \to \mathrm{Map}(M, M)$ be defined by $(\theta(r))(x) = rx$, $\forall\, r \in R$, $x \in M$. Condition (a) asserts that the image of θ is contained in the set $\mathrm{Hom}(M, M)$. Condition (b) asserts that θ is a group homomorphism of $R, +$ into $\mathrm{Hom}(M, M), +$. Condition (c) asserts that θ is a homomorphism of the multiplicative system $R, \cdot$ into the multiplicative system $\mathrm{Hom}(M, M), \circ$. Finally, condition (d) asserts that θ sends the identity element of $R, \cdot$ onto the identity element of $\mathrm{Hom}(M, M), \circ$. Thus θ is a ring homomorphism of $R, +, \cdot$ into $\mathrm{Hom}(M, M), +, \circ$. In view of this interpretation we now make the following final definition.

DEFINITION 4 · Let $M, +$ be a commutative group. Let $\theta : R \to \mathrm{Hom}(M, M)$ be a ring homomorphism. Then M is called a **left R-module** (through θ). If $r \in R$ and $x \in M$, then $(\theta(r))(x)$ will be abbreviated to rx. When there is no possibility of confusion, we call M an R-module.

Let A, B be left R-modules. An element $f \in \text{Hom}(A, B)$ is called an ***R*-module homomorphism** or simply an ***R*-homomorphism** if and only if $f(ra) = rf(a)\ \forall\, r \in R$ and $a \in A$. The set of all R-homomorphisms of A into B is denoted by $\text{Hom}_R(A, B)$; it is a subgroup of $\text{Hom}(A, B), +$. If $A = B = M$, then $\text{Hom}_R(M, M) = C_{\text{Hom}(M,M)}(\theta(R))$. Thus $\text{Hom}_R(M, M)$ is a subring of $\text{Hom}(M, M)$.

If R is a field, it is customary to call R-modules ***vector spaces over R***. It is also customary to call R-homomorphisms ***linear transformations over R***. We investigate this case in more detail later.

Example 1 · Let $A, +$ be any commutative group. Let $m \in \mathbf{Z}$ and $a \in A$. Then, define ma as in Chapter II. Under this definition A becomes a $\mathbf{Z}$-module and $\text{Hom}(A, A) = \text{Hom}_{\mathbf{Z}}(A, A)$.

Exercise 5 · Let R be a ring. Verify the following assertions:

(a) There is a unique ring homomorphism of $\mathbf{Z}$ into R.

(b) Let $\theta : R \to \text{Hom}(M, M)$ be a ring homomorphism. Let ρ be the ring homomorphism of (a). Then $\theta \circ \rho$ is the unique ring homomorphism of $\mathbf{Z}$ into $\text{Hom}(M, M)$. Thus every R-module is also a $\mathbf{Z}$-module. (This procedure is called "forgetting the R-module structure.")

Example 2 · Let I be a left ideal of the ring R. Then the map sending $r \in R$ onto h_r converts R/I and I into left R-modules.

Example 3 · Let R be a subring of the ring S. Then the map sending $r \in R$ onto h_r defined as left multiplication by r converts $S, +$ and $S/R, +$ into left R-modules.

Example 4 · Let $\mathfrak{F}$ be the set of all functions from the real numbers into the real numbers. Let $\mathfrak{D}$ be the subset of all differentiable functions in $\mathfrak{F}$. Under the definition $(f + g)(x) = f(x) + g(x)$, $(cf)(x) = c \cdot f(x)\ \forall\, f, g \in \mathfrak{F}$, where c and x are real numbers, $\mathfrak{F}$ and $\mathfrak{D}$ are vector spaces over the field $\mathbf{R}$ of real numbers. The map sending $f \in \mathfrak{D}$ onto its derivative $Df \in \mathfrak{F}$ is an $\mathbf{R}$-linear transformation.

Exercise 6 · Let $M, +$ be a commutative group and let R be a ring. Define the concept of a right module over R in terms of a map

$\# : M \times R \to M$. Let $\rho : R \to \text{Hom}(M, M)$ be defined by $(\rho(r))(x) = x \# r$, $\forall r \in R$, and $x \in M$. Show that M is a right R-module under $\#$ if and only if ρ is an opposite homomorphism of the ring R into $\text{Hom}(M, M), +, \circ$. Show that this is equivalent to "ρ is homomorphism of the ring R into the opposite of the ring $\text{Hom}(M, M), +, \circ$". Thus show that every right R-module may be considered as a left R°-module, where R° is the opposite of the ring R.

Exercise 7 · Define the concepts of R-submodules and R-quotient modules of a given R-module M. State and prove the first isomorphism theorem for R-modules. State and prove the factorization theorem of R-homomorphisms between R-modules.

The reader should realize by now that the first isomorphism theorem and the factorization for homomorphisms should be proved in a general setting so that the various versions may be obtained as special cases. The interested reader may either work this out as an exercise or consult [6; Chapter 5, vol. 1].

In any event, the point of the first isomorphism theorem is that surjective homomorphisms from a given R-module M (or a group, or a ring, etc.) can be described internally by knowing the R-submodules of M (or a normal subgroup, or a two-sided ideal, etc.) The image of a homomorphism from a given R-module M (or a group, or a ring, etc.) is described as an isomorphic copy of a quotient module of M (or a quotient group, or a quotient ring, etc.). If we consider injective homomorphisms into a given R-module M (or a group, or a ring, etc.), the images are the R-submodules of M (or the subgroups, or the subrings, etc.). The factorization theorem for a homomorphism then tells us the relation among these concepts. The reader should detect a distinction between R-modules and groups (or rings); namely, in the case of R-modules, to each R-submodule of M, we can form a quotient module of M with the given R-submodule as the kernel. Equivalently, the image of an injective R-module homomorphism is exactly the kernel of a canonical surjective R-module homomorphism. The analogous statement is not true for groups (or for rings). The point is that the kernel of a group homomorphism must be a normal subgroup. (The kernel of a ring homomorphism must be a two-sided ideal, whereas a subring must contain the identity element. Thus the image of an injective ring homomorphism can be the kernel of a surjective ring homomorphism if and only if the injective ring homomorphism is an isomorphism.)

We shall now fix our attention on a single ring R and consider the problem of constructing R-modules and describing R-homomorphisms. We can imitate the procedure for constructing direct products of groups to construct direct products of R-modules. However, it turns out that the more important concept for modules is that of the direct sum of R-modules. This is the imitation of the construction of direct sum of commutative groups described in Excursion III, Section III.5.

DEFINITION 5 · Let A_i, $i \in I$, be an indexed set of modules over the ring R. An R-module A is called a **direct sum** of A_i, $i \in I$, if and only if there exist R-homomorphisms $\theta_i : A_i \to A$ that satisfy the following condition:

(*) For any R-module B and R-homomorphisms $\varphi_i : A_i \to B$, $i \in I$, there is a unique R-homomorphism $\varphi : A \to B$ such that $\varphi \circ \theta_i = \varphi_i \; \forall \, i \in I$.

It follows from the preceding definition that there is a bijection between the set $\mathrm{Hom}_R(A, B)$ and the Cartesian product $\prod_{i \in I} \mathrm{Hom}_R(A_i, B)$ of the sets $\mathrm{Hom}_R(A_i, B)$, $i \in I$. This is given by sending each $\varphi \in \mathrm{Hom}_R(A, B)$ onto the element $(\varphi \circ \theta_i)_{i \in I}$ of the Cartesian product. Indeed, this map is a group isomorphism between $\mathrm{Hom}_R(A, B), +$ and the direct product of the groups $\mathrm{Hom}_R(A_i, B)$, $i \in I$. As we observed before, it makes no difference whether we consider the direct product as one of groups or as one of commutative groups. When $R = \mathbf{Z}$, we obtain precisely the situation described in Excursion III, Section III.5.

We now proceed to state the uniqueness and existence theorems for a direct sum of R-modules.

THEOREM 1 · Let R be a ring and let A_i, $i \in I$, be an indexed set of R-modules. Then the following assertions hold:

(a) The direct sum of A_i, $i \in I$, is unique up to R-isomorphism in a natural way. The R-homomorphisms $\theta_i : A_i \to A$ are in fact R-monomorphisms $\forall \, i \in I$.

(b) Let $A = \{(a_i)_{i \in I} \in \prod_{i \in I} A_i \mid a_i = 0$ for all but a finite number of indices $i \in I$, in which the finite number may vary from element to element$\}$. Define addition in A coordinate by coordinate. If $r \in R$, define $r \cdot (a_i)_{i \in I}$ as $(ra_i)_{i \in I}$. Then A is a direct sum of A_i, $i \in I$.

Proof · (a) involves a diagram-chasing argument similar to that used in proving the uniqueness of the direct product of groups.

(b) We note that each element of A is *uniquely* represented as a *finite* sum of elements of the form $(\ldots, 0, a_i, 0, \ldots)$, $a_i \in A_i$, $i \in I$.

The remaining steps are similar to those used in proving Theorem III.5.3.

Again the important point to remember is that only finite sums make sense in an R-module.

DEFINITION 6 · The direct sum of the R-modules A_i, $i \in I$, constructed in Theorem 2 is denoted by $\coprod_{i\in I} A_i$. (Not to be confused with the disjoint union of the sets A_i.) It is also called the ***external direct sum.*** As in Theorem III.5.3, A_i may be identified with the R-submodule $\{(..., 0, a_i, 0,...) \mid a_i \in A_i\}$. We can then prove the theorem corresponding to Theorem III.5.3 for an arbitrary indexed set of R-modules. When the identification is carried out, we shall often use the terminology of an ***internal direct sum*** of R-submodules.

We now deliberately restate the theorem corresponding to Theorem III.5.3 for R-modules.

THEOREM 2 · Let A be a module over the ring R. Let A_i, $i \in I$, be an indexed set of R-modules. Then $A \cong \coprod_{i\in I} A_i$ if and only if there exist R-submodules B_i, $i \in I$, of A that satisfy the following conditions:

(a) $B_i \cong A_i \; \forall\, i \in I$.

(b) Every element of A may be *uniquely* represented as a *finite* sum $\sum a_i$, $a_i \in B_i$, $i \in I$.

If B_i' is the R-submodule generated by B_j, $j \neq i$, then (b) may be replaced by the following:

(b*) $A = B_i + B_i'$ and $0 = B_i \cap B_i' \; \forall\, i \in I$.

DEFINITION 7 · Let A be a module over the ring R. Let B be any subset of A. The R-submodule of A generated by B is denoted by RB. It is the subgroup of A, $+$ generated by $\{rb \mid r \in R,\, b \in B\}$. An R-submodule generated by a single element is called a **cyclic submodule.**

The subset B is said to be ***free*** if and only if the following condition holds:

(*) For each R-module C and each *map* $\theta : B \to C$ there is a unique R-homomorphism $\varphi : RB \to C$ such that $\varphi(b) = \theta(b) \; \forall\, b \in B$.

If B is free and $RB = A$, then A is called a ***free R-module*** and B is called a ***free R-basis*** of A.

From Definition 7 we see that if A is a free R-module, with the free R-basis B, there is a natural bijection between the sets $\text{Hom}_R(A, C)$ and $\text{Map}(B, C)$ in which C is any R-module. If we let C_b, $b \in B$, be an indexed set (indexed by the elements of B) of R-modules such that $C_b = C \ \forall\, b \in B$, there is a natural bijection between the set $\text{Hom}_R(A, C)$ and the Cartesian product $\prod_{b \in B} C_b$. This bijection is, in fact, an isomorphism between the group $\text{Hom}_R(A, C), +$ and the direct product of the groups $C_b, +, b \in B$. Indeed, the bijection is given by sending each $f \in \text{Hom}_R(A, C)$ onto its table of values on the subset B, that is, onto the element $(f(b))_{b \in B}$ of the Cartesian product. The point here is that each such f is uniquely determined by its values on B because B generates A. Hence the map is injective. The definition of freeness then implies that the map is surjective.

Example 5 · Let R be a ring. As we mentioned in Example 3 (with $S = R$), R is a left R-module under left multiplication by elements of R; namely, $(\theta(r))(x) = rx \ \forall\, r, x \in R$. With this definition, the R-submodules of R are precisely the left ideals of R.

Let $u \in R$ be any invertible element with inverse v; that is, $uv = 1 = vu$. If $x \in R$, then $x = (xv)u$; thus the R-submodule (left ideal) generated by u in R is R. If $ru = su$, then $r = ruv = suv = s$; thus every element of R is uniquely represented as ru for some (uniquely determined!) $r \in R$. Let C be any R-module and $c \in C$; we can then send $ru \in R$ onto $rc \in C$. Since each element of R is uniquely represented as ru for some $r \in R$, it is easy to see that the map so defined is an R-homomorphism of R into C. It follows that $\{u\}$ is a free R-basis of R. In particular, u may be taken to be the identity element 1 of R. Thus R is a free R-module, and there exists a free R-basis with only one element in the basis.

Conversely, let $\{u\}$ be a free R-basis for R. Then $Ru = R$. Hence we can find $v \in R$ such that $vu = 1$. Consider the map that sends u onto the element 1 of R. Since $\{u\}$ is free, this map may be extended to an R-homomorphism of Ru into the R-module R. Thus the extension must send $(uv)u$ onto $(uv) \cdot 1$. However, $uvu = u \cdot 1 = u$. Since u is sent onto 1, we see that $(uv) \cdot 1 = 1$ or $uv = 1$. Thus u is an invertible element of R with inverse v.

We have verified in the preceding paragraphs that there is a bijection between the group of units in R and the set of free R-bases of R consisting of one element in each basis. We next connect the concept of free R-basis of a free R-module with the concept of direct sum of R-modules. Before doing this, we shall show that free R-modules have the following interesting property.

THEOREM 3 · Let R be a ring. Let $\theta : A \to F$ be a surjective R-module homomorphism. Suppose that F is a free R-module with free R-basis $B = \{b_i \mid i \in I\}$. Let $\{a_i \mid i \in I\}$ be any subset of A such that $\theta(a_i) = b_i \ \forall\, i \in I$ and let $K = \ker \theta$. Then the following assertions hold:

(a) $\{a_i \mid i \in I\}$ is free in A.

(b) A is the direct sum of K and G, where G is the R-submodule of A generated by $\{a_i \mid i \in I\}$ in A.

(c) The restriction of θ to G is an R-isomorphism between G and F.

Proof · Consider the map $\sigma : B \to A$ given by $\sigma(b_i) = a_i \ \forall\, i \in I$. From the hypothesis that B is a free R-basis for F we see that σ may be extended to an R-homomorphism $\rho : F \to A$. It is clear that $G = \operatorname{im} \rho$. We now consider the map $\theta \circ \rho : F \to F$. This is an R-homomorphism. Moreover, $\theta(\rho(b_i)) = \theta(\sigma(b_i)) = \theta(a_i) = b_i \ \forall\, i \in I$. Since B generates F, it follows that $\theta \circ \rho$ is the identity map on F. Hence ρ is injective and an R-isomorphism between F and G. It is clear that ρ is the inverse of the restriction of θ to G. Thus both (a) and (c) hold.

Let $x \in K \cap G$. Thus $\theta(x) = 0$. Since the restriction of θ to G is injective, it follows that $x = 0$, and we have shown that $K \cap G = 0$. Let $z \in A$ and set $u = z - \rho(\theta(z))$. Since $\theta \circ \rho$ is the identity map on F, we see that $\theta(u) = \theta(z) - \theta(\rho(\theta(z))) = \theta(z) - \theta(z) = 0$. Hence $u \in K$. Since $\rho(\theta(z)) \in \operatorname{im} \rho = G$, we see that $A = K + G$. Hence (b) holds. «

THEOREM 4 · Let A be a module over the ring R. Then A is a free R-module with free R-basis $B = \{b_i \mid i \in I\}$ if and only if the following conditions hold:

(a) The map that sends 1 onto b_i may be extended uniquely to an R-isomorphism between the R-module R of Example 5 and the submodule Rb_i of $A \ \forall\, i \in I$,

(b) A is the internal direct sum of the submodules Rb_i, $i \in I$.

Theorem 4 follows rather easily from the argument used in proving Theorem 3. We shall leave the details to the reader as an exercise.

Combining Theorem 4 with Theorem 2, we see that an R-module A is a free R-module with free R-basis $B = \{b_i \mid i \in I\}$ if and only if every element of A is *uniquely* representable as a *finite* sum $\sum r_i b_i$, where $r_i \in R$, $i \in I$. This feature makes free R-modules somewhat more manageable than the direct products of R-modules. The reader should be aware that there is no distinction between the "direct product" and the direct sum of a *finite* number of R-modules. Direct sums of R-modules admit internal descriptions; the "direct product" of an infinite number of nonzero R-modules does not admit any "internal" description.

The reader may raise the question: "What R-modules enjoy the property (b) stated in Theorem 4?" The answer is simply that the R-modules should be direct summands of free R-modules. These are usually called ***projective R-modules.*** There exist rings R for which projective R-modules are not free R-modules. However, we shall make no attempt to study this question in further detail.

The next question that arises naturally is: "Does the cardinality of a free R-basis of a free R-module depend on the choice of the particular basis?" If the answer is *no*, then we would have a reasonable way of measuring the size of a free R-module. Unfortunately, the answer is *yes*. It will be shown later that the answer is *no* when R is a commutative ring. In any event, the reader should become convinced that the problem of relating two sets of free R-bases of a free R-module leads naturally to the problem of solving a system of equations over the ring R.

We shall now see that "matrices" arise rather naturally when we attempt to describe homomorphisms from one free module with a finite set for free basis into another.

DEFINITION 8 · Let $m, n \in \mathbf{P}^+$ and let I_m, I_n denote the sets $\{1, \ldots, m\}$ and $\{1, \ldots, n\}$, respectively. Let R be a ring. Then an $m \times n$ ***matrix*** with entries from R is a map from $I_m \times I_n$ to R. We identify the map with its table of values $a_{ij} = f(i, j)$.

$$\begin{pmatrix} a_{11}, & a_{12}, & \ldots, & a_{1n} \\ a_{21}, & a_{22}, & \ldots, & a_{2n} \\ \cdots & & & \\ a_{m1}, & a_{m2}, & \ldots, & a_{mn} \end{pmatrix} = (a_{ij}), \qquad \text{where } a_{ij} \in R$$

i is called the ***row index*** and j is the ***column index.*** The element $a_{ij} \in$ is called the ***(i, j)-th entry*** of the matrix (a_{ij}). The set of all $m \times n$ matrices with entries from R is denoted by $M_{m,n}(R)$. When $m = n$, we often use $M_m(R)$ for $M_{m,m}(R)$.

If (a_{ij}) and $(b_{ij}) \in M_{m,n}(R)$, we define $(a_{ij}) + (b_{ij}) = (c_{ij})$, where $c_{ij} = a_{ij} + b_{ij} \ \forall\, i, j$.

If $(a_{ij}) \in M_{m,n}(R)$ and $(b_{jk}) \in M_{n,p}(R)$, then $(c_{ik}) \in M_{m,p}(R)$ such that $c_{ik} = \sum_j a_{ij} b_{jk} \ \forall\, i, k$ is called the ***product*** of (a_{ij}) and (b_{jk}), and we write $(a_{ij})(b_{jk}) = (c_{ik})$.

We now have the following important theorem.

THEOREM 5 · Let R° be the opposite of the ring R. Let m, n, $p \in \mathbf{P}^+$. Suppose that F_m, G_n, and H_p are free left R-modules with free R-bases $\{x_1, \ldots, x_m\}$, $\{y_1, \ldots, y_n\}$, and $\{z_1, \ldots, z_p\}$, respectively. Then the following assertions hold:

(a) There is a natural bijection between $\mathrm{Hom}_R(F_m, G_n)$ and $M_{n,m}(R^\circ)$ given by associating to $\sigma \in \mathrm{Hom}_R(F_m, G_n)$ the matrix (a_{ji}) such that $\sigma(x_i) = \sum_j a_{ji} y_j$, $1 \leqslant j \leqslant n$. (Note the order of the subscripts.)

(b) Let the bijection of (a) be denoted by Mat. Then the following diagram is commutative:

$$\begin{array}{ccc}
\mathrm{Hom}_R(G_n, H_p) \times \mathrm{Hom}_R(F_m, G_n) & \xrightarrow{\ \circ\ } & \mathrm{Hom}_R(F_m, H_p) \\
\Big\downarrow {\scriptstyle \mathrm{Mat}\times\mathrm{Mat}} & & \Big\downarrow {\scriptstyle \mathrm{Mat}} \\
M_{p,n}(R^\circ) \times M_{n,m}(R^\circ) & \xrightarrow{\ \cdot\ } & M_{p,m}(R^\circ)
\end{array}$$

where $\circ$ denotes the composition of homomorphisms and $\cdot$ denotes the product of matrices.

(c) The bijection of (a) is an isomorphism of the group $\mathrm{Hom}_R(F_m, G_n), +$ with the group $M_{n,m}(R^\circ)$. If $m = n = p$ and $x_i = y_i = z_i\ \forall\, i$, the bijection of (a) is a ring isomorphism of $\mathrm{Hom}_R(F_m, F_m), +, \circ$ with the ring $M_m(R^\circ), +, \cdot$. In particular, matrix multiplication is associative.

Proof · We first recall that the underlying set of R° is the same as R. The multiplication of R° is denoted by $\circ$ and defined by $a \circ b = ba\ \forall\, a, b \in R^\circ = R$.

(a) Because $X = \{x_1, \ldots, x_m\}$ is a free R-basis for F_m, it follows from the discussion after Definition 7 that there is a bijection between $\mathrm{Hom}_R(F_m, G_n)$ and $\mathrm{Map}(X, G_n)$. Since n is finite and $Y = \{y_1, \ldots, y_n\}$ is a free R-basis for G_n, it is easy to see that there is a natural bijection between G_n and $\mathrm{Map}(Y, R)$. From Exercise I.1.7, there exists a natural bijection between $\mathrm{Map}(X, \mathrm{Map}(Y, R))$ and $\mathrm{Map}(Y \times X, R)$; namely, "a function of two variables is the same as attaching to each fixed value of the second variable a function of the first variable"; $Y \times X$ may be identified with $I_n \times I_m$ by the indices of the bases elements. Putting all these natural bijections together, we obtain precisely the bijection described in (a).

We now trace through the steps indicated above. Let $\sigma \in \mathrm{Hom}_R(F_m, G_n)$. Since X is a set of generators of F_m, it is immediately clear that σ is determined uniquely by the values $\sigma(x_i)$,

Let $\sigma \in \text{Hom}_R(F_m, b_n)$. $Mat \in Map(X, b_n)$ given by $x_i \xrightarrow{} \sigma(x_i) \le \sum a_{ji} y_i$;

Let $\alpha \in Map(Y, R)$ given by $y_i \xrightarrow{\alpha} a_{ji}$, $\beta \in Map(Y \times X, R)$ given by $(y_i, x_i) \xrightarrow{\beta} a_{ji}$

$\therefore \sigma \xrightarrow{x_i} \sum a_{ji} y_i$ or $x_i \xrightarrow{} \alpha$, But γ comes to β and β comes a_{ji}. $\therefore \sigma \xrightarrow{} a_{ji}$

IV · 4 MODULES AND THEIR ENDOMORPHISM RINGS » 133

$i \in I_m$, in G_n. Since Y is a free R-basis for G_n, it follows from Theorem 2 that there exists a unique $(a_{ji}) \in M_{n,m}(R^\circ)$ such that $\sigma(x_i) = \sum_j a_{ji} y_j$, $i \in I_m$, $j \in I_n$. Thus Mat : $\text{Hom}_R(F_m, G_n) \to M_{n,m}(R^0)$ is a map. The earlier statement that σ is determined by the values $\sigma(x_i)$, $i \in I_m$, implies that Mat is injective. Suppose that (a_{ji}) is an arbitrary matrix of $M_{n,m}(R^\circ)$. We first define $\rho : X \to G_n$ by setting $\rho(x_i) = \sum_j a_{ji} y_j$, $i \in I_m$, $j \in I_n$. Since X is a free R-basis of F_m, this map ρ may be extended to an R-homomorphism $\sigma \in \text{Hom}_R(F_m, G_n)$. It is obvious that $\text{Mat}(\sigma) = (a_{ji})$. Thus Mat is surjective. We have completed the proof of (a).

(b) Let $\sigma \in \text{Hom}_R(F_m, G_n)$ be such that $\text{Mat}(\sigma) = (a_{ji})$. Let $\tau \in \text{Hom}_R(G_n, H_p)$ be such that $\text{Mat}(\tau) = (b_{kj})$. We now compute as follows:

$$\tau(\sigma(x_i)) = \tau\left(\sum_j a_{ji} y_j\right) = \sum_j \tau(a_{ji} y_j) = \sum_j a_{ji}(\tau(y_j))$$

$$= \sum_j a_{ji}\left(\sum_k b_{kj} z_k\right) = \sum_k \left(\sum_j a_{ji} b_{kj}\right) z_k$$

In the second and third of the equalities we have used the fact that τ is an R-homomorphism. We now observe that $a_{ji} b_{kj}$ is the product in R. By the definition of the product of R° we have $a_{ji} b_{kj} = b_{kj} \circ a_{ji}$. Thus the matrix of $\tau \circ \sigma$ is (c_{ki}), where $c_{ki} = \sum_j b_{kj} \circ a_{ji}$. From the definition of the product of matrices, we conclude that $\text{Mat}(\tau \circ \sigma) = \text{Mat}(\tau) \cdot \text{Mat}(\sigma)$. Thus (b) holds.

(c) The same type of calculation shows that $\text{Mat}(\sigma + \sigma') = \text{Mat}(\sigma) + \text{Mat}(\sigma')$. This, together with (b), now shows that addition and multiplication of matrices are precisely those transported from $\text{Hom}_R(F_m, F_m)$, $+$, $\circ$. Thus $M_{m,m}(R^\circ)$ is a ring and Mat is a ring isomorphism. «

Exercise 8 · In the notation of Theorem 5 verify the following assertions:

(a) If $\sigma \in \text{Hom}_R(F_m, G_n)$ and $\text{Mat}(\sigma) = (a_{ji})$, then $\sigma(\sum_i a_i x_i) = \sum_j(\sum_i a_i a_{ji}) y_j = \sum_j(\sum_i a_{ji} \circ a_i) y_j$; namely, if $x \in F_m$ is identified with the "column vector" formed by the components of x with respect to X, then $\sigma(x)$ has components with respect to Y given by the column vector obtained by multiplication of $\text{Mat}(\sigma)$ on the right by the column vector associated to x.

(b) Let $R = \mathbf{Z}$, $m = 2$, $n = 3$. Suppose that $\sigma \in \operatorname{Hom}_R(F_m, G_n)$ is given by $\sigma(x_1) = 2y_1 + y_2 - y_3$ and $\sigma(x_2) = 3y_1 + y_3$. Then

$$\operatorname{Mat}(\sigma) = \begin{pmatrix} 2 & 3 \\ 1 & 0 \\ -1 & 1 \end{pmatrix}$$

Exercise 9 · Let $\mathbf{R}$ be the field of real numbers. Let P_n be the set of all polynomials of degree less than n in the indeterminate X over $\mathbf{R}$. Show that $1, X, \ldots, X^{n-1}$ is a free $\mathbf{R}$-basis for P_n. Let $D : P_n \to P_n$ be the $\mathbf{R}$-homomorphism defined by $DX^i = iX^{i-1}$. Find $\operatorname{Mat}(D)$ with respect to the basis $\{1, \ldots, X^{n-1}\}$.

Exercise 10 · Let $\mathcal{F}$ be the $\mathbf{R}$-module consisting of all functions from the real numbers to the real numbers of the form $u \cos + v \sin$ where $u, v \in \mathbf{R}$ = the set of real numbers. Let $D : \mathcal{F} \to \mathcal{F}$ be the derivative map. Show that cos and sin form a free $\mathbf{R}$-basis for $\mathcal{F}$. Find the matrix of D with respect to the basis $\{\cos, \sin\}$.

Exercise 11 · Let R be a ring and let F be a free R-module with free basis $\{x\}$. Let $\sigma : R \to \operatorname{Hom}(F, F)$ be the ring homomorphism that turns F into a left R-module. Show that $C_{\operatorname{Hom}(F,F)}(\sigma(R))$ is isomorphic to R°. *Hint.* Show that each element of $C_{\operatorname{Hom}(F,F)}(\sigma(R))$ is uniquely determined by its effect on x. Thus there is a map $\rho : C_{\operatorname{Hom}(F,F)}(\sigma(R)) \to R$ such that $f(x) = \sigma(\rho(f))(x)\ \forall\, f \in C_{\operatorname{Hom}(F,F)}(\sigma(R))$. This exercise is analogous to Exercise 4. $C_{\operatorname{Hom}(F,F)}(\sigma(R))$ is a complicated way of writing $\operatorname{Hom}_R(F, F)$.

Exercise 12 · Let F_n be a free module over the ring R with free R-basis $\{x_1, \ldots, x_n\}$. Show that left multiplication by $r \in R$ is an R-homomorphism of F_n into F_n if and only if r lies in the **center** of R. The center of R is defined as $\{x \in R \mid xy = yx\ \forall\, y \in R\}$; it is a subring of R.

We now make several remarks concerning the notations. It is rather unpleasant to have to drag in the opposite of the ring R in Theorem 5. This could have been avoided by adopting the exponential notation for maps; namely, instead of writing $\sigma(x)$ for the image of x under the map σ, we could have written $x\sigma$ or x^σ. By interchanging the rows and columns in the definition of a matrix, we would then have been able to state Theorem 5 without having to drag in R°. As can be seen from Exercises 11 and 12, the ring R does not occur in any natural way as a subring of $\operatorname{Hom}_R(F_n, F_n)$. It does occur when R is commutative. However, R° does occur in a natural way as a subring of $\operatorname{Hom}_R(F_1, F_1)$. Of course, when R is commutative, R° and R are identical as rings, not just merely as groups.

Exercise 13   ·   Show that the identity element of $M_n(R^\circ)$ is the matrix (δ_{ij}), where δ_{ij} are the **Kronecker deltas;** that is,

$$\delta_{ij} = \begin{cases} 1 & \text{when } i = j \\ 0 & \text{when } i \neq j \end{cases}$$

Show that the zero element of $M_n(R^\circ)$ is a matrix, all of whose entries are 0. Show that the map which sends $r \in R$ onto the matrix $(r\delta_{ij})$ is an injective opposite ring homomorphism of R into $M_n(R^\circ)$. The image is then called the set of **scalar matrices.**

We note that the isomorphism between $\mathrm{Hom}_R(F_m, G_n)$ and $M_{n,m}(R^\circ)$ as groups and the isomorphism between $\mathrm{Hom}_R(F_m, F_m)$ and $M_m(R^\circ)$ as rings depend strongly on the selection of free R-bases. In particular, only a single free R-basis is selected for F_m in the consideration of $\mathrm{Hom}_R(F_m, F_m)$. To emphasize our point we state the following definition:

DEFINITION 9   ·   Let F_m, G_n be free modules over the ring R with free R-bases $X = \{x_1, ..., x_m\}$ and $Y = \{y_1, ..., y_n\}$, respectively. If $\sigma \in \mathrm{Hom}_R(F_m, G_n)$ is defined by $\sigma(x_i) = \sum_j a_{ji} y_j \ \forall \ i$, then the matrix $(a_{ji}) \in M_{n,m}(R^\circ)$ is called the **matrix of σ with respect to the free R-bases X and Y.** If $F_m = G_n$ and $x_i = y_i \ \forall \ i$, then we call $(a_{ji}) \in M_m(R^\circ)$ the matrix of σ with respect to the free R-basis X of F_m.

Exercise 14   ·   Let A be the direct product (or the direct sum) of two cyclic groups of order 2. Let R be the ring $\mathrm{Hom}(A, A)$. Verify the following assertions:

(a) A is isomorphic to the direct sum of two **Z**-modules; each is cyclic and has order 2 as a group. Moreover, A is not a free **Z**-module.

(b) A is isomorphic to the direct sum of two $\mathbf{Z}/(2)$-modules, each of which is isomorphic to $\mathbf{Z}/(2)$ as a $\mathbf{Z}/(2)$-module. Thus A is a free $\mathbf{Z}/(2)$-module with a free $\mathbf{Z}/(2)$-basis consisting of two elements.

(c) R is a noncommutative ring with 16 elements.

(d) R is isomorphic to $M_2(\mathbf{Z}/(2))$.   *Use Thm S(C), since* $\mathrm{Hom}(A, A)$ *= $\mathrm{Hom}_{\mathbf{Z}/2}(A, A)$*

(e) $I = \{ \left(\begin{smallmatrix} a & 0 \\ c & 0 \end{smallmatrix} \right) |\ a, c \in \mathbf{Z}/(2) \}$ is a left ideal of $M_2(\mathbf{Z}/(2))$.   *stfd*

(f)   Every left ideal of $M_2(\mathbf{Z}/(2))$ distinct from 0 and $M_2(\mathbf{Z}/(2))$ has the form IV for some $V \in M_2(\mathbf{Z}/(2))$; I is given in (e).

(g)   If $J = \{ \left(\begin{smallmatrix} 0 & b \\ 0 & d \end{smallmatrix} \right) |\ b, d \in \mathbf{Z}/(2) \}$, then under left multiplication by

First note that sets of form IV are left ideals in which $\left(\begin{smallmatrix} a & b \\ c & d \end{smallmatrix} \right) \notin IV$ rows iff the rows are linearly depend. ∴ suppose K is a left ideal with $\left(\begin{smallmatrix} n_1 \\ n_2 \end{smallmatrix} \right) = \left(\begin{smallmatrix} a & b \\ c & d \end{smallmatrix} \right)$ $\in K$ with n_1, n_2 linearly indep. Then closure under outer left mult. ⟹ $K = M_2(\mathbf{Z}/2)$

elements of $M_2(\mathbf{Z}/(2))$, the left $M_2(\mathbf{Z}/(2))$-module $M_2(\mathbf{Z}/(2))$ is the direct sum of the left $M_2(\mathbf{Z}/(2))$-modules I and J.

(h) 0 and $M_2(\mathbf{Z}/(2))$ are the only two-sided ideals of $M_2(\mathbf{Z}/(2))$.

(i) The map that sends $\left(\begin{smallmatrix} a & b \\ c & d \end{smallmatrix}\right) \in M_2(\mathbf{Z}/(2))$ onto $\left(\begin{smallmatrix} a & c \\ b & d \end{smallmatrix}\right)$ is an opposite ring automorphism of $M_2(\mathbf{Z}/(2))$.

(j) The set $T = \{\left(\begin{smallmatrix} a & 0 \\ c & d \end{smallmatrix}\right) \mid a, c, d \in \mathbf{Z}/(2)\}$ is a subring of $M_2(\mathbf{Z}/(2))$.

(k) The set I of (e) is a two-sided ideal of T; moreover, T is the largest subring of $M_2(\mathbf{Z}/(2))$ that contains I as a two-sided ideal.

(l) If I of (e) is identified with A as a $\mathbf{Z}/(2)$-module, then left multiplication on I by elements of $M_2(\mathbf{Z}/(2))$ identifies $\operatorname{Hom}(A, A)$ with $M_2(\mathbf{Z}/(2))$.

We now describe an example of a ring R and a free R-module A such that A has free R-bases of different cardinalities.

Example 6 · Let M be a free S-module with $X = \{x_i \mid i \in \mathbf{Z}\}$ as a free S-basis, where S is a nonzero ring. R is the ring $\operatorname{Hom}_S(M, M), +, \circ$. A will be the left R-module $\operatorname{Hom}_S(M, M)$, where R acts on A by left multiplication in $\operatorname{Hom}_S(M, M), +, \circ$. Thus A is a free R-module with $\{I_M\}$ as a free R-basis, where I_M is the identity map of M. Let $j \in \{0, 1\}$ and define $I_j \in \operatorname{Hom}_S(M, M)$ by setting $I_j(x_{2i+j}) = x_i$ and $I_j(x_{2i+1+j}) = 0 \ \forall\, i \in \mathbf{Z}$. It is clear that I_j is surjective. Thus $\sigma \circ I_j = 0$ if and only if $\sigma = 0$, where $\sigma \in \operatorname{Hom}_S(M, M) = R$. It follows that $\{I_j\}$ is free in A. Let $j \in \{0, 1\}$ and define $J_j \in \operatorname{Hom}_S(M, M)$ by setting $J_j(x_i) = x_{2i+j} \ \forall\, i \in J$. It is easy to see that $I_M = J_0 I_0 + J_1 I_1$. Hence $\sigma \in A = \operatorname{Hom}_S(M, M)$ implies that $\sigma = (\sigma \circ J_0) \circ I_0 + (\sigma \circ J_1) \circ I_1$ and that $A = RI_0 + RI_1$. Suppose that $\sigma \in RI_0 \cap RI_1$; then there exist $\rho_0, \rho_1 \in R$ such that $\sigma = \rho_0 \circ I_0 = \rho_1 \circ I_1$. It follows that $\sigma(x_{2i}) = \rho_1(I_1(x_{2i})) = 0$ and that $\sigma(x_{2i+1}) = \rho_0(I_0(x_{2i+1})) = 0$. Thus $RI_0 \cap RI_1 = 0$, and A is the direct sum of RI_0 and RI_1. Since $\{I_j\}$ is R-free in A, we conclude that $\{I_0, I_1\}$ is a free R-basis for A.

The only reason for including the hypothesis that $S \neq 0$ is that the only module over the zero ring is the zero module. This module may be considered free, with the zero element as a free basis. Any other free basis is merely a repetition of the zero element an arbitrary number of times. In the example described RI_j is R-isomorphic to A. Thus we can break up RI_j into the direct sum of $RI_{j,0}$ and $RI_{j,1}$ where $\{I_{j,k}\}$ is R-free in A. Replacing one or both of RI_j with the corresponding direct sum decomposition, we see that A also has a free R-basis with three or four elements. By repeating this procedure it is easy to show that A has a free R-basis consisting of n elements for each integer $n \in \mathbf{P}^+$. We shall see in Excursion IV, Section V.2, that this example is essentially the "only" example. More precisely, such example must occur for a noncommutative ring and the module can have free basis with only finite cardinality.

» IV · 5 RINGS OF FUNCTIONS

So far we have ignored the investigation of the direct product of modules over a ring R, as well as the direct product of rings. We shall now show that the latter leads to some interesting results.

Exercise 1 · Define the direct product of an indexed set of rings R_i, $i \in I$, by imitating the definition for groups. Prove the uniqueness and the existence of the direct product of rings. (Again, this is done by imitating the corresponding statements for groups. Indeed, the additive group of the direct product of rings is isomorphic to the direct product of the additive groups of the given rings in a natural way.)

Exercise 2 · (Chinese remainder theorem). Let I_i, $1 \leqslant i \leqslant n$, be a finite set of two-sided ideals of the ring R. Suppose that $I_i + I_j = R \; \forall \, i \neq j$. Show that R/I is isomorphic to the direct product of R/I_i, $1 \leqslant i \leqslant n$, where $I = I_1 \cap \cdots \cap I_n$.

Hint. Let the direct product of R/I_i be represented as the set of all n-tuples $(x_1 + I_1, \ldots, x_n + I_n)$, $x_i \in R$. Show that the map sending $x \in R$ onto $(x + I_1, \ldots, x + I_n)$ is a ring homomorphism with kernel I. It remains for us to show that this map is surjective. Fix j temporarily; since $I_i + I_j = R \; \forall \, i \neq j$, we see that there exists $f_i \in I_i$ such that $f_i + z_i = 1$ for some $z_i \in I_j$. Hence we conclude from the fact that each I_i is a two-sided ideal in R that $f_1 \cdots f_{j-1} f_{j+1} \cdots f_n = y_j$ is an element of $\bigcap_{i \neq j} I_i$. Since $f_i + I_j = 1 + I_j$, we see from applying to y_j the natural homomorphism of R onto R/I_j that $y_j + I_j = 1 + I_j$. Now let $x_i \in R$, $1 \leqslant i \leqslant n$, be random elements. We assert that $(x + I_1, \ldots, x + I_n) = (x_1 + I_1, \ldots, x_n + I_n)$, where $x = \sum_j x_j y_j \in R$. To see this we note that $x + I_j = \sum_{i \neq j} (x_i + I_j)(y_i + I_j) + (x_j + I_j)(y_j + I_j)$. Since $y_i \in I_j \; \forall \, i \neq j$ and $y_j + I_j = 1 + I_j$, it is immediate that $x + I_j = x_j + I_j \; \forall \, j$. Thus the map from R to the direct product of R/I_i is surjective. (We observe that the finiteness of the number of I_i's is quite important in the proof. It is used in showing that the map described is surjective. The assertion of the exercise is false when an infinite number of ideals all distinct from R are involved; for example, we may consider the ring $\mathbf{Z}$ and let $I_i = \mathbf{Z} p_i$, where $p_i > 0$ is the ith prime. The direct product of $\mathbf{Z}/\mathbf{Z} p_i$, $i \in \mathbf{P}^+$, is not a countable ring, whereas $\bigcap_{i \in \mathbf{P}^+} \mathbf{Z} p_i = 0$.)

Exercise 3 · Let R be the direct product of the rings R_i, $i \in I$. Show that the group of units $U(R)$ is naturally isomorphic to the direct product of the groups of units $U(R_i)$, $i \in I$.

Exercise 4 · Let $m = \prod_i p_i^{\nu(i)}$ be the factorization of $m \in \mathbf{P}^+$, where $p_i > 0$ is the ith prime and $\nu(i) \in \mathbf{P}$. Use Exercise 2 to verify that $\mathbf{Z}/(m)$ is the direct product of the rings $\mathbf{Z}/(p_i^{\nu(i)})$. Use Exercise 3 to verify that the Euler φ-function satisfies the relation $\varphi(mn) = \varphi(m)\varphi(n)$ whenever $m, n \in \mathbf{P}^+$, are relatively prime.

DEFINITION 1 · Let R be a ring and let I be a set. If f $g \in \text{Map}(I, R)$, define $f + g \in \text{Map}(I, R)$ by setting $(f + g)(i) = f(i) + g(i)$, $\forall\, i \in I$; and define $fg \in \text{Map}(I, R)$ by setting $(fg)(i) = f(i)\, g(i)$, $\forall\, i \in I$. $\text{Map}(I, R)$ can be easily checked to be a ring under the addition and multiplication defined. This ring is called the ***ring of R-valued functions on the set I.***

Exercise 5 · In the notation of Definition 1 show that the ring $\text{Map}(I, R)$ is isomorphic to the direct product of the rings R_i, $i \in I$, where $R_i = R$, $\forall\, i \in I$.

DEFINITION 2 · Let R be a commutative ring. For each $n \in \mathbf{P}^+$ let $R^n = \{(a_1, ..., a_n) | \, a_i \in R\}$ and let $X_1, ..., X_n$ be indeterminates over R. If $f(X_1, ..., X_n) \in R[X_1, ..., X_n]$, let $\bar{f} : R^n \to R$ be given by $\bar{f}(a_1, ..., a_n) = f(a_1, ..., a_n)$, where the right side is the image of $(a_1, ..., a_n)$ under the substitution homomorphism; $\bar{f} \in \text{Map}(R^n, R)$ is then called a ***polynomial function*** in n variables over the ring R.

Exercise 6 · In the notation of Definition 2 show that the map that sends f onto $\bar{f}$ is a ring homomorphism of $R[X_1, ..., X_n]$ into the ring $\text{Map}(R^n, R)$.

Exercise 7 · (Lagrange interpolation theorem). Let $a_0, ..., a_n$ be $n + 1$ distinct elements of the field F. Show that there exists a unique polynomial $f \in F[X]$ that satisfies the following conditions:

(a) $\deg f \leqslant n$.

(b) $f(a_i) = r_i$, $0 \leqslant i \leqslant n$, where r_i, $0 \leqslant i \leqslant n$, are arbitrarily prescribed elements of F.

Hint. For the uniqueness use (a) with the factor theorem applied to the difference of two polynomials which satisfy (a) and (b). For the existence consider the following polynomial:

$$f(X) = \sum_{0 \leqslant i \leqslant n} \left\{ r_i \prod_{\substack{j \neq i \\ 0 \leqslant j \leqslant n}} \frac{(X - a_j)}{(a_i - a_j)} \right\}$$

Exercise 8 · Let R be a finite field with q elements. Show that the ring homomorphism described in Exercise 6 is surjective with a kernel equal to the ideal generated by $X_i^q - X_i$, $1 \leqslant i \leqslant n$.

Hint. When $n = 1$, use Exercise 7 to show that the homomorphism is surjective. Use the Euclidean division algorithm in $R[X]$ to show that $R[X]/(X^q - X)$ and Map(R, R) have the same number of elements. Use this and the fact that $X^q - X$ is in the kernel to conclude that the kernel is generated by $X^q - X$.

Exercise 9 · Let $R = \mathbf{Q}$. Use the factor theorem to show that the map from $R[X]$ to Map(R, R) of Exercise 6 is injective but not surjective. In particular, show that a polynomial function has an infinite set of zeroes if and only if it is the zero function.

References

Rings may be considered as groups with operators. In this way they may be classified as a generalization of groups. The reader may consult [6] for a discussion of groups with operators. For a detailed study of rings in general he may consult [7].

In many interesting cases rings occur as "operators" on other "structures." We have already mentioned the ring of endomorphisms of a commutative group. The commutative groups often has additional structures; for example, the reader may consult [9] to investigate the rings that occur frequently in functional analysis.

The formalisms involved in the definition of direct sums of modules are based on those used in the theory of categories. The reader may consult [2] as before.

Polynomial rings and commutative rings are quite important in algebraic geometry. The reader may consult [11] for more results on commutative rings.

Divisibility theory in integral domains is important in arithmetics and number theory. The reader may consult [10] for an extensive study of

UFD's. For results and examples on the connection between divisibility theory and number theory he may consult [4]. The same reference may be consulted for transcendental and algebraic numbers. For a more advanced study of these objects the reader may refer to [1], [3], and [5].

1. E. Artin, *Theory of Algebraic Numbers*, Göttingen, Germany, 1959.
2. P. Freyd, *Abelian Categories*, Harper and Row, New York, 1964.
3. A. O. Gelfond, *Transcendental and Algebraic Numbers*, Dover, New York, 1960.
4. G. H. Hardy and E. M. Wright, *An Introduction to the Theory of Numbers*, 4th ed., Oxford University Press, London, 1960.
5. D. Hilbert, *Gesammelte Abhandlungen*, Vol. 1, Springer, Berlin, 1932.
6. N. Jacobson, *Lectures on Abstract Algebra*, Vol. 1, Van Nostrand, Princeton, N. J., 1951.
7. N. Jacobson, *Structure of Rings*, American Mathematical Society, Providence, 1956.
8. T. Motzkin, "The Euclidean algorithm," *Bulletin of the American Mathematical Society*, **55**, 1142–1146 (1949).
9. M. A. Naimark, *Normed Rings*, P. Noordhoff, Groningen, 1964.
10. P. Samuel, *Anneaux factoriels*, Sociedade Matematica de Sao Paulo, 1963.
11. O. Zariski and P. Samuel, *Commutative Algebras*, Vols, 1 and 2, Van Nostrand, Princeton, N. J., 1962.

CHAPTER V Modules and Associated Algebras over Commutative Rings

In this chapter we shall study modules over a commutative ring R and the R-homomorphisms between such modules. To facilitate our investigations we shall construct some important (generally non-commutative) rings, to be called R-algebras, associated with the given module. The most important case of our general investigation is the structure of a module of finite type over a PID. It is shown that the structure of these modules is determined by a set of invariants, called the *elementary ideals*. In the process of our development we shall also study the concepts of the determinant, the trace, the dual of a module, and the dual of a module homomorphism.

In Chapter VI we consider a few applications of the results of this chapter; in particular, we shall consider the linear transformations of a finite dimensional vector space over a field; the decomposition of such a vector space with respect to a particular linear transformation; the solutions of a system of linear homogeneous equations over a field; and several other related problems.

The reader may raise the question: "Why do we restrict ourselves to commutative rings?" The answer lies in the following observation:

(*) If M is a module over the commutative ring R and $a \in R$, the map $aI : M \to M$ given by $(aI)(x) = ax, \forall\, x \in M$, is an element of the center of $\mathrm{Hom}_R(M, M), +, \circ$. Moreover, the map that sends $a \in R$ onto aI is a ring homomorphism of R into the center of $\mathrm{Hom}_R(M, M), +, \circ$.

When R is not commutative, we can only say that there is a ring homomorphism of R into the ring $\mathrm{Hom}(M, M), +, \circ$. As a result, we can no longer examine the image of R in $\mathrm{Hom}_R(M, M)$ and its relation to $\mathrm{Hom}_R(M, M)$, and therefore we must examine the larger ring $\mathrm{Hom}(M, M), +, \circ$.

In general, if S is a ring, an S-module may be considered as an R-module, in which R is the center of S. In this sense the noncommutative situation can be broken down into two stages.

(1) The study of R-modules.

(2) The study of the relations between S and its center R.

The second problem should include a study of the relations between the S-modules and the R-modules.

Unless some restriction is placed on R and/or S, both problems become hopelessly complicated. The problem that we shall investigate in some detail is the first of these two under the added hypotheses that R is a PID and that the modules to be considered are of finite type.

CONVENTIONS · We remind the reader that the conventions of Chapter IV remain in force throughout this chapter (as well as the rest of the book); namely, rings are assumed to have identity elements, and ring homomorphisms are assumed to preserve these identity elements. Since R-algebras are rings of a special type, the same conventions apply to R-algebras and R-algebra homomorphisms as well. We shall use functional notations for maps throughout this chapter.

» V · 1 TENSOR PRODUCT OF MODULES OVER COMMUTATIVE RINGS

We now generalize the concept of a bihomomorphism. In the process we present another procedure for constructing modules out of given ones.

DEFINITION 1 · Let A, B, and C be modules over the commutative ring R. A map $\theta : A \times B \to C$ is called a ***bi-R-homomorphism*** if and only if the following conditions hold:

(a) $\theta(a + a', b) = \theta(a, b) + \theta(a', b)$ and $\theta(a, b + b') = \theta(a, b) + \theta(a, b')$,

(b) $\theta(ra, b) = r(\theta(a, b)) = \theta(a, rb)$,

Here a, a' range over A, b, b' range over B, and r ranges over R.

When $R = \mathbf{Z}$ the condition (b) is a consequence of condition (a). In any event, if we forget the R-module structures on A, B, and C, a bi-R-homomorphism must always be a bihomomorphism of the commutative groups A, B, and C.

We next note that by computing $\theta(ra, sb)$ according to (b) in two different ways we would obtain $rs(\theta(a, b)) = sr(\theta(a, b))$. Thus it would not be useful to generalize Definition 1 to noncommutative rings.

Exercise 1 · Let A, B, C, and D be modules over the commutative ring R. Let $\text{Bi-hom}_R(A \times B, C)$ be the set of all bi-R-homomorphisms from $A \times B$ to C. If $\sigma, \rho \in \text{Bi-hom}_R(A \times B, C)$, define $\sigma + \rho$ by setting $(\sigma + \rho)(a, b) = \sigma(a, b) + \rho(a, b)$. Show that $\text{Bi-hom}_R(A \times B, C)$ is a commutative group under $+$. Show that the composition of maps defines a bihomomorphism, $\circ : \text{Hom}_R(C, D) \times \text{Bi-hom}_R(A \times B, C) \to \text{Bi-hom}_R(A \times B, D)$. In particular, if $C = D$, show that $\text{Bi-hom}_R(A \times B, C)$ is a left $\text{Hom}_R(C, C)$ module.

Exercise 2 · (Continuing with the notations of Exercise 1). Let $\sigma \in \text{Hom}_R(C, D)$, $\rho \in \text{Bi-hom}_R(A \times B, C)$, and $r \in R$. Define $r\sigma$ and $r\rho$ by setting $(r\sigma)(c) = r(\sigma(c))$ and $(r\rho)(a, b) = r(\rho(a, b))$, respectively. Show that $r\sigma \in \text{Hom}_R(C, D)$ and $r\rho \in \text{Bi-hom}_R(A \times B, C)$. Show that $\text{Hom}_R(C, D)$ and $\text{Bi-hom}_R(A \times B, C)$ are both R-modules under these definitions. Show that the bi-homomorphism of Exercise 1 is actually a bi-R-homomorphism.

In order to simplify the matter it is natural for us to raise the question, "Is it possible that $\text{Bi-hom}_R(A \times B, C)$ is naturally isomorphic to $\text{Hom}_R(M, C)$, where M is an R-module constructed out of A and B in some canonical way?" The answer to this question is *yes* and leads us to the following definition:

DEFINITION 2 · Let A, B be modules over the commutative ring R. An R-module M is called a ***tensor product*** of A and B over R if and only if there exists a bi-R-homomorphism $\theta : A \times B \to M$ such that the following condition is satisfied:

(*) For any R-module C and any bi-R-homomorphism $\varphi : A \times B \to C$ there exists a unique R-homomorphism $\varphi' : M \to C$ such that $\varphi = \varphi' \circ \theta$.

We now state the following existence and uniqueness theorem.

THEOREM 1 · Let A, B be modules over the commutative ring R. Then a tensor product of A and B over R exists and is unique up to a natural R-isomorphism.

Proof · As usual, the uniqueness involves a diagram-chasing argument which we leave to the reader.

For the proof of existence we let F be the free R-module with free R-basis $\{x_{a,b} \mid a \in A, b \in B\}$. Thus $A \times B$ is used as the index set. Let T be the R-submodule of F generated by all elements of the form $x_{a+a',b} - x_{a,b} - x_{a',b}$; $x_{a,b+b'} - x_{a,b} - x_{a,b'}$; $x_{ra,b} - rx_{a,b}$; $x_{a,rb} - rx_{a,b}$, where a, a' range over A, b, b' range over B, and r ranges over R. M is taken to be the R-module F/T and $\theta : A \times B \to M$ is defined by setting $\theta(a, b) = x_{a,b} + T$. It is easy to see that θ is a bi-R-homomorphism. If C is any R-module and $\varphi \in \text{Bi-hom}_R(A \times B, C)$, we may define $\rho \in \text{Hom}_R(F, C)$ to be the unique extension of the map ρ' given by $\rho'(x_{a,b}) = \varphi(a, b)\ \forall\, a \in A, b \in B$. Since φ is a bi-R-homomorphism, it is clear that $T \subset \ker \rho$. Thus by the factorization theorem of homomorphisms we see that ρ defines a unique R-homomorphism $\varphi' : M \to C$ such that $\varphi'(x_{a,b} + T) = \varphi(a, b)\ \forall\, a \in A, b \in B$. It is now easy to verify that $\varphi = \varphi' \circ \theta$ and that φ' is uniquely determined by this equation. Hence M is a tensor product of A and B over R. «

DEFINITION 3 · Let A, B be modules over the commutative ring R. The tensor product M of A and B constructed in Theorem 1 is denoted by $A \otimes_R B$. The element $x_{a,b} + T$ of M is denoted by $a \otimes b$. Thus $(a + a') \otimes b = a \otimes b + a' \otimes b$, $(ra) \otimes b = r(a \otimes b)$, and so on. We observe that each element of $A \otimes_R B$ admits at least one representation as a *finite* sum $\sum_i a_i \otimes b_i$, where $a_i \in A$ and $b_i \in B$.

From Theorem 1 and Definition 3 we see that $\text{Bi-hom}_R(A \times B, C)$ and $\text{Hom}_R(A \otimes_R B, C)$ are naturally isomorphic. In fact, the natural isomorphism is one of R-modules.

In general, the tensor product of two modules is not easily described in terms of the component modules. More specifically, it is rather difficult to decide when the element $\sum_i x_i \otimes y_i$ is 0. Unlike the direct sum of modules, the component modules are not embedded in the tensor product in any natural way. In fact, the tensor product of two nonzero modules may very well be the zero module. (See Exercises 5 and 6.)

We observe that the construction given in Theorem 1 is not efficient in the sense that both F and T have a large number of generators. The following exercise shows that simplification is sometimes possible.

Exercise 3 · Let A, B, and C be modules over the commutative ring R. Show that $(A \otimes_R B) \otimes_R C$ and $A \otimes_R (B \otimes_R C)$ are naturally isomorphic. Show that $R \otimes_R A$, $A \otimes_R R$, and A are naturally isomorphic, where R is a left R-module under left multiplication. Show that $A \otimes_R B$ and $B \otimes_R A$ are naturally isomorphic under a "twisting" isomorphism. (The reader should be aware that when $A = B$ the elements $a \otimes b$ and $b \otimes a$ are not always equal. However, $(a \otimes b) \otimes c$ and $a \otimes (b \otimes c)$ are usually identified as the same element of "$A \otimes_R B \otimes_R C$".) Show that $A \otimes_R (B \amalg C)$ and $(A \otimes_R B) \amalg (A \otimes_R C)$ are naturally isomorphic. Similarly, show that $(B \amalg C) \otimes_R A$ and $(B \otimes_R A) \amalg (C \otimes_R A)$ are naturally isomorphic. Let A and B be free R-modules with free R-bases $\{u_i \mid 1 \leqslant i \leqslant m\}$ and $\{v_j \mid 1 \leqslant j \leqslant n\}$, respectively. Use the preceding results to show that $A \otimes_R B$ is a free module with free R-basis $\{u_i \otimes v_j \mid 1 \leqslant i \leqslant m, 1 \leqslant j \leqslant n\}$.

We observe that under the tensor product and the direct sum R-isomorphism classes of R-modules behave in such a way that we are remined of $\mathbf{P}$, $\cdot$, $+$; namely, the zero module plays the role of $0 \in \mathbf{P}$, the module R plays the role of $1 \in \mathbf{P}$, and $\otimes_B$, $\coprod$ play the role of $\cdot$, $+$, respectively. It is tempting to consider putting an equivalence relation on the collection of R-isomorphism classes of R-modules in order to obtain a ring. However, the collection of all R-isomorphism classes of R-modules is "too large" to be a set. Any attempt to consider this collection as a set will lead to logical difficulties. By restricting ourselves to a sufficiently small subcollection and introducing a suitable equivalence relation, it is possible to obtain a ring structure. We shall not attempt to investigate this possibility at this point.

It is possible to define the tensor product of any set of R-modules. All we need is the notion of a multi-R-homomorphism. However, by using Exercise 3 it is easy to see how to define inductively the tensor product of any finite number of R-modules; we shall be content with this.

We observe that, given an R-module A, it is always possible to find a suitable free R-module F and a surjective R-homomorphism $\theta : F \to A$. For example, we may take F to be free with free R-basis x_a, $a \in A$, and let θ be the unique R-homomorphism sending x_a onto $a \; \forall \, a \in A$. Clearly, this is not very efficient in the sense that F is quite large. Actually, it is possible to do the same thing with the set A replaced by any set of generators of A as an R-module.

DEFINITION 4 · Let A be a module over the commutative ring R. A is called an ***R-module of finite type*** if and only if A is generated by a finite subset as an R-module; that is, it is possible to find $a_i \in A$, $1 \leqslant i \leqslant n$, such that $A = Ra_1 + \cdots + Ra_n$. Equivalently, A is the homomorphic image of some free R-module with a free R-basis consisting of a finite number of elements. A is called a **cyclic R-module** if and only if A may be generated by one element as an R-module; that is, $A = Ra$ for a suitable $a \in A$.

DEFINITION 5 · Let A be a module over the commutative ring R. Let $a \in A$; then $\text{Ann}(a) = \{r \in R \mid ra = 0\}$ is easily seen to be an ideal of R. $\text{Ann}(a)$ is called the **annihilator ideal** of a in R. The element $a \in A$ is said to be **torsion** if and only if $\text{Ann}(a) \neq 0$. When $\text{Ann}(a) = 0$, a is said to be **torsion-free**, or simply **free** (see Definition IV.4.7). The module A is said to be **torsion** if and only if every element of A is torsion. A is said to be **torsion-free** if and only if every nonzero element of A is torsion-free.

It is clear from the preceding definitions that a torsion-free cyclic module is a free module with a free basis consisting of at most one element. (The free module with an empty set of generators is the zero module.)

Definition 5 can be generalized to noncommutative rings, in which case the annihilator ideal is only a left ideal.

Exercise 4 · Let R be a commutative ring. Show that there is a bijection between the set of ideals of R and the set of R-isomorphism classes of cyclic R-modules. *Hint.* Let M be a cyclic R-module with a generator x, show that $\text{Ann}(x)$ is an ideal uniquely determined by M, independent of the choice of the generator x. Indeed, $\text{Ann}(x) = \{r \in R \mid ry = 0 \;\forall\, y \in M\}$. Conversely, show that R/J is a cyclic R-module for any ideal J under left multiplication by elements of R. Indeed, $1 + J$ is a generator and $\text{Ann}(1 + J) = J$. Investigate the generalization to noncommutative rings.

Exercise 5 · Let I, J be ideals of the commutative ring R. Show that, as R-modules, $R/I \otimes_R R/J$ and $R/(I + J)$ are R-isomorphic. *Hint.* Consider the R-homomorphism that sends $r \in R$ onto $r(\bar{1} \otimes \bar{1})$. Show that $I + J$ is contained in the kernel, and thus we have an element $\rho \in \text{Hom}_R(R/(I + J), R/I \otimes_R R/J)$. Consider the bi-$R$-homomorphism that sends (s, t) onto $st + I + J$. Show that it induces a bi-R-homomorphism of $R/I \times R/J$ into $R/(I + J)$. Thus it induces an element $\sigma \in \text{Hom}_R(R/I \otimes_R R/J, R/(I + J))$. Finally, show that $\sigma \circ \rho$ and $\rho \circ \sigma$ are identity maps of the respective R-modules; hence the R-modules are R-isomorphic.

Exercise 6 · Show that $\mathbf{Z}/(2) \otimes_{\mathbf{Z}} \mathbf{Z}/(3) = 0$.

Note $x_{1,0} = x_{1,0} + 0 \cdot x_{1,0} = x_{1,0} - 0 x_{1,0} \in M$. Likewise $x_{0,1}, x_{0,2}, x_{0,}$

Finally $x_{1,1+2} = x_{1,1} - x_{1,2} = x_{1,1} - x_{1,1} - x_{1,5} \in M$

so their sum $x_{1,} - 3 x_{1,1} \in M \Rightarrow$ since $x_{1,2} - x_{1,1} - x_{1,1} \in M$ that $x_{1,0} + x_{1,2} - 3 x = x_{1,0} + (x_{1,} - x_{1,1})$

But then $x_{1,1}, x_{1,2} = x_{1,} - x_{1,1} \in M \Rightarrow x_{1,1} \in M$. $\in M \Rightarrow$

We note that Exercises 4 and 5 show that the study of tensor product of cyclic modules over a commutative ring R is equivalent to the study of the additive structure among ideals of R.

Exercise 7 · Let M be a free module over an integral domain R. Show that M is torsion-free.

Exercise 8 · Show that any $\mathbf{Z}$-submodule of finite type in $\mathbf{Q}$ is free with at most one element in a free $\mathbf{Z}$-basis. Thus show that $\mathbf{Q}$ is torsion-free but not free as a $\mathbf{Z}$-module.

Hint. Let $r_1, \dots, r_n$ be a finite set of generators of the $\mathbf{Z}$-submodule M of $\mathbf{Q}$. Let $d \in \mathbf{Z}$ be a common denominator of $r_1, \dots, r_n$ in $\mathbf{Z} - \{0\}$. The map that sends $x \in M$ onto dx is an injective $\mathbf{Z}$-homomorphism of M into $\mathbf{Z}$. Since every $\mathbf{Z}$-submodule of $\mathbf{Z}$ is generated by one element (here we use the fact that $\mathbf{Z}$-submodules of $\mathbf{Z}$ are ideals of $\mathbf{Z}$ and the fact that $\mathbf{Z}$ is a PID), it follows that M is free with at most one element in a free basis. The remaining assertions now follow rather easily.

Exercise 9 · Use Exercise 5 and the fundamental theorem on finite abelian groups to describe completely the tensor product of $\mathbf{Z}$-modules with a finite number of elements (i.e., finite abelian groups).

Exercise 10 · Let $\sigma : \mathbf{Q} \to M$ be an injective homomorphism of $\mathbf{Z}$-modules. Show that $\sigma(\mathbf{Q})$ is a direct summand of M. (This is not an easy exercise; the reader should consider the set $\mathfrak{F}$ of all $\mathbf{Z}$-submodules N of M such that $\sigma(\mathbf{Q}) \cap N = 0$. Since $0 \in \mathfrak{F}$, $\mathfrak{F}$ is nonempty. Next, partially order the set $\mathfrak{F}$ by inclusion. Use Zorn's lemma to find a maximal element N in $\mathfrak{F}$. Finally, use the maximality of N to conclude that M is the direct sum of $\sigma(\mathbf{Q})$ and N. The critical property of $\mathbf{Q}$ is that $\mathbf{Q}$ is "divisible"; namely, for each $x \in \mathbf{Q}$ and $n \in \mathbf{Z}$ there exists $y \in \mathbf{Q}$ such that $ny = x$.)

The reader should observe that Exercise 10 shows that $\mathbf{Q}$ is "dual" to the concept of a free module or a projective module over $\mathbf{Z}$. (See Theorem IV.4.3.)

» V · 2 FREE MODULES OVER A PID

In Chapter IV we discussed the procedure for constructing free modules. In Section V.1 we presented an explicit description of cyclic modules and the construction of modules out of given modules by way of the tensor product. The question that remains to be studied is, "How do we 'describe' a module?" The answer lies in the following theorem: which has already made its appearance in the construction of the tensor product.

THEOREM 1 · Let M be a module over the commutative ring R. There then exists a free R-module F and a surjective R-homomorphism $\rho : F \to M$.

Proof · Let F be the free R-module with free R-basis x_m, $m \in M$. We may then let ρ be the unique R-homomorphism, extending the map which sends x_m onto $m\ \forall\ m \in M$. It is clear that ρ is surjective. «

If K is the kernel of ρ in Theorem 1, it follows from the first isomorphism theorem that M is isomorphic to F/K. Thus Theorem 1 converts the description of R-modules to the description of R-submodules of free R-modules. Just as in the case of polynomials we may refer to K as the "module of relations" among the elements of M. In general, we may replace the index set M for the free R-basis of F by any set of generators of M. The effect is that F is replaced by a "smaller" free module. The kernel is then called the module of relations among the given generators of M. We may now repeat Theorem 1 in order to describe the module of relations; the new kernel may then be called the "module of relations of the module of relations," and so on. At this point we see that it is necessary to have some kind of shorthand notation to describe the situation. Schematically, this is done by what is known as an **exact sequence**. Briefly, suppose that we are given a sequence of R-modules A_i, $i \in \mathbf{Z}$, and R-homomorphism $\rho_i : A_i \to A_{i+1}$. The sequence

$$\cdots \longrightarrow A_{i-1} \xrightarrow{\rho_{i-1}} A_i \xrightarrow{\rho_i} A_{i+1} \longrightarrow \cdots$$

is then said to be **exact at A_i** if and only if $\ker \rho_i = \operatorname{im} \rho_{i-1}$. The sequence is said to be **exact** if and only if it is exact at each A_i.

We note that exactness refers to a relation between two successive homomorphisms. Often the same terminology will be used for sequences that terminate. In such cases we ignore the question of exactness at the ends. For example, a sequence of the form

$$0 \longrightarrow K \xrightarrow{\rho} F \xrightarrow{\sigma} M \longrightarrow 0$$

is exact if and only if the following conditions hold:

(a) ρ is an injective R-homomorphism (exactness at K).

(b) σ is a surjective R-homomorphism (exactness at M).

(c) $\ker \sigma = \operatorname{im} \rho$ (exactness at F).

Thus $F/\operatorname{im} \rho$ is naturally isomorphic to M under the R-homomorphism induced by σ.

We note that there is a unique R-homomorphism from the zero module into any R-module; namely, the zero element is sent onto the zero element. Similarly, there is a unique R-homomorphism from any R-module onto the zero module; namely, every element is sent onto the zero element. Thus these R-homomorphisms have been deleted from our diagram. In any case, the existence of the short exact sequence with F free over R is a summary of Theorem 1.

The procedure described after Theorem 1 by iteration may be summarized by saying that there is a long exact sequence of R-modules, where F_i are R-free for $i \in \mathbf{P}$.

$$\cdots \longrightarrow F_i \xrightarrow{\rho_i} F_{i-1} \longrightarrow \cdots \longrightarrow F_0 \xrightarrow{\rho_0} M \longrightarrow 0$$

This is usually called a ***free resolution*** of M. If there exists an integer $i \in \mathbf{P}$ such that $\operatorname{im} \rho_i = \ker \rho_{i-1}$ is free, we may select F_i and ρ_i such that ρ_i is injective. Thus we may select F_j, $j > i$, to be 0. In effect, the resolution terminates. A study of this phenomenon leads to what is known as the ***homological dimension of a module***. We shall make no attempt to discuss this aspect of the theory of modules. Indeed, we restrict ourselves to modules over PID's; the principal result is that F_1 is free when M is of finite type. Thus M may be described by a matrix, provided that M is of finite type; namely, if F_0 has free basis y_j, $1 \leqslant j \leqslant n$, and F_1 has free basis x_i, $1 \leqslant i \leqslant m$, such that ρ_1 is injective, sending x_i onto $\sum_j a_{ji} y_j$, the short exact sequence is then completely described by the matrix $(a_{ji}) \in M_{n,m}(R)$. We observe that for an arbitrary ring R there is no reason to expect $\ker \rho_0$ to be a submodule of finite type. Moreover, when $\ker \rho_0$ is of finite type, there is no reason to expect it to be free. When all F_i may be chosen to be free with a finite free basis, we can associate a sequence of matrices to describe the exact sequence. The exactness may then be described partially by imposing the condition that the product of each matrix by the preceding matrix is 0.

We now return to the problem of studying modules over PID's. The entire study is based on the following result.

THEOREM 2 · Let R be a PID and let M be a free R-module with free R-basis y_j, $1 \leqslant j \leqslant n$, $n \in \mathbf{P}^+$. Let $x_1 = \sum_i a_i y_i$, $a_i \in R$. Then there exist $x_2, \ldots, x_n \in M$ such that $\{x_i \mid 1 \leqslant j \leqslant n\}$ is a free

R-basis for M if and only if $R = Ra_1 + \cdots + Ra_n$; that is, 1 is a g.c.d. of $a_1, \ldots, a_n$.

Proof · We recall that Theorem IV.4.4 asserts that y_i, $1 \leqslant i \leqslant n$, is a free R-basis if and only if y_i is torsion-free $\forall\, i$ and M is the internal direct sum of the R-submodules Ry_i, $1 \leqslant i \leqslant n$.

Necessity · We consider the quotient module M/Rx_1. This is a free R-module with free R-basis $x_2 + Rx_1, \ldots, x_n + Rx_1$. Thus it is a torsion-free R-module. Suppose that $a_i = db_i\ \forall\, i$, where $d \in R$. We need to show that $d \mid 1$. Since x_1 is part of a free R-basis, we have $x_1 \neq 0$, and thus $d \neq 0$. However, $d(\sum_i b_i y_i + Rx_1) = x_1 + Rx_1 = Rx_1$. Since $d \neq 0$, we see that the torsion-freeness of M/Rx_1 implies that $\sum_i b_i y_i \in Rx_1$. This means that $\sum_i b_i y_i = c(\sum_i a_i y_i)$ for some $c \in R$. Since $y_1, \ldots, y_n$ is a free R-basis for M, it follows that $b_i = ca_i\ \forall\, i$; hence $b_i = cdb_i\ \forall\, i$. Since $x_1 \neq 0$, at least one $b_i \neq 0$. Since R is an integral domain, it follows that $cd = 1$ or $d \mid 1$. Thus we see that 1 is a g.c.d. of $a_1, \ldots, a_n$. Since R is a PID, this means that $R = Ra_1 + \cdots + Ra_n$.

Sufficiency · If $n = 1$, then $Ra_1 = R$ implies that a_1 is a unit. As we observed before, $a_1 y_1$ must be a free R-basis for $M = Ry_1$. We now proceed by induction on n. We may therefore assume that $n > 1$ and $a_n \neq 0$. Let $d \in R$ such that $Rd = Ra_2 + \cdots + Ra_n$ and $a_i = db_i$, $i > 1$. The hypothesis that R is a PID implies that d may be found. The hypothesis that $a_n \neq 0$ implies that $d \neq 0$. It follows that $R = Rb_2 + \cdots + Rb_n$. If we let $z_2 = \sum_{i>1} b_i y_i$ and consider the submodule $Ry_2 + \cdots + Ry_n$, then by induction we can find a free R-basis $z_2, \ldots, z_n$ for $Ry_2 + \cdots + Ry_n$. It follows that $y_1, z_2, \ldots, z_n$ is a free R-basis for M such that $x_1 = a_1 y_1 + dz_2$, $R = Ra_1 + Rd$. Therefore we may assume that $n = 2$.

Let $n = 2$, $1 = fa_1 + ga_2$, where $f, g \in R$. We then let $x_2 = -gy_1 + fy_2$. Since y_1, y_2 is a free R-basis for M and $1 = fa_1 + ga_2$, we see that x_1 and x_2 are both torsion-free; that is, Rx_1 and Rx_2 are free cyclic R-modules with x_1 and x_2 as free R-bases, respectively. It remains for us to show that M is the internal direct sum of Rx_1 and Rx_2 ; that is, to show that $M = Rx_1 + Rx_2$ and $0 = Rx_1 \cap Rx_2$. Since $fx_1 - a_2 x_2 = fa_1 y_1 + fa_2 y_2 + ga_2 y_1 - fa_2 y_2 = y_1$ and, similarly, $gx_1 + a_1 x_2 = ga_1 y_1 + ga_2 y_2 - ga_1 y_1 + fa_1 y_2 = y_2$, we see that $M = Rx_1 + Rx_2$. Now suppose that $z \in Rx_1 \cap Rx_2$; then $z = s(a_1 y_1 + a_2 y_2) = t(-gy_1 + fy_2)$ for suitable $s, t \in R$. Since y_1, y_2 is a free R-basis for M, it follows that $sa_1 = -gt$ and $sa_2 = ft$. However,

$s = s(fa_1 + ga_2) = -fgt + fgt = 0$. Thus $z = 0$ and $Rx_1 \cap Rx_2 = 0$ as desired. «

COROLLARY · Let R be a PID and let M be a free R-module with free R-basis $\{y_j \mid 1 \leqslant j \leqslant n\}$, $n \in \mathbf{P}$. Then any free R-basis for M has n elements.

Proof · Let $\{x_j \mid i \in I\}$ be a free R-basis for M. Each y_j can then be expressed as a *finite* sum $\sum_i b_{ij} x_i$. Thus a finite number of x_i's already generate M. This shows that I is a finite set. We may assume that $I = \{1, 2, \ldots, m\}$, $m \in \mathbf{P}$.

We make the agreement that the zero module is free with an empty set as a free R-basis. Thus we may assume that $n > 0$, hence $m > 0$. Let $x_1 = \sum_j a_j y_j$. Since M/Rx_1 is free with a free R-basis $x_2 + Rx_1, \ldots, x_m + Rx_1$ and $x_1 \neq 0$, the argument used in the necessity proof of Theorem 2 shows that $R = Ra_1 + \cdots + Ra_n$. Using Theorem 2 again, we can find a free R-basis $z_1, \ldots, z_n$ for M such that $z_1 = x_1$. Thus we may replace $\{y_1, \ldots, y_n\}$ with $\{z_1, \ldots, z_n\}$. Now, $M/Rz_1 = M/Rx_1$ has a free R-basis $z_2 + Rz_1, \ldots, z_n + Rz_1$. It follows from induction that $m - 1 = n - 1$, hence $m = n$. «

DEFINITION 1 · Let M be a free module with a finite set B as a free basis over the PID R. The cardinality of B is called the ***dimension*** of M over R.

The corollary of Theorem 2 shows that the dimension of the free module M is independent of the choice of B in the preceding definition. Actually, the assumption on the finiteness of B is not necessary. The details involve the use of the corollary and an argument from set theory. The interested reader may consult Excursion IV below.

The next question that we could raise is, "Can we define the dimension of a free R-module for an arbitrary commutative ring R?" The answer is *yes*, provided that $R \neq 0$. The case $R = 0$ is uninteresting, for the only module over the zero ring is the zero module. The details may be found in Excursion IV.

Excursion IV

LEMMA 1 · Let I be any infinite set. Let $\mathcal{F}(I)$ be the set of all finite subsets of I. Then I and $\mathcal{F}(I)$ have the same cardinality.

Proof · Let $\mathcal{F}_n(I)$ denote the set of all n-element subsets of I, $n \in \mathbf{P}$. Let $\rho : I \to \mathcal{F}$ be defined by $\rho(i) = \{i\} \in \mathcal{F}_1(I)\ \forall\, i \in I$. It is clear that ρ is an injection; thus $|I| \leqslant |\mathcal{F}(I)|$. Let I^n denote the cartesian product of I with itself n times, $n \in \mathbf{P}^+$. Let $\sigma_n : I^n \to \bigcup_{1 \leqslant j \leqslant n} \mathcal{F}_j(I)$ be defined by sending each element of I^n onto the subset formed by the components. It is clear that σ_n is surjective $\forall\, n \in \mathbf{P}^+$. It follows that $|\mathcal{F}_n(I)| \leqslant |I^n|$, $\forall\, n \in \mathbf{P}^+$.

Since I is infinite, it is a standard fact in set theory that $|I^n| = |I|\ \forall\, n \in \mathbf{P}^+$ and that a countable sum of $|I|$ is equal to $|I|$. The last statement is equivalent to $|\mathbf{Z} \times I| = |I|$. Since $\mathcal{F}(I)$ is the disjoint union of $\mathcal{F}_n(I)$, $n \in \mathbf{P}$, and since $\mathcal{F}_0(I)$ consists of the empty subset of I, it follows that $|\mathcal{F}(I)| \leqslant |I|$. Lemma 1 now follows from the Schröder-Bernstein theorem. «

LEMMA 2 · Let R be a nonzero commutative ring. Then R has a maximal ideal.

Proof · An ideal of R is distinct from R if and only if it does not contain the identity element 1 of R. Let $\mathcal{F}$ be the set of all ideals of R distinct from R. Since $R \neq 0$, the zero ideal is an element of $\mathcal{F}$. We partially order $\mathcal{F}$ by inclusion. From the preceding remark it is clear that the union of any linearly ordered set of proper ideals of R is again a proper ideal. (See the proof of Theorem IV.2.4.) Thus $\mathcal{F}$ is inductive in the sense of Zorn's lemma. From Zorn's lemma and Exercise IV.2.4, we see that a maximal element of $\mathcal{F}$ exists, and it is a maximal ideal of R. «

LEMMA 3 · Let R be a commutative ring and let A, B_i, $i \in I$, be R-modules. Then $A \otimes_R (\coprod_{i \in I} B_i)$ is R-isomorphic to $\coprod_{i \in I} (A \otimes_R B_i)$ in a natural way.

Lemma 3 is a generalization of Exercise 1.3. The details are left to the interested reader.

We now consider a procedure for constructing an S-module out of an S-module A, an R-module B, and a ring homomorphism $\iota : R \to S$, where R and S are both commutative rings. (The commutativity of S can be weakened slightly to the case in which $\iota(R)$ is contained in the center of S. Indeed, the most general situation requires the following given data: A is a left S-module and a right R-module such that the action of S and R commute; B is a left R-module. We leave the details to the interested reader.)

Since A is an S-module, we see that A is also an R-module through ι; namely, if $r \in A$, then the effect of r on $a \in A$ is that of $\iota(r)a$. We now let $A \otimes_R B$ be the R-module F/T described in Theorem 1.1. To each $s \in S$ we associate $\beta(s) \in \mathrm{Hom}_R(F, F)$ such that $(\beta(s))(x_{a,b}) = x_{sa,b}\ \forall\ a \in A,\ b \in B$. If we examine the effect of $\beta(s)$ on the generators of T, we see that $(\beta(s))(T) \subset T$. For example, $(\beta(s))(x_{\iota(r)a,b} - rx_{a,b}) = x_{s\iota(r)a,b} - rx_{sa,b} = x_{\iota(r)(sa),b} - rx_{sa,b} \in T$. The last equality requires that $\iota(r)s = s\iota(r)$. Thus $\beta(s)$ defines an element $\gamma(s)$ in $\mathrm{Hom}_R(F/T, F/T)$; namely, $(\gamma(s))(a \otimes b) = (sa) \otimes b\ \forall\ a \in A,\ b \in B$. It is easy to see that $A \otimes_R B = F/T$ is an S-module through γ; that is to say, $\gamma : S \to \mathrm{Hom}_R(A \otimes_R B, A \otimes_R B)$ is a homomorphism of rings. It is also easy to see that by restricting γ to $\iota(R)$ we obtain the precise structure of $A \otimes_R B$ as an R-module defined in Definition 1.3. We abbreviate $(\gamma(s))(a \otimes b)$ to $s(a \otimes b)$ and say that S acts on $A \otimes_R B$ by its action on the first component.

LEMMA 4 (Continuing with the notation of the preceding paragraph) · (a) If B is the direct sum of R-modules B_i, $i \in I$, then $A \otimes_R B$ is the direct sum of the S-modules $A \otimes_R B_i$, $i \in I$, where S acts on each $A \otimes_R B_i$ by acting on A.

(b) Let $A = S$ where S acts on A through left multiplication. Let $\theta \in \mathrm{Hom}_R(B, S \otimes_R B)$ be given by $\theta(b) = 1 \otimes b\ \forall\ b \in B$. Then $S \otimes_R B$ and θ have the following universal mapping property:

(*) Let C be any S-module. Consider C as an R-module through ι. Let $\varphi : B \to C$ be any R-module homomorphism. Then there exists a unique S-homomorphism $\varphi' : S \otimes_R B \to C$ such that $\varphi = \varphi' \circ \theta$.

Proof · The proof of (a) is straightforward. We omit the details.

(b) Since $S \otimes_R B$ is generated as an R-module by $s \otimes b = s(1 \otimes b)$, $s \in S$ and $b \in B$, it is clear that if φ' exists, then φ' must be the map which sends $1 \otimes b$ onto $\varphi(b)$. Thus it remains for us to show that φ' exists. To do this we consider the map $\rho : S \times B \to C$ given by setting $\rho(s, b) = s\,\theta(b)$, $\forall\ s \in S,\ b \in B$. Since $\iota(r)s = s\,\iota(r)\ \forall\ r \in R$ and $s \in S$ and since $\theta(rb) = \iota(r)\,\theta(b)\ \forall\ r \in R,\ b \in B$, according to the definition of C as an R-module, we see that ρ is a bi-R-homomorphism. Thus we can find $\varphi' : S \otimes_R B \to C$ such that $\rho = \varphi' \circ \otimes$, where $\otimes(s, b) = s \otimes b\ \forall\ s \in S,\ b \in B$. By taking s to be 1 we see that $\theta(b) = \rho(1, b) = \varphi'(1 \otimes b)\ \forall\ b \in B$. «

The S-module $S \otimes_R B$ is said to be the S-module obtained by ***changing the ground ring*** or by ***extending the ground ring***.

THEOREM 1 · Let R be a commutative ring distinct from zero. Let $X = \{x_i \mid i \in I\}$ and $Y = \{y_j \mid j \in J\}$ be free R-bases of the free R-module M. Then I and J have the same cardinality.

Proof · **Case 1** · R is a PID. From the corollary of Theorem 2.2, if either I or J is a finite set, then both I and J are finite sets and I and J have the same cardinality. Thus we may assume that I and J are both infinite sets. Let $\mathcal{F}(I)$ and $\mathcal{F}(J)$ be the set of all finite subsets of I and J, respectively. From Lemma 1 we know that $|I| = |\mathcal{F}(I)|$ and $|J| = |\mathcal{F}(J)|$.

Since Y is a free R-basis for M, each x_i may be written uniquely as a *finite* sum $\sum_j b_j y_j$, where $b_j \in R, j \in J$. We now define $f : I \to \mathcal{F}(J)$ by setting $f(i) = \{j \in J \mid b_j \neq 0$ in the equation $x_i = \sum_j b_j y_j\}$. We assert that if $T \in \mathcal{F}(J)$ then $f^{-1}(T) \in \mathcal{F}(I)$. To see this we observe that $i \in f^{-1}(T)$ implies that $x_i \in \sum_{t \in T} Ry_t$. Since each y_t can be expressed in terms of a finite number of x_k's, it follows that $x_i \in \sum_{s \in S} Rx_s$, where S is a sufficiently large finite subset of I. Thus $f^{-1}(T) \subset S$ and $f^{-1}(T) \in \mathcal{F}(I)$. It now follows that f^{-1} partitions I into the disjoint union of finite subsets. We claim that $|I| \leqslant |\mathbf{Z} \times \operatorname{im} f| \leqslant |\mathcal{F}(J)| = |J|$. The first of the inequalities follows from replacing each finite nonempty subset $f^{-1}(T)$ with a countably infinite set. Since the situation is symmetric, we also have $|J| \leqslant |I|$. Thus from the Schröder-Bernstein Theorem we have $|I| = |J|$.

Case 2 · R is arbitrary. By Lemma 2 we let N be a maximal ideal in R. Thus $S = R/N$ is a field; in particular, S is a PID. Let $\rho : R \to S$ be the natural projection map. We observe that if B is a free R-module with $\{u\}$ as a free R-basis the S-module $S \otimes_R B$ is a free S-module with $\{1 \otimes u\}$ as a free S-basis. This observation can be verified as follows:

Let $\varphi : B \to S$ be defined as the R-homomorphism such that $\varphi(u) = 1$, where S is considered as an R-module through left multiplication. From Lemma 4(b) we can find $\varphi' \in \operatorname{Hom}_S(S \otimes_R B, S)$ such that $\varphi'(1 \otimes u) = \varphi(u) = 1$. Since S is free as an S-module and has $\{1\}$ as a free S-basis, we can find $\sigma \in \operatorname{Hom}_S(S, S \otimes_R B)$ such that $\sigma(1) = 1 \otimes u$. Since $1 \otimes u$ generates $S \otimes_R B$ as an S-module, it follows that $\sigma \circ \varphi'$ and $\varphi' \circ \sigma$ are the respective identity maps. Thus our assertion follows.

From Lemma 3 we can conclude that $S \otimes_R M$ is a free S-module with $1 \otimes X$ and $1 \otimes Y$ as free S-bases. From Case 1 we see that

$| 1 \otimes X | = | 1 \otimes Y |$. It follows that $| I | = | 1 \otimes X | = | 1 \otimes Y | = | J |$. «

If the reader examines the proof of case 1 in the preceding theorem, he will find it easy to see that the following amusing result holds:

THEOREM 2 · Let M be a free module with an *infinite* set B as a free basis over the nonzero ring R. Then any free R-basis of M must have the same cardinality as B.

DEFINITION 1 · Let M be a free module over the nonzero commutative ring R. The cardinality of a free R-basis for M is called the ***dimension of M over R***. It is denoted by $\dim_R M$.

This concludes Excursion IV.

THEOREM 3 · Let R be a PID. Then M is a free R-module of finite dimension if and only if M is a torsion-free R-module of finite type.

Proof · The necessity follows from Exercise 7 and the hypothesis that M is R-free of finite type.

Conversely, let M be a torsion-free R-module of finite type. From Theorem 1 we let $\rho : F \to M$ be a surjective R-homomorphism such that F is a free R-module of minimal dimension over R. Let $\{y_j \mid 1 \leqslant j \leqslant n\}$ be a free R-basis for F. Since M is of finite type, we see that $n \in \mathbf{P}$. If $K = \ker \rho$ is zero, then M is isomorphic to F and we are done. Thus, proceeding by contradiction, we assume that $K \neq 0$ and $x = \sum_j a_j y_j \in K$, $x \neq 0$. Because R is a PID, $Ra_1 + \cdots + Ra_n = Rd$. Since $x \neq 0$, we see that $d \neq 0$, and we can find $b_i \in R$ such that $db_i = a_i \; \forall \, i$ and $R = Rb_1 + \cdots + Rb_n$. Let $x_1 = \sum_j b_j y_j$. Since ρ is an R-homomorphism and $x \in K$, we see that $d(\rho(x_1)) = \rho(x) = 0$. Since M is torsion-free and $d \neq 0$, we see that $\rho(x_1) = 0$ and $x_1 \in K$. From Theorem 2 we can find $x_2, \ldots, x_n \in F$ such that $x_1, \ldots, x_n$ form a free R-basis for F. Let $F' = Rx_2 + \cdots + Rx_n$. Since $\rho(x_1) = 0$, we see that $\rho(F') = \rho(F) = M$. Since F' is a free R-module of dimension less than that of F, we have arrived at a contradiction. Thus $K = 0$ and F is isomorphic to M. «

DEFINITION 2 · Let R be a commutative ring. Define R^0 as the zero module. If $n \in \mathbf{P}^+$, then R^n is defined as the set $M_{n,1}(R)$ together with addition defined by matrix addition. R^n is turned into an R-module by setting $r(a_i) = (ra_i)$. R^n is a free R-module of dimension n; it has the ***standard free R-basis*** e_i, $1 \leqslant i \leqslant n$, where e_i is the column vector, with 1 located at the ith row and 0's elsewhere.

Exercise 1 · In the notations of Definition 2 verify the following assertions:

(a) R^n is an R-module through the matrix multiplication, $\cdot : M_{n,n}(R) \times M_{n,1}(R) \to M_{n,1}(R)$, where $r \in R$ is identified with the scalar matrix $(r\delta_{ij})$.

(b) Let $\sigma \in \operatorname{Hom}_R(R^n, R^n)$ have matrix (a_{ji}) with respect to the standard R-basis so that $\sigma(e_i) = \sum_j a_{ji} e_j$. Then the action of σ on R^n can be described as the multiplication by (a_{ji}) in the map $\cdot : M_{n,n}(R) \times M_{n,1}(R) \to M_{n,1}(R)$.

Exercise 2 · In the notation of Definition 2 show that the following assertions are valid:

(a) $\sigma \in \operatorname{Hom}_R(R^n, R^n)$ is an R-automorphism (i.e., σ is a unit in the ring $\operatorname{Hom}_R(R^n, R^n)$.) if and only if the matrix (a_{ji}) of σ relative to the standard basis is invertible [that is, there exists a matrix $(b_{kj}) \in M_{n,n}(R)$ such that $(a_{ji})(b_{kj}) = (\delta_{ij}) = (b_{kj})(a_{ji})$].

(b) $\{\sum_j a_{ji} e_j \mid 1 \leqslant i \leqslant n, (a_{ji}) \in M_{n,n}(R)\}$ is a free R-basis for R^n if and only if (a_{ji}) is invertible.

(c) There is a bijection between the set of all free R-bases of R^n and the set of all invertible matrices in $M_{n,n}(R)$.

(d) The group of all R-automorphisms of R^n is transitive on the set of free R-bases of R^n. The stabilizer of a free R-basis is the identity subgroup.

Exercise 3 · Let R be a PID and let $x_1, \ldots, x_m \in R^n$. Show that if $x_1, \ldots, x_m$ generate R^n as an R-module then $m \geqslant n$. Show that equality holds if and only if $x_1, \ldots, x_m$ is a free R-basis for R^n. A set X of generators of an R-module M is called a ***minimal set of generators*** if and only if no proper subset of X can be a set of generators for M. Show that in the situation given it is possible that X is a minimal set of generators without being a free R-basis for M. Show that every free basis for an R-module is always a minimal set of generators. *Hint.* For the first assertion use Theorem IV.4.3 and Theorem 3 above. For the next to the last assertion consider the generators 2 and 3 of the **Z**-module **Z**.

DEFINITION 3 · Let M be a module over the commutative ring R. The group of all R-automorphisms of M is denoted by $GL_R(M)$

or by $\mathrm{Aut}_R(M)$. It is called the ***general linear group*** of M over R. If $M = R^n$ and the R-automorphisms are identified with their matrices relative to the standard basis, then $GL_R(M)$ is denoted by $GL(n, R)$.

DEFINITION 4 · Let R be a ring and $n \in \mathbf{P}^+$. Let M be a free R-module of dimension n with $B = \{x_i \mid 1 \leqslant i \leqslant n\}$ as a free R-basis of M. The following maps of B into M are called ***elementary transformations relative to B***:

$$\begin{aligned} T_{ji}(a) : x_i &\to x_i + ax_j \qquad j \neq i, a \in R \\ x_k &\to x_k \qquad k \neq i \\ D_i(a) : x_i &\to ax_i \qquad a \in U(R) \\ x_k &\to x_k \qquad k \neq i \\ P_{ij} : x_i &\to x_j \\ x_j &\to x_i \\ x_k &\to x_k \qquad k \neq i \text{ or } j \end{aligned}$$

The unique extensions of these maps to R-homomorphisms of M into M are denoted by the same symbol; they are also called ***elementary transformations*** relative to B.

The matrices associated with these elementary transformations with respect to the basis B are called ***elementary matrices***.

The R-endomorphisms of M defined by the equation $E_{kj}x_i = \delta_{ij}x_k$ are called "matrix unit" transformations with respect to B. The matrix of E_{kj} with respect to the basis B is then called a ***matrix unit***.

Exercise 4 · Write out explicitly the elementary matrices and the matrix units in $M_n(R)$.

Exercise 5 · In the notation of Definition 4 show that the matrix unit transformations form a free R-basis for the R-module $\mathrm{Hom}_R(M, M)$, where elements of R act according to multiplication by scalar matrices from the left. Show that the E_{ji}'s satisfy the relations $E_{ji} \circ E_{qp} = \delta_{iq}E_{jp}$. Express the elementary transformations in terms of the matrix unit transformations. Show that $T_{ji}(a) \circ T_{ji}(b) = T_{ji}(a + b)$, $D_i(a) \circ D_i(b) = D_i(ab)$, and $P_{ij}P_{ij} = (\delta_{ij}) = \sum_{i,j}\delta_{ij}E_{ij}$. Show that the elementary transformations of M are elements of $GL_R(M)$. Show that the inverse of an elementary transformation is again an elementary transformation.

Exercise 6 · In the notation of Definition 4 let $\theta \in \mathrm{Hom}_R(M, M)$ have matrix (a_{ji}) relative to the basis B. Verify the following assertions:

(a) The matrix of $\theta \circ T_{ji}(a)$ relative to B is obtained from (a_{ji}) by multiplying the jth column of (a_{ji}) by a and adding the result to the ith column. All columns other than the ith are unchanged.

(b) The matrix of $\theta \circ D_i(a)$ relative to B is obtained from (a_{ji}) by multiplying the ith column by a and leaving all other columns unchanged.

(c) The matrix of $\theta \circ P_{ji}$ is obtained from (a_{ji}) by interchanging the ith and the jth column and leaving all other columns unchanged.

(d) Analogous statements for $T_{ji}(a) \circ \theta$, $D_i(a) \circ \theta$, and $P_{ji} \circ \theta$ hold; where the roles of i and j are interchanged, the word "column" is replaced throughout by the word "row."

(We observe that as far as $T_{ji}(a)$ is concerned the index farthest away from θ is the index of the column or row of (a_{ji}) which is modified.)

The preceding exercise may be carried out also for the non-commutative case. However, the reader should be aware that multiplication of the entries of the matrices is the product in the opposite ring R°. Moreover, we must also keep track of the sides when we say "multiply a column by a and add it to another column." The reader should realize that it is sufficient to consider the case of 2×2 matrices to obtain the appropriate generalization of the assertions in Exercise 6.

We next observe that there is nothing special about the elementary transformations as elements of $GL_R(M)$. They all refer to a particular free basis of M. The point is that their matrices with respect to the selected free R-basis have special forms.

THEOREM 4 · Let R and $l: R \to \mathbf{Z}$ be a Euclidean domain. Let M be a free module with free R-basis $B = \{x_i \mid 1 \leqslant i \leqslant n\}$, $n \in \mathbf{P}^+$. Then $GL_R(M)$ is generated by the elementary transformations with respect to B.

Proof · In effect, the theorem asserts that every invertible matrix is representable as a finite product of elementary matrices.

We proceed by induction on n. Let H be the subgroup of $GL_R(M)$ generated by the elementary transformations with respect to B. Let $\theta \in GL_R(M)$. It is then sufficient to show that there exist $\rho, \sigma \in H$ such that $\sigma \circ \theta \circ \rho = 1$.

Let θ have the matrix (a_{ji}) with respect to B. Define $l(\theta)$ as $\min\{l(a_{ji}) \mid a_{ji}$ is a nonzero entry of $(a_{ji})\}$. Since (a_{ji}) is an invertible matrix, we see that $l(\theta) > l(0)$.

We now consider the "double coset" $H\theta H = \{\sigma \circ \theta \circ \rho \mid \sigma, \rho \in H\}$. From the preceding paragraph we see that $l(\gamma) > l(0)\ \forall\ \gamma \in H\theta H$. Let $\gamma \in H\theta H$ such that $l(\gamma) = \min\{l(\alpha) \mid \alpha \in H\theta H\}$. From Exercise 6 we see that left and right multiplication of the element γ by $P_{ji} \in H$ will interchange only two rows or two columns of the matrix of γ with respect to B. Thus $l(P_{qp} \circ \gamma \circ P_{ji}) = l(\gamma)$. We may therefore assume that the matrix (b_{ji}) of γ with respect to B satisfies the condition $l(\gamma) = l(b_{11}) \leqslant l(b_{ji})$ when $b_{ji} \neq 0$.

From Theorem 2 and Exercise 2 we see that $Rb_{11} + \cdots + Rb_{n1} = R$. Suppose that $b_{i1} \neq 0$ for some $i > 1$. We apply the Euclidean division algorithm to b_{11} and b_{i1}. Thus we can find $q, r \in R$ such that $b_{i1} = qb_{11} + r$, where $l(0) \leqslant l(r) < l(b_{11})$. Consider $T_{i1}(-q) \circ \gamma$; its matrix with respect to B then has b_{11} in the (1, 1)-position and r in the $(i, 1)$-position. Since $T_{i1}(-q) \in H$, we see that $T_{i1}(-q) \circ \gamma \in H\theta H$. Since $l(\gamma)$ is minimal, we see that $l(r) < l(b_{11}) = l(\gamma)$ implies that $r = 0$. Since the matrix of $T_{i1}(-q) \circ \gamma$ has b_{11} in the (1, 1)-position, we see that $l(T_{i1}(-q) \circ \gamma)$ must in fact be $l(b_{11}) = l(\gamma)$. Thus we may assume that γ has been chosen so that $b_{i1} = 0\ \forall\ i > 1$. It follows that $R = Rb_{11} + Rb_{21} + \cdots + Rb_{n1} = Rb_{11}$ or $b_{11} \in U(R)$. Thus $b_{11} \mid b_{1j}\ \forall\ j > 1$. From Exercise 6 we can right-multiply γ by a finite sequence of T_{1j}'s to obtain an element of $H\theta H$ whose matrix with respect to B has 0's in all $(1, j)$-positions, $j > 1$, and entries identical to that of γ in all other positions. Thus we may assume that γ has been chosen so that $l(b_{11}) = l(\gamma)$, $b_{11} \in U(R)$, and $b_{i1} = 0 = b_{1j}$, $\forall\ i, j > 1$. It follows that $\gamma(x_1) = b_{11}x_1$ and $\gamma(Rx_2 + \cdots + Rx_n) \subset Rx_2 + \cdots + Rx_n$. Since γ is an R-automorphism, it follows that the restriction of γ to $Rx_2 + \cdots + Rx_n$ must be an R-automorphism. Thus, by induction on n, we can find σ', $\rho' \in H$ such that $\sigma'(x_1) = x_1$, $\rho'(x_1) = 1$ and $\sigma' \circ \gamma \circ \rho'$ is the identity on $Rx_2 + \cdots + Rx_n$. It follows that $\sigma' \circ \gamma \circ \rho' = D_1(b_{11}) \in H$; hence γ and $\theta \in H$ as desired. «

When R is not a Euclidean domain, the relation between $GL_R(M)$ and the subgroup generated by the elementary transformations (with respect to some free R-basis of M) is not known in general. With some restrictions, results have recently been obtained concerning this problem. The interested reader may consult [5] and [6].

Exercise 7 · Let R be the field $\mathbf{Z}/(2)$. Show that $GL(2, R)$ is isomorphic to $\mathbf{S}_3$, the symmetric group of degree 3. Show that $T_{12}(1)$, $T_{21}(1)$, and P_{12} are not in the commutator subgroup of $GL(2, R)$.

Exercise 8 · Let R be a field and $n > 1$. Show that $D_i(c)\, D_j(c^{-1})$ is a commutator by computing $[D_j(c), P_{ij}]$. Compute $[D_i(a), T_{ij}(b)]$ and show that $T_{ij}(c)$ is a commutator whenever R has more than 2 elements. When R has more than two elements, show that $P_{ij}D_i(-1)$ is in the commutator subgroup of $GL(n, R)$ by computing $D_i(-1)\, D_j(-1)\, T_{ij}(-1)\, T_{ji}(1)\, T_{ij}(-1)$.

Exercise 9 · Let R be the field $\mathbf{Z}/(2)$ and $n > 2$. Show that $T_{ij}(1)$ and $T_{st}(1)$ are conjugate in $GL(n, R)$. Show that $T_{ij}(1)$ is a commutator by computing $[T_{ij}(1), T_{jk}(1)]$, i, j, k distinct. Show that P_{ij} is in the commutator subgroup as in Exercise 8, and thus show that $GL(n, R)$ is its own commutator subgroup.

Exercise 10 · Let R be a field, $n \in \mathbf{P}^+$. Let K be the subgroup of $GL(n, R)$ generated by all $T_{ij}(c)$, $D_i(d)\, D_i(d^{-1})$, and $P_{ij}D_i(-1)$. Let D be the subgroup generated by all $D_1(c)$. Show that K is a subgroup of the commutator subgroup of $GL(n, R)$ in all cases, except when $n = 2$ and R has two elements. Show that $GL(n, R) = KD$.

Eventually we shall see that $K \cap D = 1$ and K is the kernel of the "determinant" epimorphism from $GL(n, R)$ to $U(R) = R^\star$. K is then called the ***special linear group***, denoted by $SL(n, R)$, whereas $GL(n, R)$ is called the ***general linear group***. Except in the case when $n = 2$ and the field R has two elements, $SL(n, R)$ is the commutator subgroup of $GL(n, R)$.

» V·3 MODULES OF FINITE TYPE OVER A PID

We shall now obtain a structure theorem for modules of finite type over a PID.

THEOREM 1 · Let R be a PID and let M be an R-module of finite type. If M can be generated by m elements, then every R-submodule N of M may be generated by n elements, where $n \leqslant m$.

Proof · Form the exact sequence of R-modules $0 \to K \to F \to M \to 0$, where F is a free R-module of dimension n. Using the first isomorphism theorem, we may replace M by F. Thus we assume that M is a free R-module with free R-basis, $y_1, \ldots, y_m$. We now proceed by induction on m. Since N is an R-submodule, we see that $I_1(N) = \{a \in R \mid \exists\, y \in N$ such that $y - ay_1 \in Ry_2 + \cdots + Ry_m\}$ is an ideal of R. Indeed, $I_1(N)$ is the annihilator ideal of $y_1 + N + Ry_2 + \cdots + Ry_m$ in $M/(N + Ry_2 + \cdots + Ry_m)$. Since R

is a PID, we have $I_1(N) = Ra_1$, and there exists $x_1 \in N$ such that $x_1 - a_1 y_1 \in Ry_2 + \cdots + Ry_m$. Let $N_1 = N \cap (Ry_2 + \cdots + Ry_m)$. We assert that $N = Rx_1 + N_1$, for if $z = b_1 y_1 + \cdots + b_m y_m \in N$ then $b_1 \in I_1(N)$, hence $b_1 = da_1$ for some $d \in R$. It follows that $z - dx_1 = z - d(x_1 - a_1 y_1) - b_1 y_1 \in N_1$, hence $z \in Rx_1 + N_1$ and $N \subset Rx_1 + N_1$. It is obvious that $Rx_1 + N_1 \subset N$. By induction N_1 may be generated by $n - 1$ elements, $n - 1 \leqslant m - 1$. Hence N may be generated by n elements, $n \leqslant m$. «

COROLLARY · Let R be a PID and let M be a free R-module of dimension m. Then every R-submodule N of M is free and has dimension n, $n \leqslant m$. If M/N is also free, then $\dim_R(M) = \dim_R(N) + \dim_R(M/N)$.

Proof · The first part follows from Theorem 1, Theorem 2.3 and Exercise 2.3.

The second part follows from Theorem IV.2.4 and the fact that the dimension of the direct sum of two free modules is the sum of the dimensions. «

In view of the discussions carried out at the beginning of Section 2, we now state the following definition:

DEFINITION 1 · Let M be a module over the commutative ring R. A ***presentation*** of M is a short exact sequence of R-modules $F_1 \xrightarrow{\rho} F_0 \xrightarrow{\sigma} M \to 0$, where F_0 and F_1 are free R-modules, and ρ, σ are R-homomorphisms. (Thus σ is surjective and $\ker \sigma = \operatorname{im} \rho$.) The presentation is said to be of ***finite type*** if and only if both F_0 and F_1 are free R-modules of finite dimension. When the presentation is of finite type and $X = \{x_1, \ldots, x_m\}$ and $Y = \{y_1, \ldots, y_n\}$ are free R-bases of F_0 and F_1, respectively, then the matrix of ρ with respect to Y and X is called a ***presentation matrix*** of M. (Thus M is isomorphic to $F_0/\rho(F_1)$, where $\rho(F_1)$ is generated by $\rho(y_i) = \sum_j a_{ji} x_j$, $1 \leqslant i \leqslant n$; we note that the columns of the presentation matrix (a_{ji}) give the coefficients of the generators of $\rho(F_1)$ in terms of the basis X of M.)

The corollary of Theorem 1 can be restated in the following form:

THEOREM 2 · Let M be a module of finite type over a PID R. Then M admits a finite presentation. Indeed, the presentation can be chosen to be an exact sequence of R-modules of the form,

$$0 \to F_1 \xrightarrow{\rho} F_0 \xrightarrow{\sigma} M \to 0$$

The first statement in Theorem 2 actually holds for a much larger family of rings. The second statement, that we can select ρ to be an injective homomorphism, depends very much on the hypothesis that R is a PID. Our next task is to extract some common information from all possible finite presentations of the module M.

THEOREM 3 · Let F be a free module of dimension m over the PID R. Let E be an R-submodule of F. Then there is a free R-basis $\{x_1, \ldots, x_n\}$ of F and $d_i \in R$, $1 \leqslant i \leqslant n$, which satisfies the following conditions:

(a) $d_i \mid d_{i+1}$, $1 \leqslant i \leqslant n$, $d_m \neq 0$, $d_{m+1} = \cdots = d_n = 0$.
(b) $d_1x_1, \ldots, d_mx_m$ form a free R-basis for E.

Proof · From the corollary to Theorem 1 we see that E is a free R-module of dimension m, $m \leqslant n$. Let $Y = \{y_i \mid 1 \leqslant i \leqslant m\}$ and $Z = \{z_j \mid 1 \leqslant j \leqslant n\}$ be free R-bases of E and F, respectively. Thus there exists a matrix $(a_{ji}) \in M_{n,m}(R)$ such that $y_i = \sum_j a_{ji}z_j$, $1 \leqslant i \leqslant m$. We note in passing that (a_{ji}) is the presentation matrix of the inclusion map of E into F with respect to the bases Y and Z. We now consider the ideal $\sum_{i,j} Ra_{ji}$. Since R is a PID, this ideal is equal to Rd_1, where d_1 is a g.c.d. of the entries of the presentation matrix (a_{ji}). We show in the next paragraph that Rd_1 is independent of the choice of the bases Y and Z.

Let $Y' = \{y'_i \mid 1 \leqslant i \leqslant m\}$ and $Z' = \{z'_j \mid 1 \leqslant j \leqslant n\}$ be another pair of free R-bases. Then $y'_i = \sum_j b_{ji}y_j$ and $z'_j = \sum_k c_{kj}z_k$. It follows from Exercise 2.2 that $(b_{ji}) \in GL(m, R)$ and $(c_{kj}) \in GL(n, R)$. The presentation matrix of the inclusion map of E into F with respect to the bases Y', Z' is easily seen to be $(c_{kj})^{-1}(a_{ji})(b_{is}) = (a'_{ks})$. Thus by multiplying out the product of the matrices we see that $a'_{ks} \in Rd_1$ $\forall\, k, s$. Hence $Rd'_1 = \sum_{k,s} Ra_{ks} \subset Rd_1$. By symmetry we see that $Rd_1 = Rd'_1$. This proves the assertion that Rd_1 is independent of the choice of free bases for E and for F.

We now recall that for $a \in R - \{0\}$, the length of a, denoted by $l(a)$, is the total number of prime factors in the unique factorization of a in R (namely, if $a = up_1 \cdots p_t$, $u \in U(R)$, p_i is a prime in R, then $l(a) = t$). If (a_{ji}) is an arbitrary matrix in $M_{s,t}(R)$, then we define $l((a_{ji}))$ as the minimum length of the nonzero entries of (a_{ji}), provided that $(a_{ji}) \neq (0)$, and we let $l((0)) = -1$, where (0) denotes the zero matrix.

We observe that $d_1 = 0$ if and only if the presentation matrix (a_{ji}) is the zero matrix. This is equivalent to the assertion that $E = 0$.

In this case we simply take all d_i to be 0 and the proof is complete. Thus we may assume that $d_1 \neq 0$. The remaining steps of our proof are analogous to those used in the proof of Theorem 2.2.

We select the free R-bases Y and Z so that the presentation matrix has minimal length. By permuting the bases elements we may assume that $l(a_{11}) = l((a_{ji}))$. We assert that for such a choice $a_{11} \mid a_{j1}$ and $a_{11} \mid a_{1i}$ $\forall\, i, j$.

Suppose that $a_{11} \nmid a_{1i}$. Let $Ra_1 = Ra_{11} + Ra_{1i}$. Thus $a_1 \neq 0$ is a g.c.d. of a_{11} and a_{1i}. Since $a_{11} \nmid a_{1i}$, a_1 must be a proper divisor of a_{11}. Thus $l(a_1) < l(a_{11})$. Let $a_1 = b_1 a_{11} + b_i a_{1i}$ and set $y_1' = b_1 y_1 + b_i y_i$. Since $a_1 \mid a_{11}$ and $a_1 \mid a_{1i}$, we obtain $R = Rb_1 + Rb_i$ from the equation $a_1 = b_1 a_{11} + b_i a_{1i}$ by dividing out a_1 from both sides. From Theorem 2.2 we may complete y_1' to a free basis Y' for E. By substitution we see that $y_1' = a_1 y_1 + \sum_{i>1} r_i y_i$. Thus the presentation matrix with respect to Y' and Z has a_1 at the (1, 1)-position. Since $l(a_1) < l(a_{11}) = l((a_{ji}))$ and $a_1 \neq 0$, we see that the new presentation matrix has shorter length. This contradicts the choice of Y and Z. Thus $a_{11} \mid a_{1i}$ $\forall\, i$. Similarly, by working with the basis Z we can prove that $a_{11} \mid a_{j1}$ $\forall\, j$.

By using Exercise 2.6 we may assume that the presentation matrix (a_{ji}) satisfies $a_{j1} = 0 = a_{1i}$ $\forall\, i, j > 1$; namely, $y_1 = a_{11} z_1$ and $y_i = \sum_{j>1} a_{ji} z_j$ for $i > 1$.

We now assert that $a_{11} \mid a_{ij}$ $\forall\, i, j$. Suppose that $a_{11} \nmid a_{ji}$. Thus $i > 1$. From Exercise 2.6 we may obtain a new presentation matrix by adding the ith column of (a_{ji}) to the first column. This new presentation matrix would have a_{11} in the (1, 1)-position and a_{ji} in the (j, 1)-position. This would contradict the assertion proved two paragraphs earlier. Hence we conclude that $Ra_{11} = Rd_1$. By replacing z_1 with uz_1, $u \in U(R)$ such that $ua_{11} = d_1$ we may assume that $a_{11} = d_1$.

By working with the submodules $\sum_{i>1} Ry_i$ and $\sum_{j>1} Rz_j$ and using induction we may assume that $y_i = d_i z_i$, $2 \leqslant i \leqslant m$, and $d_i \mid d_{i+1}$, $2 \leqslant i \leqslant m - 1$. From the preceding paragraph we see that $d_1 \mid d_2$ also must hold. By setting $d_{m+1} = \cdots = d_n = 0$ we see that the assertions of our theorem are valid. «

This proof may be summarized as "diagonalizing a matrix by row and column operations." If R is a Euclidean domain, the diagonalization can be carried out in a finite number of steps, using only the operations described in Exercise 2.6.

We note that in the process of proving Theorem 3 we have shown Rd_1 as a uniquely determined ideal associated to the pair E, F. It is precisely the ideal generated by the entries of any presentation matrix. It is indeed true that the ideals Rd_i are all uniquely determined by the pair E, F independent of the free bases. However, we shall not give a direct description of these ideals at this time. $Rd_1 \cdots d_i$ is actually the ideal generated by the "determinants of the $i \times i$ minors of any presentation matrix."

In order to show that the ideals Rd_i are uniquely associated with the pair E, F, we introduce the following definition, in analogy with finite commutative groups.

DEFINITION 2 · Let M be a module over an integral domain R. If $r \in R$, $n \in \mathbf{P}^+$, then let $M(r^n) = \{x \in M \mid r^n x = 0\}$. (Using the commutativity of R, we see that $M(r^n)$ is an R-submodule.) Let $M_r = \bigcup_{n \in \mathbf{P}^+} M(r^n)$. [Since $M(r^n) \subset M(r^{n+1})$, it is easy to see that M_r is an R-submodule of M.] M_r is called the ***r*-torsion**, or ***r*-primary** component of M. M is said to be ***r*-torsion**, or ***r*-primary**, if and only if $M = M_r$. (The word *primary* is usually reserved for the case in which r is a prime in R.)

THEOREM 4 · Let M be a module over the PID R. Then the following assertions hold:

(a) If $a \mid b$ in R, then $M_a \subset M_b$.
(b) If $Rd = Ra + Rb$, then $M_d = M_a \cap M_b$.
(c) If $R = Ra + Rb$, then M_{ab} is the direct sum of M_a and M_b.

Proof · (a) Let $b = ac$, $c \in R$. If $x \in M_a$, then $a^m x = 0$ for some $m \in \mathbf{P}^+$. Thus $b^m x = c^m a^m x = 0$ and $x \in M_b$.

(b) From (a) we obtain $M_d \subset M_a \cap M_b$. Let $d = af + bg$ and $x \in M_a \cap M_b$. Thus we can find $m, n \in \mathbf{P}^+$, such that $a^m x = 0 = b^n x$. From the binomial theorem we have $d^{m+n} x = 0$; hence $x \in M_d$.

(c) Since $1^n x = x \ \forall\, x$, we have $M_1 = 0$. Using (a) and (b), we see that $0 = M_a \cap M_b$ and $M_a + M_b \subset M_{ab}$. Thus it remains for us to verify that $M_{ab} \subset M_a + M_b$. Let $x \in M_{ab}$ and $s \in \mathbf{P}^+$ such that $(ab)^s x = 0$. From $R = Ra + Rb$ we conclude that a and b have g.c.d. 1. Thus a^s and b^s have g.c.d. 1. Since R is a PID, this means that $R = Ra^s + Rb^s$. (This is the only place in the entire proof where we have used the hypothesis that R is a PID.) It follows that $1 = fa^s + gb^s$ for some $f, g \in R$. It is clear that $a^s x \in M_b$ and $b^s x \in M_a$. Thus $x = fa^s x + gb^s x \in M_a + M_b$. «

Exercise 1 · Let M be a module over an integral domain R. Show that the r-torsion component of M depends only on Rr.

THEOREM 5 · Let M be a torsion module over a PID R. Let $\{Rp_i \mid i \in I\}$ be the set of all nonzero prime ideals of R such that $M_{p_i} \neq 0$. Then M is the internal direct sum of the (uniquely determined) R-submodules M_{p_i}, $i \in I$.

Proof · Let $x \in M$ and $x \neq 0$. Since M is torsion, we see that $I(x)$, the annihilator ideal of x in R, is not zero. Since $x \neq 0$, we see that $I(x) \neq R$. Thus $I(x) = Rd$, where $d \neq 0$ and $d \nmid 1$. Let q_j, $1 \leqslant j \leqslant t$, be the distinct and nonassociate prime divisors of d. By induction on t and Theorem 4(c) we see that $x \in M_d$ and M_d is the direct sum of M_{q_j}, $1 \leqslant j \leqslant t$. If $M_{q_j} = 0$ for some j, then x would lie in M_r, where $r = \prod_{i \neq j} q_i$. This would imply that $r^n \in I(x)$ for some $n \in \mathbf{P}^+$. Thus $d \mid r^n$ and $q_j \mid r^n$, contradicting the form of r. Thus we see that $Rq_j = Rp_{i(j)}$ for suitable $i(j) \in I$. The argument just carried out shows that M is generated by M_{p_i}, $i \in I$; that is, every element of M is representable as a finite sum of elements from M_{p_i} for i ranging over a suitable finite subset of I. Furthermore, the submodule generated by any finite number of M_{p_i}'s is a direct sum according to Theorem 4(c). Thus each element of M has a unique representation as a finite sum of elements of M_{p_i}, $i \in I$. «

Exercise 2 · Let d be a nonzero element of the PID R. Suppose that $d = u(d) \prod_{1 \leqslant i \leqslant t} p_i^{\nu(i)}$ is the unique factorization of d in R, where p_i's are pairwise nonassociate primes in R. Show that the ring R/Rd is isomorphic to the direct product of the rings $R/Rp_i^{\nu(i)}$. Thus, in particular, they are R-isomorphic as modules under left multiplication by element of R. *Hint.* Use the Chinese remainder theorem (Exercise IV.5.2) and the hypothesis that R is a PID. (In particular, c is a g.c.d. of a and b if and only if $Rc = Ra + Rb$.)

THEOREM 6 (Fundamental theorem for modules of finite type over a PID) · Let M be a module of finite type over the PID R. Then M is isomorphic to the external direct sum of cyclic modules R/Rd_i, $1 \leqslant i \leqslant n$, $d_1 \nmid 1$, and $d_i \mid d_{i+1}$, $1 \leqslant i \leqslant n-1$, $n \in \mathbf{P}$. Moreover, the ideals Rd_i, $1 \leqslant i \leqslant n$, are uniquely determined by M; equivalently, the elements d_i, $1 \leqslant i \leqslant n$, are unique up to some unit factors in R.

Proof · From Theorem 2 we form a finite presentation of M corresponding to the exact sequence of R-modules:

$$0 \to E \xrightarrow{\iota} F \xrightarrow{\rho} M \to 0,$$

where ι is the inclusion map of E into F.

From Theorem 3 we can select a free R-basis $x_1, \ldots, x_n$ for F such that $d_1x_1, \ldots, d_mx_m$ form a free R-basis for E, where $d_i \mid d_{i+1}$,

$1 \leqslant i \leqslant m - 1$, $d_m \neq 0$, $m \leqslant n$. If $d_i \mid 1$, then $x_1, \ldots, x_i \in \ker \rho$ and we may delete $x_1, \ldots, x_i$ simultaneously from E and F. Thus we may assume that $d_1 \nmid 1$. If $m < n$, the we set $d_{m+1} = \cdots = d_n = 0$ as in Theorem 3. It is now immediate that $M \simeq F/E$ is R-isomorphic to the external direct sum of R/Rd_i, $1 \leqslant i \leqslant n$.

If $t(M)$ denotes the set of all torsion elements in M, then $t(M)$ is easily seen to be a uniquely determined R-submodule. From the preceding description it is clear that $t(M)$ is R-isomorphic to the external direct sum of R/Rd_i, $1 \leqslant i \leqslant m$, and that $t(M) = M_{d_m}$. The point is that $t(M) = \rho(Rx_1 + \cdots + Rx_m)$. Moreover, from the preceding description we see that $M/t(M)$ is a free R-module of dimension $n - m$. It follows that $n - m$ = number of zeros among the d_i's is uniquely determined by $M/t(M)$, hence by M. From Theorem 2.2 and Theorem IV.4.3 we see that M is R-isomorphic to the external direct sum of $t(M)$ and $M/t(M)$. Thus the structure theorem is reduced to the case in which $M = t(M)$; that is, M is a torsion-module.

By using Theorem 5 the case of a torsion-module M may be further reduced to the case in which M is p-primary for some prime $p \in R - \{0\}$. The point is that Exercise 2 may be used to extract the d's for each primary component of M from the d's for M; and, conversely, the d's for M can be built up from the d's of the various primary components of M.

We now assume that M is p-primary. Thus $d_i = p^{a(i)}$, $0 < a(1) \leqslant \cdots \leqslant a(n)$. The R-submodules $M(p^j)$, $j \in \mathbf{P}$, are uniquely determined, independent of any direct sum decomposition of M. If we select $k \in \mathbf{P}$ such that $a(k) \leqslant j < a(k+1)$, it is easy to see that $M(p^j) = \rho(Rx_1 + \cdots + Rx_k + Rp^{a(k+1)-j}x_{k+1} + \cdots + Rp^{a(n)-j})$. In fact, we see that $M(p^j)$ is R-isomorphic to the external direct sum of $R/Rp^{a(1)}, \ldots, R/Rp^{a(k)}, Rp^{a(k+1)-j}/Rp^{a(k+1)}, \ldots, Rp^{a(n)-j}/Rp^{a(n)}$. The uniquely determined R-module $M(p^{j+1})/M(p^j)$ may be considered as an R/Rp-module. Since Rp is a nonzero prime ideal in the PID R, R/Rd is a field. Thus $b_j = \dim_{R/Rp} M(p^{j+1})/M(p^j)$ is dependent only on M. If $s(j)$ denotes the number of $a(i)$'s greater than or equal to j, then $b_j = s(j) - s(j+1)$, $\forall j \in \mathbf{P}$; namely, b_j is precisely the number of $a(i)$'s equal to j. Hence $a(i)$'s are uniquely determined by M. Since the p-primary component of any module depends only on Rp, we see that the ideals $Rp^{a(i)}$ are uniquely determined by M. «

Exercise 3 · (a) Suppose that M is the direct sum of $\mathbf{Z}$-modules, $\mathbf{Z}/2\mathbf{Z}$, $\mathbf{Z}/12\mathbf{Z}$, $\mathbf{Z}/36\mathbf{Z}$, and $\mathbf{Z}/432\mathbf{Z}$. Find the direct sum decomposition of the primary components of M according to the fundamental theorem.

(b) Suppose that the primary components of the **Z**-module M have the direct sum decompositions given below:

$$M_2 \cong \mathbf{Z}/2\mathbf{Z} \amalg \mathbf{Z}/2\mathbf{Z} \amalg \mathbf{Z}/8\mathbf{Z}$$

$$M_3 \cong \mathbf{Z}/9\mathbf{Z} \amalg \mathbf{Z}/27\mathbf{Z} \amalg \mathbf{Z}/27\mathbf{Z}$$

Find the direct sum decomposition of M according to the fundamental theorem.

Exercise 4 · Let R be a PID and let F be a free R-module of finite type. Let E be a submodule of F. Show that the ideals Rd_i, where d_i are described in Theorem 3, are uniquely determined by E. Show that, for two submodules E_1 and E_2 of F, there is an R-automorphism of F sending E_1 onto E_2 if and only if the sequence of ideals associated to E_1 is the same as the sequence of ideals associated to E_2.

DEFINITION 3 · Let M be a module of finite type over a PID R. The ideals Rd_i, $1 \leqslant i \leqslant n$, determined in Theorem 6 are called the ***elementary ideals*** of the module M over R. The sequence of elements d_i, $1 \leqslant i \leqslant n$, determined (unique up to unit factors) in Theorem 6 are called the ***elementary divisors*** of M.

If we examine the various theorems leading up to the fundamental theorem, we would notice that we conveniently chose a finite presentation of the form $0 \to E \to F \to M \to 0$, where E had been considered as a submodule of F and $M \cong F/E$. In practice, it is much more convenient to give a finite presentation in the form of an exact sequence $F_1 \xrightarrow{\rho} F_0 \xrightarrow{\sigma} M \to 0$. In fact, as we mentioned before, it is enough to give the matrix of ρ with respect to free bases of F_0 and F_1 selected in some way. The problem is to extract the elementary divisors from the presentation matrix for ρ. Before we proceed any further, we remind the reader that $\dim_R F_0$ equals the number of rows in the matrix of ρ and that $\dim_R F_1$ equals the number of columns in the matrix of ρ. If we were to examine the proof of Theorem 3, or if we simply verified it directly, we would see that a replacement of the free basis $\{x_i \mid 1 \leqslant i \leqslant n\}$ of F_0 by a new free basis $x_i' = \sum_j b_{ji} x_j$, $1 \leqslant i \leqslant n$, would lead to the new presentation matrix $(b_{ji})^{-1}\mathrm{Mat}(\rho)$; whereas a replacement of the free basis $\{y_j \mid 1 \leqslant j \leqslant m\}$ of F_1 by a new free basis $y_j' = \sum_k c_{kj} y_k$ would lead to the new presentation matrix $\mathrm{Mat}(\rho)(c_{kj})$. The argument carried out in Theorem 3 may be adapted to show that the matrix of ρ can be diagonalized after a suitable change of bases in F_0 and in F_1; namely, we may assume that $\mathrm{Mat}(\rho) = (a_{ji})$ such that $a_{ji} = \delta_{ji}\, d_i$ and $d_i \mid d_{i+1}$, $1 \leqslant i < \min(m, n)$. It is now clear that the elementary ideals of M are precisely the proper ideals among $Rd_1, \ldots, Rd_n$, where $d_i = 0$ for $i > m = \dim_R F_0$. The point is that if ρ is not injective, then the kernel of ρ will show up in the form of several columns of zeros at the end of the diagonalization process. This may be verified as follows:

From the corollary to Theorem 1 we see that $\operatorname{im} \rho$ is a free R-module of dimension k, $k \leqslant n$. Using Theorem 3, we can choose free bases Z and X for $\operatorname{im} \rho$ and F_0, respectively, such that the presentation matrix of the inclusion map of $\operatorname{im} \rho$ into F_0 has the form described in Theorem 3. From Theorem IV.4.3 and the corollary to Theorem 1 we can find a free R-basis Y for F_1 such that the presentation matrix of $\rho : F_1 \to \operatorname{im} \rho$ with respect to Y, Z is a diagonal matrix with k ones supplemented by $m - k$ columns consisting of zeros. The presentation matrix of ρ with respect to Y, X is then the product of the first matrix on the right by the second matrix. The net result is that the first matrix has $m - k$ columns of zeros added onto its right. This concludes the proof of our assertion.

We summarize our discussions into the following theorem.

THEOREM 7 · Let M be a module of finite type over a PID. Let $(a_{ji}) \in M_{n,m}(R)$ be a presentation matrix of M. Then the following assertions hold:

(a) (a_{ji}) can be diagonalized by right multiplying with suitable elements of $GL(n, R)$ and left multiplying with suitable elements of $GL(m, R)$.

(b) The diagonalization can be carried out so that $d_i \mid d_{i+1}$ for each i, where d_i denotes the (i, i)-entry of the diagonalized matrix.

(c) Let t be chosen such that $d_t \mid 1$ and $d_{t+1} \nmid 1$. Define $d_i = 0$ for $i > m$. Then $Rd_{t+1}, \ldots, Rd_n$ are the elementary ideals of M.

Exercise 5 · The presentation matrices of some **Z**-modules are given below. Find the elementary ideals of the **Z**-modules and find the direct decomposition of the corresponding **Z**-modules according to the fundamental theorem.

$$\begin{pmatrix} 2 & 4 \\ 6 & 6 \\ 0 & 6 \end{pmatrix}, \quad \begin{pmatrix} 3 & 0 & 15 \\ 0 & -6 & 9 \end{pmatrix}, \quad \begin{pmatrix} 4 & 0 & 0 & 0 \\ 2 & 2 & 0 & 0 \\ 8 & 0 & 6 & 2 \end{pmatrix}, \quad \begin{pmatrix} 1 & 0 & 0 & 1 \\ 1 & 1 & 2 & 1 \\ 3 & 6 & 0 & 0 \\ 0 & 0 & 4 & 2 \\ 0 & 0 & 0 & 1 \end{pmatrix}.$$

Exercise 6 · Let $R = \mathbf{Q}[\lambda]$. The presentation matrices of some R-modules are given below. Find the elementary ideals of the R-modules and the direct decomposition of the corresponding R-modules according to the fundamental theorem.

$$\begin{pmatrix} \lambda - 1 & 5 \\ 4 & \lambda - 2 \end{pmatrix}, \quad \begin{pmatrix} \lambda & 1 & 0 \\ 0 & \lambda & 1 \\ 0 & 0 & \lambda \end{pmatrix}, \quad \begin{pmatrix} \lambda & 1 & 0 \\ 0 & \lambda & 0 \\ 0 & 0 & \lambda \end{pmatrix}, \quad \begin{pmatrix} \lambda & 1 \\ -1 & \lambda \end{pmatrix}, \quad \begin{pmatrix} \lambda & 1 \\ 1 & \lambda \end{pmatrix}.$$

Exercise 7 · Find the primary components of the modules described in Exercise 5 and Exercise 6.

Excursion V

Some of the results on modules of finite type over a PID can be generalized qualitatively to the class of "Noetherian rings". Quantitative results also exist; however, they are much more elaborate. Interested reader may consult [7].

LEMMA 1 · Let M be a module over the ring R. (R does not have to be commutative.) Then the following conditions are equivalent:

(a) Ascending chain condition holds for R-submodules of M.
(b) Maximum condition holds for R-submodules of M.
(c) Every R-submodule of M is of finite type.

Proof · (a) and (b) are equivalent according to Lemma IV.2.3.

(b) *implies* (c). Let N be an R-submodule of M. Let $\mathfrak{F}$ be the set of all R-submodule of finite type contained in N. Because 0 is such a submodule, it follows that $\mathfrak{F}$ is nonempty. Let A be a maximal element of $\mathfrak{F}$. Thus $A = Ra_1 + \cdots + Ra_n$. If $A \neq N$, we select $a_{n+1} \in N - A$ and take B to be $A + Ra_{n+1}$. It is clear that $B \in \mathfrak{F}$ and that A is a proper R-submodule of B. This contradicts the maximality of A in $\mathfrak{F}$. Thus $A = N$ and N is of finite type.

(c) *implies* (a). Let $M_0 \subset \cdots \subset M_i \subset M_{i+1} \subset \cdots$ be an increasing sequence of R-submodules of M. Let $N = \bigcup_i M_i$. Just as in the case of a PID, N is an R-submodule. Thus $N = Ra_1 + \cdots + Ra_n$. Since $M_i \subset M_{i+1}\ \forall\, i$, $\exists\, m \in \mathbf{P}$ such that $a_i \in M_m$ for each i. Thus $N \subset M_m \subset M_{m+k} \subset N\ \forall\, k \in \mathbf{P}$. It follows that the given sequence has at most a finite number of distinct R-submodules. Thus (c) implies (a). «

DEFINITION 1 · Let M be a module over the ring R (commutative or not). M is called a ***Noetherian R-module*** if and only if one of the three equivalent conditions of Lemma 1 holds in M. (Therefore all three conditions hold for M.) R is called a (left) ***Noetherian ring*** if and only if R is a Noetherian module over itself under left multiplication. (Thus we see that R is a (left) Noetherian ring if and only if every left ideal of R is finitely generated. In particular, a PID is a Noetherian ring.)

Exercise 1 · Let M be a module over the commutative ring R. Let S be the direct sum of R and M as R-modules. Define multiplication in S by the equation $(a, x)(b, y) = (ab, ay + bx) \ \forall\ a, b \in R, x, y \in M$. Verify the following assertions:

(a) The map that sends $a \in R$ onto $(a, 0)$ is an injective ring homomorphism of commutative rings.

(b) The map that sends $x \in M$ onto $(0, x)$ is an injective R-module homomorphism. The image is an ideal I such that $I^2 = 0$.

(c) Let $N \subset M$. Then N is an R-submodule of M if and only if its image under the map described in (b) is an ideal in S.

(d) The projection of S onto R is a surjective ring homomorphism such that the following sequence of R-modules is exact:

$$0 \to M \to S \to R \to 0,$$

where the first homomorphism is that described in (b).

Exercise 1 shows that modules can be converted to ideals in a bigger ring.

Exercise 2 · Let $0 \to A \to B \to C \to 0$ be an exact sequence of modules over the ring R (commutative or not). Show that B is a Noetherian R-module if and only if both A and C are Noetherian R-modules.

Exercise 3 · Use Exercises 1 and 2 to verify the following assertions:

(a) The direct sum of a finite number of Noetherian R-modules is again a Noetherian R-module.

(b) The ring S of Exercise 1 is a Noetherian ring if and only if the ring R is Noetherian and the R-module M is Noetherian.

(c) If R is a Noetherian ring, then an R-module M is Noetherian if and only if it is of finite type over R.

(d) If R is a Noetherian ring, every homomorphic image of R is again a Noetherian ring.

THEOREM 1 (Hilbert basis theorem) · Let X be a commuting indeterminate over the ring R. Then R is a left Noetherian ring if and only if $R[X]$ is a left Noetherian ring.

Proof · Since the substitution homomorphism that sends $f(X) \in R[X]$ onto $f(0)$ is a surjective ring homomorphism of $R[X]$ onto R, we may use Exercise 3(d) to conclude that $R[X]$ is left Noetherian implies that R is Noetherian.

Suppose that I is a left ideal of $R[X]$. We then define $I(j)$, $j \in \mathbf{P}$, to be the set $\{a \in R \mid a$ is the leading coefficient of a polynomial of degree j in $I\} \cup \{0\}$. It is easy to see that $I(j)$ is a left ideal of R and $I(j) \subset I(j+1)\ \forall\, j \in \mathbf{P}$. For the first of these two assertions we use the fact that I is closed under addition and left multiplication by elements of R; for the second of these two assertions we use the fact that I is closed under multiplication by X.

Before proving the remaining part of Theorem 1 we verify the following:

LEMMA 2 · Let X be a commuting indeterminate over the ring R. Let $I \subset J$ be left ideals of $R[X]$. Then $I(j) \subset J(j)\ \forall\, j \in \mathbf{P}$; moreover, $I = J$ if and only if $I(j) = J(j)\ \forall\, j \in \mathbf{P}$.

Proof · The first of the two assertions is obvious. Thus we need only verify the assertion that $I(j) = J(j)\ \forall\, j \in \mathbf{P}$ implies that $I = J$.

Suppose that $I \neq J$. Then we let $f(X)$ be a polynomial of least degree in $J - I$. Let $\deg f(X) = n$ and let a be the leading coefficient of $f(X)$. Thus $a \neq 0$ and $a \in J(n) = I(n)$. It follows that we can find $g(X) \in I$ such that $\deg g(X) = n$ and that $g(X)$ has a leading coefficient equal to a. Since $I \subset J$, we see that $f(X) - g(X) = h(X) \in J$. Since $f(X)$ and $g(X)$ both have the same degree and the same leading coefficient, it follows that $\deg h(X) < \deg f(X)$. Since $f(X) = g(X) + h(X)$ and $g(X) \in I$, we see that $f(X) \notin I$ implies that $h(X) \notin I$. Thus we have arrived at a contradiction to the choice of $f(X)$. It follows that I must be equal to J. «

We now return to the proof of Theorem 1. We let I_i, $i \in \mathbf{P}$, be an increasing sequence of left ideals of $R[X]$. Thus we have a doubly infinite array of left ideals of R as follows:

$$\begin{array}{ccccccc}
I_0(0) & \subset & I_0(1) & \subset \cdots \subset & I_0(j) & \subset & \cdots \\
\cap & & \cap & & \cap & & \\
I_1(0) & \subset & I_1(1) & \subset \cdots \subset & I_1(j) & \subset & \cdots \\
\cdots & & & & & & \\
I_i(0) & \subset & I_i(1) & \subset \cdots \subset & I_i(j) & \subset & \cdots \\
\cdots & & & & & &
\end{array}$$

Suppose that R is left Noetherian. Then, from Lemma 1, we let $I_m(n)$ be a maximal element of the set of left ideals $\{I_i(j) \mid i, j \in \mathbf{P}\}$. It follows that $I_p(q) = I_m(n)$ when $p \geqslant m$ and $q \geqslant n$. We now consider the set $\mathcal{F}(j) = \{I_i(j) \mid i \in \mathbf{P}\}$, $0 \leqslant j \leqslant n - 1$. From Lemma 1 we let $I_{T(j)}(j)$ be a maximal element of $\mathcal{F}(j)$. Thus $I_s(j) = I_{T(j)}(j)$ whenever $s \geqslant T(j)$. Finally, we let $N = \max\{T(0), ..., T(n-1), m\}$. We assert that $I_s(j) = I_N(j)\ \forall j \in \mathbf{P}$ whenever $s > N$. To see this we have the following cases:

Case 1 · $j \geqslant n$. Since $s > N \geqslant m$, we see that $I_s(j) = I_m(n) = I_N(j)$.

Case 2 · $j < n$. Since $s > N \geqslant T(j)$, we see that $I_s(j) = I_{T(j)} = I_N(j)$.

Using Lemma 2, we see that $I_s = I_N$ whenever $s > N$. Thus, from Lemma 1, we conclude that $R[X]$ is a left Noetherian ring. «

Exercise 4 · Let S be a ring. Suppose that R is a subring of S such that R is left Noetherian and that S is generated by R together with a finite set of elements of the center of S as a ring. Show that S is a left Noetherian ring.

Exercise 5 · Let R be a ring distinct from 0. Let X_i, $i \in I$, be a set of commuting indeterminates over R. Show that $R[X_i]_{i \in I}$ is left Noetherian if and only if (a) R is left Noetherian, and (b) I is a finite set.

Exercise 6 · Let X and Y be indeterminates over the field $\mathbf{Q}$. Show that the ideal generated by $X^n, X^{n-1}Y, ..., XY^{n-1}, Y^n$ in $\mathbf{Q}[X, Y] = R$ can not be generated by less than $n + 1$ elements, where $n \in \mathbf{P}$. *Hint.* Let this ideal be denoted by I_n. Show that I_n/I_{n+1} cannot be generated by less than $n + 1$ elements in R/I_{n+1}. The "total degree" of a polynomial in X and Y is a useful concept in this problem.

» V · 4 TENSOR ALGEBRAS, EXTERIOR ALGEBRAS, AND DETERMINANTS

If we examine the structure of $\mathrm{Hom}_R(M, M)$ as a ring, where M is a module over the commutative ring R, we see immediately that the map sending each $r \in R$ onto $h_r \in \mathrm{Hom}_R(M, M)$ (where h_r is the left multiplication by r on elements of M) leads to a ring homomorphism of R into the center of the ring $\mathrm{Hom}_R(M, M)$. We wish to formalize this concept.

DEFINITION 1 · Let A be a module over the commutative ring R. A together with a map $\cdot : A \times A \to A$ will be called an ***R-algebra*** if and only if $\cdot$ is a bi-R-homomorphism. Unless stated to the contrary, an R-algebra is assumed to be associative and to have an identity element. If A, B are R-algebras, then $\rho : A \to B$ is called an R-algebra homomorphism if and only if (a) ρ is an R-module homomorphism, (b) $\rho(a_1 a_2) = \rho(a_1)\,\rho(a_2)\ \forall\, a_1, a_2 \in A$, and (c) $\rho(1_A) = 1_B$. In particular, A is an R-subalgebra of B if and only if the inclusion map is an R-algebra homomorphism. Thus an R-subalgebra of B must contain the identity element of B.

Exercise 1 · Let A be a ring and let R be a commutative ring. Show that A is an R-algebra if and only if there is a specified ring homomorphism of R into the center of A.

Example 1 · A ring S is an R-algebra for each subring R of the center of S, where R acts on S through multiplication.

Example 2 · A ring S is a $\mathbf{Z}$-algebra through the unique ring homomorphism of $\mathbf{Z}$ into S.

We now repeat the example cited at the beginning of this section in order to fix our notation.

Example 3 · Let R be a commutative ring and let M be an R-module. If $r \in R$, then $rI : M \to M$ is defined by $(rI)(x) = rx\ \forall\, x \in M$. The map that sends r onto rI is easily seen to be a ring homomorphism of R into the center of $\mathrm{Hom}_R(M, M)$. Thus $\mathrm{Hom}_R(M, M)$ is an R-algebra through this ring homomorphism. The element $(rI) \circ \sigma$, $\sigma \in \mathrm{Hom}_R(M, M)$ is often written as $r\sigma$.

Since an R-algebra is, in particular, a ring, we can define an R-algebra module as a module over the ring structure. Since there is a specified ring homomorphism of R into the R-algebra, it is clear that every R-algebra module is automatically an R-module through the ring homomorphism described.

Exercise 2 · Let S be an R-algebra through $\sigma : R \to \mathfrak{Z}(S)$, where R is a commutative ring. Show that $\rho : S \times M \to M$ defines an R-algebra module structure on M if and only if (a) the restriction of ρ to $\sigma(R)$ turns M into an R-module and (b) the map that sends $s \in S$ into $\rho(s,\ ) : M \to M$, where $(\rho(s,\ ))(x) = \rho(s, x)\ \forall\, x \in M$, is an R-algebra homomorphism of S into $\mathrm{Hom}_R(M, M)$.

We now have the following very important special case.

Example 4 · Let V be a free module of finite dimension over the field R. Let T be a fixed element of $\mathrm{Hom}_R(V, V)$ and let $S = R[X]$ be the polynomial ring in the indeterminate X over the field R. From Exercise II.4.4 and Example 3 we see that there exists a unique R-algebra homomorphism $\rho : R[X] \to \mathrm{Hom}_R(V, V)$ such that $\rho(r) = rI\ \forall\, r \in R$ and such that $\rho(X) = T$.

The homomorphism ρ sends $f(X) = a_0 + a_1X + \cdots + a_nX^n$ onto $a_0I + a_1T + \cdots + a_nT^n$, where T^i is the composition of T with itself i times. We usually abbreviate the image of $f(X)$ into $f(T)$.

So far, we have not needed to assume the finite dimensionality of V. In Chapter VI we shall see that this assumption can be very useful. In any event, V becomes a module over $S = R[X]$. Since S is a PID, the results from the preceding sections can be applied in this situation. The interpretation of the finite dimensionality of V is simply that V is a torsion module of finite type over S.

DEFINITION 2 · Let M be a module over the commutative ring R. An R-algebra T together with an R-module homomorphism $\theta : M \to T$ is called a ***tensor algebra*** of M over R if and only if the following universal mapping property holds:

(*) For each R-algebra A and each R-module homomorphism $\varphi : M \to A$ there exists a unique R-algebra homomorphism $\varphi' : T \to A$ such that $\varphi = \varphi' \circ \theta$.

THEOREM 1 · Let M be a module over the commutative ring R. Then a tensor algebra of M over R exists and is unique up to a natural R-algebra isomorphism. Moreover, the map $\theta : M \to T$ associated with a tensor algebra T of M over R is injective.

Proof · As usual, the uniqueness involves a diagram-chasing argument. The details are left to the reader.

For the existence we let $T^0(M) = R$, $T^1(M) = M$, and by induction we set $T^{i+1}(M) = T^i(M) \otimes_R M$ for $i \in \mathbf{P}^+$. Thus each $T^i(M)$ is an R-module. We then let $T(M)$ be the direct sum of the R-modules $T^i(M)$, $i \in \mathbf{P}$. Using Exercise 1.3, we may identify $T^i(M) \otimes_R T^j(M)$

with $T^{i+j}(M)\ \forall\, i, j \in \mathbf{P}$. By using extension by linearity we can extend this identification to a map $\cdot : T(M) \times T(M) \to T(M)$ such that $a \cdot b = a \otimes b\ \forall\, a \in T^i(M),\ b \in T^j(M),\ i, j \in \mathbf{P}$. This map is clearly a bi-R-homomorphism; it satisfies the associative law and has an identity element $1 \in T^0(M) = R$. [All these are consequences of the identification of $T^i(M) \otimes T^j(M)$ with $T^{i+j}(M)$.] Thus $T(M)$ is an R-algebra. To illustrate the R-algebra structure of $T(M)$, we consider the following cases as examples:

(a) Let $r \in R$, $x_i \in M$, $1 \leqslant i \leqslant n$. Then $r(x_1 \otimes x_2 \otimes \cdots \otimes x_n) = r \otimes x_1 \otimes \cdots \otimes x_n = 1 \otimes x_1 \otimes \cdots \otimes x_{i-1} \otimes (rx_i) \otimes x_{i+1} \otimes \cdots \otimes x_n = x_1 \otimes \cdots \otimes x_{i-1} \otimes (rx_i) \otimes x_{i+1} \otimes \cdots \otimes x_n \in T^n(M)$. The long string of tensor products is to be read from left to right.

(b) Let x_1, x_2, and $x_3 \in M$; then $(x_1 \otimes x_2) \cdot x_3 = (x_1 \otimes x_2) \otimes x_3 = x_1 \otimes (x_2 \otimes x_3) = x_1 \cdot (x_2 \otimes x_3)$ under the identification. Indeed, we can obtain the result $(x_1 \cdot x_2) \cdot x_3 = x_1 \cdot (x_2 \cdot x_3)$.

(c) Let $x_1, x_2 \in M$. In general, $x_1 \otimes x_2$ and $x_2 \otimes x_1$ are not equal; namely, we do *not* use the identification of $A \otimes_R B$ with $B \otimes_R A$. The reader should view elements of $T(M)$ as noncommutative polynomials in M; namely, elements of $T(M)$ are finite sums of formal products of elements from M, where elements of M do not commute in general. [They may commute in special cases; for example, $(rx) \otimes (sx) = rs(x \otimes x) = (sx) \otimes (rx)$.]

In view of the equations in (b), we usually denote the multiplication in $T(M)$ by $\otimes$ rather than by $\cdot$.

The map $\theta : M \to T(M)$ is taken to be the identity map between M and $T^1(M)$. Thus θ is injective.

Suppose that $\varphi : M \to A$ is an R-module homomorphism of M into an R-algebra A. We define $\varphi' : T(M) \to A$ as follows:

(a) Since $T^0(M) = R$ is a free R-module with $\{1\}$ as a free R-basis, there exists a unique R-homomorphism $\varphi_0' : T^0(M) \to A$ such that $\varphi_0'(1) = 1_A$; φ_0' is precisely the ring homomorphism of R into the center of A that turns A into an R-algebra.

(b) Suppose that $\varphi_i' : T^i(M) \to A$ has been defined as an R-module homomorphism. Consider the map of $T^i(M) \times T^1(M)$ into A given by sending (s, x) onto $(\varphi_i'(s))(\varphi(x)) \in A$, $\forall\, s \in T^i(M), x \in T^1(M) = M$; since multiplication in A is a bi-R-homomorphism of $A \times A$ into A, it follows that the map just defined is also a bi-R-homomorphism. Thus from the definition of tensor product of modules we see that there exists a unique R-homomorphism $\varphi_{i+1}' : T^{i+1}(M) \to A$ such that $\varphi_{i+1}'(s \otimes x) = (\varphi_i'(s))(\varphi(x))\ \forall\, s \in T^i(M), x \in M$.

(c) Since $T(M)$ is the direct sum of $T^i(M)$, $i \in \mathbf{P}$, we see that the R-module homomorphisms of (a) and (b) define a unique R-module homomorphism $\varphi' : T(M) \to A$ such that the restriction of φ' to $T^i(M)$ is precisely φ'_i. By induction on n we quickly see that $\varphi'(x_1 \otimes \cdots \otimes x_n) = \varphi(x_1) \cdots \varphi(x_n)$. Since $T(M)$ satisfies the associative law under $\otimes$ by our definition, we see that φ' is an R-algebra homomorphism. It is clear that $\varphi' \circ \theta = \varphi$. Thus we have proved the existence of φ'. The uniqueness is an easy consequence of the equation $\varphi' \circ \theta = \varphi$ and the fact that φ' is an R-algebra homomorphism. «

DEFINITION 3 · Let M be a module over a commutative ring R. The tensor algebra of M over R constructed in Theorem 1 is called *the* tensor algebra of M over R. It is denoted by $T(M)$ or by $T_R(M)$; M is identified with $T^1(M)$, and the multiplication in $T(M)$ is denoted by $\otimes$.

It follows from Definition 1 that there is a bijection between the set of all R-algebra homomorphisms of $T(M)$ into a given R-algebra A and the set $\mathrm{Hom}_R(M, A)$. We observe that the latter has been given the structure of an R-module. However, the former is merely a set. If we wished, we could transport the structure, but we should note that the "sum" of two R-algebra homomorphisms between R-algebras is not in any natural way another R-algebra homomorphism. The transported sum does not correspond to the sum in the sense of adding the values of the homomorphisms for each element of $T(M)$. It does so only for elements in $T^1(M)$.

Exercise 3 · Let M be a module over a commutative ring R. Show that $T(M)$ is the R-subalgebra generated by M. [Note that under our convention an R-subalgebra must necessarily contain $T^0(M)$.] Show that $\coprod_{i \in \mathbf{P}^+} T^i(M)$ is an ideal of the R-algebra $T(M)$, where an ideal of an R-algebra is defined as an R-submodule of the R-algebra that is closed under both left and right multiplication by elements of the R-algebra given.

Exercise 4 · Let M be a free module over a commutative ring R with free R-basis B. Let $B^0 = \{1\}$; and for $i \in \mathbf{P}^+$ let B^i be the Cartesian product of the set B with itself i-times. Show that $T^i(M)$ is R-isomorphic to a free R-module with free R-basis B^i. Thus show that $\dim_R(T^i(M)) = (\dim_R(M))^i$. Show that when $\dim_R(M) = 1$ then $T(M)$ is isomorphic to the polynomial ring in one indeterminate over R. Show that when $\dim_R(M) > 1$, $T(M)$ is not commutative.

Exercise 5 · Let M and N be modules over a commutative ring R. Let $\rho \in \operatorname{Hom}_R(M, N)$. Show that ρ may be extended uniquely to an R-algebra homomorphism $T(\rho) : T(M) \to T(N)$. Show that the following assertions hold:

(a) If A, B, and C are R-modules and $f \in \operatorname{Hom}_R(A, B)$, $g \in \operatorname{Hom}_R(B, C)$, then $T(g \circ f) = T(g) \circ T(f)$. If $A = B$ and f is the identity map on A, then $T(f)$ is the identity map on $T(A)$.

(b) $T(\rho)$ sends elements of $T^i(M)$ into $T^i(N) \, \forall \, i \in \mathbf{P}$. Elements of $T^i(M)$ are called ***homogeneous tensors of degree i*** in M. Tensors of degree 0 are called ***scalars***. The restriction of $T(\rho)$ to $T^i(M)$ is denoted by $T^i(\rho)$. If $x_1, \ldots, x_n \in M$, then $(T(\rho))(x_1 \otimes \cdots \otimes x_n) = (\rho(x_1)) \otimes \cdots \otimes (\rho(x_n))$.

(c) $T(\rho)$ is surjective if and only if $\rho = T^1(\rho)$ is surjective.

(d) Every R-algebra is the R-algebra homomorphic image of a suitable $T(M)$, where M is a free R-module.

We see from Exercise 5(d) that $T(M)$ plays a role "dual" to that of $\operatorname{Hom}_R(A, A)$, where A is an R-module; namely, we saw that every R-algebra may be considered as an R-subalgebra of a suitable $\operatorname{Hom}_R(A, A)$; for example, A is the left R-module R under multiplication.

Exercise 6 · Let M, N be free modules over a commutative ring R with free R-bases $\{x_i \mid 1 \leqslant i \leqslant m\}$ and $\{y_j \mid 1 \leqslant j \leqslant n\}$, respectively. Let $\rho \in \operatorname{Hom}_R(M, N)$ have the matrix (a_{ji}) relative to these bases. Show that $T^2(\rho)$ has the matrix $(a_{ji}a_{lk})$ relative to the bases $\{x_i \otimes x_k \mid 1 \leqslant i, k \leqslant m\}$ and $\{y_j \otimes y_l \mid 1 \leqslant j, l \leqslant n\}$. Describe $T^i(\rho)$ in general. Compute $(x_1 + x_2) \otimes (x_2 \otimes x_3 + x_4 \otimes (-x_5) \otimes x_6)$.

Exercise 7 · Let M be a module of finite type over PID R. Assume that the elementary ideals of M are $Rd_1, \ldots, Rd_n$, where $d_i \mid d_{i+1}$, $d_1 \nmid 1$ and $d_m \neq 0$, $d_{m+1} = 0$. Show that the elementary ideals of $T^2(M)$ are $Rd_i + Rd_j$, $1 \leqslant i, j \leqslant n$, with the agreement that they are to be arranged according to divisibility. Thus $Rd_i + Rd_j = Rd_l$, where $l = \min(i, j)$ and there are n^2 elementary ideals. Find the elementary ideals of $T^i(M)$ in general. *Hint.* Use Exercise V.1.5. and Exercise 1.3 (tensor product is distributive with respect to direct sum).

DEFINITION 4 · Let M be a module over a commutative ring R. An R-algebra Λ is called an ***exterior algebra*** of M over R if and only if there exists an R-module homomorphism $\theta : M \to \Lambda$ that satisfies the following conditions:

(a) $(\theta(x))^2 = 0$, $\forall \, x \in M$,

(b) If S is any R-algebra and $\varphi : M \to S$ is any R-module homomorphism with $(\varphi(x))^2 = 0$, $\forall\, x \in M$, then there exists a unique R-algebra homomorphism $\varphi' : \Lambda \to S$ such that $\varphi = \varphi' \circ \theta$.

THEOREM 2 · Let M be a module over a commutative ring R. Then an exterior algebra of M over R exists and is unique up to a natural R-algebra isomorphism. Moreover, the map θ is injective.

Proof · Uniqueness involves a diagram-chasing argument and is omitted.

For existence we proceed as follows:

First, assume that $\varphi : M \to S$ is any R-module homomorphism of M into an R-algebra S. From Definition 1 and Theorem 1 we can extend φ to an R-algebra homomorphism φ_T of $T(M)$ into S. Next, assume that $(\varphi(x))^2 = 0\ \forall\, x \in M$. Because $\varphi_T(x \otimes x) = (\varphi(x))^2$, we see that $x \otimes x$ lies in $\ker \varphi_T$. It follows that the ideal of $T(M)$ generated by $\{x \otimes x \mid x \in M\}$ lies in the kernel of φ_T. If we let E be this ideal, it follows that $T(M)/E$ has the property (b) for an exterior algebra. If we let θ be the inclusion of M into $T(M)$, followed by the projection of $T(M)$ onto $T(M)/E$, then it is also clear that property (a) of an exterior algebra is satisfied by $T(M)/E$. Thus $T(M)/E$ is an exterior algebra of M.

The ideal E coincides with the additive subgroup generated by all $t(x \otimes x)t'$, where $x \in M$, $t, t' \in T(M)$. Using the distributive laws, we may assume that $t \in T^i(M)$, $t' \in T^j(M)$, $i, j \in \mathbf{P}$. Since $T^0(M) = R$, the subgroup so constructed is in fact an R-submodule. We note further that the generators of the subgroup all lie in $T^i(M)$, $i > 1$. Thus $E \cap T^i(M) = 0$ for $i = 0, 1$. It follows that the map θ is injective. «

We now give a more explicit description of the ideal E in $T(M)$.

LEMMA 1 · Let M be a module over a commutative ring R. Let E be the ideal of $T(M)$ generated by $\{x \otimes x \mid x \in M\}$ and let $E^i = E \cap T^i(M)$, $i \in \mathbf{P}$. Then the following hold:

(a) E is the internal direct sum of the R-submodules E^i, $i \in \mathbf{P}$.

(b) $T(M)/E$ is isomorphic, as an R-module, to the external direct sum of the R-modules $T^i(M)/E^i$, $i \in \mathbf{P}$, in a natural way.

Proof · We have already seen that $E^0 = E^1 = 0$. Let $E^{(2)}$ be the R-submodule of $T(M)$ generated by $\{x \otimes x \mid x \in M\}$. If A, B are R-submodules of $T(M)$, then let AB denote the R-submodule of $T(M)$ generated by $\{ab \mid a \in A, b \in B\}$. We now define inductively $E^{(i+1)} = T^1(M)E^{(i)} + E^{(i)}\, T^1(M)$. It follows by induction that $E^{(i)} \subset E^i$, $i \in \mathbf{P}$, where $E^{(0)} = E^{(1)} = 0$. Since the R-algebra $T(M)$ is generated by $T^0(M)$ and $T^1(M)$, we see that the internal direct sum of $E^{(i)}$, $i \in \mathbf{P}$, is an ideal of $T(M)$. This ideal contains $\{x \otimes x \mid x \in M\}$; hence it contains E. Since $E^{(i)} \subset E^i \ \forall\, i \in \mathbf{P}$, it is also contained in E. Thus we may conclude that $E^i = E^{(i)} \ \forall\, i \in \mathbf{P}$ and (a) holds.

(b) We now let $G^j = T(M)/(\sum_{i \neq j} T^i(M) + E^j), j \in \mathbf{P}$. Let G be the external direct sum of G^j, $j \in \mathbf{P}$, as an R-module. Let $\theta_j : T(M) \to G^j$ be the natural R-homomorphism of $T(M)$ onto G^j, $j \in \mathbf{P}$. Finally, let $\theta : T(M) \to G$ be given by $\theta(t) = (\theta_j(t))_{j \in \mathbf{P}}$. The map θ is uniquely determined by θ_j, $j \in \mathbf{P}$, because $T(M)$ is the direct sum of the R-modules $T^j(M)$ so that each $t \in T(M)$ is mapped onto 0 under θ_j for all but at most a finite number of indices $j \in \mathbf{P}$. This same reasoning also shows that θ is surjective and $\ker \theta = E$. Thus G and $T(M)/E$ are isomorphic as R-modules. Applying the first isomorphism theorem to the restriction of θ_i to $T^i(M)$, we see that $T^i(M)/E^i$ is isomorphic to G^i as R-modules. «

DEFINITION 5 · Let M be a module over a commutative ring R. The exterior algebra of M over R constructed in Theorem 2 is called *the* exterior algebra of M over R. It is denoted by $\Lambda_R(M)$ of simply by $\Lambda(E)$. The product of x and y in $\Lambda(M)$ is denoted by $x \wedge y$; that is, if $x = a + E$ and $y = b + E$, then $x \wedge y = a \otimes b + E$. $\Lambda^i(M)$ denotes the R-submodule $(T^i(M) + E)/E$. M is identified with $\Lambda^1(M)$.

Exercise 8 · Let M be a module over a commutative ring R. Show that, as an R-module, $\Lambda(M)$ is the internal direct sum of $\Lambda^i(M)$, $i \in \mathbf{P}$, corresponding to the external direct sum described in Lemma 1. Show that the following hold:

(a) $\Lambda^i(M) \wedge \Lambda^j(M) \subset \Lambda^{i+j}(M) \ \forall\, i, j \in \mathbf{P}$.

(b) Let $x_i \in \Lambda^i(M)$, $x_j \in \Lambda^j(M)$; then $x_i \wedge x_j = (-1)^{ij} x_j \wedge x_i$. *Hint.* Let $x, y \in M = \Lambda^1(M)$ and use $x \wedge x = y \wedge y = (x + y) \wedge (x + y) = 0$ to conclude that $x \wedge y = -y \wedge x$. Next use the fact that elements of $\Lambda^i(M)$ are finite sums of "exterior monomials of degree i," where an exterior monomial of degree i is any product of i elements from M.

Exercise 9 · Let M, N be modules over a commutative ring R. Let $\rho \in \mathrm{Hom}_R(M, N)$. Show that there exists a unique extension of ρ to an R-algebra homomorphism $\Lambda(\rho) : \Lambda(M) \to \Lambda(N)$. Show that the following assertions hold:

(a) If A, B, and C are R-modules and $f \in \text{Hom}_R(A, B)$, $g \in \text{Hom}_R(B, C)$, then $\Lambda(g \circ f) = \Lambda(g) \circ \Lambda(f)$; if $A = B$ and f is the identity map on A, then $\Lambda(f)$ is the identity map on $\Lambda(A)$.

(b) $\Lambda(\rho)$ sends elements of $\Lambda^i(M)$ into $\Lambda^i(N) \, \forall \, i \in \mathbf{P}$. Elements of $\Lambda^i(M)$ are called ***homogeneous exterior polynomials of degree i*** in M. The restriction of $\Lambda(\rho)$ to $\Lambda^i(M)$ is denoted by $\Lambda^i(\rho)$. If $x_1, \ldots, x_n \in M$, then $(\Lambda(\rho))(x_1 \wedge \ldots \wedge x_n) = (\rho(x_1)) \wedge \ldots \wedge (\rho(x_n))$.

(c) $\Lambda(\rho)$ is surjective if and only if $\rho = \Lambda^1(\rho)$ is surjective.

(d) Every $\Lambda(N)$ is the homomorphic image of a suitable $\Lambda(M)$, where M is a free R-module.

In Exercise 4 we obtained the R-module structure of $T^i(M)$ when M is a free R-module. We now describe the structure of $\Lambda^i(M)$, in which M is a free R-module and for which we prove the following lemma.

LEMMA 2 · Let B be the internal direct sum of submodules M and N as a module over a commutative ring R. Then the following assertions hold:

(a) The inclusion maps of M and N into B induce injective R-algebra homomorphisms of $\Lambda(M)$ and $\Lambda(N)$ into $\Lambda(B)$.

(b) If $\Lambda(M)$ and $\Lambda(N)$ are identified with R-subalgebras of $\Lambda(B)$ as in (a), then $\Lambda(B)$ is R-isomorphic to $\Lambda(M) \otimes_R \Lambda(N)$ as R-modules such that the following conditions are satisfied:

(1) $\Lambda^k(M)$ is naturally isomorphic to the direct sum of $\Lambda^i(M) \otimes_R \Lambda^j(N)$, where $i + j = k$.

(2) If $x \in M$ and $y \in N$, then $x + y$ is identified with $x \otimes 1 + 1 \otimes y$.

(3) If $x(i) \in \Lambda^i(M)$, $x(k) \in \Lambda^k(M)$, $y(j) \in \Lambda^j(N)$, $y(l) \in \Lambda^l(N)$, the product in $\Lambda(B)$ of the images of $x(i) \otimes y(j)$ and $x(k) \otimes y(l)$ is the image of $(-1)^{jk}(x(i) \wedge x(k)) \otimes (y(j) \wedge y(l))$.

Proof · (a) We have the exact sequence of R-modules, $0 \to M \xrightarrow{\rho} B \xrightarrow{\sigma} M \to 0$, where ρ is the inclusion and σ is the projection. The composition $\sigma \circ \rho$ is the identity on M. From Exercise 9 we conclude that $\Lambda(\sigma) \circ \Lambda(\rho) = \Lambda(\sigma \circ \rho)$ is the identity map of $\Lambda(M)$. Thus $\Lambda(\rho)$ is an injective R-algebra homomorphism of $\Lambda(M)$ into $\Lambda(B)$. Similarly, we may carry out the same argument for N. Thus (a) holds.

(b) We now identify $\Lambda(M)$ and $\Lambda(N)$ with R-subalgebras of $\Lambda(B)$. Thus $\wedge : \Lambda(M) \times \Lambda(N) \to \Lambda(B)$ defined by the multiplication $\wedge$

in $\Lambda(B)$ is a bi-R-homomorphism. Hence $\wedge$ induces an R-homomorphism of $\Lambda(M) \otimes_R \Lambda(N)$ into $\Lambda(B)$ as R-modules. In order to show that this is an R-isomorphism that satisfies (1), (2) and (3), we proceed to define an R-algebra structure on $A = \Lambda(M) \otimes_R \Lambda(N)$ and to construct the inverse map explicitly. In the process we show that (1), (2) and (3) hold.

From Exercise 8 we see that A is naturally the direct sum of A^k, $k \in \mathbf{P}$, where A^k is the direct sum of $\Lambda^i(M) \otimes_R \Lambda^j(N)$, $i + j = k$. We next note that $\Lambda^i(M) \otimes_R \Lambda^j(N) \otimes_R \Lambda^m(M) \otimes_R \Lambda^n(N)$ is R-isomorphic to $\Lambda^i(M) \otimes_R \Lambda^m(M) \otimes_R \Lambda^j(N) \otimes_R \Lambda^n(N)$ under a "twisting" isomorphism; namely, the two middle factors are interchanged *and* a factor $(-1)^{jm}$ is introduced. Thus the element $x \otimes y \otimes u \otimes v$ is sent onto the element $(-1)^{jm}x \otimes u \otimes y \otimes v$. Next we can construct an R-homomorphism of $\Lambda^i(M) \otimes_R \Lambda^m(M) \otimes_R \Lambda^j(N) \otimes_R \Lambda^n(N)$ into $\Lambda^{i+m}(M) \otimes_R \Lambda^{j+n}(N)$ by using the multiplications in $\Lambda(M)$ and $\Lambda(N)$ on the first two and the last two factors, respectively. The composition of the two R-homomorphisms then sends $x \otimes y \otimes u \otimes v$ onto $(-1)^{jm}(x \wedge u) \otimes (y \wedge v) \in A^{i+m+j+n}$. Using the direct sum decomposition of A, we may extend these R-homomorphisms uniquely to an R-homomorphism of $A \otimes_R A \to A$. Using Exercise 8 and the associativity of $\wedge$ on $\Lambda(M)$ and $\Lambda(N)$, we see that the corresponding bi-R-homomorphism of $A \times A$ into A is associative. The element $1 \otimes 1$ is clearly the identity element of the corresponding bi-R-homomorphism. Thus A becomes an R-algebra.

Let $x \in M$, $y \in N$ and consider the map $\theta : B \to A$ such that $\theta(x + y) = x \otimes 1 + 1 \otimes y$; θ is clearly an R-module homomorphism. Moreover, $\theta(x + y) \wedge \theta(x + y)$ is equal to the element $(-1)^{0 \cdot 1}(x \wedge x) \otimes (1 \wedge 1) + (-1)^{0 \cdot 0}(x \wedge 1) \otimes (1 \wedge y) + (-1)^{1 \cdot 1}(1 \wedge x) \otimes (y \wedge 1) + (-1)^{1 \cdot 0}(1 \wedge 1) \otimes (y \wedge y) = 0$. Thus θ may be extended uniquely to an R-algebra homomorphism from $\Lambda(B)$ into $A = \Lambda(M) \otimes_R \Lambda(N)$. Conversely, because the R-homomorphism of A into $\Lambda(B)$ induced by $\wedge$ is the multiplication of the elements of $\Lambda(M)$ by the elements of $\Lambda(N)$, it follows from Exercise 8 and the definition of the algebra structure on A that the R-homomorphism of A into $\Lambda(B)$ is an R-algebra homomorphism. Composition in one direction will give an R-algebra homomorphism of $\Lambda(B)$ into $\Lambda(B)$ that gives the identity on B. From the universal property of $\Lambda(B)$, this means that the composition is, in fact, the identity map. Composition in the other direction will give an R-algebra homomorphism of A into A that gives the identity map on $A^1 \cong B$. Because $\Lambda(M)$ and $\Lambda(N)$ are generated by M and N as R-algebras, the definition of multiplication in A shows that A is generated by A^1 as an R-algebra. This shows that the composition is the identity map on A. Thus we have proved that A and $\Lambda(B)$

are R-isomorphic as R-algebras. It follows directly from the definition of A, as an R-algebra, that all parts of (b) hold. «

We now give the explicit structure of $\Lambda(M)$, where M is a free R-module with a finite number of elements in a free R-basis. The structure shows that the number of elements in a free R-basis is independent of the choice of the free R-basis. Earlier we had arrived at this conclusion by way of Zorn's lemma. This time the proof does not directly involve its use.

THEOREM 3 · Let M be a free module with free basis $\{x_i \mid 1 \leqslant i \leqslant m\}$ over a commutative nonzero ring R. Then the following assertions hold:

(a) $\Lambda^i(M) = 0$ for $i > m$ and $\Lambda^i(M)$ is a free R-module with free R-basis $\{x_{j(1)} \wedge x_{j(2)} \wedge \cdots \wedge x_{j(i)} \mid 1 \leqslant j(1) < \cdots < j(i) \leqslant m\}$ when $0 \leqslant i \leqslant m$. The agreement is that when $i = 0$ the set consists of the identity element of $\Lambda(M)$.

(b) Any free R-basis of M consists of exactly m elements. Thus $\dim_R(M)$ is well-defined.

(c) $\Lambda^i(M)$ is a free R-module of dimension $\binom{m}{i}$ for $0 \leqslant i \leqslant m$.

Proof · (a) Let $m = 1$. It is immediate from Lemma 1 that $\Lambda(M)$ is R-isomorphic to $R \cdot 1 \amalg Rx_1$ as an R-module, where $\Lambda^0(M)$ is R-isomorphic to R, $\Lambda^1(M)$ is R-isomorphic to M, and $\Lambda^i(M) = 0$ for $i > 1$. The point is that, as an R-algebra, $\Lambda(M)$ is R-isomorphic to $R[X]/X^2R[X]$, where X is an indeterminate over R. Using induction and Lemma 2, we obtain all the parts of (a).

(b) Since R is not the zero ring, the number m is recognized as the largest integer n such that $\Lambda^n(M) \neq 0$.

(c) This follows from (a) and (b). «

COROLLARY · Let R be a commutative nonzero ring. Let M be a free R-module with the free R-basis $\{x_i \mid i \in I\}$, where I is linearly ordered by $<$. Then $\Lambda^i(M)$ is a free R-module with free R-basis $\{x_{j(1)} \wedge \cdots \wedge x_{j(i)} \mid j(1) < \cdots < j(i)$, where the j's lie in $I\}$.

Proof · Because each element of $\Lambda(M)$ is a finite sum of exterior monomials of finite degrees in the R-basis given, the assertion follows easily from Theorem 3. «

Exercise 10 · Let M be a free module over a commutative ring R with the free R-basis $\{x_i \mid 1 \leqslant i \leqslant m\}$. Compute the product

$(x_1 + x_2 \wedge x_5) \wedge (x_3 \wedge x_4 + x_2 \wedge x_6 \wedge x_5)$ and put the final expression in the form of a finite sum of the exterior monomials given in Theorem 3.

Exercise 11 · Let M be a module of finite type over a PID R having the elementary ideals $Rd_1, \ldots, Rd_n$, $d_1 \nmid 1$, $d_i \mid d_{i+1}$, $d_m \neq 0$, and $d_{m+1} = 0$. Show that $\Lambda^2(M)$ has elementary ideals $Rd_i + Rd_j$, $1 \leqslant i < j \leqslant n$. Thus the total number of elementary ideals is $\binom{n}{2}$ and $Rd_i + Rd_j = Rd_i$ when $i < j$. Describe $\Lambda^i(M)$ for all i.

Exercise 12 · Let M be a free module over a commutative ring R with free R-basis $\{x_i \mid 1 \leqslant i \leqslant m\}$. Let $\rho \in \operatorname{Hom}(M, M)$ have the matrix (a_{ji}) with respect to this basis. Show that the matrix of $\Lambda^2(\rho)$ with respect to the basis $\{x_i \wedge x_j \mid 1 \leqslant i < j \leqslant m\}$ is $(d_{j,i;l,k})$, $i < j$ and $k < l$, where $d_{j,i;l,k} = a_{jl}a_{ik} - a_{il}a_{jk}$.

LEMMA 3 . Let M be a free module of dimension 1 over a commutative ring R. Then the map that sends $r \in R$ onto $rI \in \operatorname{Hom}_R(M, M)$ is an R-algebra isomorphism.

Proof · Let $x \in M$ be a free R-basis. Then $(rI)(sx) = rsx$. Since x is R-free, we see that the map is an injective R-module homomorphism. If $\rho \in \operatorname{Hom}_R(M, M)$, then $\rho(x) = rx$ for a uniquely determined $r \in R$. Thus $\rho(sx) = s\rho(x) = srx = rsx = (rI)(sx)$; hence $\rho = rI$. It follows that our map is surjective. It is easily seen to be an R-algebra homomorphism. Thus our assertion follows. «

DEFINITION 6 · Let M be a free module of dimension m, $m \in \mathbf{P}^+$, over a nonzero commutative ring R. Let $\rho \in \operatorname{Hom}_R(M, M)$. From Theorem 3(c) and Lemma 3, there exists a unique element $\det(\rho) \in R$ such that $\Lambda^m(\rho) = \det(\rho)I$, where I is the identity map on $\Lambda^m(M)$. The element $\det(\rho)$ is called the ***determinant of*** ρ.

THEOREM 4 · Let R be a nonzero commutative ring. Let M be a free R-module with free R-basis $\{x_i \mid 1 \leqslant i \leqslant m\}$. Let ρ, σ, and $\tau \in \operatorname{Hom}_R(M, M)$. Then the following assertions hold:

(a) If, for some fixed i, $\rho(x_i) = \sigma(x_i) + r\tau(x_i)$ and $\rho(x_j) = \sigma(x_j) = \tau(x_j)$ for all $j \neq i$, then $\det(\rho) = \det(\sigma) + r \cdot \det(\tau)$.

(b) If, for some fixed i, j, $i \neq j$, $\rho(x_i) = \rho(x_j)$, then $\det(\rho) = 0$.

(c) $\det(\rho \circ \sigma) = \det(\sigma) \cdot \det(\sigma)$.

(d) $\det(I) = 1$, where I is the identity map of M.

Proof · Use Exercise 9(b).

Exercise 13 · Translate the statements in Theorem 4 into statements about matrices in $M_m(R)$. Compute the determinant of elementary transformations. Let ρ have the matrix (a_{ji}) with respect to the basis given in Theorem 4 and compute the determinant of ρ in terms of the a_{ji}'s when $m = 1, 2$, or 3. Show that the determinant produces a surjective group homomorphism from $GL_R(M)$ to $U(R)$. The kernel of this homomorphism is usually denoted by $SL_R(M)$; it is called the ***special linear group*** of the free R-module M. Assume that R is a field and show that $SL_R(M)$ coincides with the subgroup K defined in Exercise 2.10 after identifying $GL_R(M)$ with $GL(m, R)$ through the given basis.

We now give a second proof in the following exercise of the existence of a subgroup of index 2 in $\mathbf{S}_n$, $n > 1$.

Exercise 14 · Let M be a free $\mathbf{Z}$-module of dimension n. Let $\{x_i \mid 1 \leqslant i \leqslant n\}$ be a free $\mathbf{Z}$-basis for M. If $\rho \in \mathbf{S}_n$, define $f(\rho) \in \mathrm{Hom}_{\mathbf{Z}}(M, M)$ as the unique element such that $(f(\rho))(x_i) = x_{\rho(i)}\ \forall\, i$. Show that if $n > 1$, the map that sends ρ onto $\det(f(\rho))$ is a surjective homomorphism of $\mathbf{S}_n$ onto $U(\mathbf{Z}) = \{1, -1\}$. Thus show that the kernel of this homomorphism is a subgroup of index 2 in $\mathbf{S}_n$.

Exercise 15 · Let M be a free module of dimension n over a commutative ring R, where $n \in \mathbf{P}^+$. Let $(a_{ji}) \in M_n(R)$. To each free R-basis X of M we associate $\rho((a_{ji}), X) \in \mathrm{Hom}_R(M, M)$ such that the matrix of $\rho((a_{ji}), X)$ with respect to X is (a_{ji}). Let $\sigma \in GL_R(M)$ so that $X' = \sigma(X)$ is another free R-basis for M. Show that $\rho((a_{ji}), X') = \sigma \circ \rho((a_{ji}), X) \circ \sigma^{-1}$. Thus show that $\det(\rho((a_{ji}), X')) = \det(\rho((a_{ji}), X))$.

DEFINITION 7 · Let R be a commutative ring and let $(a_{ji}) \in M_n(R)$. Then the ***determinant*** of the matrix (a_{ji}) is defined as $\det(\rho((a_{ji}), X))$ in the notation of Exercise 15. This element of R is usually abbreviated to $\det(a_{ji})$.

Exercise 16 · Verify the following assertions for a commutative ring R:

(a) If $(a_{ji}), (b_{ji}) \in M_n(R)$, then $\det((a_{ji})(b_{ji})) = \det(a_{ji}) \cdot \det(b_{ji})$.

(b) If (b_{ji}) is obtained from $(a_{ji}) \in M_n(R)$ by multiplying the ith column of (a_{ji}) by $r \in R$, then $\det(b_{ji}) = r \cdot \det(a_{ji})$.

(d) If $(a_{ji}) \in M_n(R)$ has two identical columns, then $\det(a_{ji}) = 0$.

(e) If (a_{ji}), (b_{ji}), and (c_{ji}), and $(c_{ji}) \in M_n(R)$ have identical columns for $k \neq i$ and the ith column of (a_{ji}) is the sum of the ith column of (b_{ji}) and the ith column of (c_{ji}), then $\det(a_{ji}) = \det(b_{ji}) + \det(c_{ji})$.

(f) If (a_{ji}) is a diagonal matrix, that is, $a_{ji} = 0$ for $i \neq j$, then $\det(a_{ji}) = \prod_i a_{ii}$.

DEFINITION 8 · Let $(a_{ji}) \in M_{n,m}(R)$, R a nonzero commutative ring. If $1 \leqslant s \leqslant \min(m, n)$, then an $s \times s$ minor of (a_{ji}) is the matrix in $M_s(R)$ obtained from (a_{ji}) by deleting simultaneously $m - s$ columns and $n - s$ rows.

Exercise 17 · Write down some of the 2×2 minors for the matrices given in Exercise 3.6.

THEOREM 5 · Let E and F be free modules of dimension m, n with free bases X and Y over a nonzero commutative ring R, respectively. Suppose that $\rho \in \mathrm{Hom}_R(E, F)$ has the matrix (a_{ji}) with respect to X and Y. Then the following assertions hold:

(a) With respect to the "standard" free R-bases of $\Lambda^k(E)$ and $\Lambda^k(F)$ constructed out of X and Y according to Theorem 3, the entries of the matrix of $\Lambda^k(\rho)$ are precisely the determinants of the $k \times k$ minors of (a_{ji}). If $k > \min(m, n)$, these determinants are understood to be 0.

(b) The ideal $\mathfrak{D}_k$ of R generated by the determinants of the $k \times k$ minors of (a_{ji}) is independent of the choice of the free bases X and Y.

Proof · (a) Let $X = \{x_1, \ldots, x_m\}$ and $Y = \{y_1, \ldots, y_n\}$, respectively. Thus $\rho(x_i) = \sum_j a_{ji} y_j$. If we select the basis element $x_{i(1)} \wedge \cdots \wedge x_{i(k)}$ of $\Lambda^k(E)$ and the basis element $y_{j(1)} \wedge \cdots \wedge y_{j(k)}$ and examine the coefficient of $y_{j(1)} \wedge \cdots \wedge y_{j(k)}$ in the expansion of $\rho(x_{i(1)}) \wedge \cdots \wedge \rho(x_{i(k)})$, it is easy to see that the coefficient is the determinant of the $k \times k$ minor obtained by deleting the columns other than $i(1)$th,..., $i(k)$th columns and by deleting the rows other than $j(1)$th,..., $j(k)$th. To be more precise, we may let $\alpha : Rx_{i(1)} + \cdots + Rx_{i(k)} \to E$ be the inclusion map and let $\beta : F \to Ry_{j(1)} + \cdots + Ry_{j(k)}$ be the projection defined by $\beta(y_{j(t)}) = y_{j(t)}$, $1 \leqslant t \leqslant k$, and $\beta(y_s) = 0$ for $s \notin \{j(1), \ldots, j(k)\}$. It is then clear that the matrix of $\beta \circ \rho \circ \alpha$ with respect to the free bases exhibited is the $k \times k$ minor just described. Moreover, the coefficient of $y_{j(1)} \wedge \cdots \wedge y_{j(k)}$ in $\rho(x_{i(1)}) \wedge \cdots \wedge \rho(x_{i(k)})$ is the same as the coefficient of $y_{j(1)} \wedge \cdots \wedge y_{j(k)}$ in $(\beta \circ \rho \circ \alpha)(x_{i(1)} \wedge \cdots \wedge x_{i(k)})$. If we identify the free module $Rx_{i(1)} + \cdots + Rx_{i(k)}$ and the free module $Ry_{j(1)} + \cdots + Ry_{j(k)}$ by identifying their free bases in the order given, it is clear that the coefficient in question is the determinant of the minor mentioned earlier. This concludes the proof of (a).

(b) Let X' and Y' be free R-bases for E and F. Then we can find $\sigma \in GL_R(E)$ and $\tau \in GL_R(F)$ such that $\sigma(X) = X'$ and $\tau(Y) = Y'$. It is now easy to see that the matrix of ρ with respect to X' and Y' is the same as the matrix of $\tau^{-1} \circ \rho \circ \sigma$ with respect to X and Y; namely, if $x_i' = \sigma(x_i) = \sum_j b_{ji}x_j$ and $y_j' = \tau(y_j) = \sum_l c_{lj}y_l$, then the matrix of ρ with respect to X' and Y' is $(c_{lj})^{-1}(a_{ji})(b_{ji})$. From Exercise 9 we see that the matrix of $\Lambda^k(\rho)$ with respect to the standard bases constructed out of X' and Y' is the same as the matrix of $\Lambda^k(\tau^{-1} \circ \rho \circ \sigma) = \Lambda^k(\tau)^{-1} \circ \Lambda^k(\rho) \circ \Lambda^k(\sigma)$ with respect to the standard bases constructed from X and Y.

If we let $\mathfrak{D}_k(X, Y)$ denote the ideal in R generated by the entries of $\Lambda^k(\rho)$ with respect to the standard bases constructed from the free bases X and Y, the preceding paragraph shows that $\mathfrak{D}_k(X', Y') \subset \mathfrak{D}_k(X, Y)$. Since the situation is symmetric, we see that equality must hold. This shows that (b) holds. «

DEFINITION 9 · Let E, F be free modules of dimensions m and n over a nonzero commutative ring R. Let $\rho \in \mathrm{Hom}_R(E, F)$. The ideal in R generated by the entries of $\Lambda^k(\rho)$ with respect to some standard free R-bases is called the kth ***determinantal ideal of*** ρ. This ideal is denoted by $\mathfrak{D}(\Lambda^k(\rho))$. If $k > \min(m, n)$, then $\mathfrak{D}(\Lambda^k(\rho)) = 0$.

Exercise 18 · In the situation described in Definition 9 show that $\mathfrak{D}(\Lambda^k(\rho))$ is the ideal generated by the entries of the matrix of $\Lambda^k(\rho)$ with respect to any free R-bases for $\Lambda^k(E)$ and $\Lambda^k(F)$. (The point is that $\Lambda^k(E)$ in general may have free bases that do not occur among the standard bases constructed out of free bases of E.)

Exercise 19 · Let $0 \to E \xrightarrow{\rho} F \to M \to 0$ be a finite presentation of the module M over a PID R; namely, the sequence is an exact sequence of R-modules with E and F as free R-modules of finite dimension m and n, respectively. Let $Rd_1, \ldots, Rd_t$, $d_1 \nmid 1$, $d_i \mid d_{i+1}$, be the elementary ideals of M. Verify the following relations between Rd_i and the determinantal ideals of ρ:

(*) Let s be an integer such that $R = \mathfrak{D}(\Lambda^s(\rho)) \neq \mathfrak{D}(\Lambda^{s+1}(\rho))$. Then $R = \mathfrak{D}(\Lambda^1(\rho)) = \cdots = \mathfrak{D}(\Lambda^s(\rho))$; $\mathfrak{D}(\Lambda^{s+1}(\rho)) = Rd_1, \ldots, \mathfrak{D}(\Lambda^{s+t}(\rho)) = Rd_1 d_2 \cdots d_t$, and $s + t = n = \dim_R(F)$.

Hint. Select bases for E and F so that the matrix of ρ has the diagonal form described in Theorem 3.7.

DEFINITION 10 · Let M and N be modules over a ring R. Let ρ, $\sigma \in \mathrm{Hom}_R(M, N)$: ρ and σ are said to be ***GL*$_R$(*M*)-equivalent**, or simply ***M*-equivalent**, if and only if $\exists\, \tau \in GL_R(M)$ such that $\sigma = \rho \circ \tau$; ρ and σ are said to ***GL*$_R$(*N*)-equivalent**, or simply ***N*-equivalent**, if and only if $\exists\, \eta \in GL_R(N)$ such that $\eta^{-1} \circ \rho = \sigma$.

Exercise 20 · Let A and B be submodules of the module C over a ring R. A and B are said to be ***GL*$_R$(*C*)-equivalent** if and only if there is an R-automorphism θ of C such that $\theta(A) = B$. Verify the following assertions:

(a) If A and B are $GL_R(C)$-equivalent, then (1) A and B are R-isomorphic and (2) C/A and B/A are R-isomorphic.

(b) Let $R = \mathbf{Z}$, $C =$ direct sum of M_i, $i \in \mathbf{P}^+$, where M_{2j} is a cyclic group of order 4 generated additively by y_j, M_{2j+1} is a cyclic group of order 2 generated additively by x_j. Let A be the subgroup generated by x_1 and let B be the subgroup generated by $2y_1$. Then $A \cong B$, $C/A \cong C/B$, but A and B are not $GL_{\mathbf{Z}}(C)$ equivalent.

(c) In the notations of Definition 10, ρ and σ are $GL_R(M)$-equivalent if and only if $\ker \rho$ and $\ker \sigma$ are $GL_R(M)$-equivalent; ρ and σ are $GL_R(N)$-equivalent if and only if $\mathrm{im}\,\rho$ and $\mathrm{im}\,\sigma$ are $GL_R(N)$-equivalent.

Draw commutative diagrams to illustrate the definition introduced at the beginning of this exercise.

Exercise 21 · Let M and N be free R-modules of finite type over a PID R. Let ρ, $\sigma \in \mathrm{Hom}_R(M, N)$. Verify the following assertions:

(a) Two submodules A and B of M are $GL_R(M)$-equivalent if and only if M/A and M/B are R-isomorphic.

(b) ρ and σ are $GL_R(M)$-equivalent if and only if $M/\ker \rho$ and $M/\ker \sigma$ have the same elementary ideals.

(c) ρ and σ are $GL_R(N)$-equivalent if and only if $N/\mathrm{im}\,\rho$ and $N/\mathrm{im}\,\sigma$ have the same elementary ideals.

Interpret the concepts of $GL_R(M)$- and $GL_R(N)$-equivalence of ρ and σ in terms of change of bases in M and in N, respectively.

» V · 5 DERIVATIONS, TRACES, AND CHARACTERISTIC POLYNOMIALS

In Section V.4 we obtained the determinant of a matrix in $M_n(R)$ by way of the determinant of an element $\rho \in \text{Hom}_R(M, M)$, where M is a free module of dimension n over the commutative ring R. We now define the trace of a matrix by a similar procedure. Eventually, we shall see that these invariants are the coefficients of a polynomial associated to the given matrix. They are invariants in the sense that they do not depend on the choice of a free basis for the free module M.

DEFINITION 1 · Let A be an algebra over a commutative ring R. A map $D : A \to A$ is called an R-***derivation*** of A if and only if the following conditions hold:

(a) D is an R-module homomorphism.

(b) $D(ab) = D(a) \cdot b + a \cdot D(b) \; \forall \, a, b \in A$.

In the preceding definition we do not need to assume that A is an associative algebra nor that A has an identity element.

Example 1 · Let A be the polynomial ring in the indeterminate X over the commutative ring R. Let $D : R[X] \to R[X]$ be the R-module homomorphism defined by $D(X^n) = nX^{n-1} \; \forall \, n \in \mathbf{P}$. It is easy to verify that D is a derivation.

Example 2 · Let A be the set of all "infinitely differentiable" real-valued functions on the entire real line; then $D = d/dx$ is an $\mathbf{R}$-derivation of A, where $\mathbf{R}$ is the "field of real numbers" and A is considered as a subring of the ring of all $\mathbf{R}$-valued functions on $\mathbf{R}$.

Example 3 · Let A be any (associative and with an identity element) algebra over a commutative ring R. For each $x \in A$, let $I_x : A \to A$ be defined by $I_x(a) = xa - ax \; \forall \, a \in A$. Then I_x is an R-derivation of A. It is called the ***inner derivation*** induced by the element x of A.

Exercise 1 · Let D be a $\mathbf{Z}$-derivation of an R-algebra A with the identity element 1. Show that D is an R-derivation of A if and only if $D(r) = 0 \; \forall \, r \in R$. *Hint.* Apply D to $r = r \cdot 1$ and $1 = 1 \cdot 1$.

Exercise 2 · (Leibniz rule) Let A be a commutative, associative R-algebra with the identity element 1, where R is a commutative ring. Let D be an R-derivation of A. Verify the following assertions:

(a) $D(r \cdot 1) = 0 \;\forall\, r \in R$.

(b) If $a \in A$ and $n \in \mathbf{P}$, then $D(a^n) = na^{n-1} \cdot D(a)$, where $a^0 = 1$.

(c) $D^n(ab) = \sum_{0 \leqslant i \leqslant n} \binom{n}{i} D^{n-i}(a) \cdot D^i(b)$, where D^0 is the identity map on A and $D^{i+1} = D \circ D^i \;\forall\, i \in \mathbf{P}$.

We may raise the question, "What kind of algebraic structures can we place on the set of all R-derivations of an R-algebra?" By looking at the example furnished by Exercise 2(c) it is easy to become convinced that the composition of two derivations is generally not a derivation. We will now collect some of the properties of the set of R-derivations of the R-algebra A into the following exercise:

Exercise 3 · Let L be a module over a commutative ring R. L together with the map $[\ ,\ ] : L \times L \to L$ is called a ***Lie algebra*** over R if and only if the following conditions hold:

(a) $[\ ,\ ]$ is a bi-R-homomorphism. The image of (x, y) under $[\ ,\ ]$ will be denoted by $[x, y]$.

(b) (Antireflexive law) $[x, x] = 0 \;\forall\, x \in L$.

(c) (Jacobi identity) $[[x, y], z] + [[y, z], x] + [[z, x], y] = 0 \;\forall\, x, y, z \in L$.

Verify the following assertions:

(1) Let A be an associative R-algebra. Define $[a, b]$ to be $ab - ba \;\forall\, a, b \in A$. Then $A, +, [\ ,\ ]$ is a Lie algebra over R. This is usually denoted by A_L.

(2) Let B be an arbitrary R-algebra. Let $\mathrm{Der}_R(B)$ denote the set of all R-derivations of B. Then $\mathrm{Der}_R(B)$ is a Lie subalgebra of $\mathrm{Hom}_R(B, B)_L$.

(3) Let L be a Lie algebra over R. For each $x \in L$, define $\mathrm{ad}\, x : L \to L$ by setting $(\mathrm{ad}\, x)(y) = [x, y]$. Then ad x is an R-derivation of L. It is usually called the ***inner derivation*** of L induced by x. The map that sends $x \in L$ onto ad $x \in \mathrm{Der}_R(L)$ is a Lie algebra homomorphism over R. This homomorphism is called the ***adjoint homomorphism***; its kernel is called the ***center*** of L.

THEOREM 2 · Let M be a free module of finite dimension n over a commutative ring R. Let $\rho \in \mathrm{Hom}_R(M, M)$. Then there exist unique derivations D_T and D_Λ on $T(M)$ and $\Lambda(M)$ respectively such that the following assertions hold:

(a) The restrictions of D_T and D_Λ to $T^1(M) = M$ and to $\Lambda^1(M) = M$ are both equal to ρ.

(b) $D_T(T^i(M)) \subset T^i(M)$ and $D_\Lambda(\Lambda^i(M)) \subset \Lambda^i(M)\ \forall\, i \in \mathbf{P}$.

(c) D_T induces D_Λ.

Proof · If D is an R-derivation of the associative algebra A, then, by using induction, it is easy to see that for $a_1, \ldots, a_k \in A$, $D(a_1 \cdots a_k) = \sum_{1 \leqslant i \leqslant k} a_1 \cdots a_{i-1} D(a_i) a_{i+1} \cdots a_k$. It follows easily that the derivation D is uniquely determined by its value on any set of generators of the R-algebra A. The point is that any element of A is a finite sum of R-multiples of finite product of the generators. Since $T(M)$ and $\Lambda(M)$ are both generated by M, and therefore by a free R-basis for M, it follows that D_T and D_Λ, if they exist, must be uniquely determined by the condition (a).

Let $x_1, \ldots, x_n$ be a free R-basis for M. Because $\{x_{j(1)} \otimes \cdots \otimes x_{j(1)} \mid 1 \leqslant j(k) \leqslant n,\ 1 \leqslant k \leqslant i\}$ is a free R-basis for $T^i(M)$ and since $T(M)$ is the direct sum of the R-modules $T^i(M)$, $i \in \mathbf{P}$, there exists a unique R-homomorphism $D_T : T(M) \to T(M)$ such that $D_T(x_{j(1)} \otimes \cdots \otimes x_{j(i)}) = \sum_{1 \leqslant k \leqslant i} x_{j(1)} \otimes \cdots \otimes x_{j(k-1)} \otimes \rho(x_{j(k)}) \otimes x_{j(k+1)} \otimes \cdots \otimes x_{j(i)}$ for $1 \leqslant j(k) \leqslant n$, $1 \leqslant k \leqslant i$, $i \in \mathbf{P}$. If we group the first l factors together and call it a and then group the last $i - l$ factors together and call it b, it is clear that the first l terms on the right hand side give $D_T(a) \cdot b$, whereas the last $i - l$ terms on the right-hand side give $a \cdot D_T(b)$. Using the fact that D_T is an R-homomorphism and the fact that the elements exhibited above form an R-basis for $T(M)$, we see quickly that D_T is an R-derivation of $T(M)$ that satisfies (a) and (b).

Suppose that $x \in M$, then $D_T(x \otimes x) = \rho(x) \otimes x + x \otimes \rho(x) = (\rho(x) + x) \otimes (\rho(x) \otimes x) - \rho(x) \otimes \rho(x) - x \otimes x$. It follows that the ideal E in $T(M)$ generated by $x \otimes x$, $x \in M$ is mapped into itself under D_T. Thus we see that D_T induces a derivation D_Λ on $\Lambda(M) = T(M)/E$. Since $T^1(M) \cap E = 0$, it is clear that D_Λ coincides with ρ on $M = \Lambda^1(M)$. Indeed, if we substitute $\wedge$ for $\otimes$ in the defining equation for D_T, we would obtain the defining equation for D_Λ. It is now clear that (a), (b) and (c) all hold. «

DEFINITION 2 · Let M be a free module of dimension n over a commutative ring R. Let $\rho \in \mathrm{Hom}_R(M, M)$. There exists a unique element $\mathrm{tr}\,\rho \in R$ such that the restriction of D_Λ defined in Theorem 3 to $\Lambda^n(M)$ is equal to $(\mathrm{tr}\,\rho)I$. This element $\mathrm{tr}\,\rho$ is called the ***trace*** of ρ. [The existence and uniqueness of $\mathrm{tr}\,\rho$ follows from Theorem 4.3(c) and Lemma 4.3.]

THEOREM 3 · Let M be a free module with the free basis $X = \{x_i \mid 1 \leqslant i \leqslant m\}$ over a commutative ring R. Let $\rho \in \mathrm{Hom}_R(M, M)$ have the matrix $(a_{ji}) \in M_m(R)$ with respect to X. Then $\mathrm{tr}\, \rho = \sum_i a_{ii}$.

Proof · From hypothesis, $\rho(x_i) = \sum_j a_{ji} x_j$. Thus we see that $D_\Lambda(x_1 \wedge \cdots \wedge x_m) = \sum_i x_1 \wedge \cdots \wedge x_{i-1} \wedge \sum_j a_{ji} x_j \wedge x_{i+1} \wedge \cdots \wedge x_m = (\mathrm{tr}\, \rho) x_1 \wedge \cdots \wedge x_m$. Using the fact that $x_i \wedge x_i = 0$ and $x_i \wedge x_k = -x_k \wedge x_i$, the assertion follows immediately. «

DEFINITION 3 · Let M be a module over a commutative ring R; ρ and σ are said to be ***conjugate elements*** of $\mathrm{Hom}_R(M, M)$ if and only if there exists $\tau \in GL_R(M)$ such that $\sigma = \tau^{-1} \circ \rho \circ \tau$. Similarly, (a_{ji}), $(b_{ji}) \in M_m(R)$ are said to be ***conjugate*** if and only if there exists $(c_{ji}) \in GL(m, R)$ such that $(b_{ji}) = (c_{ji})^{-1}(a_{ji})(c_{ji})$.

Exercise 4 · In the situation described in Definition 3 assume that M is R-free of dimension m. Verify the following assertions:

(a) If X, X' are free R-bases for M, the matrix of ρ with respect to X is conjugate to the matrix of ρ with respect to X'.

(b) If ρ and $\rho' \in \mathrm{Hom}_R(M, M)$ have the same matrix with respect to the free bases X and X', then ρ and ρ' are conjugate.

(c) There exists a bijection μ between the set of conjugacy classes in $\mathrm{Hom}_R(M, M)$ and the conjugacy classes of $M_m(R)$ such that if ρ lies in the conjugacy class C the matrix of ρ with respect to any free basis of M lies in the conjugacy class $\mu(C)$.

Exercise 5 · Let M be a free module of dimension m over a commutative ring R. Let $\rho \in \mathrm{Hom}_R(M, M)$. Show that $\det \rho$ and $\mathrm{tr}\, \rho$ depend only on the conjugacy class of ρ in $\mathrm{Hom}_R(M, M)$. Show that the sum of the diagonal entries of a matrix and the determinant of a matrix depend only on the conjugacy class of the matrix in $GL(m, R)$.

DEFINITION 4 · Let R be a commutative ring. If $(a_{ji}) \in M_m(R)$, then $\mathrm{tr}(a_{ji}) = \sum_i a_{ii}$ is called the ***trace*** of the matrix (a_{ji}).

THEOREM 4 · Let M be a free module with the free basis $X = \{x_i \mid 1 \leqslant i \leqslant m\}$ over a commutative ring R. Then the following assertions hold:

(a) tr : $\mathrm{Hom}_R(M, M) \to R$ is an R-module homomorphism.

(b) tr is symmetric; that is, $\mathrm{tr}(\rho \circ \sigma) = \mathrm{tr}(\sigma \circ \rho)\ \forall\ \rho, \sigma \in \mathrm{Hom}_R(M, M)$.

(c) $\mathrm{Hom}_R(M, M)$ is a free module of dimension m^2 with the free basis $\{E_{ji} \mid 1 \leqslant i, j \leqslant m\}$.

(d) tr is surjective.

(e) If $m \in \mathbf{P}^+$, then ker tr has the following properties:

(1) It is a direct summand of $\mathrm{Hom}_R(M, M)$.

(2) It is a free module of dimension $m^2 - 1$ and E_{ji}, $i \neq j$, $E_{ii} - E_{11}$, $i > 1$, form a free basis for ker tr, where $E_{ji} \in \mathrm{Hom}_R(M, M)$ is characterized by $E_{ji}(x_k) = \delta_{ik} x_j\ \forall\ i, j, k$.

(3) It is generated by $\rho \circ \sigma - \sigma \circ \rho\ \forall\ \rho, \sigma \in \mathrm{Hom}_R(M, M)$.

(f) If $\pi \in \mathbf{S}_m$ and $\rho_\pi \in \mathrm{Hom}_R(M, M)$ is defined by $\rho_\pi(x_i) = x_{\pi(i)}\ \forall\ i$, then tr ρ_π is the number of fixed points of π on the set $\{1, \ldots, m\}$.

Proof · We first make the observation that $D_\Lambda(\rho) + D_\Lambda(\sigma)$ and $D_\Lambda(\rho + \sigma)$ are both R-derivations of $\Lambda(M)$ which extend $\rho + \sigma$ on M. Thus they are identical. By looking at $\Lambda^m(M)$, we obtain (a); (a) can also be verified directly by looking at the traces of the various matrices with respect to X.

(b) From Exercise 3(2) we see that $[D_\Lambda(\rho), D_\Lambda(\sigma)] = D_\Lambda(\rho) \circ D_\Lambda(\sigma) - D_\Lambda(\sigma) \circ D_\Lambda(\rho)$ and $D_\Lambda([\rho, \sigma]) = D_\Lambda(\rho \circ \sigma - \sigma \circ \rho)$ are both R-derivations of $\Lambda(M)$ which extend $\rho \circ \sigma - \sigma \circ \rho$ on M. Thus they must be equal. Because $\mathrm{Hom}_R(\Lambda^m(M), \Lambda^m(M))$ is isomorphic to the commutative ring R, we see that the effect of $D_\Lambda(\rho \circ \sigma - \sigma \circ \rho)$ on $\Lambda^m(M)$ must be 0; namely, $\mathrm{tr}(\rho \circ \sigma - \sigma \circ \rho) = 0$. (b) now follows from (a). We can also verify (b) directly by looking at the trace of the product of two matrices in $M_m(R)$.

(c) is obvious through the identification of $\mathrm{Hom}_R(M, M)$ with $M_m(R)$.

(d) is obvious through the observation that $\mathrm{tr}(aE_{11}) = a\ \forall\ a \in R$.

(e) Since R is a free R-module of dimension 1, (1) is a consequence of (d) and Theorem IV.4.3; (2) follows directly from the fact that $\mathrm{tr}(\sum_{i,j} a_{ji} E_{ji}) = \sum_i a_{ii}$. We already know from (b) that $\rho \circ \sigma - \sigma \circ \rho \in \ker \mathrm{tr}\ \forall\ \rho, \sigma \in \mathrm{Hom}_R(M, M)$. Conversely, we see that $[E_{ji}, E_{lk}] = \delta_{il} E_{jk} - \delta_{jk} E_{li}$. Thus the free basis for ker tr exhibited in (2) lie in the R-submodule generated by $\rho \circ \sigma - \sigma \circ \rho$, $\rho, \sigma \in \mathrm{Hom}_R(M, M)$. Hence (3) holds.

(f) is completely elementary. «

Exercise 6 · Let R be a commutative ring. Suppose that A is an R-algebra. A map $\rho : A \to R$ is called a ***symmetric linear function*** on A if and only if the following conditions hold:

(a) ρ is an R-module homomorphism.

(b) $\rho(ab) = \rho(ba) \; \forall \; a, b \in A$.

Verify the following assertions:

(1) The set of all symmetric linear functions on A is an R-submodule of $\mathrm{Hom}_R(A, R)$.

(2) If $A = \mathrm{Hom}_R(M, M)$, where M is a free R-module of finite positive dimension, the set of all symmetric linear functions on A is a free module of dimension 1 with $\{\mathrm{tr}\}$ as a free basis.

DEFINITION 5 · Let λ be an indeterminate over a commutative ring R. Let $(a_{ji}) \in M_n(R)$ so that $\lambda I_n - (a_{ji}) \in M_n(R[\lambda])$. The polynomial $\chi(\lambda, (a_{ji})) = \det(\lambda I_n - (a_{ji})) \in R[\lambda]$ is called the ***characteristic polynomial*** of the matrix (a_{ji}). By expanding the determinant it is easy to see that $\chi(\lambda, (a_{ji})) = \lambda^n - \mathrm{tr}(a_{ji})\lambda^{n-1} \pm \cdots + (-1)^n \det(a_{ji})$.

If M is a free R-module of dimension n and if $\rho \in \mathrm{Hom}_R(M, M)$ has the matrix (a_{ji}) with respect to some free R-basis of M, then $\chi(\lambda, \rho)$ is defined to be $\chi(\lambda, (a_{ji}))$ and it is called the ***characteristic polynomial*** of ρ.

We observe that, from the multiplicativity of the determinant function, the characteristic polynomial of a matrix depends only on its conjugacy class. It follows from Exercise 4(c) that the characteristic polynomial of ρ is well defined; moreover, this polynomial depends only on the conjugacy class of ρ in $\mathrm{Hom}_R(M, M)$. As a result, each of the coefficients of the characteristic polynomial defines a function from the conjugacy classes of $\mathrm{Hom}_R(M, M)$ to R. The determinant function and the trace function are especially interesting. The main reasons can be found in Theorem 4.4 and Theorem 4 already.

Exercise 7 · Let R be a subring of a commutative ring S. Let λ be an indeterminate over R. Show that under the substitution homomorphism $R[\lambda] \to R[a]/R$, $a \in S$, $\chi(a, (a_{ji})) = \det(b_{ji})$, where $b_{ji} = a\,\delta_{ji} - a_{ji} \; \forall \; i, j$, $(a_{ji}) \in M_n(R)$, $(b_{ji}) \in M_n(S)$.

Definition 5 is not very satisfactory because it depends on choosing a basis for M. In the following excursion we give another definition of the characteristic polynomial of $\rho \in \mathrm{Hom}_R(M, M)$, where M is a free module of finite dimension over the commutative ring R.

Excursion VI

DEFINITION 1 · Let M be a free module of finite dimension m over a commutative ring R. Let λ be an indeterminate over R and let $\rho \in \mathrm{Hom}_R(M, M)$. Let $S = R[\lambda]$. Then let $1 \otimes \rho$ be the S-homomorphism in $\mathrm{Hom}_S(S \otimes_R M, S \otimes_R M)$ which extends ρ. (Recall that $S \otimes_R M$ is the S-module obtained from R by ground ring extension; cf. Lemma 4 and its discussions in Excursion IV.) The polynomial $\chi(\lambda, \rho) = \det(\lambda I_m - 1 \otimes \rho)$ in $R[\lambda] = S$ is called the ***characteristic polynomial*** of ρ. It is monic of degree m.

The easiest way to understand Definition 1 is to work backward; namely, if we identify M with the free R-module $M_{m,1}(R)$, then ρ corresponds to left multiplication by the matrix $(a_{ji}) \in M_m(R)$. Because R is a subring of S, $M_m(R) \subset M_m(S)$. Thus multiplication by (a_{ji}) on $M_{m,1}(S)$ also makes sense. This corresponds to the action of $1 \otimes \rho$ on the module $S \otimes_R M$. The action of $\lambda I_m - 1 \otimes \rho$ on $S \otimes_R M$ is left multiplication of $M_{m,1}(S)$ by the matrix (b_{ji}), where $b_{ji} = \lambda\delta_{ji} - a_{ji}\ \forall\, i, j$. Thus we see that Definition 1 coincides with the definition introduced previously.

From Definition 5 of the preceding section we see that $\mathrm{tr}\,\rho$ and $\det \rho$ are the coefficients (up to a sign) of the characteristic polynomial of ρ. Now, $\mathrm{tr}\,\rho$ and $\det \rho$ have been defined by way of the exterior algebra $\Lambda(M)$, whereas $\det(\lambda I_m - 1 \otimes \rho)$ is defined by way of the exterior algebra $\Lambda_S(S \otimes_R M)$, $S = R[\lambda]$. It is rather natural to ask, "How are these entities related?" We shall investigate this question in the following paragraphs.

DEFINITION 2 · Let M be a free module of dimension m, $m \in \mathbf{P}$, over a commutative ring R. Let $S = R[\lambda]$ be the polynomial ring in the indeterminate λ over R. If $\rho \in \mathrm{Hom}_R(M, M)$, the element of $\mathrm{Hom}_S(S \otimes_R M, S \otimes_R M)$ which sends $s \otimes x$ onto $\lambda s \otimes \rho(x)$, $\forall\, s \in S$, $x \in M$, will be denoted by $\lambda \otimes \rho$; $\det(1 + \lambda \otimes \rho) \in S$ will then be called the ***d.t. characteristic polynomial*** of ρ, namely, $\Lambda_S^m(1 + \lambda \otimes \rho) = \det(1 + \lambda \otimes \rho)I$, where I stands for the identity map on $\Lambda_S^m(S \otimes_R M)$. (The initials d.t. stand for "determinant-trace.")

THEOREM 1 · Let $\sigma : R \to S$ be a ring homomorphism of a commutative ring R into a commutative ring S. Let M be a free module of dimension m over R with the free basis $X = \{x_i \mid 1 \leqslant i \leqslant m\}$. Suppose that S is not the zero ring. Then the following assertions hold:

(a) $S \otimes_R M$ is a free module of dimension m over S under the action of S acting on the first factor; $1 \otimes X = \{1 \otimes x_i \mid 1 \leqslant i \leqslant m\}$ is a free S-basis for $S \otimes_R M$.

(b) $S \otimes_R \Lambda_R(M)$ becomes an S-algebra under the definition given by setting $(s \otimes x) \cdot (t \otimes y) = (st) \otimes (x \wedge y)$, $\forall\, s,\ t \in S,\ x,\ y \in \Lambda_R(M)$. (This assertion holds whether M is free or not.)

(c) Let $\theta : S \otimes_R M \to S \otimes_R \Lambda_R(M)$ be defined by identifying $s \otimes x$ with the element $s \otimes x$ in $S \otimes_R \Lambda_R^1(M)$, $s \in S$, $x \in M$. Then $\Lambda(\theta)$ is an isomorphism between $\Lambda_S(S \otimes_R M)$ and $S \otimes_R \Lambda_R(M)$. (Again, this assertion holds whether M is free or not.)

The proof of Theorem 1 can be supplied easily by using the various universal mapping properties connected with the tensor product, with the exterior algebra, and with the freeness of a basis.

THEOREM 2 (Determinant-trace formula) · In the situation described in Definition 2 the following relation holds:

$$\det(1 + \lambda \otimes \rho) = \textstyle\sum_{i \in \mathbf{P}} \operatorname{tr}(\Lambda^i(\rho)) \cdot \lambda^i,$$

where the traces on the right side refer to the free R-modules $\Lambda^i(M)$, $i \in \mathbf{P}$. Moreover, if ρ has the matrix (a_{ji}) with respect to the free basis $X = \{x_1, \ldots, x_m\}$ of M, then $\operatorname{tr}(\Lambda^i(\rho))$ is the sum of the determinants of the $i \times i$ ***principal minors*** of (a_{ji}), where a principal $i \times i$ minor is obtained by deleting simultaneously the j_1th,..., j_{m-i}th row and column of (a_{ji}), $1 \leqslant j_1 < \cdots < j_{m-i} \leqslant m$.

Proof · By using Theorem 1 we obtain the following equation:

$$\begin{aligned} &\det(1 + \lambda \otimes \rho) \cdot (1 \otimes x_1) \wedge \cdots \wedge (1 \otimes x_m) \\ &= (1 + \lambda \otimes \rho)(1 \otimes x_1) \wedge \cdots \wedge (1 + \lambda \otimes \rho)(1 \otimes x_m) \\ &= (1 \otimes x_1 + \lambda \otimes \rho(x_1)) \wedge \cdots \wedge (1 \otimes x_m + \lambda \otimes \rho(x_m)). \end{aligned}$$

By expanding this last expression we obtain $\sum_{i \in \mathbf{P}} \lambda^i \otimes t_i$ where t_i is equal to the sum of all terms of the following form:

$$x_1 \wedge \cdots \wedge x_{j(1)-1} \wedge \rho(x_{j(1)}) \wedge x_{j(1)+1} \wedge \cdots \wedge x_{j(i)-1} \wedge \rho(x_{j(i)}) \wedge x_{j(i)+1} \wedge \cdots \wedge x_n\,,\ 1 \leqslant j(1) < \cdots < j(i) \leqslant n;\ t_i = 0 \text{ when } i > m.$$

It is clear that this term is simply $d_{j(1),\ldots,j(i)} x_1 \wedge \cdots \wedge x_n$, where $d_{j(1),\ldots,j(i)}$ is the determinant of the principal $i \times i$ minor of (a_{ji}) obtained by retaining only the $j(1)$th,..., $j(i)$th row and column.

Since the matrix of $\Lambda^i(\rho)$ with respect to the standard basis of $\Lambda^i(M)$ constructed from X has entries equal to the $i \times i$ minor determinants of (a_{ji}), it is clear that the diagonal entries of this matrix are exactly the principal $i \times i$ minor determinants. Thus our assertions are verified. «

» V · 6 DUAL MODULES

If we are given an $n \times n$ matrix over a ring R, then by interchanging the rows with the corresponding columns we obtain another matrix. By direct calculation we can show that this leads to an opposite isomorphism between $M_n(R)$ and $M_n(R^\circ)$. Our purpose is to interpret the meaning of this result. We first recall the following exercise:

Exercise 1 · Let S be a ring (commutative or not). Consider S as a left S-module under left multiplication by elements of S. Show that $\mathrm{Hom}_S(S, S)$ is oppositely isomorphic to S. Let $\sigma \in \mathrm{Hom}_S(S, S)$ and let $s \in S$; define $\sigma s : S \to S$ by setting $(\sigma s)(t) = \sigma(t) \cdot s \; \forall \, t \in S$. Show that this definition turns $\mathrm{Hom}_S(S, S)$ into a right S-module. Moreover, show that $\mathrm{Hom}_S(S, S)$ is a free module with the identity map of S as a free basis.

In the preceding exercise the important point is that S is a free *left* S-module with a single element in a free S-basis. The result is that $\mathrm{Hom}_S(S, S)$ is a free *right* S-module with a single element in a free S-basis. The result can be generalized to free S-modules with any finite set for a free S-basis. We recall that a right S-module can be considered as a left S°-module. This then gives a hint toward the interpretation of the process of interchanging rows and columns of a matrix. In order to avoid the complication arising from the lack of dimension for a free module over a general noncommutative ring, we concern ourselves with the commutative case only. The interested reader can carry out the noncommutative case by generalizing Exercise 1.

DEFINITION 1 · Let M be a module over a commutative ring R. $\mathrm{Hom}_R(M, R)$ is called the ***dual module*** of M or the ***R-dual*** of M. In this setup R is considered as a module over itself under left multiplication. We often write M^* for $\mathrm{Hom}_R(M, R)$ and the elements of M^* are often called the ***R-linear functions*** on M. We recall that the action of R on $\mathrm{Hom}_R(M, R)$ is given by $(rf)(x) = r \cdot f(x) \; \forall \, r \in R, f \in M^*$ and $x \in M$.

Exercise 2 · Let M and N be modules over a commutative ring R. Let $\rho \in \mathrm{Hom}_R(M, N)$. If $f \in N^*$, define $\rho^*(f)$ as $f \circ \rho$. Show that $\rho^* \in \mathrm{Hom}_R(N^*, M^*)$.

Exercise 3 · Let M be a module over a commutative ring R. Define $\langle \ , \ \rangle_M : M^* \times M \to R$ by setting $\langle f, x \rangle_M = f(x) \ \forall f \in M^*, x \in M$. Show that $\langle \ , \ \rangle_M$ is a bi-R-homomorphism.

DEFINITION 2 · Let M and N be modules over a commutative ring R. If $\rho \in \mathrm{Hom}_R(M, N)$, the element $\rho^* \in \mathrm{Hom}_R(N^*, M^*)$ defined in Exercise 2 is called the ***dual*** of ρ or the ***transpose*** of ρ; ρ^* is characterized by the equation $\langle f, \rho(x) \rangle_N = \langle \rho^*(f), x \rangle_M \ \forall f \in N^*, x \in M$, where $\langle \ , \ \rangle_M$ and $\langle \ , \ \rangle_N$ are defined as in Exercise 3. We often call $\langle \ , \ \rangle_M$ the ***evaluation map***. When there is no possibility of confusion, we often write $\langle \ , \ \rangle$ for $\langle \ , \ \rangle_M$.

Exercise 4 · Let M be a module of finite type over a PID M. Suppose that the elementary ideals of M are $Rd_1, \dots, Rd_m$, where $d_1 \nmid 1$, $d_i \mid d_{i+1}$, $d_n \neq 0$, and $d_{n+1} = 0$. Show that M^* is a free R-module of dimension $m - n$.

Exercise 5 · Let M be a free module over a commutative ring R with the free basis $X = \{x_i \mid i \in I\}$. Show that there exist unique elements $x_i^* \in M^*$, $i \in I$, such that $\langle x_i^*, x_j \rangle = \delta_{ij} \ \forall i, j \in I$. Show that the R-submodule of M^* generated by $\{x^* \mid i \in I\}$ is a free R-module with $\{x_i^* \mid i \in I\}$ as a free basis. Show that when I is a finite set this R-submodule of M^* is in fact all of M^*. In particular, when $\dim_R M$ is finite, M and M^* are isomorphic as R-modules. (The isomorphism depends on a choice of the free bases.)

Exercises 4 and 5 show that the dual module of a module can be determined explicitly in some special cases.

DEFINITION 3 · Let M be a free module over a commutative ring R with free basis $X = \{x_i \mid 1 \leqslant i \leqslant m\}$, $m \in \mathbf{P}^+$. Let $X^* = \{x^* \mid 1 \leqslant i \leqslant m\}$ be a free basis of M^* such that $\langle x^*, x_j \rangle = \delta_{ij} \ \forall i, j$. Then X and X^* are called ***dual bases*** for M and M^*. Often we also say that X^* is the free basis of M^* ***dual*** to the free basis X of M.

THEOREM 1 · Let M be a free module over a commutative ring R. Then the following assertions hold:

(a) The map $** : M \to M^{**}$ defined by $\langle x^{**}, f \rangle_{M^*} = \langle f, x \rangle_M = f(x) \ \forall x \in M, f \in M^*$ is an injective R-homomorphism of M into M^{**}.

(b) If $\dim_R M$ is finite, the map $**$ defined in (a) is a "natural" isomorphism.

(c) If $\dim_R M$ is finite, then, by selecting dual bases of M and M^*, there exists an R-isomorphism between M and M^*. The "natural" isomorphism between M and M^{**} is the composition of these dual bases isomorphisms.

Proof · All the assertions follow easily from Exercise 5. The word "natural" in (b) refers to the fact that the isomorphism does not depend on the choice of a basis. «

When $\dim_R M$ is infinite, Theorem 1(b) definitely fails. The point is that $\mathrm{Hom}_R(\coprod_{i \in I} M_i, R)$ is R-isomorphic to $\prod_{i \in I} \mathrm{Hom}_R(M_i, R)$. Thus, if R is a field and each M_i is one-dimensional, then $\dim_R \coprod_{i \in I} M_i$ is equal to the cardinality $|I|$. However, if $|I|$ is infinite, it can be shown that the dimension of the direct product is strictly greater than $|I|$. The general case may be reduced to the case of a field by considering the ground ring extension procedure mentioned in Excursion IV. We shall not pursue the details.

Some of the properties of the dual are completely formal. We collect the important ones into the following theorem.

THEOREM 2 · Let P be a fixed module over a commutative ring R. If M and N are R-modules and $\rho \in \mathrm{Hom}_R(M, N)$, define $\rho^{\#} : \mathrm{Hom}_R(N, P) \to \mathrm{Hom}_R(M, P)$ by setting $\rho^{\#}(f) = f \circ \rho \ \forall f \in \mathrm{Hom}_R(N, P) = N^{\#}$. (Thus the map $*$ is the special case in which $P = R$.) Then the following assertions hold:

(a) If $\sigma \in \mathrm{Hom}_R(M, M)$ is the identity map, then $\sigma^{\#}$ is the identity map on $M^{\#} = \mathrm{Hom}_R(M, P)$.

(b) If $\sigma \in \mathrm{Hom}_R(A, B)$ and $\tau \in \mathrm{Hom}_R(B, C)$, where A, B, and C are R-modules, then $(\tau \circ \sigma)^{\#} = \sigma^{\#} \circ \tau^{\#}$.

(c) If $A \xrightarrow{\sigma} B \xrightarrow{\tau} C \to 0$ is an exact sequence of R-modules, then $0 \to \mathrm{Hom}_R(C, P) \xrightarrow{\tau^{\#}} \mathrm{Hom}_R(B, P) \xrightarrow{\sigma^{\#}} \mathrm{Hom}_R(A, P)$ is an exact sequence of R-modules.

(d) If $0 \to A \xrightarrow{\sigma} B \xrightarrow{\tau} C \to 0$ is a ***split exact sequence*** of R-modules (that is, it is an exact sequence of R-modules and there exists $\theta \in \mathrm{Hom}_R(C, B)$ such that $\tau \circ \theta$ is the identity map on C; equivalently, $\sigma(A)$ is a direct summand of B.), then

$$0 \to \mathrm{Hom}_R(C, P) \xrightarrow{\tau^{\#}} \mathrm{Hom}_R(B, P) \xrightarrow{\sigma^{\#}} \mathrm{Hom}_R(A, P) \to 0$$

is a split exact sequence of R-modules.

Proof · (a) and (b) are straightforward.

(c) Since τ is surjective, it is immediate that $\tau^{\#}$ is injective. Since $\tau \circ \sigma$ is the zero map, it follows from (b) that $\sigma^{\#} \circ \tau^{\#}$ is the zero map. Thus $\operatorname{im} \tau^{\#} \subset \ker \sigma^{\#}$. Conversely, let $f \in \ker \sigma^{\#}$; thus $(\sigma^{\#}(f))(a) = f(\sigma(a)) = 0 \;\forall\, a \in A$. Therefore f may be considered as an R-homomorphism of $B/\sigma(A)$ into P; but by the exactness hypothesis and the first isomorphism theorem $B/\sigma(A)$ is isomorphic to C under the map induced by τ. It now follows easily that there exists $g \in \operatorname{Hom}_R(C, P)$ such that $\tau^{\#}(g) = f$. Hence $\ker \sigma^{\#} \subset \operatorname{im} \tau^{\#}$ and (c) holds.

(d) The exactness of the first four terms is a consequence of (c). If we use the same argument as in the proof of Theorem IV.4.3, the hypothesis that the sequence is split and exact can be seen to be equivalent to the statement that B is the internal direct sum of $\operatorname{im} \sigma = \sigma(A) = \ker \tau$ and $\operatorname{im} \theta = \theta(C)$. If we let $f \in \operatorname{Hom}_R(A, P)$, we may define $g \in \operatorname{Hom}_R(B, P)$ by setting $g(b) = 0$ for $b \in \operatorname{im} \theta$ and $g(\sigma(a)) = f(a) \;\forall\, a \in A$. Since σ is injective and B is the internal direct sum of $\sigma(A)$ and $\operatorname{im} \theta$, it is easily seen that g exists and is uniquely determined by these requirements. Thus we can define $\varphi : \operatorname{Hom}_R(A, P) \to \operatorname{Hom}_R(B, P)$ by setting $\varphi(f) = g$. It is easy to verify that $\sigma^{\#} \circ \varphi$ is the identity map on $\operatorname{Hom}_R(A, P)$. This shows that the second sequence is split and exact. «

DEFINITION 4 · Let R be a nonzero commutative ring. If $T = (a_{ji}) \in M_{n,m}(R)$, then $T^t = (b_{ij}) \in M_{m,n}(R)$ is defined by setting $b_{ij} = a_{ji} \;\forall\, i, j$. T^t is called the ***transpose*** of the matrix T. It is obvious that $T = (T^t)^t$. (If R is noncommutative, then $T^t \in M_{m,n}(R^\circ)$.)

THEOREM 3 · Let M, N be free modules of finite type with free bases X and Y, respectively, over a commutative nonzero ring R. Let $\operatorname{Hom}_R(M, N)$ have the matrix $T = (a_{ji}) \in M_{n,m}(R)$. Then the matrix of ρ^* with respect to the dual bases Y^* and X^* is $T^t \in M_{m,n}(R)$.

Proof · From the definition we have $\langle \rho^*(y_j^*), x_i \rangle = \langle y_j^*, \rho(x_i) \rangle = \langle y_j^*, \sum_k a_{ki} y_k \rangle = a_{ji}$. Computing backward, we also have that $\langle \sum_k a_{jk} x_k^*, x_i \rangle = a_{ji}$. It follows that $\rho^*(y_j^*) = \sum_k a_{jk} x_k^*$ as desired. «

COROLLARY · Let R be a nonzero commutative ring. If $S \in M_{p,n}(R)$ and $T \in M_{n,m}(P)$, then $(ST)^t = T^t S^t$.

Proof · Choose dual bases for appropriate free modules and apply Theorems 2 and 3.

Exercise 6 · Let M, N be free modules of finite type with free bases X and Y over a nonzero commutative ring R. Identify M with $M_{m,1}(R)$ through the basis X; that is, $x = \sum_i a_i x_i$ is identified with $(a_i) \in M_{m,1}(R)$. Identify M^* with $M_{1,m}(R)$ by the dual basis X^*. Similarly, identify N and N^* with $M_{n,1}(R)$ and $M_{1,n}(R)$, respectively. Show that the evaluation map $\langle\ ,\ \rangle_M$ corresponds to the matrix multiplication, $\cdot : M_{1,m}(R) \times M_{m,1}(R) \to M_{1,1}(R)$, where 1×1 matrices are identified with their entries in R. Let $\rho \in \mathrm{Hom}_R(M, N)$ have the matrix (a_{ji}) with respect to X and Y. Show that $\rho^* \in \mathrm{Hom}_R(N^*, M^*)$ corresponds to right multiplication of elements of $M_{1,n}(R)$ by $(a_{ji}) \in M_{n,m}(R)$.

DEFINITION 5 · Let R be a nonzero commutative ring. Let $T \in M_{n,m}(R)$. The $(n-1) \times (m-1)$ minor of T obtained by deleting the jth row and ith column of T is denoted by M_{ji}. If $m = n$, then $(-1)^{i+j} \det M_{ji} = T_{ji}$ is called the ***(j, i)-cofactor*** of the matrix T.

THEOREM 4 · Let R be a nonzero commutative ring. Let $T = (t_{ji}) \in M_{n,n}(R)$. Let S be the transpose of the matrix of cofactors of T; that is, $S = (s_{ij})$, $s_{ij} = (-1)^{i+j} \det M_{ji} = T_{ji}$. Let $I_n = (\delta_{ij})$ be the identity matrix. If $\pi \in \boldsymbol{S}_n$, then define $\mathrm{sgn}(\pi) = 1$ when $\pi \in \boldsymbol{A}_n$ and $\mathrm{sgn}(\pi) = -1$ when $\pi \notin \boldsymbol{A}_n$. Then the following assertions hold:

(a) $\det T = \sum_{\pi \in \boldsymbol{S}_n} \mathrm{sgn}(\pi) t_{\pi(1),1} t_{\pi(2),2} \cdots t_{\pi(n),n}$
$\qquad = \sum_{\pi \in \boldsymbol{S}_n} \mathrm{sgn}(\pi) t_{1,\pi(1)} t_{2,\pi(2)} \cdots t_{n,\pi(n)}$.

(b) $\det T = \det T^t$.

(c) $ST = (\det T) I_n = TS = (\det T \cdot \delta_{ij})$. Thus T is invertible if and only if $\det T$ is invertible.

(d) Let M be a free R-module of dimension n. Then $\rho \in \mathrm{Hom}_R(M, M)$ is in $GL_R(M)$ (that is, ρ is invertible) if and only if ρ is surjective.

Proof · Let M be a free R-module with free R-basis $\{x_i \mid 1 \leqslant i \leqslant n\}$. Let $\rho \in \mathrm{Hom}_R(M, M)$ have the matrix T with respect to this free basis.

(a) $\det T = \det \rho$ by definition. Thus we have $\rho(x_1) \wedge \cdots \wedge \rho(x_n) = (\det \rho) x_1 \wedge \cdots \wedge x_n$. Since $\rho(x_i) = \sum_j t_{ji} x_j$, we see that a consequence of $x_i \wedge x_i = 0$ and $x_j \wedge x_i = -x_i \wedge x_j$ is that the only possible nonzero contribution comes from $t_{\pi(1),1} x_{\pi(1)} \wedge \cdots \wedge t_{\pi(n),n} x_{\pi(n)}$, where $\pi \in \boldsymbol{S}_n$. Because each transposition of two factors leads to a multiplicative factor of -1, we obtain the first equality immediately. For the second equality we observe that the commutativity of multiplication in R implies that $t_{\pi(1),1} \cdots t_{\pi(n),n} = t_{1,\tau(1)} \cdots t_{n,\tau(n)}$, where $\tau = \pi^{-1}$. However, since

$\operatorname{sgn}(\pi) = \operatorname{sgn}(\pi^{-1}) = \operatorname{sgn}(\tau)$ and each element of a group has a unique inverse, it follows that the second equality also holds.

(b) follows immediately from (a).

(c) We first assert that $\det T = t_{1i}T_{1i} + \cdots + t_{ni}T_{ni}$ for $1 \leqslant i \leqslant n$. To obtain this, we evaluate $\rho(x_1) \wedge \cdots \wedge \rho(x_n)$ by substituting $\sum_j t_{ji}x_j$ for $\rho(x_i)$ and expanding the result. Thus $\det T \cdot (x_1 \wedge \cdots \wedge x_n) = \sum_j \rho(x_1) \wedge \cdots \wedge \rho(x_{i-1}) \wedge t_{ji}x_j \wedge \rho(x_{i+1}) \wedge \cdots \wedge \rho(x_n)$. Since $x_j \wedge x_j = 0$ and $x_j \wedge x_k = -x_k \wedge x_j$, it follows that for $p \neq i$, each $\rho(x_p)$ may be replaced by $\sum_{q \neq j} a_{qp}x_q$ in the jth term of the sum. Let

$$\rho_{ji} : Rx_1 + \cdots + Rx_{i-1} + Rx_{i+1} + \cdots + R_n \to Rx_1 + \cdots + Rx_{j-1} + Rx_{j+1} + \cdots Rx_n$$

be the R-homomorphism with the matrix T_{ji} with respect to the R-bases exhibited. If we now move $t_{ji}x_j$ to the front, it follows that the jth term is $(-1)^{i-1}t_{ji}x_j \wedge \rho_{ji}(x_1) \wedge \cdots \wedge \rho_{ji}(x_{i-1}) \wedge \rho_{ji}(x_{i+1}) \wedge \cdots \wedge \rho(x_n)$.

If we now identify the domain and the image of ρ_{ji} by identifying their free bases in the order exhibited, it is then clear that the jth term of the sum is precisely $(-1)^{i-1}t_{ji} \det M_{ji}x_j \wedge x_1 \wedge \cdots \wedge x_{j-1} \wedge x_{j+1} \wedge \cdots \wedge x_n$. If we move x_j back to the jth position, the jth term of the sum then becomes $(-1)^{i+j}t_{ji} \det M_{ji}x_1 \wedge \cdots \wedge x_n$. Summing these terms over j, we obtain the desired assertion.

Next, we assert that $t_{1i}T_{1j} + \cdots + t_{ni}T_{nj} = 0$ for $i \neq j$. We first replace the jth column of T by the ith column of T and leave the other columns of T unchanged. This operation does not change the cofactors T_{pj}, $1 \leqslant p \leqslant n$. (The point is that $i \neq j$ and the (p, j)-cofactor is obtained by crossing out the jth column and the pth row.) Our present assertion, under the application of the computations carried out in the preceding paragraphs, becomes the assertion that the new matrix should have determinant 0. However, the new matrix has two identical columns, namely the ith and jth. Thus our assertion follows from Exercise 4.16(b).

By combining these two assertions we have verified that $ST = (\det T) \cdot I_n$.

Since S^t is the matrix of cofactors of T, it follows from (b) that S is the matrix of cofactors of T^t. Thus from the preceding result we have $S^tT^t = (\det T^t) \cdot I_n$. Using (b) again, we see that $TS = (S^tT^t)^t = (\det T) \cdot I_n^t = (\det T) \cdot I_n$. This completes the proof of (c).

(d) Of course, if ρ is an R-automorphism, it is surjective. Conversely, if ρ is surjective, then, from Exercise 4.9(c), $\Lambda^n(\rho)$ must be surjective. Thus $\exists\, u \in R$ such that $x_1 \wedge \cdots \wedge x_n = \Lambda^n(\rho)(ux_1 \wedge \cdots \wedge x_n) = u \det(\rho)x_1 \wedge \cdots \wedge x_n$. Hence $u \det(\rho) = 1$. Since R is commutative, we see that $\det(\rho) = u^{-1} \in U(R)$. Let σ have the matrix $u^{-1}S$. It follows from (c) that σ is the inverse of ρ. «

In Section V.2 we studied the structure of $GL_R(M)$ and $SL_R(M)$ when R is a field and M is of finite dimension over R. It follows from Theorem 4(c) that

$$GL_R(M) = \{\rho \in \mathrm{Hom}_R(M, M) \mid \det \rho \in U(R)\},$$

where M is a free R-module of finite dimension. Moreover, we have an exact sequence of groups,

$$1 \to SL_R(M) \to GL_R(M) \xrightarrow{\det} U(R) \to 1.$$

When R is a Euclidean domain, Theorem V.2.4 gives us a set of generators for $GL_R(M)$. It is an easy matter to show that in such a case the generators with determinant 1 generate $SL_R(M)$.

In Theorem 4 assertion (d) depends strongly on the finite dimensionality of the free R-module M; (d) fails when this dimension is infinite. We may raise the question of generalizing Theorem 4 to noncommutative R-algebras. There are two problems involved. First, we must restrict ourselves to those R-algebras for which the notion of dimension can be defined. This may be taken care of by restricting ourselves to division algebras. We can, in fact, generalize (d) without any difficulty. However, a second problem now arises; we need a generalization of the determinant. If we examine the proof of Theorem 4 and the construction of the determinant, we see that the commutativity of R has been used several times. Actually, the notion of a determinant may be generalized to the case in which R is a division algebra. The value of the determinant is an $U(R)$-orbit in R, where $U(R)$ acts on R via inner automorphism. The interested reader may consult [1; Chapter 4].

THEOREM 5 · Let M be a free module of finite dimension over the commutative ring R. Then the map $\gamma : M^* \times M \to \mathrm{Hom}_R(M, M)$ defined by $(\gamma(f, x))(y) = f(y) \cdot x$ is a bi-R-homomorphism and it induces an isomorphism between $M^* \otimes_R M$ and $\mathrm{Hom}_R(M, M)$ as R-modules. Moreover, the composition of the inverse isomorphism with the evaluation map $\langle\ ,\ \rangle_M : M^* \otimes_R M \to R$ is precisely the trace function on $\mathrm{Hom}_R(M, M)$.

Proof · It is obvious that γ is a bi-R-homomorphism. Let X and X^* be dual bases for M and M^*. We then have $(x_i^* \otimes x_j)(x_k) =$

$\delta_{ik}x_j = E_{ji}x_k \; \forall\, i, j, k$. Thus the map induced by γ sends the free R-basis $\{x_i^* \otimes x_j \mid 1 \leqslant i, j \leqslant m\}$ bijectively onto the free R-basis $\{E_{ji} \mid 1 \leqslant i, j \leqslant m\}$. It follows that we have an R-isomorphism between $M^* \otimes_R M$ and $\mathrm{Hom}_R(M, M)$.

If $\rho \in \mathrm{Hom}_R(M, M)$ has the matrix (a_{ji}) with respect to the basis X, then $\rho = \sum_{i,j} a_{ji}E_{ji}$. Thus the preimage of ρ is $\sum_{i,j} a_{ji}x_i^* \otimes x_j$. The evaluation map sends the preimage onto $\sum_{i,j} a_{ji}\delta_{ij} = \sum_i a_{ii} = \mathrm{tr}\, \rho$. «

We note that the assertions of Theorem 5 are independent of the choice of a basis for M. However, it is very easy to give a proof based on the choice of dual bases for M and M^*.

The map from $M^* \otimes M$ to R induced by the evaluation map is often called the ***contraction map***. It can be generalized to $T(M)$ and to $\Lambda(M)$. However, we shall not go into this generalization.

We conclude this section with some exercises that develop the duality theory of torsion modules of finite type over a PID.

Exercise 7 · Let R be an integral domain. Let $a, b \in R - \{0\}$. Verify the following assertions:

(a) $\mathrm{Hom}_R(R/Ra, R/Rab)$ is generated by f as an R-module, where f is defined by $f(r + Ra) = br + Rab$.

(b) The annihilator ideal of f in R is Ra. Thus $\mathrm{Hom}_R(R/Ra, R/Rab)$ is isomorphic to R/Ra.

We remark that the assumption that R is an integral domain is essential in the preceding exercise.

Exercise 8 · Let R be a PID. Suppose that M is a module of finite type with elementary ideals $Rd_1, \ldots, Rd_t$, $d_1 \nmid 1$, $d_i \mid d_{i+1}$, $d_t \neq 0$. Let P be the module R/Rd, where $d \neq 0$ and $d_t \mid d$. Show that M is a torsion module and that $\mathrm{Hom}_R(M, P)$ has the elementary ideals $Rd_1, \ldots, Rd_t$. Thus show that M and $\mathrm{Hom}_R(M, P)$ are R-isomorphic. *Hint*. $\mathrm{Hom}_R(A \amalg B, P)$ is isomorphic to $\mathrm{Hom}_R(A, P) \amalg \mathrm{Hom}_R(B, P)$. Apply Exercise 7 and the fundamental theorem on modules of finite type over a PID to the torsion module M.

Exercise 9 · (continuing with the notation of Exercise 8). Let $M^\# = \mathrm{Hom}_R(M, P)$. Show that the evaluation map $\langle\ ,\ \rangle : M^\# \times M \to P$ is a ***dual pairing*** in the following sense:

(a) $\langle\ ,\ \rangle$ is a bi-R-homomorphism.

(b) If $x \in M$ such that $x \neq 0$, then there exists $f \in M^\#$ such that $\langle f, x\rangle = f(x) \neq 0$.

(c) If $f \in M$ such that $f \neq 0$, then there exists $x \in M$ such that $\langle f, x \rangle = f(x) \neq 0$.

(d) If $\rho \in \text{Hom}_R(M, P)$, then there exists $f \in M^\#$ such that $\rho(x) = \langle f, x \rangle \ \forall\, x \in M$.

(e) If $\sigma \in \text{Hom}_R(M^\#, P)$, then there exists $x \in M$ such that $\sigma(f) = \langle f, x \rangle \ \forall\, f \in M^\#$.

Moreover, suppose that A and B are arbitrary modules and that $\langle\ ,\ \rangle : A \times B \to P$ satisfies the conditions (a) through (e) with A and B in place of $M^\#$ and M, respectively. Then show that $B \cong \text{Hom}_R(A, P) = A^\#$ and $A \cong \text{Hom}_R(B, P)$ in a natural way. [Naturality refers to the fact that a map from $A \times B \to P$ defines naturally maps from A to $\text{Map}(B, P)$ and from B to $\text{Map}(A, P)$.]

Hint. Carry out the proofs of (a) through (e) for the case in which $t = 1$. Reduce the general case to this special case by using the hints in Exercise 8.

Exercise 10 · (continuing with the notations of Exercises 8 and 9). Assume that A, B are R-modules over an arbitrary commutative ring R. Suppose that $\langle\ ,\ \rangle : A \times B \to P$ is a dual pairing; that is, conditions (a) through (e) hold with A and B in place of $M^\#$ and M, respectively. Verify the following assertions:

(a) If C is an R-submodule of A, then $C^! = \{b \in B \mid \langle c, b \rangle = 0 \ \forall\, c \in C\}$ is an R-submodule of B and $C^!$ is R-isomorphic to $\text{Hom}_R(A/C, P)$ under the map that sends each $b \in C^!$ onto $\langle\ , b \rangle : A/C \to P$ given by $\langle a + C, b \rangle = \langle a, b \rangle \ \forall\, a \in A$.

(b) If D is an R-submodule of B, then $D^! = \{a \in A \mid \langle a, d \rangle = 0 \ \forall\, d \in D\}$ is an R-submodule of A and $D^!$ is R-isomorphic to $\text{Hom}_R(B/D, P)$ under the map that sends each $a \in D^!$ onto $\langle a, b \rangle : B/D \to P$ given by $\langle a, b + D \rangle = \langle a, b \rangle \ \forall\, b \in B$.

Exercise 11 · Let R be a PID. If d is a nonzero element of R, then $l(d)$ is defined as the total number of prime factors in a factorization of d into a product of primes with a unit in R. Let M be a torsion-module of finite type over R with elementary ideals $Rd_1, \ldots, Rd_t$, where $d_1 \nmid 1$, $d_i \mid d_{i+1}$ and $d_t \neq 0$. Then $l(M) = \sum_i l(d_i)$ is called the length of M. Verify the following assertions:

(a) $l(M) \in \mathbf{P}$ and $l(M) = 0$ if and only if $M = 0$.

(b) Let $p_1, \ldots, p_s$ be the set of nonassociate prime divisors of d_t; then $l(M) = \sum_j l(M_{p_j})$, where M_{p_j} is the p_j-primary component of M.

(c) If N is any R-submodule of M, then $N_{p_j} = N \cap M_{p_j}$ and N is the direct sum of $N_{\mathfrak{p}_j}$; moreover, $(M/N)_{\mathfrak{p}_j} = (N + M_{\mathfrak{p}_j})/N$ and M/N is the direct sum of $(M/N)_{\mathfrak{p}_j}$.

(d) If M is a p-primary module, p a nonzero prime in R, then for each R-submodule N of $M, l(N) = \sum_i \dim_{R/R\mathfrak{p}} N(p^{i+1})/N(p^i)$, where $N(p^i) = \{x \in N \mid p^i x = 0\}$; moreover, $N(p^i) = N \cap M(p^i)$.

(e) If N is a submodule of the p-primary module M, then $l(N) \leqslant l(M)$ and equality holds if and only if $N = M$; moreover, $l(M/N) \leqslant l(M)$ and equality holds if and only if $N = 0$.

(f) $l(M) = l(M/N) + l(N)$ holds for any R-submodule of M.

Hint. Theorem 3.5 and Exercise 3.2 are useful in the proofs of (b) and (c). The proof of Theorem 3.6 should be examined in proving (d). In proving (e) the isomorphism theorems should be used in showing that $\dim_{R/R\mathfrak{p}} N(p^{i+1})/N(p^i) \leqslant \dim_{R/R\mathfrak{p}} M(p^{i+1})/M(p^i)$. Observe the fact that N is the union of $N(p^i)$ and that M is the union of $M(p^i)$; furthermore, $N(p^i)$ is a submodule of $M(p^i)$. As for the second assertion in (e), use Exercise 8 to conclude that $l(M/N) = l((M/N)^*)$; then use Exercise 9 and 10(b) to conclude that $l((M/N)^*) = l(N^\circ)$, where $N^\circ = \{f \in M^* \mid f(N) = 0\}$, Finally, use the fact that $l(N^\circ) \leqslant l(M^*) = l(M)$ to conclude that the second assertion holds.

The following steps may be followed to obtain a proof of (f).

(1) (b) and (c) may be used to reduce us to the case in which M is a p-primary module. Thus we may assume that $d_i = p^{\nu(i)}$, $1 \leqslant \nu(1) \leqslant \cdots \leqslant \nu(t) < \infty$.

(2) Proceed by induction and assume that (f) holds for all p-primary modules of length less than $l(M)$. We may assume that $N \neq 0, M$), Thus let $x \in N(p) - \{0\}$. It follows from the induction hypothesis that $l(M/N) = l((M/Rx)/(N/Rx)) = l(M/Rx) - l(N/Rx)$.

(3) Use Theorem 3.6 to conclude that $l(M/M(p)) = \sum_i(\nu(i) - 1) = \sum_i \nu(i) - t = l(M) - l(M(p))$. Use Corollary 5.3 to conclude that $l(M(p)/Rx) = l(M(p)) - l(Rx)$. Thus, with $M(p)$ playing the role of N, we obtain $l(M/Rx) = l(M/M(p)) + l(M(p)/Rx) = l(M) - l(Rx)$. Since $l(N) < l(M)$, from the induction hypothesis, we have $l(N/Rx) = l(N) - l(Rx)$. Feeding this information back into the conclusion of (2), we see that (f) holds.

The length $l(M)$ is the "composition length" of M. Had we proved the "Jordan-Hölder-Schreier-Zassenhaus" theorem, (f) would have followed easily. For more information on the length of a module, the interested reader may consult [7].

Exercise 12 · Let R be a PID. Suppose that A, B are torsion R-modules of finite type. Let $d \in R - \{0\}$ such that $dA = 0 = dB$. Suppose that $\langle\ ,\ \rangle : A \times B \to R/Rd$ is a bi-R-homomorphism. Then $\langle\ ,\ \rangle$ induces a dual pairing $\langle\ ,\ \rangle : \bar{A} \times \bar{B} \to P$, where $\bar{A} = A/\{a \in A \mid \langle a, B\rangle = 0\}$, $\bar{B} = B/\{b \in B \mid \langle A, b\rangle = 0\}$, $P = R/Rd$, and $\langle \bar{a}, \bar{b}\rangle = \langle a, b\rangle$, where $\bar{a}$ and $\bar{b}$ are the cosets of a and b in $\bar{A}$ and $\bar{B}$, respectively. In particular, $\bar{A}$ is isomorphic to $\mathrm{Hom}_R(\bar{B}, P)$ and $\bar{B}$ is isomorphic to $\mathrm{Hom}_R(\bar{A}, P)$ in a natural way.

Hint. Conditions (a), (b), and (c) are satisfied by $\langle\ ,\ \rangle : \bar{A} \times \bar{B} \to P$. We need to verify (d) and (e). Using symmetry, it suffices to verify (d), From condition (c) the map that sends $u \in \bar{A}$ onto the map $\langle u,\ \rangle : \bar{B} \to P$ is an injective R-homomorphism of $\bar{A}$ into $\mathrm{Hom}_R(\bar{B}, P)$. It follows from Exercises 8 and 11 that $l(\bar{A}) \leqslant l(\bar{B}^\#) = l(\bar{B})$; moreover, equality holds if and only if the preceding R-homomorphism is an R-isomorphism. From condition (b) we then deduce that $l(\bar{B}) \leqslant l(\bar{A})$. Thus equality holds, hence (d) and (e) hold.

Exercise 13 · In the situation described in Exercise 12 suppose that $\langle\ ,\ \rangle : A \times B \to P$ is a dual pairing. Let C be an R-submodule of A and let $C^! = \{b \in B \mid \langle C, b\rangle = 0\}$. Verify the following assertions:

(a) $\langle\ ,\ \rangle$ induces a dual pairing $\langle\ ,\ \rangle : C \times (B/C^!) \to P$.

(b) $\langle\ ,\ \rangle$ induces a dual pairing $\langle\ ,\ \rangle : (A/C) \times C^! \to P$.

In particular, $C = C^{!!}$, that is, $C = \{a \in A \mid \langle a, C^!\rangle = 0\}$.

Hint. (a) follows easily from Exercise 12. Thus from Exercises 11 and 12 we obtain $l(C) = l(B) - l(C^!) = l(A) - l(C^!)$. By symmetry we have $l(C^!) = l(B) - l(C^{!!}) = l(A) - l(C^{!!})$. Thus $l(C) = l(C^{!!})$. But it is obvious that $C \subset C^{!!}$. From Exercise 11(e) we conclude that $C = C^{!!}$. The assertion (b) is then the symmetric statement of (a).

We observe that the net result of the preceding exercise is that there exists a bijection between the set of all submodules of A and the set of all quotient modules of B such that the corresponding modules are isomorphic. However, there is no natural isomorphism between the corresponding modules. In particular, there is no natural isomorphism between A and B such that the bijection is induced by this isomorphism. To be more precise we summarize the preceding exercises into the following theorem.

THEOREM 6 (Duality theorem for torsion modules of finite type over a PID) · Let R be a PID. Let A, B be torsion R-modules of finite type and let d be a nonzero element of R such that $dA = 0 = dB$. Suppose that $\langle\ ,\ \rangle : A \times B \to R/Rd$ is a bi-R-homomorphism such that (1) $\{a \in A \mid \langle a, B\rangle = 0\} = 0$ and (2) $\{b \in B \mid \langle A, b\rangle = 0\} = 0$. Then the following assertions hold:

(a) $\langle\ ,\ \rangle$ is a dual pairing, that is, $\langle\ ,\ \rangle$ induces natural isomorphisms, $A \cong B^\# = \mathrm{Hom}_R(B, P)$, $B \cong A^\# = \mathrm{Hom}_R(B, P)$, where $P = R/Rd$.

(b) Let $\mathcal{A}$ be the set of all R-submodules of A and let $\mathcal{B}$ be the set of all R-submodules of B. Let $! : \mathcal{A} \to \mathcal{B}$ and $\S : \mathcal{B} \to \mathcal{A}$ be defined by setting $C^! = \{b \in B \mid \langle C, b\rangle = 0\}$ and by setting $D^\S = \{a \in A \mid \langle a, D\rangle = 0\}$. Then

(1) $C_1 \subset C_2$ are submodules of A imdlies that $C_2^! \subset C_1^!$.
(2) $D_1 \subset D_2$ are submodules of B implies that $D_2^\S \subset D_1^\S$.
(3) $(C^!)^\S = C \ \forall\ C \in \mathcal{A}$ and $(D^\S)^! = D \ \forall\ D \in \mathcal{B}$.
(4) If $C \in \mathcal{A}$, then $\langle\ ,\ \rangle$ induces dual pairings

$$\langle\ ,\ \rangle : C \times (B/C^!) \to P \qquad \text{and} \qquad \langle\ ,\ \rangle : (A/C) \times C^! \to P.$$

(5) If $D \in \mathcal{B}$, then $\langle\ ,\ \rangle$ induces dual pairings

$$\langle\ ,\ \rangle : (A/D^\S) \times D \to P \qquad \text{and} \qquad \langle\ ,\ \rangle : D^\S \times (B/D) \to P.$$

We remark that the module $P = R/Rd$ is selected in such a way that it depends on the choice of A and B. It is a natural question for us to ask, "Can we replace P by a universal module that depends only on R?" It should be clear that this universal module should contain a unique submodule isomorphic to R/Rd for each ideal $Rd \neq R$ of R. Since the image of a torsion module under an R-homomorphism is always a torsion module, we can assume that the universal module, if it exists, is a torsion module.

Exercise 14 · Let K be the field of fractions of a PID R. Let U be the R-module K/R. Verify the following assertions:

(a) U is a torsion R-module.

(b) If $d \in R - \{0\}$, then Rd^{-1}/R is the unique R-submodule of U which is R-isomorphic to R/Rd.

(c) Every R-submodule of finite type in U has the form Rd^{-1}/R for a suitable $d \in R - \{0\}$.

Hint. (a) is the statement that every element of K may be represented as a quotient of elements of R. In (b) Rd^{-1} is the set of all elements of K that admit d as a denominator. In (*c*) we may use the fact that any finite number of fractions have a least common denominator in R.

Exercise 14 shows that a universal module exists. Indeed, U is the minimal universal module. In some sense it plays a role dual to the R-module R. We shall not investigate this problem any further at this point.

Exercise 15 · Let the ring $\boldsymbol{Z}$ be considered as a $\boldsymbol{Z}$-module. Verify the following assertions:

(a) The multiplication in $\boldsymbol{Z}$ defines a dual pairing of $\boldsymbol{Z} \times \boldsymbol{Z} \to \boldsymbol{Z}$.

(b) If $n \in \boldsymbol{Z}$ and $n \neq 0$, then $(n\boldsymbol{Z})^! = 0$; moreover, $\mathrm{Hom}_{\boldsymbol{Z}}(\boldsymbol{Z}/n\boldsymbol{Z}, \boldsymbol{Z}) = 0$.

(c) If $n \in \boldsymbol{Z}$ and $n > 1$, then the dual pairing of (a) does not induce a dual pairing from $\boldsymbol{Z}/n\boldsymbol{Z} \times (n\boldsymbol{Z})^!$ to $\boldsymbol{Z}$.

Exercise 16 · What happens when the ring $\boldsymbol{Z}$ of Exercise 15 is replaced by a commutative ring R? In particular, consider the case of an integral domain that is not a field and the case of a field separately.

Exercise 17 · Restate Theorem 6 for the case of a finite abelian group of order n.

References

The concept of a tensor product of modules is quite important. It is not a total exaggeration to say that nearly all of homological algebra is an investigation of the tensor product of modules and the module $\mathrm{Hom}_R(M, N)$. The interested reader may consult [3].

The use of exact sequences and diagrams to describe a complicated collection of maps has become indispensable in algebra as well as in other fields of mathematics. We mentioned earlier that the "description" of a module by an exact sequence of free modules leads to the notion of homological dimension of a module. The interested reader may consult [3] for an introduction to this subject.

The general linear group and the special linear group are important in geometry and arithmetic. The interested reader may consult [1], [4], [5] and [6].

For a detailed treatment of modules over a PID the reader may consult [2]. For a general treatment of modules over commutative rings the reader may consult [7].

1. E. Artin, *Geometric Algebra*, Interscience, New York, 1957.
2. N. Bourbaki, *Eléments de mathématique, algèbre*, Chapter 7, Hermann, Paris, 1952.
3. H. Cartan and S. Eilenberg, *Homological Algebra*, Princeton University Press, Princeton, N.J., 1956.
4. J. Dieudonne, *La geometrie des groupes classiques*, Springer, Berlin, 1955.

5. O. T. O'Meara, "On the finite generation of linear groups over Hasse domains," *Journal für die reine und angewandte Mathematik*, **217**, 79–108, (1965).
6. O. T. O'Meara, "Finiteness of SL_n/TL_n over Hasse domains for $n \geqslant 4$," *Mathematisches Zeitschrift*, **86**, 273–284, (1964).
7. O. Zariski and P. Samuel, *Commutative Algebras*, Vols. 1 and 2, Van Nostrand, Princeton, N.J., 1962.

CHAPTER VI Vector Spaces

The goal in this chapter is to consider the special case of a module V over a field k. Our attention is again centered on the ring $\mathrm{Hom}_k(V, V)$. Nearly all of the results in this chapter are corollaries of the results obtained in preceding chapters. Our main task is the interpretation of our earlier results. In addition to this interpretation, we indicate, in the form of exercises and excursions, some of the uses of vector spaces in other branches of mathematics.

In passing it should be noted that, for the purposes of computation, it is often convenient to use matrices. However, the study of vector spaces should not be considered the same as the study of matrices. Results concerning matrices arising from our investigations should be viewed as bonuses. Matrices that satisfy additional restrictions, for example, "symmetric matrices," "positive definite matrices," and "doubly stochastic matrices," and so on, occur naturally in the study of certain mathematical objects; often, these objects are special subsets of special vector spaces. However, our interest is in the study of vector spaces without any additional restrictions other than that of looking at only finite dimensional vector spaces.

Once more we remind the reader that the blanket conventions of Chapters IV and V are in effect; namely, ring means ring with an identity element; ring homomorphisms preserve the identity elements; algebra means associative algebra with an identity element.

» VI · 1 BASIC CONCEPTS

For the sake of convenience we recall the definition of a module in the special case of a module over a field.

DEFINITION 1 · Let V be a commutative group under $+$. Let k be a field. V together with a map $\cdot : k \times V \to V$ is called a ***vector space*** if and only if the following conditions are satisfied:

(a) $a(x + y) = ax + ay$,
(b) $(a + b)x = ax + bx$,
(c) $(ab)x = a(bx)$,
(d) $1x = x$,

where $a, b \in k$, $x, y \in V$ and 1 is the identity element of the field k. [We have again used the notation in which $\cdot\ (a, x)$ is written as ax.] The elements of k are often called ***scalars*** and the elements of V are often called ***vectors***. Left multiplication by elements of k on elements of V is often called ***scalar multiplication***. Elements of $\mathrm{Hom}_k(V, V)$ are often called ***linear transformations***.

In any event, the following statements are all equivalent:

(a) V is a vector space over a field k.
(b) V is a k-module, where k is a field.
(c) Left multiplication by elements of k leads to a ring homomorphism of the field k into the ring $\mathrm{Hom}(V, V), +, \circ$.

Since every field is a commutative ring, the image of k under the map described in (c) lies in the center of the ring $\mathrm{Hom}_k(V, V)$. Since k is a field, the ring homomorphism of (c) is actually injective. Thus we may identify k with a subset of $\mathrm{Hom}_k(V, V)$. If we set $I : V \to V$ as the identity map of V, then $a \in k$ may be identified with $aI : V \to V$, where $(aI)(x) = ax\ \forall\ x \in V$.

DEFINITION 2 · Let V be a vector space over a field k. A subset B of V is said to be ***linearly independent over k*** if and only if the following condition holds:

(*) For every finite subset $\{x_i \mid 1 \leqslant i \leqslant m\}$ contained in B, the equation $\sum_i a_i x_i = 0$, $a_i \in k$, can be satisfied only by setting $a_i = 0$ for each i.

Subsets that are not linearly independent over k are called ***linearly dependent subsets***. Free k-basis is abbreviated to k-basis.

We observe that the following statements are equivalent:

(a) B is linearly independent in V.
(b) B is k-free in the module V over k.

Exercise 1 · Let V be a vector space over a field k. Verify the following assertions:

(a) The following conditions are equivalent for the subset B of V:

(1) B is linearly independent.
(2) Every finite subset of B is linearly independent.
(3) If $x \in B$, then x is not in the k-subspace generated by $B - \{x\}$, that is, x is not a finite sum $\sum_i a_i x_i$, $a_i \in k$, $x_i \in B - \{x\}$.

(b) If B_i, $i \in I$, are subsets of V which are linearly ordered by inclusion, then $\bigcup_{i \in I} B_i$ is linearly independent if and only if each B_i is linearly independent.

THEOREM 1 · Let V be a vector space over a field k. Then the following assertions hold:

(a) Let G be a set of generators of V; that is, $kG = V$. Let B be a k-free subset of G; for example, $B = \varnothing$. Let $\mathcal{F} = \{C \mid B \subset C \subset G$ and C is k-free$\}$ be partially ordered by inclusion. Then $\mathcal{F}$ is inductive in the sense of Zorn's lemma, and any maximal element of $\mathcal{F}$ is a k-free basis of V.

(b) Every k-subspace of V is a direct summand of V.

(c) If V_1 and V_2 are k-subspaces of V, then

(1) $\dim_k V = \dim_k(V/V_1) + \dim_k(V_1)$,
(2) $\dim_k(V_1) + \dim_k(V_2) = \dim_k(V_1 + V_2) + \dim_k(V_1 \cap V_2)$.

Proof · It follows from Exercise 1(b) that $\mathcal{F}$ is inductive. Let C be a maximal element of $\mathcal{F}$. Then, by its definition, C is a k-free basis of $W = kC$. Suppose that $W \neq V$. From the hypothesis we can find $x \in G - kC$. Since k is a field, it is clear that $kx \cap kC = 0$. Again, since k is a field, kx is k-free with basis $\{x\}$. Thus $kx + kC$ is the direct sum of kx and kC; moreover, it has $C \cup \{x\}$ as a free k-basis. This contradicts the maximality of C in $\mathcal{F}$.

(b) and (c) (1) are now easy consequences of (a) and the Corollary to Theorem V.3.1.

We now consider the map $\sigma : V_1 \amalg V_2 \to V_1 + V_2$ by setting $\sigma(x_1, x_2) = x_1 - x_2$. It is immediate that σ is a surjective k-homomorphism with $\ker \sigma \cong V_1 \cap V_2$. (c)(2) follows from (c)(1) and the first isomorphism theorem. «

Exercise 2 · Let G be a group. Show that $|\operatorname{Aut}(G)| = 1$ if and only if $|G| \leqslant 2$.

Exercise 3 · Let X be an indeterminate over a field k. Let $n \in \mathbf{P}$. Suppose that $q(X) \in k[X]$ is a monic polynomial of degree n and let P_n denote the set $\{f \in k[X] \mid \deg f < n\}$. Verify the following assertions:

(a) P_n is a k-subspace of dimension n over k.

(b) If $f_i \in k[X]$ is a monic polynomial of degree i, then $\{f_i \mid 0 \leqslant i < n\}$ is a k-basis for P_n.

(c) If $V = \{g \in k(X) \mid gq \in P_n\}$, then V is a k-subspace of the field of fraction $k(X)$ of $k[X]$.

(d) Let $q = \prod_{1 \leqslant i \leqslant t} q^{\nu(i)}$ be the unique factorization of q in $k[X]$, where q_i are monic, irreducible and $q_i \neq q_j$ for $i \neq j$. Let $V_i = \{g \in k(X) \mid gq_i^{\nu(i)} \in P_{\nu(i)\deg q_i}\}$. Then V is the direct sum of the k-subspaces V_i, $1 \leqslant i \leqslant t$.

(e) $\{X^j/q_i^l \mid 0 \leqslant j < \deg q_i, 1 \leqslant l \leqslant \nu(i)\}$ is a k-basis for V_i, $1 \leqslant i \leqslant t$.

We observe that (d) and (e) are simply translations of the partial fraction theorem.

Exercise 4 · Let V be a vector space over a field k. For each subspace W of V define $W^! = \{f \in V^* \mid f(W) = 0\}$, where $V^* = \operatorname{Hom}_k(V, k)$. Verify the following assertions:

(a) $W_1 \subset W_2$ if and only if $W_2^! \subset W_1^!$.

(b) $W^!$ is naturally isomorphic to $(V/W)^*$.

(c) If $\dim_k V$ is finite, then $\dim_k W + \dim_k W^* = \dim_k V$.

(d) If $\dim_k V$ is finite, then $\langle\ ,\ \rangle_V : V^* \times V \to k$ is a dual pairing. (Compare with Theorem V.6.6.)

Exercise 5 · Let V be a vector space over a field k. To each $\rho \in \operatorname{Hom}_k(V, V^*)$, let $\langle\ ,\ \rangle_\rho : V \times V \to k$ be defined by setting $\langle x, y\rangle = \rho(x) \cdot y$. Show that the map sending ρ onto $\langle\ ,\ \rangle_\rho$ is a k-isomorphism between $\operatorname{Hom}_k(V, V^*)$ and $\text{Bi-hom}_k(V \times V, k)$. Thus show that $\operatorname{Hom}_k(V, V^*)$ is k-isomorphic to $(V \otimes_k V)^*$. Generalize this and show that $\operatorname{Hom}_k(V, W^*)$ is k-isomorphic to $(V \otimes_k W)^*$, where W is a second vector space over k.

Exercise 6 · Let V and W be vector spaces over k. Show that $\langle\ ,\ \rangle : V^* \times W \to \operatorname{Hom}_k(V, W)$ defined by $\langle f, w\rangle(v) = f(v) \cdot w$ is a bi-k-homomorphism. Show that it induces an injective k-homomorphism from $V^* \otimes_k W$ into $\operatorname{Hom}_k(V, W)$. Suppose that $\dim_k V$ or $\dim_k W$ is finite and show that the preceding map is a k-isomorphism.

Exercise 7 · Let V be a vector space over k. Show that V is k-isomorphic to V^* if and only if $\dim_k V$ is finite.

If V is a vector space of finite dimension over the field k, we may select a particular isomorphism between V^* and V. This then leads to a "self-dual pairing," $< , > : V \times V \to k$. Much of geometry is devoted to the study of such self-dual pairings. The interested reader may consult [1].

Exercise 8 · Let $\mathbf{R}$ be the field of "real numbers." Let V be a three-dimensional vector space over $\mathbf{R}$ with basis I, J, and K. Identify V with its dual V^* by the isomorphism that sends I, J, and K onto I^*, J^*, and K^*, respectively. Verify the following assertions:

(a) The self dual pairing $\langle \, , \, \rangle : V \times V \to \mathbf{R}$ is the "usual inner product" in the three-dimensional Euclidean space; namely, $\langle \, , \, \rangle$ is a bi-$\mathbf{R}$-homomorphism, $\langle v, v \rangle \geqslant 0$ and equality holds if and only if $v = 0$; moreover, $\| v \| = \sqrt{\langle v, v \rangle}$ satisfies the triangle inequality $\| v + w \| \leqslant \| v \| + \| w \|$ and the condition $\| rv \| = | r | \cdot \| v \|$, $\forall\, v, w \in V$, and $r \in \mathbf{R}$.

(b) V^* may be identified with $\Lambda^2(V)$ by the bi-$\mathbf{R}$-homomorphism $\wedge : \Lambda^2(V) \times \Lambda^1(V) \to \Lambda^3(V)$, where $\Lambda^1(V) = V$ and $\Lambda^3(V)$ is identified with $\mathbf{R}$ through the choice of the basis $I \wedge J \wedge K$. By the identification of V^* and V the map $\wedge : V \times V \to \Lambda^2(V)$ becomes identified with the "usual cross product" in the three-dimensional Euclidean space.

In general, if V is a finite dimensional vector space over a field k, then $\Lambda^i(V^*)$ may be shown to be "naturally" isomorphic to $\Lambda^i(V)^*$. This is the content of the following exercise. For more details in the case that k has "characteristic 0" the reader may consult [7].

Exercise 9 · Let V be a vector space of finite dimension m over a field k. For $n \in \mathbf{P}$ define $\cdot : \mathbf{S}_n \times T^n(V) \to T^n(V)$ by setting it to be the map induced by $\pi(v_1, \ldots, v_n) = v_{\pi(1)} \otimes \cdots \otimes v_{\pi(n)}$ $\forall\, \pi \in \mathbf{S}_n$ and $v_1, \ldots, v_n \in V$; namely, $\pi \cdot (v_1 \otimes \cdots \otimes v_n) = v_{\pi(1)} \otimes \cdots \otimes v_{\pi(n)}$. Show that this defines a group homomorphism of $\mathbf{S}_n$ into $GL_k(T^n(V))$. Let ι denote this group homomorphism and set $\mathcal{A}_n = \sum_{\pi \in \mathbf{S}_n} \operatorname{sgn}(\pi)\, \iota(\pi)$. Show that $\mathcal{A}_n$ maps $E^n = T^n(V) \cap E$ into itself, where E is the ideal of $T(V)$ generated by $v \otimes v$, $v \in V$. Thus show that $\mathcal{A}_n$ defines an element, also denoted by $\mathcal{A}_n$, of $\operatorname{Hom}_k(\Lambda^n(V), \Lambda^n(V))$. Show that $\langle \, , \, \rangle : T^n(V^*) \times T^n(V) \to k$ given by the equation

$$\langle f_1 \otimes \cdots \otimes f_n, v_1 \otimes \cdots \otimes v_n \rangle = f_1(v_1) \cdot \cdots \cdot f_n(v_n)$$

is a bi-k-homomorphism.

Hint. Show that the map that sends $(f_1, \ldots, f_n, v_1, \ldots, v_n)$ onto $f_1(v_1) \cdot \cdots \cdot f_n(v_n)$ is a multi-k-homomorphism, hence may be extended to $T^n(V^*) \otimes_k T^n(V)$ as a k-homomorphism in a unique way.

Show that the map $\langle \mid \rangle : \Lambda^n(V^*) \times \Lambda^n(V) \to k$ induced by the map that sends $(f_1 \otimes \cdots \otimes f_n, v_1 \otimes \cdots \otimes v_n)$ onto $\langle f_1 \otimes \cdots \otimes f_n, \mathcal{A}_n(v_1 \otimes \cdots \otimes v_n)\rangle = \langle \mathcal{A}_n(f_1 \otimes \cdots \otimes f_n), v_1 \otimes \cdots \otimes v_n\rangle$ is a dual pairing. [In fact,

$$\langle f_1 \wedge \cdots \wedge f_n \mid v_1 \wedge \cdots \wedge v_n\rangle = \textstyle\sum_{\pi \in S_n} \operatorname{sgn}(\pi) f_1(v_{\pi(1)}) \cdot \cdots \cdot f_n(v_{\pi(n)}).]$$

Suppose that $x_1, \ldots, x_m$ and $x_1^*, \ldots, x_m^*$ are dual bases for V and V^*, respectively. Show that for each $\rho \in \operatorname{Hom}_k(V, V)$, $\langle x_1^* \wedge \cdots \wedge x_m^* \mid \rho(x_1) \wedge \cdots \wedge \rho(x_m)\rangle = \det \rho$. Show that $\langle X^* \mid \rho(X)\rangle = \det \rho$ for any dual bases X^* and X of $\Lambda^m(V^*)$ and $\Lambda^m(V)$ in the sense of the dual pairing $\langle \mid \rangle$ defined above.

We saw in Theorem 1 that every k-free, or equivalently k-linearly independent, subset of a k-vector space V can be enlarged to a k-basis for V. We now give a necessary and sufficient condition for a subset of a k-vector space V to be k-free. Because a subset B is k-free if and only if every finite subset of B is k-free, it suffices to phrase the condition for finite subsets.

THEOREM 2 · Let V be a vector space over a field k. Let $v_1, \ldots, v_n$ be a finite subset of V. Then $v_1, \ldots, v_n$ are k-linearly independent if and only if $v_1 \wedge \cdots \wedge v_n \neq 0$ in $\Lambda(V)$.

Proof · We may clearly replace V by the k-subspace generated by $v_1, \ldots, v_n$. Hence we may assume that $V = kv_1 + \cdots + kv_n$. If $v_1, \ldots, v_n$ are k-linearly independent, they must form a k-basis for V. Thus $v_1 \wedge \cdots \wedge v_n$ is a k-basis for the nonzero k-vector space $\Lambda^n(V)$. Hence $v_1 \wedge \cdots \wedge v_n \neq 0$. Conversely, suppose that $v_1, \ldots v_n$ are k-linearly dependent; we may then express $v_i = \sum_{j \neq i} a_j v_j$. Thus $v_1 \wedge \cdots \wedge v_n = v_1 \wedge \cdots \wedge \sum_{j \neq i} a_j v_j \wedge \cdots \wedge v_n = 0$ would follow from $x_j \wedge x_j = 0$, $x_j \wedge x_l = -x_l \wedge x_j$.

Exercise 10 · Let V be a vector space over a field k. An element $w \neq 0$ of $\Lambda^m(V)$ is said to be ***decomposable*** if and only if there exist m nonzero elements of V, say $v_1, \ldots, v_m$, such that $w = v_1 \wedge \cdots \wedge v_m$. Show that each decomposable element w of $\Lambda^m(V)$ determines a unique k-subspace W of dimension m in V such that $\Lambda^m(W)$ has w as a k-basis. Show that $v_1, \ldots, v_m \in V$ satisfies $v_1 \wedge \cdots \wedge v_m = aw$, $a \in k - \{0\}$ if and only if $v_1, \ldots, v_m$ form a k-basis for W, where w is a decomposable element of $\Lambda^m(V)$ and W is determined as above.

Exercise 11 · Let V be a vector space of dimension m, $m \in \mathbf{P}$, over the field k. Suppose that $x_1, \ldots, x_m$ is a fixed k-basis for V. For each subspace W of dimension n in V we select a decomposable element w of $\Lambda^n(V)$ such that $kw = \Lambda^n(W)$. The coefficients of w in terms of the standard k-basis for $\Lambda^n(V)$ constructed from the given k-basis $x_1, \ldots, x_m$ are then called the ***Grassmann coordinates*** of W. Show that the coordinates so defined are unique up to a constant nonzero factor in k. Compute the Grassmann coordinates of the subspace generated by $x_1 + \cdots + x_m$ and $x_1 + 2x_2 + \cdots + mx_m$ in V, where $m > 1$. (The Grassmann coordinates lead to a uniquely determined element of $\Lambda^n(V) - \{0\}$ modulo the equivalence relation defined by the action of the group $k - \{0\}$ under multiplication; namely, two elements of $\Lambda^n(V) - \{0\}$ are equivalent if and only if they differ by a nonzero factor in k. For this reason the coordinates are usually called the ***homogeneous Grassmann coordinates*** of W. These coordinates were used in "classical" algebraic geometry. The reader interested in more details may consult [5].)

DEFINITION 3 · Let V and W be vector spaces over a field k. If $\rho \in \mathrm{Hom}_k(V, W)$, then $\dim_k \ker \rho$ is called the ***nullity*** of ρ and $\dim_k \mathrm{im}\ \rho$ is called the ***rank*** of ρ.

THEOREM 3 · Let V and W be vector spaces over a field k. Let $\rho, \sigma \in \mathrm{Hom}_k(V, W)$. Then the following assertions hold (cf. Definition V.4.10):

(a) ρ and σ are $GL_k(V)$-equivalent if and only if (1) $\mathrm{im}\ \rho = \mathrm{im}\ \sigma$ and (2) nullity of ρ = nullity of σ.

(b) ρ and σ are $GL_k(W)$-equivalent if and only if, (1) $\ker \rho = \ker \sigma$ and (2) $\dim_k(W/\mathrm{im}\ \rho) = \dim_k(W/\mathrm{im}\ \sigma)$.

(c) If $\dim_k V$ is finite, then $\dim_k V$ = rank of ρ + nullity of ρ.

(d) If either $\dim_k V$ or $\dim_k W$ is finite, then conditions (2) in (a) and (b) may be deleted.

Proof · All the assertions follow easily from Theorem 1; we leave the details to the reader.

Exercise 12 · Let V and W be vector spaces over a field k; $\rho, \sigma \in \mathrm{Hom}_k(V, W)$ are said to be ***V-W-equivalent*** if and only if $\exists\ \alpha \in GL_k(V)$,

$\beta \in GL_k(W)$ such that $\rho = \beta^{-1} \circ \sigma \circ \alpha$. Show that the following assertions are equivalent when V is a finite-dimensional vector space:

(a) ρ and σ are V-W-equivalent.

(b) Nullity of ρ = nullity of σ.

(c) Rank of ρ = rank of σ.

DEFINITION 4 · Let k be a field and let $(a_{ji}) \in M_{n,m}(k)$. The ***column rank*** of the matrix (a_{ji}) is the dimension of the subspace of $M_{n,1}(k)$ (considered as a k-vector space under coordinatewise multiplication by elements of k) generated by the columns of (a_{ji}). The ***row rank*** of (a_{ji}) is the dimension of the subspace of $M_{1,m}(k)$ generated by the rows of (a_{ji}).

The following operations on (a_{ji}) are referred to as ***column operations***:

(a) Adding a k-multiple of the jth column of (a_{ji}) to the ith column, $i \neq j$.

(b) Multiplying the jth column of (a_{ji}) by a nonzero element of k.

(c) Interchanging the ith column with the jth column.

Similarly, ***row operations*** are defined as the operations on (a_{ji}) obtained by substituting the word "row" for the word "column" throughout the above definitions.

Exercise 13 · Let k be a field. Verify the following assertions:

(a) Column operations on elements of $M_{n,m}(k)$ correspond to right multiplication by elementary matrices in $GL(m, k)$.

(b) Row operations on elements of $M_{n,m}(k)$ correspond to left multiplication by elementary matrices in $GL(n, k)$.

(c) Every element of $M_{n,m}(k)$ can be "diagonalized" by using row and column operations.

(d) Every element of $GL(m, k)$ can be changed into the identity matrix by using only column or only row operations.

Hint. Every field is a Euclidean domain, hence also a PID. Thus elementary divisor theory is applicable; similarly, the result on the generation of a general linear group of a free module of finite dimension over a Euclidean domain is also applicable.

Exercise 14 · Let V, W be vector spaces of dimensions m, n over a field k, respectively. Let $\rho, \sigma \in \operatorname{Hom}_k(V, W)$ have matrices (a_{ji}) and (b_{ji}) with respect to k-bases X and Y of V and W, respectively. Verify the following assertions:

(a) ρ and σ are $GL_k(V)$-equivalent if and only if (a_{ji}) and (b_{ji}) are column equivalent in the sense that (a_{ji}) can be transformed into (b_{ji}) by a finite sequence of column operations.

(b) ρ and σ are $GL_k(W)$-equivalent if and only if (a_{ji}) and (b_{ji}) are row equivalent in the sense that (a_{ji}) can be transformed into (b_{ji}) by a finite sequence of row operations.

(c) The column rank of (a_{ji}) is equal to rank ρ.

(d) The row rank of (a_{ji}) is equal to rank ρ^*, where ρ^* is the transpose of ρ.

(e) The column rank of (a_{ji}) is unchanged by column operations.

(f) The row rank of (a_{ji}) is unchanged by row operations.

(g) The column rank of (a_{ji}) and the row rank of (a_{ji}) are equal. *Hint*. Use Exercise 13(c) with (a) through (f) above.

(h) Rank ρ = rank ρ^*, m − nullity $\rho = n$ − nullity ρ^*.

(i) ρ is surjective if and only if ρ^* is injective and ρ is injective if and only if ρ^* is surjective.

We can now combine Theorem 2 and Exercise 14 into the following theorem.

THEOREM 3 · Let V and W be finite dimensional vector spaces over a field k. Let $\rho \in \operatorname{Hom}_k(V, W)$ have the matrix (a_{ji}) with respect to the k-basis X and Y of V and W, respectively. Then the following numbers are equal:

(a) Rank of ρ.

(b) Rank of ρ^*.

(c) Column rank of (a_{ji}).

(d) Row rank of (a_{ji}).

(e) $\operatorname{Max}\{r \mid$ there exists an $r \times r$ minor of (a_{ji}) with nonzero determinant$\}$.

Proof · (a), (b), (c), and (d) are all equal according to Exercise 14. The point is that (a) and (c) are equal by looking at the definition; (*b*) and (*d*) are equal by using the fact that $(a_{ji})^t$ is the matrix of ρ^* with respect to the dual bases Y^* and X^* and looking at the definition; finally, (a) and (b) are equal by diagonalization.

If we examine $\rho(x_{i(1)}) \wedge \cdots \wedge \rho(x_{i(r)})$, $1 \leqslant i(1) < \cdots < i(r) \leqslant m$, and expand it in terms of the standard basis for $\Lambda^r(W)$ obtained from Y, it is then clear that the coefficients are precisely the $r \times r$ minor determinants obtained from the $i(1)$- ,..., $i(r)$th columns of (a_{ji}). Since im ρ is generated by $\rho(x_1),\dots, \rho(x_m)$, it follows clearly from the proof of Theorem 1 that $\dim_k$ im ρ = maximum number of k-linear independent elements selected out of $\rho(x_1),\dots, \rho(x_m)$. Our equality of (a) and (d) now follow from the above discussion, and from Theorem 2. «

Exercise 15 · Compute the row rank of the following matrices over the field **Q**.

$$\begin{pmatrix} 1 & 0 & 0 & 5 \\ 2 & 3 & 0 & 1 \\ 0 & 0 & 1 & 2 \end{pmatrix}, \quad \begin{pmatrix} 1 & 0 & 1 & 2 \\ 2 & 9 & 1 & 2 \\ 3 & 9 & 1 & 2 \\ 4 & 0 & 0 & 2 \end{pmatrix}, \quad \begin{pmatrix} 1 & 0 & 0 & 0 & 0 \\ 2 & 3 & 0 & 0 & 0 \\ 0 & 0 & 0 & 1 & 1 \\ 0 & 0 & 0 & 0 & 1 \\ 0 & 1 & 1 & 0 & 0 \end{pmatrix}.$$

Exercise 16 · Let k be a subfield of a field K. Suppose that the matrix $(a_{ji}) \in M_{n,m}(k)$ has row rank r. Show that the matrix (a_{ji}), considered as an element of $M_{n,m}(K)$, also has row rank r. Let $\rho \in \mathrm{Hom}_k(V, W)$, where V and W are k-vector spaces. Show that rank ρ = rank $1 \otimes \rho$, where $1 \otimes \rho \in \mathrm{Hom}_K(K \otimes_k V, K \otimes_k W)$ is defined by setting

$$(1 \otimes \rho)(\gamma \otimes v) = \gamma \otimes \rho(v) \;\forall\, \gamma \in K, v \in V.$$

Exercise 17 · Let V be the vector space of all "infinitely differentiable" real-valued functions on the line over the field of real numbers. Show that $\{e^{rt} \mid r \text{ is a real number}\}$ considered as a set of functions in t is linearly independent over the field of real numbers. *Hint*. Use the fact that $e^{rt} \cdot e^{st} = e^{(r+s)t}$ and that $D_t e^{rt} = re^{rt}$ to conclude that $e^{r(1)t},\dots, e^{r(n)t}$ being dependent would imply that $1, e^{r(1)t-r(n)t},\dots, e^{r(n-1)t-r(n)t}$, and therefore $e^{r(1)t-r(n)t},\dots, e^{r(n-1)t-r(n)t}$ are dependent over the real numbers.

» VI · 2 SYSTEMS OF LINEAR EQUATIONS

We now consider the problem of solving a system of linear equations over a field k; namely, we wish to find all m-tuples of elements $t_1, \ldots, t_m \in k$ such that they satisfy the follow system of equations:

$$(*) \qquad \begin{cases} a_{11}t_1 + \cdots + a_{1m}t_m = b_1 , \\ \cdots \\ a_{n1}t_1 + \cdots + a_{nm}t_m = b_n , \end{cases}$$

where a_{ji} and b_j are prescribed elements of k.

We translate the given problem into a problem involving vector spaces as follows:

Let V and W be vector spaces with k-bases $X = \{x_1 \ldots, x_m\}$ and $Y = \{y_1, \ldots, y_n\}$, respectively. Let $\rho \in \mathrm{Hom}_k(V, W)$ have the matrix $(a_{ji}) \in M_{n,m}(k)$ as given in (*) with respect to the bases X and Y. It then follows that the solutions of (*) are exactly the elements of the set $\{(t_i) \in M_{m,1}(k) \mid \rho(\sum_i t_i x_i) = \sum_{i,j} t_i a_{ji} y_j = \sum_j b_j y_j\}$. In other words, we are trying to describe $\rho^{-1}(w)$ for a particular element w of W.

If we now identify V with $M_{m,1}(k)$ and W with $M_{n,1}(k)$ by sending each $\sum_i t_i x_i$ onto the column vector (t_i) and by sending each $\sum_j b_j y_j$ onto the column vector (b_j), then the given equation (*) can be written as $AT = B$, where $A = (a_{ji}) \in M_{n,m}(k)$, $T = (t_i) \in M_{m,1}(k)$, and $B = (b_j) \in M_{n,1}(k)$. Under this identification we see that im ρ is generated by the columns of A in $M_{n,1}(k)$. In fact, (*) merely asserts that B must lie in the image of ρ; namely, $B = \sum_i t_i A_{,i}$, where $A_{,i}$ stands for the ith column of A.

THEOREM 1 · Continuing with the notations above, the following assertions hold:

(a) If $v \in V$ is such that $\rho(v) = w$, then $v + \ker \rho = \rho^{-1}(w)$.

(b) There exists $v \in \rho^{-1}(w)$ if an only if rank A = rank (A, B), where $A = (a_{ji})$, $B = (b_j) \in M_{n,1}(k)$ and (A, B) is the matrix in $M_{n,m+1}(k)$ obtained by adding the column B to the right of the matrix A.

Proof · (a) is obvious; (b) follows from the observation that $\rho^{-1}(w)$ is nonempty if and only if $w \in \mathrm{im}\, \rho$. Equivalently, $\rho^{-1}(w)$ is nonempty if and only if im ρ and w generate the subspace im ρ of W. Since im ρ is contained in the subspace generated by im ρ and w, we see that im ρ = im $\rho + kw$ if and only if they have the same dimension. The latter is equivalent to the assertion that A and (A, B) should have the same column rank. «

COROLLARY · If $B = 0$ in (*) and if $m > n$, then the solutions form a subspace of V of positive dimension; namely, if the number of unknowns exceeds the number of equations, then every "homogeneous" system of equations has a nontrivial solution.

The word "homogeneous" refers to the case in which each $b_j = 0$. The word "nontrivial" refers to a solution (t_i) such that at least one t_i is nonzero. It follows from (a) of Theorem 1 that the solution set is either empty or the coset with respect to a subspace of V. Such a coset may be viewed as a "plane parallel to the subspace ker ρ." In any event, the problem (*) is broken down into two parts. The first is to find a single element in $\rho^{-1}(w)$. The second is to find ker ρ.

If the first part has a negative solution, then (*) has no solution and we are done; (b) of Theorem 1 converts the first part into a problem about the computation of the rank of matrices. By using Theorem 1.3 we convert problem into a mechanical problem of computing the determinants of the minors of the matrix $A = (a_{ji})$.

We now describe the mechanical procedure for solving (*) completely.

Continuing with the preceding notations, we assume that rank $A = r =$ rank A', where A' is the "first" $r \times r$ minor of A. We block off the matrix (A, B) as follows:

$$\left(\begin{array}{ccc|ccc|c} a_{11} & \cdots & a_{1r} & a_{1,r+1} & \cdots & a_{1m} & b_1 \\ a_{r1} & \cdots & a_{rr} & a_{r,r+1} & \cdots & a_{rm} & b_r \\ \hline \cdots & & & & & & \\ a_{n1} & \cdots & a_{nr} & a_{n,r+1} & \cdots & a_{nm} & b_n \end{array}\right).$$

We now assert that the column vector $C = (c_i) \in M_{n,1}(k)$ is in the image of ρ if and only if there are uniquely determined elements, $e_1, \ldots, e_r \in k$ such that $\sum_{1 \leqslant i \leqslant r} a_{ji} e_i = c_j$ for $1 \leqslant j \leqslant n$. It is obvious that the existence of the e_i's is both necessary and sufficient for C to be in im ρ. Since rank $\rho = r =$ rank $A =$ rank A', the first r column vectors are k-linearly independent in W. Thus they form a k-basis for im ρ and we deduce from this the uniqueness of the e_i's.

In order to find these e_i's, we consider only the first r equations: $\sum_{1 \leqslant i \leqslant r} a_{ji} e_i = c_j$, $1 \leqslant j \leqslant r$. We can write them in matrix form as $A'E = C'$, where $'$ indicates that we have truncated the matrices. Since rank $A' = r$, we see that det $A' = d \neq 0$. Thus, by multiplying the matrix equation on the left by the transpose of the cofactor matrix of A' and applying Theorem V.6.4 we see that $de_i = \sum_{1 \leqslant j \leqslant r} (-1)^{i+j} M_{ji} c_j$, $1 \leqslant i \leqslant r$. Since $d \neq 0$, we see that e_i is already determined from the first r equations. Since the e_i's are uniquely determined when $C \in \operatorname{im} \rho$, we conclude that the remaining $n - r$ equations must automatically be satisfied for these values of e_i. By using B in place of C we see that the procedure mentioned indeed may be used to solve the first part; namely, we use $b_1, \ldots, b_r$ to determine the e_i's. Using these e_i's for the last $n - r$ equations, we obtain either an identity or a contradiction. In the first case B must be in the image. In the second case B is not in the image. We can actually write out the determination of e_i's in the following form:

$$e_i = \frac{\det \begin{pmatrix} a_{11} & \cdots & c_1 & \cdots & a_{1r} \\ \vdots & & & & \vdots \\ a_{r1} & \cdots & c_r & \cdots & a_{rr} \end{pmatrix}}{\det \begin{pmatrix} a_{11} & \cdots & a_{1r} \\ \vdots & \cdots & \vdots \\ a_{r1} & \cdots & a_{rr} \end{pmatrix}}, \qquad 1 \leqslant i \leqslant r,$$

(the c's standing in the ith column)

where the c's have replaced the ith column of A'.

We now proceed to the problem of finding $\ker \rho$. This is independent of the first part. We let $A_{,i}$ denote the ith column of the matrix A. The statement that rank A = rank $A' = r$ is equivalent to the statement that $A_{,1}, \ldots, A_{,r}$ is a k-basis of $\operatorname{im} \rho$. Thus $A_{,r+1}, \ldots, A_{,m}$ are all in $\operatorname{im} \rho$. Hence, we may use $A_{,s}$ in place of C, $r < s \leqslant m$. Let $e_{i,s}$ be the elements of k obtained from the preceding procedure, $1 \leqslant i \leqslant r$, $r < s \leqslant m$. Define $e_{i,s}$ as $-\delta_{i,s}$ for $r < i$, $s \leqslant m$. Thus we have the following $m \times (m - r)$ matrix D:

$$D = \begin{pmatrix} e_{1,r+1} & \cdots & e_{1,m} \\ \vdots & & \vdots \\ e_{r,r+1} & \cdots & e_{r,m} \\ -1 & 0 \cdots & 0 \\ 0 & -1 \cdots & 0 \\ \vdots & & \vdots \\ 0 & \cdots \quad 0 \cdots & -1 \end{pmatrix}, \qquad e_{i,s} = \frac{\det \begin{pmatrix} a_{11} & \cdots & a_{1s} & \cdots & a_{1r} \\ \vdots & & & & \vdots \\ a_{r1} & \cdots & a_{rs} & \cdots & a_{rr} \end{pmatrix}}{\det \begin{pmatrix} a_{11} & \cdots & a_{1r} \\ \vdots & & \vdots \\ a_{r1} & \cdots & a_{rr} \end{pmatrix}}.$$

(in the numerator, the a_{js} stand in the ith column)

It is clear that rank $D = m - r = \dim_k V -$ rank ρ = nullity of ρ. By the construction of $e_{i,s}$, $1 \leqslant i \leqslant r$ we see that $\sum_{1 \leqslant i \leqslant r} a_{ji} e_{i,s} = a_{js}$ holds for $1 \leqslant j \leqslant r$. The equation also holds for $r < j \leqslant n$, since $A_{,s}$ is in the image of ρ. Since $e_{i,s} = -\delta_{js}$ for $j > r$, it follows that the columns of D are in $\ker \rho$. Since rank D = nullity of $\rho = \dim_k \ker \rho$, it follows that the columns of D form a k-basis for $\ker \rho$.

The description given above is a generalization of Cramer's rule, which is the procedure for the case $m = n$ and rank $A = m$; namely, the solutions are represented as the ratio of two determinants. In the future we shall loosely refer to our procedure as "Cramer's Rule."

Exercise 1 · Solve the following system of equations over the field **Q**:

$$\begin{cases} x + 3y + 5z + u = 6 \\ \quad 5y - 2z \quad = 3 \\ 2x \quad + z + u = -2 \end{cases}$$

Exercise 2 · Suppose that $A \in GL(n, k)$, where k is a field. Consider the matrix $(A, I) \in M_{n,2n}(k)$, where I is the identity matrix of $GL(n, k)$. Show that by using only row operations the matrix (A, I) can be converted into the matrix (I, B), where B must necessarily be the inverse of A. *Hint*. Recall that row operations correspond to left multiplication by elementary matrices and that $GL(n, k)$ is generated by elementary matrices.

Exercise 3 · Use the technique mentioned in Exercise 2 to compute the inverse of the following matrix:

$$\begin{pmatrix} 1 & 5 & 0 & 3 \\ 2 & 9 & 3 & 2 \\ 4 & 18 & 5 & 3 \\ 3 & 14 & 3 & 4 \end{pmatrix}.$$

Exercise 4 · Use the technique mentioned in Exercise 2 to describe a procedure for computing $A^{-1}C$, where $A \in GL(n, k)$ and $C \in M_{n,m}(k)$. Describe how one might use the technique to solve a system of linear equations.

Exercise 5 · Use the technique mentioned in Exercise 2 to describe a procedure that could lead to the calculation of the determinant of an $n \times n$ matrix.

» VI · 3 DECOMPOSITION OF A VECTOR SPACE WITH RESPECT TO A LINEAR ENDOMORPHISM

In Section VI.1 we considered and solved the equivalence problem of elements in $\mathrm{Hom}_k(V, W)$ under the action of $GL_k(V)$ and $GL_k(W)$. We now consider the conjugacy problem of elements in $\mathrm{Hom}_k(V, V)$. We recall that $\rho, \sigma \in \mathrm{Hom}_k(V, V)$ are said to be ***conjugate*** if and only if there exists $\theta \in GL_k(V)$ such that $\rho = \theta^{-1} \circ \sigma \circ \theta$. In terms of matrices, we have seen that this is equivalent to the statement that ρ

and σ should have the same matrix with respect to suitably selected bases for the k-vector space V. The solution of this problem depends on the conversion of V into a torsion module over the PID $k[\lambda]$, where λ is an indeterminate over the field k.

DEFINITION 1 · Let V be a vector space over a field k. Suppose that W is a k-subspace of V and that $T \subset \mathrm{Hom}_k(V, V)$.

(a) W is said to be T-***invariant***, or T-***stable***, if and only if $\rho(W) \subset W \; \forall \rho \in T$.

(b) W is said to be T-***irreducible***, or T-***simple***, if and only if (1) $W \neq 0$, (2) W is T-stable, and (3) 0, W are the only T-stable subspaces of W.

(c) W is said to be T-***indecomposable*** if and only if (1) $W \neq 0$, (2) W is T-stable, and (3) W is not the direct sum of two nonzero T-stable subspaces of W.

(d) W is said to be T-***cyclic*** if and only if W is the T-stable subspace generated by a single element.

Exercise 1 · Continuing with the notations of Definition 1, show that all the concepts are unchanged if we replace T by the k-subalgebra of $\mathrm{Hom}_k(V, V)$ generated by the subset T, where $\mathrm{Hom}_k(V, V)$ is considered as a k-algebra through the map that sends $a \in k$ onto $aI : V \to V$ such that $(aI)(x) = ax \; \forall x \in V$.

Exercise 1 has the following important special case:

If, in the notations of Definition 1, $T = \{\rho\}$, then T may be replaced by the commutative k-subalgebra $k[\rho]$ of $\mathrm{Hom}_k(V, V)$; $k[\rho]$ is precisely the image of the polynomial ring $k[\lambda]$ under the "substitution" map that sends $a \in k$ onto aI and λ onto ρ.

Exercise 2 · Continuing with the notation of Definition 1, show that each T-stable subspace W of V is a left S-module, where S is the k-subalgebra of $\mathrm{Hom}_k(V, V)$ generated by T. Show that the T-cyclic (equivalently, the S-cyclic) subspace generated by $v \in V$ is $\{\rho(v) | \rho \in S\}$.

THEOREM 1 · Let V be a finite-dimensional vector space over a field k. Let λ be an indeterminate over the field k. Then, for each $\rho \in \mathrm{Hom}_k(V, V)$, the "substitution" homomorphism $k[\lambda] \to k[\rho]/k$ converts V into a torsion-module of finite type over the PID $k[\lambda]$. (In our notation we have identified k with a subfield contained in the center of $\text{Hom}_k(V, V)$ through the map that sends $a \in k$ onto $aI : V \to V$ such that $(aI)(x) = ax \; \forall \; x \in V$.)

Proof · From Exercises 1 and 2 we already know that V is a $k[\lambda]$-module. Since $\dim_k V$ is finite, it is clear that V is of finite type. Since $\dim_k V$ is finite, we see that $\dim_k \text{Hom}_k(V, V) = (\dim_k V)^2$ is also finite. Thus the kernel of the substitution homomorphism must be a nonzero ideal of $k[\lambda]$. It follows that a nonzero element of the kernel must lie in the annihilator ideal of every element $v \in V$. «

DEFINITION 2 · Let V be a k-vector space of finite dimension. Let λ be an indeterminate over the field k. If $\rho \in \text{Hom}_k(V, V)$, the monic polynomial $m(\lambda, \rho) \in k[\lambda]$ that generates the kernel of the substitution homomorphism described in Theorem 1 is called the ***minimal-polynomial*** of ρ. Similarly, if ρ has the matrix $(a_{ji}) \in M_m(k)$ with respect to some k-basis of V, then $m(\lambda, \rho)$ is also called the ***minimal-polynomial*** of (a_{ji}). In this case we often write $m(\lambda, (a_{ji}))$.

THEOREM 2 · Let V be a finite-dimensional vector space over a field k. Then the following assertions hold:

(a) If $\sigma \in GL_k(V)$, then $\iota(\sigma) : \text{Hom}_k(V, V) \to \text{Hom}_k(V, V)$, defined by $\iota(\sigma)(\rho) = \sigma \circ \rho \circ \sigma^{-1} \; \forall \; \rho \in \text{Hom}_k(V, V)$, is a k-algebra automorphism of $\text{Hom}_k(V, V)$. The map ι is a group homomorphism of $GL_k(V)$ into the group of all k-algebra automorphisms of $\text{Hom}_k(V, V)$; $\ker \iota$ is the image of $k - \{0\}$ under the identification of $a \in k$ with $aI \in \text{Hom}_k(V, V)$. (In fact, j is surjective, but we shall not prove this assertion.)

(b) The minimal polynomial $m(\lambda, \rho)$ and the characteristic polynomial $\chi(\lambda, \rho)$ are monic polynomials that depend only on the conjugacy class of ρ in $\text{Hom}_k(V, V)$.

Proof · The verification of (a) is straightforward. Since $m(\lambda, \rho)$ generated the kernel of an algebra homomorphism, it is easy to see that $m(\lambda, \rho)$ is unchanged by algebra automorphisms of $\text{Hom}_k(V, V)$. The statement concerning the characteristic polynomial has already been verified. «

Exercise V.1.4 can now be rephrased into the following theorem.

THEOREM 3 · Let λ be an indeterminate over a field k. Suppose that $f(\lambda)$ is a monic polynomial of degree m, $m \in \mathbf{P}^+$. Then the following assertions hold:

(a) Under left multiplication by elements of $k[\lambda]$, $k[\lambda]/(f(\lambda)) = V$ is a $k[\lambda]$-cyclic module. V is a ρ-cyclic vector space of dimension n, where $\rho \in \operatorname{Hom}_k(V, V)$ is defined as multiplication by λ; $m(\lambda, \rho) = \chi(\lambda, \rho) = f(\lambda)$. A k-basis of V is formed by the coset of $1, \lambda, \dots, \lambda^{n-1}$. With respect to this k-basis, ρ has the following matrix:

$$\begin{pmatrix} 0 & 0 & 0 \cdots 0 & -a_0 \\ 1 & 0 & 0 \cdots 0 & -a_1 \\ 0 & 1 & 0 \quad\; 0 & -a_2 \\ & \cdots & & \\ 0 & 0 & 0 \cdots 1 & -a_{n-1} \end{pmatrix},$$

where $f(\lambda) = \lambda^n + a_{n-1}\lambda^{n-1} + \cdots + a_1\lambda + a_0$.

(b) If V is a ρ-cyclic vector space of dimension n over k, where $\rho \in \operatorname{Hom}_k(V, V)$, then for each generator v of V the map that sends λ^i onto $\rho^i(v)$ leads to an isomorphism of $k[\lambda]/(m(\lambda, \rho))$ with V, where both are considered as $k[\lambda]$-modules. In particular, $m(\lambda, \rho)$ generates the annihilator ideal of v; moreover, $m(\lambda, \rho) = \chi(\lambda, \rho)$.

Proof · By using the Euclidean division algorithm we see that the cosets of $1, \lambda, \dots, \lambda^{n-1}$ form a k-basis for the vector space $k[\lambda]/(f(\lambda))$. Under the given definition of ρ it is clear that V so defined is ρ-cyclic with the coset of 1 as a generator. The remaining assertions of (a) are easy consequences of these remarks. The characteristic polynomial of ρ can be computed easily from the matrix of ρ exhibited.

We now examine the homomorphism described in (b). By considering $k[\lambda]$ as a module over itself with respect to left multiplications we see that the given map is a $k[\lambda]$-module homomorphism of $k[\lambda]$ into V. Because V is ρ-cyclic, the map is surjective. The kernel is precisely the $k[\lambda]$-submodule (namely, the ideal) generated by $m(\lambda, \rho)$. Our assertion now follows from the first isomorphism theorem. «

By combining Theorem 1, Theorem 3, and the fundamental theorem on modules of finite type over a PID, we have the following result:

THEOREM 4 · Continuing with the notations of Theorems 1 and 3, the following assertions hold:

(a) If $d_i(\lambda) \in k[\lambda]$, $1 \leqslant i \leqslant t$, are the monic elementary divisors of the $k[\lambda]$-module V, then $d_i(\lambda)$, $1 \leqslant i \leqslant t$, are uniquely determined monic polynomials satisfying the following conditions:

(1) V is $k[\lambda]$-isomorphic to the direct sum of the $k[\lambda]$-cyclic modules, $k[\lambda]/(d_i(\lambda))$, $1 \leqslant i \leqslant t$, constructed in (a) of Theorem 1.

(2) $\deg_\lambda d_i(\lambda) > 0$, $1 \leqslant i \leqslant t$ and $d_i(\lambda) \mid d_{i+1}(\lambda)$, $1 \leqslant i \leqslant t-1$.

(b) In the notation of (a) $d_t(\lambda) = m(\lambda, \rho)$ and $\prod_{1 \leqslant i \leqslant t} d_i(\lambda) = \chi(\lambda, \rho)$.

(c) (Cayley-Hamilton) $m(\lambda, \rho) \mid \chi(\lambda, \rho)$, that is, every matrix in $M_n(k)$ is a zero of its characteristic polynomial, where $n = \dim_k V$.

(d) $\chi(\lambda, \rho) \mid m(\lambda, \rho)^n$, $n = \dim_k V$. Thus $m(\lambda, \rho)$ and $\chi(\lambda, \rho)$ have the same set of irreducible factors in $k[\lambda]$.

Proof · (a) follows directly from the fundamental theorem for modules of finite type over a PID. The reader should keep in mind that V is a torsion module and that we have normalized the elementary divisors to be monic polynomials. The statement on $m(\lambda, \rho)$ in (b) follows from the fact that ρ acts through multiplication by the coset of λ on each of the direct summands. The statement on $\chi(\lambda, \rho)$ follows from taking the bases indicated in Theorem 3(a) for each of the direct summands. In any event, it is a special case of Exercise 3; (c) and (d) are immediate consequences of (b) and the fact that $k[\lambda]$ is a PID. «

Exercise 3 · Let V be a vector space of finite dimension over a field k. Let $\rho \in \mathrm{Hom}_k(V, V)$. Suppose that W is a ρ-stable subspace of V. Thus ρ induces $\rho_W \in \mathrm{Hom}_k(W, W)$ and $\rho_{V/W} \in \mathrm{Hom}_k(V/W, V/W)$. Show that $\chi(\lambda, \rho) = \chi(\lambda, \rho_W) \cdot \chi(\lambda, \rho_{V/W})$. Conclude that $\det \rho = \det \rho_W \cdot \det \rho_{V/W}$ and that $\operatorname{tr} \rho = \operatorname{tr} \rho_W + \operatorname{tr} \rho_{V/W}$. *Hint.* Start with a k-basis for W and expand it to a k-basis for V. Using the fact that W is ρ-stable, show that the matrix of ρ has a special form. Suppose that V is the direct sum of the ρ-stable subspaces V_1 and V_2. Show that $m(\lambda, \rho)$ is the least common multiple of $m(\lambda, \rho_1)$ and $m(\lambda, \rho_2)$, where ρ_i is the restriction of ρ to V_i, $i = 1, 2$.

COROLLARY · Continuing with the notations of Theorem 4, we find that the following assertions hold:

(a) If $\chi(\lambda, \rho) = g(\lambda)\, h(\lambda)$, where g and h are monic polynomials that are coprime in $k[\lambda]$, then V is the direct sum of uniquely determined ρ-stable subspaces V_g and V_h such that $\chi(\lambda, \rho_{V_g}) = g(\lambda)$ and $\chi(\lambda, \rho_{V_h}) = h(\lambda)$.

(b) V is ρ-cyclic if and only if $\chi(\lambda, \rho) = m(\lambda, \rho)$.

(c) V is ρ-irreducible if and only if $\chi(\lambda, \rho)$ is an irreducible polynomial in $k[\lambda]$.

(d) V is ρ-indecomposable if and only if (1) V is ρ-cyclic and (2) $m(\lambda, \rho)$ is a power of an irreducible polynomial in $k[\lambda]$.

Proof · Exercise.

We may now summarize our results by setting up a table of correspondence between V, $\rho \in \mathrm{Hom}_k(V, V)$, and the case of a finite abelian group G. If we wish, we may consider G as a **Z**-module and take $\rho \in \mathrm{Hom}_{\mathbf{Z}}(G, G)$ to be the identity map I.

V, ρ	G, I
$\chi(\lambda, \rho)$	$\lvert G \rvert$
$m(\lambda, \rho)$, the monic polynomial that generates the least common multiple of the annihilator ideals of the elements of V.	Least common multiple of $\lvert g \rvert$, $g \in G$; often called the **exponent** of G.
V is ρ-cyclic.	G is a cyclic group.
V is ρ-irreducible.	G is a simple group.
V is ρ-indecomposable.	G is a cyclic group of prime-power order (greater than 1).
$m(\lambda, \rho)$ is irreducible; thus $\chi(\lambda, \rho)$ is the power of an irreducible polynomial.	G is a group of prime-power order (greater than 1) and every non-identity element of G has prime order.

Exercise 4 · Consider vector spaces over **Q**. Determine the characteristic polynomial and the minimal polynomial in each of the following cases:

(a) $\begin{pmatrix} 1 & a \\ 0 & 1 \end{pmatrix}$, $\begin{pmatrix} 0 & 1 \\ a & 0 \end{pmatrix}$, $\begin{pmatrix} a & 0 \\ 0 & b \end{pmatrix}$.

(b) Let V be the **Q**-vector space of polynomials of degree less than n in the indeterminate X. Let $\rho \in \mathrm{Hom}_k(V, V)$ be given by $\rho(X^i) = iX^{i-1}$.

In each of these cases determine when the underlying vector space is indecomposable, irreducible, or cyclic with respect to the linear transformation specified.

Exercise 5 · Repeat Exercise 4 with **Q** replaced by $\mathbf{Z}/(p)$ throughout, where p is a prime in $\mathbf{P}^+$.

Exercise 6 · Set up the correspondence between V, ρ, and the case of a finite abelian p-group G together with the pth power map of G into G.

Exercise 7 · Let ρ have this matrix in $M_4(\mathbf{Q})$:

$$\begin{pmatrix} 2 & 0 & -6 & 10 \\ 0 & 0 & 0 & 8 \\ -4 & 2 & 0 & 0 \\ 0 & 2 & -4 & 0 \end{pmatrix}.$$

Find the decomposition of the four-dimensional vector space V as a module over $k[\lambda]$, where λ acts through the element ρ.

Hint. To find the internal decomposition of V is not easy. However, it is possible to calculate the elementary divisors of V as follows:

(a) $\chi(\lambda, \rho) = \det(\lambda I_4 - \rho) = \lambda^4 - 2\lambda^3 + 8\lambda^2 - 96\lambda + 256.$

(b) Since $\mathbf{Q}$ is the field of fractions of the UFD $\mathbf{Z}$, any monic irreducible factor of $\chi(\lambda, \rho)$ may be realized in $\mathbf{Z}[\lambda]$. Thus the linear factors of $\chi(\lambda, \rho)$ must have the form $\lambda - a$, $a \in \mathbf{Z}$. It follows that $a \mid 256$ and $|\, a \,|$ must be a power of 2. Use of the factor theorem makes clear that $a > 0$. Simple calculation shows that $a < 8$. A check of the cases $a = 1, 2$, and 4 will convince us that $\chi(\lambda, \rho)$ has no linear factors. Thus the only possible factorization of $\chi(\lambda, \rho)$ falls within one of the following cases:

(1) $\chi(\lambda, \rho)$ is irreducible and V is ρ-irreducible.

(2) $\chi(\lambda, \rho)$ is the product of two distinct monic irreducible polynomials of degree 2. V is then the direct sum of two nonisomorphic ρ-irreducible subspaces (see the corollary).

(3) $\chi(\lambda, \rho)$ is the square of an irreducible monic polynomial $f(\lambda)$ of degree 2. We now have two possibilities:

(α) $f(\rho) = 0$. In this case $f(\lambda)$ is the minimal polynomial of ρ and V is the direct sum of two isomorphic ρ-irreducible subspaces.

(β) $f(\rho) \neq 0$. In this case V is ρ-indecomposable but not ρ-irreducible.

In the preceding theorems we have converted the pair (V, ρ) into a torsion-module of finite type over the PID $k[\lambda]$. We still have to solve the conjugacy problem of elements of $\mathrm{Hom}_k(V, V)$. It will be shown shortly that the elementary divisors of the module V over $k[\lambda]$ form a complete set of invariants. In order to do this we must find a "reasonable" presentation matrix for the $k[\lambda]$-module V.

THEOREM 5 · Let V be a vector space of dimension n over a field k. Let $\rho \in \mathrm{Hom}_k(V, V)$ have the matrix $(a_{ji}) \in M_n(k)$ with respect to the k-basis $X = \{x_i \mid 1 \leqslant i \leqslant n\}$. Let W be the free $k[\lambda]$-module of dimension n with the free $k[\lambda]$-basis $X = \{x_i \mid 1 \leqslant i \leqslant n\}$. Define $\sigma \in \mathrm{Hom}_{k[\lambda]}(W, W)$ by setting $\sigma(x_i) = \lambda x_i - \sum_j a_{ji}x_j$, $1 \leqslant i \leqslant n$. Then the $k[\lambda]$-module V, through ρ, has the following presentation: $0 \to W \xrightarrow{\sigma} W \xrightarrow{\tau} V \to 0$, where $\tau \in \mathrm{Hom}_{k[\lambda]}(W, V)$ sends $f(\lambda)x_i$ onto $f(\rho)x_i \; \forall\, i$. In particular, the presentation matrix of σ with respect to the free $k[\lambda]$-basis X of W is $\lambda I_n - (a_{ji}) \in M_n(k[\lambda])$.

Proof · Before we proceed with the proof, the reader should observe that it is not necessary to select a k-basis for V. W is simply the $k[\lambda]$-module $k[\lambda] \otimes_k V$, σ is the map $\lambda \otimes I_V - I \otimes \rho$, and τ is the evaluation map induced by ρ, namely $\tau(f(\lambda) \otimes x) = (f(\rho))(x)$.

We first assert that σ is injective. If $w \in W$, then define $\deg w$ = maximum of the degree of the coefficients of w in terms of x_i. It is clear that $\deg(u + v) \leqslant \deg u + \deg v$, $\deg(f(\lambda)u) = \deg f(\lambda) + \deg u$, where $u, v \in W$. It is also clear that $\deg(\sigma(w)) = \deg w + 1$. Using the fact that $\deg w = -\infty$ if and only if $w = 0$, we see that σ is injective. In terms of tensor product and ground ring extension, we see that $k[\lambda] \otimes_k V = \cup_{n \in \mathbf{P}} P_n \otimes V$, where P_n is the subspace of all polynomials of degree at most n. $P_n \otimes V$ is increasing with n. Elements of $P_n \otimes V$ which are not in $P_{n-1} \otimes V$ can be given the degree n. It is clear that $\lambda \otimes I_V - 1 \otimes \rho$ increases the degree by 1, hence it is injective.

Since $\tau(\sigma(x_i)) = \tau(\lambda x_i) - \tau(\sum_j a_{ji}x_i) = \rho(x_i) - \sum_j a_{ji}x_j = 0$, we see that $\operatorname{im} \sigma \subset \ker \tau$. Since $\tau(x_i) = x_i$, we see that τ is surjective. Suppose that $\sum_i f_i(\lambda)x_i \in \ker \tau$; that is, $\sum_i f_i(\rho)(x_i) = 0$. We consider ρ also as an element of $\mathrm{Hom}_{k[\lambda]}(W, W)$ defined by reading the equations defining ρ in W; namely, $\rho(x_i) = \sum_j a_{ji}x_j$. Since λI is in the ring $\mathrm{Hom}_{k[\lambda]}(W, W)$, we see that $f(\lambda I) - f(\rho) = (\lambda I - \rho) - g$ holds for a suitable element g of $\mathrm{Hom}_{k[\lambda]}(W, W)$. The point is that the factor theorem holds for expressions of the form $\lambda^m I - \rho^m$ as long as λI and ρ lie in the same ring and λI lies in the center. Thus, $\sum_i f_i(\lambda)x_i = \sum_i (f_i(\lambda I) - f_i(\rho))x_i = \sum_i (\lambda I - \rho)(g_i(x_i)) = \sigma(\sum_i g_i(x_i))$ for suitable $g_i(x_i) \in W$, and $\ker \tau \subset \operatorname{im} \sigma$. We have verified the exactness of the sequence exhibited in the theorem. The remaining assertions are now obvious. «

DEFINITION 3 · Let V be a vector space of dimension n over a field k. Let $\rho \in \mathrm{Hom}_k(V, V)$. Then the presentation in Theorem 5 is called the ***canonical presentation*** of the $k[\lambda]$-module associated to ρ.

We observe that the map σ is injective in the canonical presentation. Thus the elementary divisors of the presentation matrix of σ are the elementary divisors of the $k[\lambda]$-module V.

THEOREM 6 · Let V be a finite dimensional vector space over a field k. Let $\rho, \sigma \in \mathrm{Hom}_k(V, V)$ have the matrices (a_{ji}) and (b_{ji}) in $M_n(k)$ with respect to the k-bases X and Y, respectively. Then the following statements are equivalent:

(a) ρ and σ are conjugate with respect to $GL_k(V)$.

(b) (a_{ji}) and (b_{ji}) are conjugate with respect to $GL(n, k)$.

(c) $\lambda I - (a_{ji})$ and $\lambda I - (b_{ji})$ are conjugate with respect to $GL(n, k[\lambda])$.

(d) The $k[\lambda]$-module V associated to ρ is $k[\lambda]$-isomorphic to the $k[\lambda]$-module V associated to σ.

(e) $\lambda I - (a_{ji})$ and $\lambda I - (b_{ji})$ have the same set of monic elementary divisors as presentation matrices in $M_n(k[\lambda])$, where $n = \dim_k V$.

Proof · We already know that (a) and (b) are equivalent. We also know that (d) and (e) are equivalent.

We now consider the substitution homomorphism $k[\lambda] \to k[0]/k$. This induces a ring homomorphism of $M_n(k[\lambda]) \to M_n(k)$.

If (b) holds, then we can find $(c_{ji}) \in GL(n, k)$ such that $(a_{ji}) = (c_{ji})^{-1}(b_{ji})(c_{ji})$. Since λI is in the center of $GL(n, k[\lambda])$, it is clear that $\lambda I - (a_{ji}) = (c_{ji})^{-1}(\lambda I - (b_{ji}))(c_{ji})$. Thus (b) implies (c). Conversely, suppose that $A(\lambda) \in M_n(k[\lambda])$ is invertible and that $\lambda I - (a_{ji}) = (A(\lambda))^{-1}(\lambda I - (b_{ji}))\, A(\lambda)$. Since $A(\lambda)^{-1}A(\lambda) = I = A(\lambda)\, A(\lambda)^{-1}$, we may apply the substitution homomorphism to this equation to conclude that $A(0) \in GL(n, k)$. Similarly, by applying the substitution homomorphism to the equation for $\lambda I - (a_{ji})$ and taking the additive inverse we see that (c) also implies (b). Thus (b) and (c) are equivalent. (d) holds if and only if there exists $\theta \in GL_k(V)$ such that $\theta(f(\rho)(x)) = f(\sigma)(\theta(x))$ $\forall\, x \in V$ and $f(\lambda) \in k[\lambda]$. The point to recall is that $f(\lambda)$ acts on V according to $f(\rho)$ and according to $f(\sigma)$ in the respective $k[\lambda]$-module structure on V. Taking the special case $f(\lambda) = \lambda$ and applying θ^{-1} to both sides of our equation, we see that (d) implies (a). Conversely, since conjugation by θ is a k-algebra automorphism of $\mathrm{Hom}_k(V, V)$, we see that $\theta^{-1} \circ \sigma \circ \theta = \rho$ implies that $\theta^{-1} \circ f(\sigma) \circ \theta = f(\rho)$ $\forall\, f(\lambda) \in k[\lambda]$. Thus (a) implies (d). We have now verified the theorem. «

Exercise 8 · Use Theorem 6 to do Exercise 7 a second time. In particular, compute the elementary divisors of the corresponding presentation matrix by using the computation involving determinantal divisors.

Exercise 9 · Let V be a finite-dimensional vector space over a field k. Consider the $k[\lambda]$-module V through $\rho \in \operatorname{Hom}_k(V, V)$. Verify the following assertions:

(a) If V is ρ-cyclic, then $\operatorname{Hom}_{k[\lambda]}(V, V)$ is isomorphic to the k-algebra $k[\lambda]/(m(\lambda, \rho))$.

(b) If V is ρ-cyclic, then every element of the centralizer of ρ in $\operatorname{Hom}_k(V, V)$ is a polynomial in ρ.

» VI · 4 CANONICAL FORMS OF MATRICES: CHARACTERISTIC VALUES: CHARACTERISTIC VECTORS

Throughout this section we assume that V is a vector space of dimension n over a field k; ρ denotes an element of $\operatorname{Hom}_k(V, V)$, and λ denotes an indeterminate over k.

DEFINITION 1 · Let $f(\lambda) = \lambda^n + a_{n-1}\lambda^{n-1} + \cdots + a_0$, $a_i \in k$. The following matrix in $M_n(k)$ is called the ***Jordan companion matrix*** associated to $f(\lambda)$.

$$\begin{pmatrix} 0 & 0 & 0 \cdots 0 & -a_0 \\ 1 & 0 & 0 \cdots 0 & -a_1 \\ 0 & 1 & 0 \cdots 0 & -a_2 \\ & \cdots & & \\ 0 & 0 & 0 \quad\; 1 & -a_{n-1} \end{pmatrix}.$$

From results in the preceding section we see that V is ρ-cyclic if and only if the matrix of ρ with respect to a suitable k-basis of V is the Jordan companion matrix associated with $\chi(\lambda, \rho)$.

DEFINITION 2 · Let $m(\lambda)$ be a monic, irreducible polynomial of degree s and $f(\lambda) = m(\lambda)^t$ such that $st = n$. Let $P \in M_s(k)$ be the Jordan companion matrix of $m(\lambda)$ and let $N \in M_s(k)$ be the matrix whose only nonzero entry is the element 1 in the $(1, s)$ position. The following matrix in $M_n(k) = M_{st}(k)$ is called the ***Jordan canonical matrix*** associated with $f(\lambda)$.

$$\begin{pmatrix} P & 0 & 0 & 0 \cdots 0 & 0 \\ N & P & 0 & 0 \cdots 0 & 0 \\ 0 & N & P & 0 \cdots 0 & 0 \\ \cdots & & & & \\ 0 & 0 & 0 & 0 \cdots N & P \end{pmatrix},$$

where 0 stands for the zero matrix in $M_s(k)$.

THEOREM 1 · V is ρ-indecomposable if and only if there is a suitable k-basis X for V such that the matrix of ρ with respect to X is the Jordan canonical matrix associated with $\chi(\lambda, \rho) = m(\lambda)^t$, where $m(\lambda)$ is a monic, irreducible polynomial in $k[\lambda]$ of degree s and $n = st$.

Proof · From the preceding section we know that V is ρ-indecomposable if and only if V is isomorphic to the $k[\lambda]$-module $k[\lambda]/(m(\lambda)^t)$, where $\chi(\lambda, \rho) = m(\lambda)^t$, $m(\lambda)$ is monic and irreducible. The action of ρ corresponds to left multiplication by the coset determined by λ. It is clear that the cosets determined by any set of monic polynomials of degrees $i = 0, 1, \ldots, st - 1$, $st = n = \dim_k V$ can be used as a k-basis for $k[\lambda]/(m(\lambda)^t)$. If we select the polynomials $f_{is+j}(\lambda) = m(\lambda)^i \lambda^j$, $0 \leqslant i < t$, $0 \leqslant j < s$, an easy calculation will show that the matrix corresponding to left multiplication by λ is precisely the Jordan canonical matrix associated with $m(\lambda)^t$. «

DEFINITION 3 · Let $\alpha \in k$. Then $\ker(\alpha I - \rho)$ is called the ***characteristic subspace*** of V corresponding to the ***characteristic value*** α in k. Nonzero elements of $\ker(\alpha I - \rho)$ are called the ***characteristic vectors*** associated with the characteristic value $\alpha \in k$; $\alpha \in k$ is called a ***characteristic root*** of ρ if and only if $(\lambda - \alpha) \mid \chi(\lambda, \rho)$ in $k[\lambda]$. By extending the ground field k to a bigger field K we may take α to lie in K. In such a case V is replaced by $K \otimes_k V$ and ρ is replaced by $1 \otimes \rho$. In the literature the word "proper" and the word "eigen" are often used in place of the word "characteristic."

THEOREM 2 · Let $\alpha \in k$. Then the following assertions hold:

(a) $\ker(\alpha I - \rho)$ is a ρ-stable subspace of V.

(b) $\ker(\alpha I - \rho)$ is nonzero if and only if α is a characteristic root of ρ.

Proof · (a) follows easily from the fact that $\alpha I - \rho$ lies in the commutative k-subalgebra generated by ρ in $\mathrm{Hom}_k(V, V)$.

From Cramer's rule we see that $\ker(\alpha I - \rho)$ is nonzero if and only if $\det(\alpha I - \rho) = 0$. From Theorem V.6.4 we see that the determinant of a matrix is a "universal" polynomial in the entries of the matrix. Thus the substitution homomorphism $k[\lambda] \to k[\alpha]/k$ sends $\det(\lambda I - \rho)$ onto $\det(\alpha I - \rho)$; (b) now follows from the factor theorem. «

The assertion (b) makes the characteristic polynomial quite useful. Moreover, because of condition (b), characteristic roots are the "interesting" characteristic values. The reader should be aware that ρ may have no characteristic root in the given field k. It may very well be necessary to "enlarge" k to a bigger field in order to find a characteristic root of ρ.

Excursion VII

We now exhibit the use of some of our results in proving the existence and uniqueness of solutions to a system of ordinary linear homogeneous differential equations with complex constant coefficients.

We assume that the following facts are known to the reader:

I. The field $\mathbf{C}$ of complex numbers contains $\mathbf{Q}$ as a subfield, and every irreducible polynomial in $\mathbf{C}[X]$ has degree 1, where X is an indeterminate over $\mathbf{C}$.

II. The function $\exp : \mathbf{C} \to \mathbf{C}$ given by $\exp(t) = e^t$ is infinitely differentiable. It has the following properties:

(a) $e^0 = 1$, $e^{(\alpha+\beta)t} = e^{\alpha t} \cdot e^{\beta t}$, $\alpha, \beta \in \mathbf{C}$.

(b) $D_t(e^{\alpha t}) = \alpha e^{\alpha t}$, $\alpha \in \mathbf{C}$, and D_t is the differentiation operator with respect to t.

I and II may be summarized into the following statement:

LEMMA · Let A be the $\mathbf{C}$-algebra of all infinitely differentiable functions from $\mathbf{C}$ to $\mathbf{C}$. Let $D_t : A \to A$ be the differentiation operator. Then the following assertions hold:

(a) Each polynomial in $\mathbf{C}[t]$ defines a polynomial function through the substitution homomorphism. $\mathbf{C}[t]$ is $\mathbf{C}$-isomorphic to the subalgebra of all polynomial functions in A.

(b) D_t is a $\mathbf{C}$-derivation of A.

(c) $e^{\alpha t} \in \ker(\alpha I - D_t)$. Moreover, $e^{\alpha t}$ is a unit of the algebra A.

(d) The map that sends t onto $e^{\alpha t}$ is a homomorphism of $\mathbf{C}, +$ into the group of units in A. Thus it leads to a homomorphism of $\mathbf{C}, +$ into the group of $\mathbf{C}$-automorphisms of the $\mathbf{C}$-vector space A.

Let $\alpha \in \mathbf{C}$ and define $(a_{ji}) \in M_n(\mathbf{C})$ as the Jordan canonical matrix associated to $(\lambda - \alpha)^n$. Thus $a_{ii} = \alpha$, $a_{i+1,i} = 1$, $1 \leqslant i \leqslant n - 1$, and all other entries of (a_{ji}) are 0. Consider $M_{n,1}(A)$ as a left **C**-vector space under coordinatewise multiplication by elements of **C**. Let $W(\alpha) = \{(y_i) \in M_{n,1}(A) \mid D_t y_i = \sum_j a_{ji} y_j\}$. Thus $W(\alpha)$ is the solution space of the following system of differential equations:

$$(*)_\alpha \qquad D_t y_i = \sum_j a_{ji} y_j \,.$$

It is clear that $W(\alpha)$ is a **C**-subspace of $M_{n,1}(A)$. If we use the lemma, it follows easily that $e^{\beta t} W(\alpha) \subset W(\alpha + \beta)$, where $M_{n,1}(A)$ is also considered as a left A-module under coordinatewise multiplication by elements of A. Since $e^{\beta t}$ has the inverse $e^{-\beta t}$, we conclude easily that $W(\alpha + \beta) = e^{\beta t}\, W(\alpha)$. In particular, $W(\alpha) = e^{\alpha t}\, W(0)$.

The system $(*)_0$ can be rewritten into the form

$$D_t^n(y_1) = 0, y_2 = D_t y_1 ,..., y_n = D_t y_{n-1} = \cdots = D_t^{n-1}(y_1).$$

Thus y_1 determines $y_2 ,..., y_n$ uniquely. It follows that $(*)_0$ is equivalent to the solution of the nth order differential equation $D_t^n(y_1) = 0$. By using induction on n and a mean value type argument it is easy to verify that y_1 must be a polynomial of degree less than or equal to $n - 1$. It follows that $W(0)$ is a **C**-vector space of dimension n with **C**-basis formed by the columns of the following matrix:

$$\begin{pmatrix} 1 & t & t^2 \cdots & t^{n-1} \\ 0 & 1 & 2t \cdots & (n-1)t^{n-2} \\ \cdots & & & \\ 0 & 0 & 0 \cdots & (n-1)! \end{pmatrix}.$$

We now consider an arbitrary system of homogeneous linear differential equations with constant coefficients in **C** as follows:

$$(**)_y \qquad D_t y_i = \sum_j a_{ji} y_j \,, 1 \leqslant i, j \leqslant n, (a_{ji}) \in M_n(\mathbf{C}).$$

The reader should be aware that the y_i's are not the basis elements of a suitable **C**-vector space. They are the components of an element of the free A-module $M_{n,1}(A)$.

Suppose that $(b_{ji}) \in GL(n, \mathbf{C})$ has the inverse $(c_{ji}) \in GL(n, \mathbf{C})$. We may consider the new elements $z_i = \sum_j b_{ji} y_j$, $1 \leqslant i, j < n$. Since (b_{ji}) has the inverse (c_{ji}), we know that $y_i = \sum_j c_{ji} z_j$, $1 \leqslant i, j \leqslant n$. By substitution we see that $(**)_y$ implies the following system:

$$(**)_z \qquad D_t z_i = \sum_{j,k,l} c_{lk} a_{kj} b_{ji} z_l \,.$$

By reversing the substitution we see that $(**)_z$ implies the system $(**)_y$ given. Indeed, the solution space $W(z)$ of $(**)_z$ is obtained from $W(y)$ by left multiplying the elements of $W(y)$ by the transpose of the matrix (b_{ji}). In any event, the coefficient matrix $(c_{lk})(a_{kj})(b_{ji})$ of $(**)_z$ is a conjugate of the coefficient matrix (a_{ji}) of $(**)_y$.

Let V be a vector space of dimension n over $\mathbf{C}$. Let $\rho \in \mathrm{Hom}_{\mathbf{C}}(V, V)$ have the matrix (a_{ji}) with respect some $\mathbf{C}$-basis of V. From Theorem 3.6 we may conclude that the $k[\lambda]$-module V through the action of ρ is independent of the change of the system $(**)_y$ obtained by applying elements of $GL(n, \mathbf{C})$ to the solution space $W(y)$ of $(**)_y$. Thus we may assume that (b_{ji}) is selected so that the following conditions are satisfied:

(a) $(b_{ji})^{-1}(a_{ji})(b_{ji})$ is the matrix of ρ with respect to k-basis of V formed from the union of k-bases of V_i, where V is the direct sum of the ρ-indecomposable subspaces V_i, $1 \leqslant i \leqslant t$.

(b) The matrix of the restriction of ρ to V_i with respect to the k-basis of V_i is in Jordan canonical form.

It follows that the matrix $(b_{ji})^{-1}(a_{ji})(b_{ji})$ has the following form:

$$\begin{pmatrix} A_1 & 0 & 0 \cdots 0 & 0 \\ 0 & A_2 & 0 \cdots 0 & 0 \\ \cdots & & & \\ 0 & 0 & 0 \cdots 0 & A_t \end{pmatrix},$$

where A_i is the Jordan canonical matrix associated with the polynomial $m_i(\lambda, \rho_i)^{n(i)}$ and ρ_i is the restriction of ρ to V_i, $1 \leqslant i \leqslant t$.

From hypothesis II, $m_i(\lambda, \rho_i) = \lambda - \alpha_i$ for suitable $\alpha_i \in \mathbf{C}$, $1 \leqslant i \leqslant t$. Thus the system $(**)_z$ is the "union" of t "independent" systems of differential equations; each of these t systems has $n(i)$ equations and is of the form discussed at the beginning. Thus each of these t systems has a solution space W_i in $M_{n(i),1}(A)$ of dimension $n(i)$ over $\mathbf{C}$. $W(z)$ is the direct sum of these W_i, $1 \leqslant i \leqslant t$, and $W(y) = (c_{ji})^t\, W(z)$. Thus we have shown that $W(y)$ is always a $\mathbf{C}$-vector space of dimension n. This corresponds to the existence and uniqueness theorem for solutions of $(**)_y$. It is easy to verify that the specification of the 'initial conditions" picks out precisely one element of $W(y)$. Indeed, the set of initial conditions can be considered as a $\mathbf{C}$-vector space isomorphic to the solution space $W(y)$.

In passing, the reader should observe that α_i is a characteristic root of the matrix of coefficient (a_{ji}). It can be verified rather easily that each W_i contains a unique characteristic subspace of dimension 1; the corresponding characteristic value is precisely α_i.

References

For a detailed study of finite dimensional vector spaces the reader may consult [3]. For an example of the study of infinite dimensional vector spaces the reader may consult [4]. For a more detailed study of the uses of vector spaces in the investigation of the solution of linear differential equations the reader may consult [2] and [6]. Exterior algebras and tensor algebras are particularly important in differential geometry; the interested reader may consult [7].

1. E. Artin, *Geometric Algebra*, Interscience, New York, 1957.
2. E. A. Coddington and N. Levinson, *Theory of Ordinary Differential Equations*, McGraw-Hill, New York, 1955.
3. P. R. Halmos, *Finite-Dimensional Vector Spaces*, 2nd ed., Van Nostrand, Princeton, N.J., 1958.
4. P. R. Halmos, *Introduction to Hilbert Space*, Chelsea, New York, 1951.
5. W. V. D. Hodge and D. Pedoe, *Methods of Algebraic Geometry*, Vols. I, II, Cambridge University Press, Cambridge, 1947.
6. S. Lefshetz, *Differential Equations: Geometric Theory*, Interscience, New York, 1957.
7. S. Sternberg, *Lectures on Differential Geometry*, Prentice-Hall, Englewood Cliffs, N. J., 1964.

CHAPTER VII

Elementary Theory of Fields

Up to now we have constructed **Z**, $+$ in order to solve equations in **P**, $+$; we have constructed **Q**, $+, \cdot$ in order to solve equations in **Z**, $\cdot$; and we have used the concepts of modules and of determinants to give a systematic procedure to solve a system of linear equations over a field and to solve a system of linear homogeneous differential equations with constant coefficients in the complex numbers. In fact, much of mathematics is devoted to the study of the solutions of equations of some kind. In doing so, many formal constructions are designed to facilitate our studies. Often these formal constructions are of independent interest and form topics of investigation themselves.

To follow up this viewpoint we next consider the study of solutions of polynomial equations in one variable, where the coefficients lie in a prescribed field. By use of the factor theorem it becomes apparent that irreducible polynomials of a degree greater than one will not have a solution in the prescribed field. We must therefore look for solutions in a larger system. If $f(X)$ is any irreducible polynomial in the ring $k[X]$, where k is a prescribed field, we know that the ideal generated by $f(X)$ in $k[X]$ is a nonzero prime ideal of the PID $k[X]$. It is easy to see that the coset of X in $K = k[X]/(f(X))$ is a solution of the equation $f(Y) = 0$, where Y is an indeterminate over K. Since we have seen that a nonzero prime ideal in a PID is a maximal ideal, it follows that K is a field. If we identify each element of k with the coset it determines in K, then k may be considered as a subfield of K. As a result, we have found, in a formal way, a field K containing k as a subfield such that $f(Y)$ has a zero in K. We may generalize this by asking the question, "Given an arbitrary polynomial of positive degree in $k[Y]$, can we find a field L containing k as a subfield such that the prescribed polynomial has a zero in L?" The answer is *yes*; namely, we replace the prescribed polynomial by one of its irreducible factors in $k[Y]$. Moreover, since L is a field, every zero of the prescribed polynomial is obtained in this way. We may conclude that the "natural" setting for the study of solutions of a polynomial equation in one variable with coefficients in a prescribed field k is to consider fields L that contain k as a subfield.

Several immediate generalizations of the problem posed in the preceding paragraph quickly come to mind. First, we may consider polynomial equations in several variables with coefficients lying in the prescribed field k. This is roughly the content of "classical" algebraic geometry. Second, we may replace fields by integral domains and insist that the solution lie in the prescribed integral domain. For example, we may consider polynomial equations in several variables with coefficients in $\mathbf{Z}$ and insist on looking for solutions in $\mathbf{Z}$. This is roughly the content of Diophantine equations. Finally, we may consider polynomial equations in several variables with coefficients in a prescribed commutative ring and hunt for solutions in bigger commutative rings. This is roughly the content of "modern" algebraic geometry. Of course, we can ultimately ask for solutions of polynomial equations in non-commutative rings; however, a unified theory in this direction does not exist. In any event, we shall not attempt to go into any of these generalizations. It will be seen that our "simple" case already embodies many interesting phenomena.

CONVENTIONS AND NOTATIONS · As before, rings are assumed to have identity elements; ring homomorphisms are assumed to preserve the identity elements. We observed sometime ago that a ring homomorphism of a field into a nonzero ring must be injective. Since this situation occurs often, we consistently abbreviate "injective homomorphism" into "monomorphism." Similarly, "surjective homomorphism" is abbreviated to "epimorphism." We remind the reader that "isomorphism" is used to describe a bijective homomorphism whose inverse is also a homomorphism. However, as we remarked earlier, in all the situations that we will encounter (and have encountered), the second condition is automatic. As a result, "isomorphism" is equivalent to "monomorphism" plus "epimorphism."

Let $\sigma : A \rightarrow B$ be a homomorphism of the algebraic system A into the algebraic system (of the same type as A). Then the image of the element a (respectively, the subset S) under σ is denoted by $\sigma(a)$ [respectively, $\sigma(S)$]. When there is no possibility of confusion, we also write σa (respectively σS).

Let $\rho : R \rightarrow S$ be a ring homomorphism of the commutative ring R into the commutative ring S. Let X be an indeterminate over R

and S simultaneously. Then the unique extension of ρ to a ring homomorphism of $R[X]$ into $S[X]$ which sends X onto X is again denoted by ρ. Formally, the extension sends the finite sequence $[a_0, \ldots, a_n, 0, \ldots]$ onto the finite sequence $[\rho(a_0), \ldots, \rho(a_n), 0, \ldots]$. In general, the image of $f \in R[X]$ under ρ is denoted by $\rho(f)$ or by ρf when there is no possibility of confusion. The image of $g \in S[X]$ under the substitution homomorphism $S[X] \to S[b]/S$ is denoted by $g\{b\}$. We view the polynomial g as a "function" on S. In general, $h\{c\}$ denotes the value of the function h on the element c. Thus, when $g = \rho f$, $(\rho f)\{b\}$ is the image of f under the composition of ρ with the subsitution homomorphism. (This composition is precisely the unique ring homomorphism of $R[X] \to S$ which extends ρ on R and sends X onto $b \in S$.) In order to be consistent we occasionally write $f\{X\}$ for f to emphasize that f is a polynomial in X. Thus $(\rho f)\{X\}$ is the polynomial obtained from f by applying ρ to the coefficients of $f\{X\}$; and $(\rho f)\{b\}$ is obtained from $f\{X\}$ by applying ρ to the coefficients of $f\{X\}$ followed by substituting b for X.

» VII · 1 BASIC CONCEPTS

In this section we consider the general ideas involved in building up a field.

DEFINITION 1 · Let k be a subfield of a field K. Then K is called an ***extension field*** of k. K is called a ***prime field*** if and only if K is the only subfield of itself. If k is a subfield of K and B is a subset of K, then $k[B]$ and $k(B)$ are the subring and subfield, respectively, of K generated by k and B. If $B = \{a_i \mid i \in I\}$ is an indexed set of elements in K, we use $k[a_i]_{i \in I}$ and $k(a_i)_{i \in I}$ to denote the subring and subfield, respectively, of K generated by k and B.

Intersection of all subrings (subfields) of K that contain k ∪ B.

The reader should observe that in an indexed set $\{a_i \mid i \in I\}$ it is permissible to have $a_i = a_j$ for $i \neq j$. The reader should also observe that a subring of a field is automatically an integral domain.

Do for class (outline of idea)

Exercise 1 · Let K be an extension field of a field k. Suppose that B is any subset of K. Show that there is a natural isomorphism between the field of fractions of the integral domain $k[B]$ and the field $k(B)$.

Show $k(B) = \{ab^{-1} \mid a, b \in k[B], b \neq 0\}$. Then show $[(a,b)] \to ab^{-1}$ is natural isom. where $[(a,b)] \in$ field of fract. of k

Exercise 2 · Let k be a field. Show that there exists a unique ring homomorphism of $\boldsymbol{Z}$ into k. Show that the kernel of this homomorphism

Map Z to k by $n \xrightarrow{\sigma} n1_k$. Uniqueness follows since $\langle 1 \rangle = Z$. Kernel of map is clearly prime ideal. Since ideals of Z principal, $\ker \sigma = (p)$ for p a prime by IV 2.

For $p \neq 0$, im $\sigma \cong Z/(p)$, by 1st isom. thm. for image. $Z/(p)$ is a field by IV.2.

is a prime ideal (p) of **Z**. Suppose that $p \neq 0$; show that the image is a subfield of k isomorphic to $Z/(p)$. Suppose that $p = 0$; show that there is a unique monomorphism of the field **Q** into k. *Hint.* Exercises II.3.7 and IV.2.12 are useful. *Let $p = 0$, $Z \to Q$ ... and σ unique homo. by first part of exercise. Thus by IV 3.7, ∃ a unique homo. (mono.) φ ∃ diagram commutes. This gives uniqueness of map from Q into k; just note $\theta(z)$, $\sigma(z) = z$, and each $\theta(z) \subseteq Q$, $\sigma(z) \in k$ to ∃ maps $\theta(z)$ to $\sigma(z)$ in same way.*

THEOREM 1 · Let k be a subfield of a field K. Then the following assertions are equivalent:

(a) k is a prime field.

(b) k is the subfield of K generated by 1.

(c) k is isomorphic to either **Q** or $Z/(p)$, where p is a prime in P^+, but not to both.

The proof is an easy consequence of Exercise 2.

(a) ⇒ (b) def of prime field.   (b) ⇒ (c) Let $Z \to k$ as in Ex. 2. Then $Z/(p) \cong \sigma(z) \subseteq k$. If $p \neq 0$, then $\sigma(z) = k$. If $p = 0$ then ∃ a unique mono. ψ: Q → k field of k. But $\psi(Q)$ is a subfield of k containing ψ surjective.   (c) ⇒ (a) clear, since subfield generated by 1 in Q (Z/(p)) is in all of Q (Z/(p)).

DEFINITION 2 · Let K be a field. The **characteristic** $\chi(K)$ of K is defined as the prime $p \in P$ that generates the kernel of the homomorphism of Exercise 2; namely, $Z/(p)$ is isomorphic to the subring of K generated by 1. In particular, $\chi(K) = 0$ when **Q** is isomorphic to the prime field of K; $\chi(K) = p > 0$ when $Z/(p)$ is isomorphic to the prime field of k, where p is a prime in **P**.

{ The structure is a direct sum of commutative gps as given on page 97.

Exercise 3 · Let k be a field. What is the structure of the additive group of k? In particular, what are the orders of the elements of k? *the elts of k are all of same order. 1st consider case where $\chi(k) = p \neq 0$. note if $a, b \in k$ with $m \cdot a = \sum n_i \cdot b$; $m, n_i \in Z$ then since $p \nmid b$ prime $\exists$ $q, g, ∃$.*

Note $[\text{ord } a \in Z] = [m \cdot a] \cdot a [m \in Z]$ $\langle a \rangle = \{ m \cdot a \mid m \in Z \}$

As a consequence of Theorem 1, every field can be considered *l m $+ q p = 1$. Hence* as an extension field of **Q** or of $Z/(p)$; p is a positive prime in **Z**. We now *$l \cdot m \cdot a = a \cdot a = \sum n_i \cdot b$* exhibit a crude procedure for contructing fields in general. *let $A_a = \langle a \rangle$, $a \in k$ and well order $\{A_a\}$. Let $J = \{A_a \mid X \text{ is ...}\}$...*

Then $k = \bigoplus_{a \in J} A_a$, where this means each elt of k is uniquely expressible as a finite sum of A_a's, ... ∴ k is a direct of cyclic gps of order p. If $\chi(k) = 0$, then define $A_a = \{qa \mid q \in Q\}$, well order $\{A_a\}$ and ... as above.

THEOREM 2 · Let K be an extension field of k. Let X be an *k is a direct sum* indeterminate over the field K. If $a \in K$, then *exactly* one of the following *of gps ≅ to Q.* two cases occur:

Define $k(X)$ to be field of fractions of $k[X]$.

(a) The substitution homomorphism $k[X] \to k[a]/k$ is injective, and $k(X)$ is isomorphic to $k(a)$ under the map induced by the substitution homomorphism.

(b) The substitution homomorphism $k[X] \to k[a]/k$ has a kernel distinct from 0. This kernel is generated by a uniquely determined monic, irreducible polynomial $f \in k[X]$, and $k[X]/(f)$ is isomorphic to $k[a] = k(a)$ under the map induced by the substitution homomorphism.

Proof · It is obvious that the two cases are mutually exclusive. If the kernel of the substitution homomorphism is zero, then, by using Exercise II.2.7, (a) holds. If the kernel of the substitution homomorphism is nonzero, it must be a nonzero prime ideal in the PID $k[X]$. It follows that there exists a unique monic, irreducible polynomial $f \in k[X]$ such that the kernel is the ideal in $k[X]$ generated by f. Since every nonzero prime ideal of a PID is a maximal ideal, we see that $k[X]/(f)$ is a field. The remaining assertion of (b) follows from the first isomorphism theorem. Thus case (b) must hold. «

DEFINITION 3 · An extension field K of k is called a ***simple extension*** of k if and only if $K = k(a)$ for some $a \in K$. The element a is then called a **generator** of K over k. If Theorem 2(a) holds for the element a, then K is called a ***simple transcendental extension*** of k and the generator a is said to be ***transcendental*** over k. If Theorem 2(b) holds for the element a, then K is called a ***simple algebraic extension*** of k and the generator a is said to be ***algebraic*** over k. In the second case the uniquely determined monic, irreducible polynomial f is called the ***irreducible polynomial*** of a over k. It is usually denoted by $\mathrm{Irr}(X, a, k)$.

Exercise 4 · Show that a simple transcendental extension K of k is necessarily an infinite dimensional vector space over k under left multiplication by elements of k. Show that a simple algebraic extension K of k is necessarily a finite dimension vector space over k under left multiplication by elements of k.

Example 1 · Let e denote the base of the natural logarithm and let π be the ratio of the circumference of a circle to its diameter. Then $\mathbf{Q}(e)$ and $\mathbf{Q}(\pi)$ are subfields of the field of real numbers which are simple transcendental extensions of $\mathbf{Q}$. The proof of these assertions is fairly intricate. We must verify that e and π are not the zeros of any polynomial equation of positive degree and with coefficient in $\mathbf{Q}$.

Example 2 · The subfield $\mathbf{Q}(\sqrt{2}, \sqrt{3})$ of the field of real numbers is a simple algebraic extension. The element $\sqrt{2} + \sqrt{3}$ is a generator. The reader may verify that $\sqrt{2} + \sqrt{3}$ is a zero of the polynomial $(X - \sqrt{2} - \sqrt{3})(X - \sqrt{2} + \sqrt{3})(X + \sqrt{2} - \sqrt{3})(X + \sqrt{2} + \sqrt{3}) = X^4 - 10X^2 + 1$. From a direct computation the reader may show that $\sqrt{2} = a/2 - 1/(2a)$ and $\sqrt{3} = a/2 + 1/(2a)$, where $a = \sqrt{2} + \sqrt{3}$. Thus $\mathbf{Q}(\sqrt{2}, \sqrt{3}) = \mathbf{Q}[\sqrt{2} + \sqrt{3}]$. Eventually, we shall verify enough theorems that will allow us to draw the conclusion of this example without doing any computation.

The following elementary result is extremely useful in our later investigations:

THEOREM 3 · (Fundamental theorem on the extendibility of field isomorphisms). Let X and Y denote indeterminates over the fields $k \subset K$ and $l \subset L$, respectively. Let $\rho : k \to l$ be a field isomorphism. Suppose that $a \in K$ and $b \in L$. Then the following assertions hold:

(a) There exists a unique ring isomorphism $\sigma : k[X] \to l[Y]$ such that $\sigma c = \rho c \ \forall\, c \in k$ and such that $\sigma X = Y$. Moreover, σ may be extended uniquely to an isomorphism between $k(X)$ and $l(Y)$.

(b) There exists a unique field isomorphism $\tau : k(a) \to l(b)$ such that $\tau c = \rho c \ \forall\, c \in k$ and $\tau a = b$ if and only if the following conditions are satisfied:

(1) a and b, respectively, are transcendental over k and l.

(2) a and b, respectively, are algebraic over k and l, and the map σ in (a) is such that $\sigma(\mathrm{Irr}(X, a, k)) = \mathrm{Irr}(Y, b, l)$.

Proof · (a) is an obvious consequence of the hypothesis that X and Y are indeterminates and of the assertion of Exercise II.4.4.

In order to verify (b) we construct the following diagram:

$$\begin{array}{ccc} k[X] & \to & k[a]/k \\ \sigma\big\downarrow & & \\ l[Y] & \to & l[b]/l \end{array}$$

where the horizontal rows are substitution homomorphisms.

If τ exists, it is certainly uniquely determined by the values it takes on the generators k and a of $k(a)$. Moreover, when τ exists, it will lead to a commutative diagram. If I and J denote the kernels of the respective substitution homomorphisms, it is immediate that $\sigma I = J$. In particular, $I = 0$ if and only if $J = 0$. This occurs precisely when a and therefore b are both transcendental. Otherwise, both I and J are distinct from 0. In this case I and J are generated by $\mathrm{Irr}(X, a, k)$ and $\mathrm{Irr}(Y, b, l)$, respectively. Since σ preserves the identity element, it is clear that $\sigma(\mathrm{Irr}(X, a, k)) = \mathrm{Irr}(Y, b, l)$.

Conversely, assume that (1) and (2) are satisfied. In case (1) the kernels I and J are both 0 and all the maps in the diagram are isomorphisms. By forming the inverse of the map in the top row and composing it with the remaining maps we obtain an isomorphism from $k[a]$ to $l[b]$. This isomorphism may be uniquely extended to an isomorphism τ from the field of fractions $k(a)$ to the field of fractions $l(b)$. It is easily checked that τ has the desired properties. In case (2) both the kernels I and J are distinct from zero. They are generated by $\mathrm{Irr}(X, a, k)$ and $\mathrm{Irr}(Y, b, l)$, respectively. From the condition stated in (2) we see that $\sigma I = J$. Thus σ induces an isomorphism between $k[X]/I$ and $l[Y]/J$ such that the coset of $c \in k$ is mapped onto the coset of σc and that the coset of X is mapped onto the coset of Y. By using the first isomorphism theorem we see that $k[X]/I$ is k-isomorphic to $k[a]$ where the coset of X is mapped onto a; similarly, $l[Y]/J$ is l-isomorphic to $l[b]$ where the coset of Y is mapped onto b. Again, by forming the inverse of the first of the preceding isomorphisms and composing it with the remaining isomorphism it is easy to see that the resulting map is the desired isomorphism τ. 〈〈

The following result generalizes the factor theorem and can be derived easily from Definition 3.

THEOREM 4 · Let K be an extension field of k. Suppose that $a \in K$ is algebraic over k. Then the following assertions hold:

(a) If $g \in k[X]$, then $g\{a\} = 0$ if and only if $\mathrm{Irr}(X, a, k)$ is a factor of g in $k[X]$.

(b) If $g \in k[X]$ is monic and irreducible, then $g\{a\} = 0$ if and only if $g = \mathrm{Irr}(X, a, k)$.

Exercise 5 · Show that the group of **Q**-automorphisms of the field $\mathbf{Q}[\sqrt{2}, \sqrt{3}]$ is transitive on the set of zeros of $X^4 - 10X^2 + 1$. Thus show that this group must have an order at least equal to 4.

Use Thm 34. applied to $Q[\sqrt{3}+\sqrt{2}]$

Exercise 6 · Find the irreducible polynomial of $\sqrt{5}$ over the field $\mathbf{Q}[\sqrt{2}, \sqrt{3}]$. $\quad x^2 + 5$. *Show $\sqrt{5} \neq (a+b\sqrt{2}) + (c+d\sqrt{2})\sqrt{3}$ for $a, b \in Q$*

Exercise 7 · Find the irreducible polynomials of $\sqrt{2} + \sqrt{3}$ over the fields $\mathbf{Q}[\sqrt{2}]$ and $\mathbf{Q}[\sqrt{3}]$, respectively. $(X + \sqrt{2} - \sqrt{3})(x - \sqrt{2} + \sqrt{3}) = x^2 - 2\sqrt{3}x$

Note $\mathrm{Irr}(X, \sqrt{2}+\sqrt{3}, Q[\sqrt{3}]) | (x^4 - 10x^2 + 1)$ since $(x - \sqrt{2} - \sqrt{3})(x + \sqrt{2} - \sqrt{3}) = x^2 - 2\sqrt{3}x$

$x^4 - 10x^2 + 1 \in Q[\sqrt{5}](x)$

Exercise 8 · Let $k \subset K \subset L$ be a tower of fields. Let $a \in L$ be algebraic over k. Verify the following assertions:

(a) $\mathrm{Irr}(X, a, K)$ is a factor of $\mathrm{Irr}(X, a, k)$ in $K[X]$. *Clear, since*

if $f = \mathrm{Irr}(X, a, K)$ and $g = \mathrm{Irr}(X, a, k)$ then $g \in K[X]$ with $g(a) = 0$ so $f | g$.

(b) If $g \in k[X]$, then $\operatorname{Irr}(X, a, K) \mid g$ in $K[X]$ if and only if $\operatorname{Irr}(X, a, k) \mid g$ in $k[X]$.

(c) $a \in k$ if and only if $\deg_X \operatorname{Irr}(X, a, k) = 1$.

DEFINITION 4 · Let I be a linearly ordered set under $<$. Suppose that K_i is a field for each $i \in I$ and that K_i is a subfield of K_j whenever $i < j$. Then $\{K_i \mid i \in I\}$ is called a ***field tower***.

Exercise 9 · Let $\{K_i \mid i \in I\}$ be a field tower. Show that the set $K = \bigcup_{i \in I} K_i$ may be given a unique field structure such that each K_i is a subfield of K. Suppose that each K_i is already a subfield of the field L. Show that the field structure defined on K coincides with the subfield in L generated by K_i, $i \in I$.

Example 3 · Let $K_i = \mathbf{Q}[2^{1/2^i}]$, $i \in \mathbf{P}$. Then each K_i is a subfield of K_{i+1}, $i \in \mathbf{P}$. It can be shown that $K_i \neq K_{i+1}$ for each i. Thus $K = \bigcup_{i \in \mathbf{P}} K_i$ is a field formed out of an infinite field tower.

Example 4 · Let p_i be the ith prime in $\mathbf{P}^+$. Let $K_0 = \mathbf{Q}$ and define inductively $K_{i+1} = K_i[\sqrt{p_i}]$. It may be shown (with some effort) that K_i is a proper subfield of K_{i+1}, $i \in \mathbf{P}$. Thus $\bigcup_{i \in \mathbf{P}} K_i$ is again a field formed out of an infinite field tower.

Exercise 10 · Let K be an extension field of k. Show that there is a set of subfields $\{K_i \mid i \in I\}$ of K which satisfies the following conditions:

(a) The set $\{K_i \mid i \in I\}$ is well ordered by strict inclusion.

(b) $K_0 = k$, where 0 is the least element of I.

(c) If $i \in I$ has an immediate predecessor $i - 1$, then K_i is a simple extension of K_{i-1}.

(d) If $i \in I$ has no immediate predecessor in I, then $K_i = \bigcup_{j<i} K_j$, $j \in I$.

(e) $K = \bigcup_{i \in I} K_i$.

Hint. Consider the set of those towers of subfields of K that satisfy (a), (b), (c), and (d). Partially order this set by the condition that the tower $\mathfrak{F}$ precedes the tower $\mathfrak{G}$ if and only if $\mathfrak{F}$ is a front segment of $\mathfrak{G}$; that is, every field in $\mathfrak{F}$ is one in $\mathfrak{G}$, and if $L_1 \subset L_2$ such that L_2 is in $\mathfrak{F}$ and L_1 is in $\mathfrak{G}$ then L_1 is also in $\mathfrak{F}$. Apply Zorn's lemma to conclude the exercise.

» VII · 2 ALGEBRAIC EXTENSION FIELDS: SPLITTING FIELDS

We shall now investigate case (b) of Theorem 1.2 in detail. The reader should have observed that every element of the field k is algebraic over k; namely, the element $a \in k$ is a zero of the polynomial $X - a \in k[X]$.

DEFINITION 1 · An extension field K of k is said to be ***algebraic*** over k if and only if every element of K is algebraic over k.

We have already observed that every ring S may be considered as a module over the subring R with respect to the left multiplications induced by the elements of R. This is a very useful concept in the case of an extension field K of the field k. Since K is commutative, it makes no difference whether we consider K as a left or as a right module over k. However, if K is a noncommutative division ring, it will make a difference whether K is considered as a k-module under left multiplication or as a k-module under right multiplication. The interested reader may consult [3] for a discussion of this case. In any event, we introduce the following definition.

DEFINITION 2 · Let K be an extension field of a field k. Then $[K : k]$ denotes the vector-space dimension of K over k, where k acts on K by left multiplication. $[K : k]$ is called the ***field degree***, or simply the ***degree***, of K over k.

Example 1 · Let $K = k[a]$ be a simple algebraic extension of k. Suppose that $\text{Irr}(X, a, k)$ has degree n over k. Then $1, a, \ldots, a^{n-1}$ form a k-basis for K. Thus $[K : k] = n$. The verification follows from Theorem 2(b) and Exercise II.4.3(d)—the division algorithm in $k[X]$.

We now collect some of the most important properties of extension fields K of k for which $[K : k]$ is finite.

THEOREM 1 · Let $k \subset K \subset L$ be a tower of fields. Then the following assertions hold:

(a) If $[K : k]$ is finite, then K is algebraic over k.

(b) $[L : k] = [L : K][K : k]$. In fact, if $\{x_i \mid i \in I\}$ is a k-basis for K and $\{y_j \mid j \in J\}$ is a K-basis for L, then $\{x_i y_j \mid i \in I, j \in J\}$ is a k-basis for L.

(c) Let $k_0 = k$, $k_{i+1} = k_i(a_{i+1})$, $a_i \in K$. If each a_i is algebraic over k_{i-1} and $\mathrm{Irr}(X, a_i, k_{i-1})$ has degree n_i, then $[k_j : k] = \prod_{1 \leqslant i \leqslant j} n_i$, $j \in \mathbf{P}^+$. Moreover, $k_j = k[a_1, \dots, a_j]$ for $j \in \mathbf{P}$.

(d) L is algebraic over k if and only if

(1) L is algebraic over K

(2) K is algebraic over k.

(e) If $K = k(a_i)_{i \in I}$, then K is algebraic over k if and only if each a_i is algebraic over k. Moreover, if K is algebraic over k, then $K = k[a_i]_{i \in I}$; the converse is in general false (see Exercise 4).

(f) $\{a \in K \mid a \text{ is algebraic over } k\}$ is a subfield of K; it is the largest subfield of K that is algebraic over k.

Proof · (a) Suppose that $[K : k]$ is finite. Then $\dim_k k[a] \leqslant [K : k]$. Thus the assertion follows from Exercise 1.4.

(b) Let $\{x_i \mid i \in I\}$ be a k-basis for K and let $\{y_j \mid j \in J\}$ be a K-basis for L. If $z \in L$, there exists a finite subset J' of J such that $z = \sum_{j \in J'} b_j y_j$, where $b_j \in K \; \forall j$. For each $j \in J'$ we can find a finite subset $I'(j)$ of I such that $b_j = \sum_{i \in I'(j)} a_{i,j} x_i$, $a_{i,j} \in k$. On substitution, we see that z lies in the k-subspace generated by $\{x_i y_j \mid i \in I, j \in J\}$. Conversely, suppose that $\sum_{i \in I', j \in J'} a_{i,j} x_i y_j = 0$, $a_{i,j} \in k$, I' is a finite subset of I, and J' is a finite subset of J. Then, from the fact that $\sum_i a_{i,j} x_i \in K$ and the fact that the y_j's are K-independent, we conclude that $0 = \sum a_{i,j} x_i \; \forall j \in J'$. Since the x_i's are k-independent, we see that $a_{i,j} = 0 \; \forall i, j$. Thus $\{x_i y_j \mid i \in I, j \in J\}$ form a k-basis for the vector space L. The assertion (b) now follows.

(c) follows from (b), Example 1 and induction.

(d) If L is algebraic over k, then (2) obviously holds; (1) holds from the observation that any polynomial in $k[X]$ is already a polynomial in $K[X]$. Conversely, suppose that (1) and (2) hold. Let $a \in L$. Consider the irreducible polynomial $X^n + a_{n-1}X^{n-1} + \cdots + a_0 = f$ of a over K. Each a_i must be algebraic over k. From (a) and (c) we see that a must be algebraic over k. Thus L must be algebraic over k as asserted.

(e) follows from (c), (d), and the observation that every element of $k(a_i)_{i \in I}$ must lie in $k(a_i)_{i \in J}$ for a suitable finite subset J of I.

(f) follows immediately from (e). «

Exercise 1 · Show that $[\mathbf{Q}[\sqrt{2}, \sqrt{3}] : \mathbf{Q}] = 4$ in two ways (by showing that $X^4 - 10X^2 + 1$ is irreducible in $\mathbf{Q}[X]$, and by showing that $X^2 - 2$ is irreducible in $\mathbf{Q}[X]$ and that $X^2 - 3$ is irreducible in $\mathbf{Q}[\sqrt{2}][X]$.)

Une Eisenstein

Exercise 2 · Show that $X^{2^i} - 2$ is irreducible in $\mathbf{Q}[X]$. Verify the assertion of Example 1.3.

In both of the exercises above, we should take advantage of the fact that $\mathbf{Q}$ is the field of fractions of the PID $\mathbf{Z}$ and use Eisenstein's criterion on irreducibility.

Exercise 3 · Let K be an integral domain containing subfield k. Suppose that $\dim_k K$ is finite. Show that K is a field. Show that every finite integral domain is a field. *Let $a \in K \setminus k$, Then since $\dim_k K$ finite $\exists$ $n \in \mathbf{Z}^+$ $\ni$ $1, a, a^2, \cdots, a^{n-1}$ dependent $\Rightarrow \exists$ poly $f(a)$ in a over $k \ni a f(a) = 1 \Rightarrow K$ is a field. For last part take subring R of finite int. domain generated by 1 and show it a field. Then apply first part of exercise.*

Exercise 4 · Let $K = k(X)$ be the field of rational functions in the indeterminate X over k. Let $\{f_i \mid i \in I\}$ be the set of all monic irreducible polynomials in $k[X]$. Show that $K = k[X][1/f_i]_{i \in I}$. *Hint.* Use the partial fraction theorem.

Colan look at this in light of partial fraction theorem on page 121.

DEFINITION 3 · Let K be an extension field of k such that $[K : k]$ is finite. Let $a \in K$. Then the characteristic polynomial of $aI \in \operatorname{Hom}_k(K, K)$ is called the **field polynomial** of a in K over k and is denoted by $\chi(X, a, K/k)$; $\det(aI)$ is called the **norm** of a from K to k and is denoted by $N_{K/k}(a)$; $\operatorname{Tr}(aI)$ is called the **trace** of a from K to k and is denoted by $\operatorname{Tr}_{K/k}(a)$. If $K = k(a)$, we use $N_k(a)$ and $\operatorname{Tr}_k(a)$, respectively. They are called the **norm** and the **trace** of a relative to k.

skip for now

Exercise 5 · Let K be an extension field of k such that $[K : k]$ is finite. Let $a, b \in K$. Verify the following assertions:

(a) K is an aI-cyclic k-vector space if and only if $K = k(a)$.

(b) $\operatorname{Irr}(X, a, k)$ is the minimal polynomial of aI.

(c) K is aI-cyclic if and only if $\operatorname{Irr}(X, a, k) = \chi(X, a, K/k)$.

(d) If λ acts on K according to aI, the $k[\lambda]$-module K has elementary divisors $\operatorname{Irr}(\lambda, a, k)$ repeated $[K : k(a)]$ times.

(e) $\chi(X, a, K/k) = (\operatorname{Irr}(X, a, k))^m$, where $m = [K : k(a)]$.

(f) $N_{K/k}(ab) = N_{K/k}(a)N_{K/k}(b)$; $N_{K/k}(a) = (N_k(a))^m$, $m = [K : k(a)]$.

(g) $\operatorname{Tr}_{K/k} \in \operatorname{Hom}_k(K, k)$ is a symmetric k-linear function on K (that is, $\operatorname{Tr}_{K/k}(ab) = \operatorname{Tr}_{K/k}(ba)$ and is k-linear). $\operatorname{Tr}_{K/k}(a) = [K : k(a)]\operatorname{Tr}_k(a)$.

In many instances, the following theorem is very useful.

THEOREM 2 · Let K be an *algebraic* extension field of k. Let $\sigma : K \to K$ be a k-algebra homomorphism. Then σ is a k-automorphism of K.

Proof · Let X be an indeterminate over K. If $a \in K$ is a zero of $f \in k[X]$, then from $0 = \sigma(f\{a\}) = (\sigma f)\{\sigma a\}$ we deduce that σa is a zero of σf. Since σ is a k-homomorphism and σf is obtained from $f \in k[X]$ by applying σ to the coefficients of f, we see that $\sigma f = f$. Thus σa is again a zero of f in K. From the factor theorem we know that f has at most $\deg f$ zeros in K. Since K is a field, σ must be injective; and since an injective map of a finite set into itself is automatically surjective, we conclude that σ induces a permutation of the set of zeros of f in K. Since K is algebraic over k, each element $a \in K$ is a zero of $\mathrm{Irr}(X, a, k)$. The preceding reasoning then shows that there exists a zero b of $\mathrm{Irr}(X, a, k)$ such that $\sigma b = a$. Thus σ is also surjective. Hence σ is a k-automorphism. «

Example 2 · Let X be an indeterminate over a field k. Let $\sigma : k[X] \to k[X^2]/k$ be the substitution homomorphism; σ is clearly a monomorphism. Hence σ may be uniquely extended to a monomorphism of $k(X)$ into $k(X)$. Using the fact that $k[X]$ is UFD, we can conclude that σ cannot be an automorphism.

We now consider the problem of finding zeros of the polynomial $f \in k[X]$ in the extension field K of k. From the factor theorem we know that f has a zero in K if and only if f has a ***linear factor*** (that is, a factor of degree 1) in $K[X]$. Thus it is natural to introduce the following definition:

DEFINITION 4 · Let f be a polynomial in $k[X]$.

(a) An extension field K of k is called a ***splitting field*** of f over k if and only if f is a product of linear factors in $K[X]$.

(b) An extension field K of k is called a ***root field*** of f over k if and only if the following conditions hold:

(1) K is a splitting field of f over k.

(2) If L is any splitting field of f over k, then there exists a k-monomorphism $\sigma : K \to L$.

Example 3 · $\mathbf{Q}[\sqrt{2}]$ is a splitting field of $X^2 - 2$ over $\mathbf{Q}$.

Example 4 · $\mathbf{Q}[2^{\frac{1}{3}}, e^{2\pi i/3}]$ is a splitting field of $X^3 - 1$ and of $X^3 - 2$ over $\mathbf{Q}$.

THEOREM 3 (Kronecker) · Let f be a monic polynomial of degree n in $k[X]$, where X is an indeterminate over the field k. Then the following assertions hold:

(a) f has a root field K such that $[K : k] \leqslant n!$.

(b) If L is any splitting field of f over k, the zeros of f in L generate a root field of f over k.

(c) A root field K of f over k is unique up to a k-isomorphism However, in general, there are no natural k-isomorphisms between two root fields of f over k.   ↑ This means several maps can be used (see end of proof)

Proof · We first show that (c) follows from (b). Let K and K' be root fields of f over k. By Definition 4 we can find k-monomorphisms $\sigma : K \to K'$ and $\sigma' : K' \to K$. Thus $\sigma' \circ \sigma$ and $\sigma \circ \sigma'$ are k-monomorphisms of K into K and of K' into K', respectively. From (b) and Theorem 1(c) we see that K and K' are both algebraic over k. Thus by Theorem 2 $\sigma' \circ \sigma$ and $\sigma \circ \sigma'$ are both k-automorphisms. Hence σ is a k-isomorphism as desired.

We now verify (a) and (b) simultaneously by using induction on n. If $n = 1$, then k is the root field of f and there is nothing to prove. Thus we may assume that (a) and (b), and therefore (c), have been verified for all monic polynomials of degree $n - 1$ over arbitrary fields.

Suppose that L is a splitting field of f over k as given in (b). Let N be the subfield of L generated by the zeros of f in L. We let Y be an indeterminate over k and take $g \in k[Y]$ to be a monic, irreducible factor of $f\{Y\}$ in $k[Y]$. Thus $\deg g \leqslant \deg f = n$. Since L is a splitting field of f over k, g has a zero, b, in N. Let $M = k[Y]/(g)$. Since g is monic and irreducible, we know that M is a field. If we identify each element of k with the coset it determines in M and let a denote the coset of Y in M, then $M = k[a]$. We know that $[M : k] = \deg g \leqslant n$ and that $\mathrm{Irr}(X, a, k) = g\{X\}$. From (b) of Theorem 1.4 we know that $\mathrm{Irr}(X, b, k) = g\{X\}$. Thus from Theorem 1.3 we can find a k-isomorphism $\sigma : M \to k[b]$ such that $\sigma(a) = b$. By the factor theorem we see that $f = (X - a)f_1$ in $M[X]$ and that $f = (X - b)g_1$ in $L[X]$. Moreover, since σ is a k-isomorphism, we have $(X - b)g_1 = f = \sigma f = \sigma((X - a)f_1) = (X - b) \cdot \sigma f_1$. Thus $\sigma f_1 = g_1$, and they are monic polynomials of degree $n - 1$. It is clear that L is a splitting field of g_1 over $k[b]$ and that N is the subfield generated by the zeros of g_1 over $k[b]$. By the induction hypothesis we know that f_1 has a root field K over $k[a] = M$ which satisfies (a), (b), and (c). It is clear that K is a splitting field of f over k, that K is generated by the zeros of f, and that $[K : k] = [K : M][M : k] \leqslant (n - 1)! \cdot n = n!$. By using (c) and the

Really here using fact that for isom. fields root fields of corresponding polynomials are isom. This follows inductively from Thm 1. 3b.

fact that $\sigma f_1 = g_1$, we know that σ can be extended to a k-isomorphism between K and M. This shows that the splitting field K of f over k is in fact a root field of f over k. The point is that with this particular field K we may repeat the argument by constructing σ one step at a time. This also shows the nonuniqueness of the map σ, because the choice of b in M is not unique. **«**

Exercise 6 · Find the root field in each of the cases mentioned in Examples 3 and 4.

Apply Thm 3.b $\mathbb{Q}[e^{\frac{2\pi i}{3}}]$. is root field of $x^3 - 1$ over $\mathbb{Q}$. Other cases splitting field given is root field.

Exercise 7 · Let f be a monic polynomial in $k[X]$. Compile the possible degrees of the root field K of f over k when $\deg f \leqslant 4$. *1, 2, 3, 4, 6, 8, 12, 24*

One can show that all these obtainable.

Exercise 8 · Find a **Q**-basis for the root field K of the polynomial f in each of the following cases:

apply Eisenstein

(a) $f = X^2 - m$, m has no square factors in **Z**. $1, \sqrt{m}$

(b) $f = X^3 + 2$. $1, -\sqrt[3]{2}, 2^{1/3}\omega, -\omega\sqrt[3]{2}, \omega^2 2^{1/3}$ *where $\omega = \sqrt[3]{2}e^{\frac{\pi}{3}i}$ (Used that $X^3 + 2$ irred over $\mathbb{Q} \Rightarrow [\mathbb{Q}(\sqrt[3]{2}), \mathbb{Q}] = 3$. Also $(-\sqrt[3]{2})$ real so doesn't contain ω or others)*

(c) $f = X^4 + X^3 + X^2 + X + 1$. *root of f. root of f. ∴ degree of root field must be 6.*

Find the multiplication tables for these **Q**-bases.

Hint. **Q** is the field of fractions of the PID **Z**. Eisenstein's criterion is very useful. *(c) By Ex 19 on Page 120, f is irred. and has zeros of $X^5 - 1$ different from 1. ∴ $\mathbb{Q}[e^{\frac{2\pi}{5}i}]$ is root field. Set basis of $1, \omega, \omega^2, \omega^3$, where $\omega = e^{\frac{2\pi i}{5}}$*

» VII · 3 ALGEBRAICALLY CLOSED FIELDS: ALGEBRAIC CLOSURE

Let X be an indeterminate over a prescribed field k. Let f_i, $i \in I$, be a finite set of polynomials in $k[X]$. We could raise the following questions:

(a) Let K be an extension field; what is the set-union of the zeros of f_i, $i \in I$, in K? (Recall that a zero of f_i is simply a solution of the equation $f_i(X) = 0$.)

(b) Let K be an extension field; what is the set-intersection of the zeros of f_i, $i \in I$, in K? (Equivalently, the common solutions of the system of simultaneous equations $f_i(X) = 0$, $i \in I$.)

The second problem is completely solved as follows: $a \in K$ is a simultaneous zero of f_i, $i \in I$, if and only if a is a simultaneous zero of the polynomials in the ideal of $k[X]$ generated by f_i, $i \in I$. Since

$k[X]$ is a PID, $a \in K$ is a simultaneous zero if and only if a is a zero of $g(X) \in k[X]$, where g is a g.c.d. of f_i, $i \in I$, in $k[X]$. Moreover, the argument presented can be extended to the case in which I is an infinite set.

As for the first problem, we see that the set-union of the sets of zeros of f_i, $i \in I$, coincides with the zeros of $f = \prod_{i \in I} f_i$. Kronecker's theorem tells that these zeros may all be found in a suitably constructed extension field K of finite degree over k. Moreover, the root field K of f over k is unique up to k-isomorphisms. In this sense the problem is converted to the study of the structure of the root field K. However, when I is an infinite set, our argument fails simply because infinite product of polynomials is not defined. Consequently, it is not clear whether there exists a universal field $\bar{k}$ containing k such that every polynomial in $k[X]$ factors into a product of linear factors in $\bar{k}[X]$; equivalently, all the zeros of f may be found in $\bar{k}$.

The goal in this section is to construct such fields $\bar{k}$. It should be realized that we shall need transfinite techniques. Two such methods are available, one of which is to use transfinite induction. The other is to use Zorn's lemma. We adopt the second approach. The reader may consult the references at the end of the chapter for a source in which the first method is used.

DEFINITION 1 · Let K be an extension field of k. The set $\{a \in K \mid a \text{ is algebraic over } k\}$ is called the ***algebraic closure of k in K***; k is said to be ***algebraically closed in K*** if and only if k is equal to its own algebraic closure in K; k is said to be ***algebraically closed*** if and only if it is algebraically closed in every extension field.

Exercise 1 · Let K be an extension field of k. Show that the following assertions hold:

(a) The algebraical closure of k in K is a subfield of K containing k.

(b) The algebraical closure of k in K is algebraically closed in K.

(c) k is algebraically closed if and only if k is the only algebraic extension field of itself.

Exercise 2 · Show that the following are equivalent for the field k.

(a) k is algebraically closed.

(b) k is the splitting field of every polynomial of positive degree in $k[X]$.

(c) Every irreducible monic polynomial in $k[X]$ has degree 1.

DEFINITION 2 · A field K is called an ***algebraic closure*** of k if and only if the following conditions are satisfied:

(a) K is algebraic over k.

(b) K is algebraically closed.

We shall soon see that an algebraic closure of k can be characterized in two different ways. One is "internal"; namely, an algebraic closure should be a "maximal" algebraic extension. The other is "external"; namely, an algebraic closure should be a "minimal" algebraically closed field extension of k.

THEOREM 1 · Let K be an *algebraic* extension field of k. Then K is an algebraic closure of k if and only if K is a splitting field of every monic polynomial in $k[X]$. In fact, we may even restrict ourselves to monic, irreducible polynomials in $k[X]$.

Proof · If K is an algebraic closure of k, then K must be algebraically closed. Since every polynomial in $k[X]$ is a polynomial in $K[X]$, the necessity of our condition follows from Exercise 2.

Conversely, assume that every monic, irreducible polynomial in $k[X]$ splits into a product of linear factors in $K[X]$. Let L be an algebraic extension of K. We must show that $L = K$. From Theorem 2.1 we know that L is algebraic over k. Let $a \in L$. From (a) of Exercise 1.8 we see that $\mathrm{Irr}(X, a, K) \mid \mathrm{Irr}(X, a, k)$ in $K[X]$. Since $\mathrm{Irr}(X, a, k)$ is a product of linear factors in $K[X]$ and since $\mathrm{Irr}(X, a, K)$ is monic, irreducible in $K[X]$, we conclude that $\deg_X \mathrm{Irr}(X, a, K) = 1$. Thus $a \in K$ as desired. «

THEOREM 2 · Let k be a field. Then the following hold:

(a) k has an algebraic closure $\bar{k}$.

(b) If K is an algebraically closed field extension of k, there exists a k-monomorphism $\sigma : \bar{k} \to K$. In general σ is not unique.

(c) $\bar{k}$ is unique up to a k-isomorphism. In general there is no natural isomorphism between two algebraic closures of k.

Proof · Our proof involves an interplay of Kronecker's Theorem and Zorn's lemma.

(a) Let $\mathcal{I}$ be the set of all monic irreducible polynomials in $k[X]$. Let $\{Y(f, i) \mid 1 \leqslant i \leqslant \deg f, f \in \mathcal{I}\}$ be indeterminates over k. For each $f \in \mathcal{I}$ we let $R_f = k[Y(f, 1),\ldots, Y(f, \deg f)]$. Let $R = k[Y(f, i)]_{f \in \mathcal{I}, 1 \leqslant i \leqslant \deg f}$;

Thus R is the polynomial ring generated by the polynomial subrings R_f, $f \in \mathcal{S}$. For each $f \in \mathcal{S}$ let k_f be a root field of f over k. Define $\sigma_f : R_f \to k_f$ as the k-homomorphism such that $f\{X\} = \prod_i (X - \sigma_f(Y(f, i)))$, where X is an indeterminate over k_f. Thus σ_f is surjective; and, since k_f is a field, the ideal $I_f = \ker \sigma_f$ is a maximal ideal in R_f. We now let I be the ideal in R generated by $\{I_f \mid f \in \mathcal{S}\}$. We assert that $I \neq R$.

Suppose that $I = R$. Then $1 \in I$; hence 1 must be representable as a *finite* sum of R-multiples of elements from I_f, $f \in \mathcal{S}$. It follows that there exists a finite subset $\mathcal{F}$ of $\mathcal{S}$ such that 1 is an element of the ideal of $R_{\mathcal{F}} = k[Y(f, i)]_{f \in \mathcal{F}, 1 \leqslant i \leqslant \deg f}$ generated by I_f, $f \in \mathcal{F}$. Let $g = \prod_{f \in \mathcal{F}} f$ and let k_g be a root field of g. From Kronecker's theorem we can find k-monomorphisms $\rho_f : k_f \to k_g$. It is clear that k_g is generated by the images $\rho_f(k_f)$, $f \in \mathcal{F}$, as a ring. It is also clear that we can define a k-homomorphism $\sigma : R_{\mathcal{F}} \to k_g$ by setting $\sigma(Y(f, i)) = \rho_f \circ \sigma_f(Y(f, i))$, $f \in \mathcal{S}$, $1 \leqslant i \leqslant \deg f$. Because each σ_f is surjective and $\operatorname{im} \rho_f$, $f \in \mathcal{S}$, generate k_g as a ring, σ is surjective. Thus $\ker \sigma$ is a maximal ideal of $R_{\mathcal{F}}$. Since ρ_f is a k-monomorphism, the restriction of σ to R_f must have the same kernel in R_f as σ_f. It follows that $R_f \cap \ker \sigma = I_f$. Thus the ideal in $R_{\mathcal{F}}$ generated by I_f, $f \in \mathcal{F}$, is contained in $\ker \sigma$. Since $\ker \sigma \neq R$, we have reached a contradiction. It follows that $I \neq R$ as asserted.

From Lemma 2 of Excursion IV we let M/I be a maximal ideal of R/I. Thus from the first isomorphism theorem M is a maximal ideal of R and R/M is a field. Let $a(f, i)$ be the coset $Y(f, i) + M$ in R/M. Since $I \subset M$, the natural homomorphism of R onto R/M induces a homomorphism $R_f \to R/M$. Since I is generated by I_f, $f \in \mathcal{S}$, we see that I_f is contained in the kernel of the map $R_f \to R/M$. Since I_f is a maximal ideal of R_f and since $R/M \neq 0$, it follows that I_f is precisely the kernel of $R_f \to R/M$. Thus $k_f \simeq R_f/I_f$ is isomorphic to a subfield of R/M. The same reasoning shows that all the monomorphisms are k-monomorphisms, in which each element of k is identified with the coset it determines in R/M and in each R_f/I_f. Consequently, R/M is a splitting field of each monic irreducible polynomial f in $k[X]$. Since R/M is generated by $a(f, i)$, $f \in \mathcal{S}$, $1 \leqslant i \leqslant \deg f$, and since each such element is algebraic over k, we see that R/M is an algebraic extension of k. By Theorem 1 we conclude that R/M is an algebraic closure of k.

(b) Suppose that $\bar{k}$ is an algebraic closure of k and that K is an algebraically closed field extension of k. Let $\mathcal{F}$ be the set of all pairs (L, θ), where L is a subfield of $\bar{k}$ that contains k and $\theta: L \to K$ is a k-monomorphism. We define a partial ordering $\leqslant$ on $\mathcal{F}$ by setting $(L_1, \theta_1) \leqslant (L_2, \theta_2)$ if and only if (1) $L_1 \subset L_2$ and (2) the restriction of θ_2 to L_1 is θ_1. Since (k, id)—id is the identity map on k—is an element of $\mathcal{F}$, we know that $\mathcal{F}$ is nonempty. Exercise 1.9 shows that $\mathcal{F}$ is inductive in the sense of Zorn's lemma. Thus we may select a maximal element (M, σ) in $\mathcal{F}$. We assert that $M = \bar{k}$.

Suppose that $a \in \bar{k} - M$. Since $\bar{k}$ is algebraic over k, $\mathrm{Irr}(X, a, M)$ is a monic, irreducible polynomial in $M[X]$. Since K is algebraically closed, we see, from Exercise 2, that $\sigma(\mathrm{Irr}(X, a, M)) = \mathrm{Irr}(X, \sigma a, \sigma M)$ has a zero b in K. From Theorem 1.3 σ may be extended to a k-monomorphism $\rho : M[a] \to K$. Since $a \in \bar{k} - M$, this contradicts the maximality of (M, σ). Thus $\bar{k} = M$ and (b) holds.

(c) Let k' and k'' be two algebraic closures of k. From (b) we can find k-monomorphisms $\sigma' : k' \to k''$ and $\sigma'' : k'' \to k'$. Thus $\sigma' \circ \sigma''$ and $\sigma'' \circ \sigma'$ are k-monomorphisms respectively of k'' and k' into themselves. From Theorem 2.2 we see that both are k-automorphisms. Thus σ' is k-isomorphism. **«**

COROLLARY · Let K be an algebraically closed field extension of k. Then the algebraic closure of k in K is an algebraic closure of k.

Proof · Exercise. Trivial. Let $K \supseteq k$, with K algebraically closed. Then $h \supseteq k$; $a \in K \mid a$ alg over k; is alg over k. Further for $f \in k[X] \subseteq K[X]$ splits in K and and hence in h. ∴ by Thm 1 h is an alg closure of k.

Exercise 3 · Let k be a countable field; that is, there exists a bijection between the set k and a subset of **P**. Show that the following hold:

(a) $k[X]$ has at most a countable number of monic, irreducible polynomials.

(b) $k[X]$ has an infinite number of monic, irreducible polynomials. (Compare with Theorem I.6.5.) Same proof as for Thm I 6.5

(c) If k is finite and $n \in \textbf{P}$, there exist an infinite number of monic irreducible polynomials in $k[X]$ of degree greater than n. apply b) together with k being finite!

(d) An algebraic closure of k is countably infinite. By (a) countably many number of monic irred poly. Each adjunction of monic

(e) Any algebraically closed field must be infinite. an inf number irred poly require inf number of deg result is countable extension.

(f) If $n \in \textbf{P}$, there exists a finite field K such that K has more than n elements. Either use enough adjunction of a finite field or for $n \in P$, n a prime, consider $Z/(n)$. by iteration we obtain a countable tower of countable fields whose union is alg closed.

✓ **Exercise 4** · Let $f(X) = X^2 + X + 1$ and $g(X) = X^3 - 2 \in \textbf{Q}[X]$.

(a) Show that $f(X)$ and $g(X)$ are irreducible in $\textbf{Q}[X]$. Use Ex 19 p 120 and Eisenstein.

(b) Let $\textbf{Q}_f$ and $\textbf{Q}_g$ be the root fields of f and g, respectively, over $\textbf{Q}$. Show that f splits into a product of two linear factors in $\textbf{Q}_g$. $\sqrt[3]{2}, \sqrt[3]{2}\,\omega \in \textbf{Q}_g$ when $\varrho = \frac{2\pi i}{3}$ Then $(X - \omega^2)(X - \omega) = X^2 + X + 1$

(c) Show that $[\textbf{Q}_f : \textbf{Q}] = 2$ and $[\textbf{Q}_g : \textbf{Q}] = 6$. Find some $\textbf{Q}$-bases for $\textbf{Q}_f$ and $\textbf{Q}_g$ as $\textbf{Q}$-vector spaces. Find the multiplication tables of these $\textbf{Q}$-bases.

$\textbf{Q}_f = \textbf{Q}(\omega)$. $\textbf{Q}(\sqrt[3]{2}) \subseteq R$ with $[\textbf{Q}(\sqrt[3]{2}) : \textbf{Q}] = 3$ also $X^2 + X + 1$ irred over $\textbf{Q}(\sqrt[3]{2})$ or $[\textbf{Q}_g : \textbf{Q}(\sqrt[3]{2})] = 2$ Basis in $1, 2^{1/3}, 2^{2/3}, \omega, \omega 2^{1/3}, \omega 2^{2/3}$.

(d) Find all the $\mathbf{Q}$-monomorphisms of the field $\mathbf{Q}_f$ into $\mathbf{Q}_g$.

(e) Find the groups of $\mathbf{Q}$-automorphisms of the fields $\mathbf{Q}_f$ and $\mathbf{Q}_g$.

Exercise 5 · Let K be an extension field of k. Show that K is an algebraic closure of k if and only if the following hold:

(a) K is algebraic over k.

(b) If L is any algebraic extension of k, then there exists a k-monomorphism $\sigma : L \to K$.

Show that (b) may be replaced by a "weaker" condition:

(b*) If L is an extension field of k such that $[L : k]$ is finite, then there exists a k-monomorphism $\sigma : L \to K$.

Exercise 6 · Let $\bar{\mathbf{Q}}$ be an algebraic closure of $\mathbf{Q}$. Show that the following hold for the fields $\mathbf{Q}_f$ and $\mathbf{Q}_g$ of Exercise 3,

(a) The images of $\mathbf{Q}_f$ (respectively, $\mathbf{Q}_g$) in $\bar{\mathbf{Q}}$ under $\mathbf{Q}$-monomorphisms are the same subfield of $\bar{\mathbf{Q}}$. Moreover, the image of $\mathbf{Q}_f$ in $\bar{\mathbf{Q}}$ is contained in the image of $\mathbf{Q}_g$.

(b) Show that $\bar{\mathbf{Q}}$ is an algebraic closure of the image of $\mathbf{Q}_f$ and $\mathbf{Q}_g$.

(c) Show $\mathbf{Q}_f$ and $\mathbf{Q}_g$ are stable under the action of the group of all $\mathbf{Q}$-automorphisms of the field $\bar{\mathbf{Q}}$, where $\mathbf{Q}_f$ and $\mathbf{Q}_g$ are identified with subfields of $\bar{\mathbf{Q}}$ through (a). Thus show that there exist group homomorphisms $\sigma_f : \mathcal{G}_{\mathbf{Q}}(\bar{\mathbf{Q}}) \to \mathcal{G}_{\mathbf{Q}}(\mathbf{Q}_f)$ and $\sigma_g : \mathcal{G}_{\mathbf{Q}}(\bar{\mathbf{Q}}) \to \mathcal{G}_{\mathbf{Q}}(\mathbf{Q}_g)$, where $\mathcal{G}_k(K)$ denotes the group of all k-automorphisms of the extension field K of k.

(d) Under the identifications of (c) show that $\mathbf{Q}_f$ is stable under the action of $\mathcal{G}_{\mathbf{Q}}(\mathbf{Q}_g)$. Thus show that there exists a group homomorphism $\sigma : \mathcal{G}_{\mathbf{Q}}(\mathbf{Q}_g) \to \mathcal{G}_{\mathbf{Q}}(\mathbf{Q}_f)$.

(e) Show that $\mathcal{G}_{\mathbf{Q}_f}(\mathbf{Q}_g)$ is a normal subgroup of $\mathcal{G}_{\mathbf{Q}}(\mathbf{Q}_g)$.

(f) Show that (d) and (e) lead to an exact sequence of groups, $1 \to \mathcal{G}_{\mathbf{Q}_f}(\mathbf{Q}_g) \to \mathcal{G}_{\mathbf{Q}}(\mathbf{Q}_g) \to \mathcal{G}_{\mathbf{Q}}(\mathbf{Q}_f) \to 1$.

Many of the ideas presented in the proofs of preceding theorems and in the statements of preceding exercises will be studied in more detail later.

» VII · 4 ALGEBRAIC INDEPENDENCE: PURELY TRANSCENDENTAL EXTENSIONS: TRANSCENDENCE BASE

We abandon the study of algebraic extension fields temporarily. The primary reason for considering nonalgebraic extension fields is simply that they are used to construct field extensions that are useful in our later investigations. A thorough investigation of nonalgebraic extensions will lead us into the study of algebraic geometry. In order that we do not stray from our goal, we shall consider only the most basic results on nonalgebraic extensions.

DEFINITION 1 · Let K be an extension field of k. Let I be an index set and $A = \{a_i \in K \mid i \in I\}$. (We note that the map that sends $i \in I$ onto $a_i \in K$ need not be injective.) Let $X = \{X_i \mid i \in I\}$ be a *set* of indeterminates over k. (Thus the map which sends $i \in I$ onto X_i is injective.) Then the k-homomorphism which sends X_i onto $a_i \; \forall \, i \in I$ is denoted by $k[X] \to k[A]/k$. The indexed set A is called ***algebraically independent over*** k if and only if $k[X] \to k[A]/k$ is a k-isomorphism of rings. In general, nonzero elements of the kernel of $k[X] \to k[A]/k$ are called (nontrivial) ***relations*** among the algebraically dependent elements of A.

K is said to be a ***purely transcendental extension of*** k if and only if $K = k(A)$, where A is algebraically independent over k. In general, A is said to be a ***transcendence base for*** K ***over*** k if and only if the following hold:

(a) A is algebraically independent over k.

(b) K is algebraic over $k(A)$.

If $f(X) = \prod_{j \in J} X_j^{n(j)}$, where J is a finite subset of I, $n(j) \in \mathbf{P}$, then $f(X)$ is called a ***monomial*** in the indeterminates X. In general, $f(A) = \prod_{j \in J} a_j^{n(j)}$ is called a ***monomial*** in A.

K is called an ***extension of finite type*** over k if and only if $K = k(A)$, where A is a finite set of elements of K.

Example 1 · Let $A = \{a_i \mid i \in I\}$ be an algebraically independent subset of the field K over the subfield k. Suppose that $\sigma : K \to L$ is a k-monomorphism. Then σA is an algebraically independent subset of the field L over the subfield k.

Example 2 · Let $K = k(X, Y)$, where X and Y are indeterminates over k. Then X, Y are algebraically independent in K over k; X^2, Y^2 are also algebraically independent over k. Using Example 1, $X + Y$, Y are algebraically independent over k; in fact the substitution homomorphism $k[X, Y] \to k[X + Y, Y]/k$ is a k-isomorphism whose inverse is the substitution homomorphism $k[X, Y] \to k[X - Y, Y]/k$. $\{X, Y\}$, $\{X + Y, Y\}$, $\{X^2, Y^2\}$ are all transcendence bases for K over k.

THEOREM 1 · Let K be an extension field of k and let $A = \{a_i \in K \mid i \in I\}$. Then the following are equivalent:

(a) A is algebraically independent over k.

(b) $A_J = \{a_i \mid i \in J\}$ is algebraically independent over k for every finite subset J of I.

(c) The indexed set $\{f(A) \mid f \text{ is a monomial in } X\}$ is k-linearly independent; that is, the monomials in A are k-free in the k-vector space K.

Proof · The equivalence of these three conditions follows easily from the definition. We leave the details to the reader as an exercise.

THEOREM 2 · Let K be an extension field of k. Let I, J be disjoint index sets and let $A = \{a_i \in K \mid i \in I\}$, $B = \{b_j \in K \mid j \in J\}$. Then $C = \{a_i, b_j \in K \mid i \in I, j \in J\}$ is algebraically independent over k if and only if the following hold:

(a) A is algebraically independent over k.

(b) B is algebraically independent over $k(A)$.

Proof · Let $Z = \{X_i, Y_j \mid i \in I, j \in J\}$ be a set of indeterminates over K. Let $X = \{X_i \mid i \in I\}$, $Y = \{Y_j \mid j \in J\}$.

Suppose that C is algebraically independent over k. Thus $k[Z] \to k[C]/k$ is an isomorphism. Restricting ourselves to $k[X]$, we obtain (a). By extending the isomorphism from $k[Z]$ to $k(Z) \to k(C)/k$ and then restricting ourselves to $k(X)[Y]$, we obtain a k-isomorphism $k(X)[Y] \to k(A)[B]$. This k-isomorphism is the composition of $k(X)[Y] \to k(A)[Y]$ and $k(A)[Y] \to k(A)[B]$. We note that by using the assertion (a) the first one is an isomorphism over $k[Y]$. It follows that the second one must be an isomorphism. Indeed, the second one is an isomorphism over $k(A)$. From this isomorphism and from the hypothesis that Y is a set of indeterminates over K we obtain (b).

Conversely, suppose that (a) and (b) hold. The homomorphism $k[Z] \to k[C]/k$ is the composition of $k[X][Y] \to k[A][Y]/k[Y]$ and $k(A)[Y] \to k(A)[B]/k(A)$. From (a) we see that the first one is an isomorphism. From (b) we see that the second one is also an isomorphism. Thus the composition is an isomorphism over k. It follows that C is algebraically independent over k. «

COROLLARY · Let K be an extension field of k and let A be a subset of K such that $K = k(A)$. Let $\mathcal{A}$ be the set of all subsets of A which are algebraically independent over k. Then the following hold:

(a) $\mathcal{A}$ has maximal elements with respect to the inclusion ordering.

(b) Every maximal element B of $\mathcal{A}$ is a transcendence base for K over k.

(c) If K is of finite type over k, there is a finite transcendence base for K over k.

(d) K is algebraic over k if and only if the empty set is a transcendence base for K over k.

Proof · (a) Since the empty set is in $\mathcal{A}$, $\mathcal{A}$ is not empty. By using Theorem 1(b) we see that the subset of A formed by the union of those subsets of A that correspond to elements of a linearly ordered subset of $\mathcal{A}$ is again in $\mathcal{A}$. (a) now follows from Zorn's lemma.

(b) follows from Definition 1 and Theorem 2.

(c) is a consequence of (b).

(d) The empty subset of A is maximal in $\mathcal{A}$ if and only if each element of A is algebraic over k. (d) now follows from Theorem 2.1. «

DEFINITION 2 · Let K be an extension field of k. Let A, B be subsets of K. The subset A is said to be ***algebraically dependent on B over k*** if and only if $k(A, B)$ is an algebraic extension of $k(B)$. The subsets A and B are said to be ***algebraically equivalent over k*** if and only if each is algebraically dependent on the other over k.

Example 3 · Let X_i, $i \in \mathbf{P}$, be a set of indeterminates over the field k. Let $K = k(X_i)_{i \in \mathbf{P}}$. Then the following hold:

(a) $\{X_i^2 \mid i \in \mathbf{P}\}$ is algebraically equivalent to $\{X_i \mid i \in \mathbf{P}\}$ over k.

(b) $\{X_i \mid i \in \mathbf{P}^+\}$ is algebraically dependent on $\{X_i^2 \mid i \in \mathbf{P}\}$ over k, but these two sets are not algebraically equivalent over k.

(c) The substitution homomorphism that sends X_i onto X_{i+1}, $i \in \mathbf{P}$, does not carry a transcendence base onto a transcendence base of K over k.

So far, all the examples about transcendental elements in a field extension K over k are given for abstract fields. For particular fields it is often very difficult to determine the algebraically independent subsets. For example, we mentioned earlier that the real numbers e and π are both transcendental over **Q**. By considering the polynomial $(X - \pi)(X - e) = X^2 - (e + \pi)X + e\pi$ we can conclude that either $e + \pi$, or $e\pi$ must be transcendental over **Q**. However, it is not known which of these is transcendental over **Q**. It is also not known whether or not e and π are algebraically independent over **Q**.

Since **Q** is countable, we know that the algebraic closure of **Q** in the complex numbers is also countable. It is known that the field of complex numbers is algebraically closed (see Chapter IX) and that the complex numbers are not countable. From this it is easy to conclude that a transcendence base of the complex numbers over **Q** must be a noncountable set. However, an explicitly constructed transcendence base for the complex numbers over **Q** is not known.

Exercise 1 · Let K be an extension field of k. Show that the following assertions hold:

(a) The relation "A is algebraically dependent on B over k" is a partial ordering on the set of subsets of K.

(b) The relation "A is algebraically equivalent to B over k" is an equivalence relation on the set of subsets of K.

(c) If $A \subset K$ and $B \subset A$ are such that B is a transcendence base for $k(A)$ over k, then A and B are algebraically equivalent over k.

From Exercise 1 it follows that in the study of algebraic equivalence over k we may restrict ourselves to algebraically independent subsets of K over k.

THEOREM 3 · Let K be an extension field of k. Let

$$A = \{a_i \mid 1 \leqslant i \leqslant m\} \qquad \text{and} \qquad B = \{b_j \mid 1 \leqslant j \leqslant n\}$$

be algebraically independent subsets of K over k, $m, n \in \mathbf{P}$. Suppose that A is algebraically dependent on B over k; then the following assertions hold:

(a) $m \leqslant n$.

(b) After a suitable permutation of the indices of B, each $A_i = \{a_1, \ldots, a_i, b_{i+1}, \ldots, b_n\}$, $0 \leqslant i \leqslant m$, has the properties of being

(1) algebraically independent over k;
(2) algebraically equivalent to B over k.

Proof · If $m = 0$, then there is nothing to prove. Thus we proceed by induction on m. Assume that the theorem has been verified for $m - 1$. By considering $\{a_i \mid 1 \leqslant i \leqslant m - 1\}$, we may assume that $m - 1 \leqslant n$ and that A_i, $0 \leqslant i \leqslant m - 1$, has properties (1) and (2). Using Exercise 1(b), we see that A is algebraically dependent on A_{m-1} over k.

Since A is an algebraically independent subset of K over k, it follows from Theorem 2 that A is not algebraically dependent on $\{a_1, \ldots, a_{m-1}\}$ over k. Thus $m - 1 < n$ or $m \leqslant n$.

We let $L = k(a_1, \ldots, a_m, b_m, \ldots, b_n)$. We know that A_{m-1} is an algebraically independent subset of L over k. Since $a_m \in A$, we see, according to Theorem 2, that $A_{m-1} \cup \{a_m\}$ is not algebraically independent over k. Thus, according to the corollary of Theorem 2, A_{m-1} is a transcendence base for L over k. Since A is algebraically independent over k, we can apply the corollary to find a subset A' such that $A \subset A' \subset C = \{a_1, \ldots, a_m, b_m, \ldots, b_n\}$ and such that A' is a transcendence base for L over k. By permuting the indices of $b_m, \ldots, b_n$, we may assume that $A' = A \cup \{b_{m+l}, \ldots, b_n\}$, where $0 \leqslant l \leqslant n - m + 1$. Because C is not algebraically independent over k, we see that $1 \leqslant l$. If $1 < l$, then the set $A'' = A' \cup \{b_{m+l-1}\}$ is algebraically dependent over k and contains a transcendence base of L over k. The subset $D = \{a_1, \ldots, a_{m-1}, b_{m+l-1}, b_{m+l}, \ldots, b_n\} \subset A_{m-1}$ of A'' is algebraically independent over k. Thus D is a transcendence base for L over k. However, A_{m-1} is known to be a transcendence base for L over k. It follows that $D = A_{m-1}$, that is, $l = 1$. This contradiction shows that $l = 1$ and $A' = A_m$. Since $A' = A_m$ is a transcendence base for L over k, we see that A_m and A_{m-1} are algebraically equivalent over k. Since A_i is algebraically equivalent to B for $1 \leqslant i \leqslant m - 1$, we see that our assertions hold. «

COROLLARY · Let K be an extension field of k. Then the following hold:

(a) If A, B are algebraically equivalent, algebraically independent subsets of K over k and A is finite, then B is finite and A, B have the same number of elements.

(b) If K has a finite transcendence base with n elements, then every transcendence base of K over k has n elements.

Proof · (a) Let A have m elements. By Theorem 3 every finite subset of B has at most m elements. Thus B must be finite with n elements, $n \leqslant m$. Interchanging A and B, we see that $m \leqslant n$. Thus (a) holds.

(b) follows from (a) immediately, since transcendence bases of K over k are algebraically independent, algebraically equivalent subsets of K over k. «

The finiteness requirement in (b) of the corollary above can be removed by using the argument presented in Excursion IV.

DEFINITION 3 · Let K be an extension field of k. The cardinality of a transcendence base of K over k is denoted by tr. deg.$_k$ K. It is called the ***transcendence degree*** of K over k.

Exercise 2 · Let K be an extension field of k such that tr. deg. $_kK = n$, $n \in \mathbf{P}$. Show that $\{a_i \in K \mid 1 \leqslant i \leqslant n\}$ is a transcendence base for K over k if and only if K is algebraic over $k(a_1, ..., a_n)$. If K is of finite type over k, show that the condition that K is algebraic over $k(a_1, ..., a_n)$ may be replaced by $[K : k(a_1, ..., a_n)]$ is finite.

Exercise 3 · Let $k \subset K \subset L$ be a tower of fields. Show that the following hold,

(a) tr. deg. $_kL$ = tr. deg. $_kK$ + tr. deg. $_KL$.

(b) If L is of finite type and tr. deg. $_kK$ = tr. deg. $_kL$, then K is of finite type over k.

We now generalize Exercise 3 in the following Excursion.

Excursion VIII

THEOREM · Let $k \subset l \subset K \subset L$ be a tower of fields. If L is of finite type over k, then K is of finite type over l.

Proof · Since L is of finite type over k, we see that L is of finite type over l. Thus we may consider the case $k = l$. Indeed, it is sufficient to show that K is of finite type over $k(A)$, where A is any finite subset of K. From Exercise 3 we may take A to be a transcendence base of K over k; it follows that we may assume that K is algebraic over k. According to Theorem 2.1 we must now show that $[K : k]$ is finite. Thus we may assume that K is the algebraic closure of k in L. Using Exercise 3, we may assume that L is a purely transcendental extension of K. Let $L = K(a_1, ..., a_n)$, where $a_1, ..., a_n$ are algebraically independent over K. Since K is the algebraic closure of k in L, we see that L is algebraic over $k(a_1, ..., a_n)$. Since L is of finite type over k, we see that L is algebraic and of finite type over $k(a_1, ..., a_n)$. Thus $[L : k(a_1, ..., a_n)] = m \in \mathbf{P}^+$. Let $b_1, ..., b_{m+1} \in K$. It follows that $b_1, ..., b_{m+1}$ must be dependent over $k(a_1, ..., a_n)$; that is, we can find $f_i \in k(a_1, ..., a_n)$, not all zero, such that $f_1 b_1 + \cdots + f_{m+1} b_{m+1} = 0$. Since $a_1, ..., a_n$ are algebraically independent over K and $k \subset K$, we see that $a_1, ..., a_n$ are algebraically independent over k. Clearing the denominators of f_i's, we may assume that all f_i lie in $k[a_1, ..., a_n]$. We may consider the elements $a_1, ..., a_n$ as indeterminates over k. Collecting terms, we see that $f_1 b_1 + \cdots + f_{m+1} b_{m+1}$ is a finite sum of multiples of monomials in the a_i's, where the coefficients of the monomials have the form $c_1 b_1 + \cdots + c_{m+1} b_{m+1}$ and $c_i \in k$ is the coefficient in f_i of the particular monomial in the a_j's selected for the argument. Since $a_1, ..., a_n$ are algebraically independent over K, the monomials in the a_j's are linearly independent over K. Thus we conclude that $c_1 b_1 + \cdots + c_{m+1} b_{m+1} = 0$. Since at least one f_i is not zero, we may select a suitable monomial in the a_j's so that its coefficient c_i in f_i is not zero. It follows that $b_1, ..., b_{m+1}$ are linearly dependent over k. From this we conclude that $[K : k] \leqslant m$. «

This theorem is useful in the study of "algebraic function fields of one variable." We shall not go into any description of this topic. Indeed, many of the theorems in this section have "geometric" meanings. Again, we shall not attempt to describe these interpretations.

» VII · 5 SEPARABLE AND INSEPARABLE ALGEBRAIC FIELD EXTENSIONS

We now return to the study of algebraic extension fields. The basic problem that we wish to consider is the following:

(*) Suppose that K and L are extension fields of k and that K is algebraic over k. How many k-monomorphisms from K to L are there?

The study on algebraic closure shows that we can assume the field L to be algebraic over k. If we examine Theorem 4.2 again, it becomes apparent that the most interesting case occurs when L is algebraically closed. Thus L is an algebraic closure of k. If we examine Exercise 1.10 and the proof of Theorem 4.2, it is clear that the problem is reducible to the case of a simple algebraic extension field $K = k(a)$, to be followed by the consideration of a field tower.

For class discussion consider only case where K is finite extension of k.

When K is a simple extension field $k(a)$ of k, it is clear that any k-monomorphism of K into the extension field L of k is uniquely determined by the image of the element $a \in K$. Theorem 1.3 immediately leads to the following result:

LEMMA 1 · Let $K = k[a]$ be a simple algebraic extension field of k. Suppose that L is any extension field of k.

(a) The following three numbers coincide:

(1) The number of distinct k-monomorphisms of K into L.

(2) The number of distinct zeros of $\text{Irr}(X, a, k)$ in L.

(3) The number of distinct monic, linear factors of $\text{Irr}(X, a, k)$ in $L[X]$.

(b) The common value of the three numbers in (a) is at most equal to $\deg_X \text{Irr}(X, a, k) = [k(a) : k]$; moreover, this number depends only on the k-isomorphism classes of the fields K and L.

The k-isom. class of the field K probably means all fields k-isom. to K. *not sure what he means by this as skip it*

DEFINITION 1 · Let X be an indeterminate over the algebraic closure $\bar{k}$ of k. Suppose that $f \in k[X]$ has degree $n > 0$ and that f has m distinct zeros in $\bar{k}$ (thus $1 \leqslant m \leqslant n$).

(a) f is said to be **separable** (respectively, **inseparable**, **purely inseparable**) in $k[X]$ when $m = n$ (respectively, $m < n$, $m = 1$).

(b) $a \in \bar{k}$ is said to be **separable** (respectively, **inseparable**, **purely inseparable**) over k if and only if $\text{Irr}(X, a, k)$ is separable (respectively, inseparable, purely inseparable) in $k[X]$.

The extension field K of k is called *separable* (purely inseparable) if each of its elements is separable (purely inseparable) over k.

COROLLARY · Let $K = k[a]$ be a simple algebraic extension field of k. Let $\bar{k}$ be an algebraic closure of k.

(a) There exist exactly $[K : k] = \deg_X \text{Irr}(X, a, k)$ distinct k-monomorphisms of K into $\bar{k}$ if and only if a is separable over k.

(b) There exists exactly one k-monomorphism of K into $\bar{k}$ if and only if a is purely inseparable over k.

(c) a lies in k if and only if a is both separable and purely inseparable over k.

Example 1 · The element $\sqrt{2}$ is separable over **Q**.

Proof clear?

Example 2 · Let l be a field of characteristic $p > 0$. Let Y be an indeterminate over l. Then Y is purely inseparable over the field $k = l(Y^p)$. In fact, $\text{Irr}(X, Y, k) = X^p - Y^p$. The point is that Y^p is a prime in the PID $l[Y^p]$; hence Eisenstein's criterion is applicable to $X^p - Y^p \in k[X]$. Applying the theorem of Frobenius to $k(Y)[X]$, we see that $X^p - Y^p = (X - Y)^p$. $(x-y)^p = (x + (-1)y)^p = x^p + (-1)^p y^p = x^p - y^p.$

The reader should observe that the separability of a polynomial in $k[X]$ is independent of the choice of $\bar{k}$. In fact, from the corollary to Theorem 4.2 we can conclude that $\bar{k}$ may be replaced by any algebraically closed field extension K of k. Similarly, the separability of the algebraic element a depends only on the k-isomorphism class of $k(a) = k[a]$. Moreover, the separability of a polynomial over a field k is unchanged when k is replaced by any extension field of k in $\bar{k}$. As for the element $a \in \bar{k}$, we can only make the following statement:

LEMMA 2 · Let $k \subset K \subset L$ be a tower of fields. Suppose $a \in L$ is algebraic over k. Then the following assertions hold:

(a) If a is separable over k, then a is separable over K.

(b) If a is purely inseparable over k, then a is purely inseparable over K.

The verification follows immediately from the observation that any algebraically closed field extension of L is also one of K.

We now give characterizations of the concepts involving separability in terms of k-derivations. This is "intrinsic" in that we do not have to consider an algebraically closed field extension of k.

DEFINITION 2 · Let X be an indeterminate over an extension field K of k. $D_X \in \text{Hom}_k(k[X], k[X])$ is defined by setting $D_X(X^n) = nX^{n-1}$ for each $n \in \mathbf{P}$. If $f \in k[X]$, then $D_X f$ is called the **derivative** of f with respect to X. The unique extension of D_X to a K-derivation of $K[X]$ is also denoted by D_X. (See Definition V.5.1.)

The following exercises are quite important.

Exercise 1 · Let X be an indeterminate over a field k. Let p denote the characteristic of k. Show that $\ker D_X$ in $k[X]$ is the set $\{f \in k[X] | f = a_0 + a_p X^p + \cdots + a_{tp} X^{tp}, a_i \in k, t \in \mathbf{P}\}$.

Exercise 2 · Let X be an indeterminate over an extension field K of k. Let $f, g \in k[X]$. Show that a g.c.d. of f and g in $k[X]$ is also a g.c.d. of f

Just note $(f_1, g_1) = 1$ *in* $k[X] \Leftrightarrow \exists h_1, h_2 \in k[X] \ni k_1 f_1 + h_2 g_1 =$ *Then if* $h \in k[X]$ *is* $\ni h | f_1$ *and* h *then* h

and g in $K[X]$. *Hint.* Let $f = df_1$, $g = dg_1$ in $k[X]$, where d is a g.c.d. of f and g in $K[X]$. Show that 1 is a g.c.d. of f_1 and g_1 in $K[X]$.

Exercise 3 · Let X be an indeterminate over an extension field K of k. Let $f \in k[X]$. Suppose that $a \in K$ is such that $(X - a) | f$ in $K[X]$; namely, $f\{a\} = 0$. Show that $(X - a)^2 | f$ in $K[X]$ if and only if $(X - a) | D_X f$ in $K[X]$; namely, a is a multiple root of the equation $f\{X\} = 0$ in K if and only if both f and $D_X f$ vanish at a. *show* $D_Z(f g) = (D_Z f) g + f(D_Z g)$. *Do this by showing it for* $f = x^i, g = x^j$ *and dev. of sum in sum of dev. and dev of const times*

From this get $(x-a)^2 | f$ *then result follows*
$D_x f = g + (x-a) D_x g$

THEOREM 1 · Let X be an indeterminate over a field k. Let $f \in k[X]$ be an irreducible polynomial. Then f is separable in $k[X]$ if and only if $D_X f \neq 0$.

Proof · By the definition of an irreducible polynomial, f is nonzero. Let $\bar{k}$ be an algebraically closed field extension of k such that X is an indeterminate over $\bar{k}$. Let $f = u \prod_i (X - a_i)$, $u \in k - \{0\}$ and $a_i \in \bar{k}$.

Suppose that f is inseparable and that $a_i = a_j$ for some $i \neq j$. From Exercise 3, we see that $(X - a_i)$ must divide a g.c.d. of f and $D_X f$ in $\bar{k}[X]$. Thus from Exercise 2 we see that a g.c.d. of f and $D_X f$ must be of positive degree. Since f is irreducible in $k[X]$, we see that f must be a g.c.d. of f and $D_X f$, namely, $f | D_X f$ in $k[X]$. Since $\deg D_X f < \deg f$, we conclude that $D_X f = 0$. The converse follows from Exercise 3. *By Ex 3* $\Rightarrow D_X f\{a\} \neq 0$ *when* $a \ni f\{a\} = 0$ »
if f *sep* $\Rightarrow D_X \neq 0$

Exercise 4 · If A is an S-algebra, where S is a commutative ring, then let $\mathrm{Der}_S(A)$ denote the set of all S-derivations of A. (See Definition V.5.1.) Let X be an indeterminate over the *commutative* ring R (considered as an **Z**-algebra). If $\sigma \in \mathrm{Der}_{\mathbf{Z}}(R)$, then let $\sigma_X \in \mathrm{Der}_{\mathbf{Z}[X]}(R[X])$ denote the unique extension of σ; namely, $\sigma_X(rX^i) = \sigma(r)X^i \, \forall \, r \in R, i \in \mathbf{P}$. Verify the following:

(a) If $\sigma \in \mathrm{Der}_{\mathbf{Z}}(R), f \in R[X]$, and $a \in R$, then

$$\sigma(f\{a\}) = (\sigma_X f)\{a\} + (D_X f)\{a\} \cdot \sigma(a).$$

(b) $\mathrm{Der}_{\mathbf{Z}}(R)$ is closed with respect to left multiplication by elements $rI \in \mathrm{Hom}_{\mathbf{Z}}(R, R), r \in R$; namely, if $\sigma \in \mathrm{Der}_{\mathbf{Z}}(R)$ and $r \in R$, the map $r\sigma : R \to R$ given by $(r\sigma)(a) = r \cdot \sigma(a) \, \forall \, a \in R$ is a **Z**-derivation of R. Thus $\mathrm{Der}_{\mathbf{Z}}(R)$ is a Lie subalgebra of the Lie algebra $\mathrm{Hom}_{\mathbf{Z}}(R, R)_L$ over the commutative ring R.

COROLLARY · Let X be an indeterminate over an extension field K of k. Let $a \in K$ be algebraic over k and let $f = \mathrm{Irr}(X, a, k) \in k[X]$. Then the following assertions hold:

Proof (a) a sep $\Rightarrow f$ sep $\therefore D_x f\{a\} \neq 0 \Rightarrow D_x f \neq 0 \Rightarrow a$ sep.
Conversely if $D_x f\{a\} = 0$, then since $f(a) = 0$, exercise 3 $\Rightarrow a$ not sep.

(a) a is separable over k if and only if $D_X f\{a\} \neq 0$.

(b) If a is separable over k and $\sigma \in \mathrm{Der}_k(K)$, then $\sigma(a) = 0$.

(c) If a is separable over k, each $\sigma \in \mathrm{Der}_z(k)$ has a unique extension to an element of $\mathrm{Der}_z(k(a))$.

Proof · (a) follows easily from Exercise 3 and Theorem 1. (b) follows easily from the preceding result, Exercise 4, and the fact that $\sigma_x f = 0$. since $\sigma \in \mathrm{Der}_k(K) \Rightarrow \sigma \in \mathrm{Der}_k(K)$ can apply eqn (a) of Ex 4 and obtain $D_x f\{a\}\sigma_x a = 0$

Suppose that σ' and $\sigma'' \in \mathrm{Der}_z(k(a))$ are extensions of σ. From Exercise V.5.1 we see that $\sigma' - \sigma'' \in \mathrm{Der}_k(k(a))$. With K replaced by $k(a)$ in (b), we conclude that $\sigma' - \sigma'' = 0$. This proves the uniqueness of an extension of σ to an element of $\mathrm{Der}_z(k(a))$. In order to show the existence of an extension of σ to an element of $\mathrm{Der}_z(k(a))$, we consider the substitution homomorphism $k[X] \to k[a]/k$. Since a is algebraic, $k[a] = k(a)$. By definition, this map is surjective and has a kernel generated by $f \in k[X]$. Since a is separable over k, we know that $(D_X f)\{a\} \in k - \{0\}$; thus $r = -((D_X f)\{a\})^{-1} \cdot (\sigma_X f)\{a\} \in k$. We now consider the derivation $\sigma_X + rD_X \in \mathrm{Der}_z(k[X])$. If $g \in k[X]$, then $(\sigma_X + rD_X)(fg) = (\sigma_X f + rD_X f)g + f(\sigma_X g + rD_X g)$. By the choice of r we see that $(\sigma_X f + rD_X f)\{a\} = 0$. Since $f = \mathrm{Irr}(X, a, k)$, we see that $\sigma_X f + rD_X f = fh$ for suitable $h \in k[X]$. Thus our calculation shows that the derivation $\sigma_X + rD_X$ maps the ideal generated by f in $k[X]$ into itself. By use of the first isomorphism theorem $\sigma_X + rD_X$ then induces a derivation of $k(a)$. If $b \in k$, then $(\sigma_X + rD_X)(b) = \sigma_X(b) + 0 = \sigma(b)$. Thus the derivation of $k(a)$ obtained in this manner is in fact an extension of σ. This concludes the proof of (c).

This wrong and $k = \mathbb{Q}(\sqrt[3]{2})$, $k = \mathbb{Q}$, and $f = x^3 - 2$ then $D_X^3 f \{\sqrt[3]{2}\}$ ... $\notin \mathbb{Q}$

This wrong in particular. $\Rightarrow = 0$, by part (a), $\sigma(a) = 0$.

Proof of existence is wrong, in particular doesn't work for $\sigma = 0$. I've used which use result (c) can be done in other ways.

THEOREM 2 · Let k be a field of characteristic 0.

(a) Every irreducible polynomial in $k[X]$ is separable.

(b) Every algebraic extension field of k is separable over k.

Proof · We simply note that $f \in k[X] - \{0\}$ implies that $\deg D_X f = \deg f - 1 \neq -\infty$. Our assertions follow from Theorem 1. «

THEOREM 3 · Let X be an indeterminate over the field k of characteristic $p > 0$. Let σ be the substitution homomorphism $k[X] \to k[X^p]/k$. Suppose that $f \in k[X]$ is monic and irreducible. Then the following assertions hold: Will let $\sigma^\circ = k[X]$

(a) σ^n is a monomorphism $\forall\, n \in \mathbf{P}^+$ and $k = \bigcap_{n \in \mathbf{P}} \mathrm{im}(\sigma^n)$.

(b) $\mathrm{im}\,\sigma = \ker D_X$; hence f is separable if and only if $f \notin \mathrm{im}\,\sigma$.

(c) If $g \in k[X]$ is such that $\sigma^n(g) = f$, then g is monic and irreducible.

(d) Suppose that X is an indeterminate over a splitting field K of k (for example, K may be taken to be the algebraic closure of k.) Let $\{a_i \mid 1 \leqslant i \leqslant n_0\}$ be the *distinct* zeros of f in K and let $e = \max\{n \in \mathbf{P} \mid f \in \operatorname{im}(\sigma^n)\}$.

(1) $f = \prod_{1 \leqslant i \leqslant n_0} (X - a_i)^{p^e}$; thus $\deg f = n_0 p^e$.

(2) $g = \prod_{1 \leqslant i \leqslant n_0} (X - a_i^{p^e})$ is a monic, irreducible, and separable polynomial in $k[X]$ such that $\sigma^n(g) = f$; thus $g = \operatorname{Irr}(X, a_i^{p^e}, k)\ \forall\, i$.

Proof · The injectivity of the map σ^n follows easily from the fact that X is an indeterminate over k. It is clear that $\deg \sigma^n(g) = p^n \cdot \deg g\ \forall\, g \in k[X]$. From this it follows that $\bigcap_{n \in \mathbf{P}} \operatorname{im}(\sigma^n) = k$.

(b) follows from Exercise 1 and Theorem 1. (c) follows from the fact that σ^n is a monomorphism of k-algebras.

The existence of e is assured by (a). If $g \in k[X]$ is such that $\sigma^e(g) = f$, the preceding assertions imply that g is a uniquely determined monic, irreducible, and separable polynomial in $k[X]$. Moreover, $\deg f = p^e \deg g$.

It is clear that $a \in K$ is a zero of f if and only if a^{p^e} is a zero of g in K. From Frobenius' theorem we see that $a^{p^e} = b^{p^e}$ implies that $(a - b)^{p^e} = a^{p^e} - b^{p^e} = 0$. Thus $a^{p^e} = b^{p^e}$ in K if and only if $a = b$ in K. It is easy to see that K is a splitting field of g and that the map sending $a \in K$ onto $a^{p^e} \in K$ leads to a bijection between the set of all zeros of f in K and the set of all zeros of g in K. Since g is monic and separable in $k[X]$, we must have the factorization in (2). Since $\sigma^e(g) = f$, we must have the factorization in (1). The remaining assertions follow from the fact that g is irreducible in $k[X]$. «

DEFINITION 3 · Let X be an indeterminate over a field k. Let $f \in k[X]$ be an *irreducible* polynomial. The number of distinct zeros of f in a splitting field of f over k (or, equivalently, in an algebraic closure of k) is called the **reduced degree** of f or the **degree of separability** of f. The ratio, $\deg f/$ reduced degree of f, is called the **degree of inseparability** of f. If $\chi(k) = 0$, then $\deg f$ is equal to reduced degree of f and 1 is equal to the degree of inseparability of f. If $\chi(k) = p > 0$, then p^e is equal to the degree of inseparability of f, where $e = \max\{n \in \mathbf{P} \mid f \in \operatorname{im} \sigma^n\}$. The integer e is called the **exponent of inseparability** of f.

Exercise 5 · Let $k = k_0(\pi)$ be a simple transcendental extension of k_0, $\chi(k_0) = 3$. Let X be an indeterminate over k and let

$$f = X^{18} + \pi^3 X^{12} + \pi^6 X^9 + \pi.$$

Show that f is irreducible in $k[X]$. Find the polynomial g described in Theorem 3. Find the reduced degree, the degree of inseparability, and the exponent of inseparability of f. *Hint.* k is the field of fractions of the PID $k_0[\pi]$.

COROLLARY · Let $K = k(a)$ be a simple algebraic extension of the field k. Let $f = \mathrm{Irr}(X, a, k)$. Suppose that n_0 and p^e are the reduced degree and the degree of inseparability of f, respectively. Then the following assertions hold:

(a) a^{p^e} is separable over k and $[k(a^{p^e}) : k] = n_0$.

(b) a is purely inseparable over $k(a^{p^e})$ and $\mathrm{Irr}(X, a, k(a^{p^e})) = X^{p^e} - a^{p^e}$; moreover, $[k(a) : k(a^{p^e})] = p^e$ and p^e is $\min\{n \in \mathbf{P}^+ \mid a^n \in k(a^{p^e})\}$.

(c) a^{p^i} is purely inseparable over $k(a^{p^{i+1}})$ and $[k(a^{p^i}) : k(a^{p^{i+1}})] = p$, $0 \leqslant i \leqslant e$.

Proof · (a) follows easily from Theorem 3. It is clear that $\mathrm{Irr}(X, a, k(a^{p^e})) | (X^{p^e} - a^{p^e})$. From this we see that a must be purely inseparable over $k(a^{p^e})$. From Theorem 2.1 we see that $[k(a) : k(a^{p^e})] = p^e$. Thus $\mathrm{Irr}(X, a, k(a^{p^e})) = X^{p^e} - a^{p^e}$. Suppose that $n \in \mathbf{P}^+$ is such that $a^n \in l = k(a^{p^e})$. Let $d \in \mathbf{P}^+$ be the g.c.d. of n and p^e. Then $d = un + vp^e$, $u, v \in \mathbf{Z}$. We may clearly assume that $a \neq 0$. Thus $a^d = (a^n)^u + (a^{p^e})^v \in l$. (The reader should observe that u, v may be negative.) Since $d \mid p^e$ implies that $d = p^c$, we see that $X^{p^e} - a^{p^e} = (X^{p^c} - a^{p^c})^m$, $m = p^{e-c} \in \mathbf{P}^+$. Hence the irreducibility of $X^{p^e} - a^{p^e}$ implies that $e = c$. Thus $p^e = \min\{n \in \mathbf{P} \mid a^n \in k(a^{p^e})\}$.

(c) follows easily from Theorem 2.1 and (b). «

LEMMA 3 · Let X be an indeterminate over a simple algebraic extension field $k(a)$ of k. Suppose that a is purely inseparable over k and that $p^e > 1$ is the degree of inseparability of $\mathrm{Irr}(X, a, k)$ over k. Then the following statements about the element $\rho \in \mathrm{Der}_{\mathbf{Z}}(k)$ are equivalent:

(a) ρ has a unique extension $\sigma \in \mathrm{Der}_{\mathbf{Z}}(k(a))$ such that $\sigma(a) = 1$.

(b) $\rho(a^{p^e}) = 0$.

Proof · Since a is a generator of $k(a) = k[a]$ over k, it is clear that the uniqueness of σ follows from the existence of σ.

Suppose that σ exists. Since $p^e > 1$, we see that $\chi(k) = p > 0$. Thus $\rho(a^{p^e}) = \sigma(a^{p^e}) = p^e a^{p^e - 1}\,\sigma(a) = 0$.

Conversely, suppose that $\rho(a^{p^e}) = 0$. We again consider the substitution homomorphism $k[X] \to k[a]/k$. We know that this map is surjective and has kernel equal to the ideal in $k[X]$ generated by $f = X^{p^e} - a^{p^e}$. The **Z**-derivation $\rho_X + D_X$ of $k[X]$ is such that $(\rho_X + D_X)(f) = -\rho(a^{p^e}) + p^e X^{p^e - 1} = 0$. If $g \in k[X]$, then $(\rho_X + D_X)(fg) = f \cdot (\rho_X + D_X)(g)$. Thus from the first isomorphism theorem we see that $\rho_X + D_X$ induces a derivation σ of $k[a]$. Since $(\rho_X + D_X)(r) = \rho_X(r) + 0 = \rho(r)\ \forall\, r \in R$, and since $(\rho_X + D_X)(X) = \rho(1)X + 1 = 1$, we see that σ has the desired properties. «

THEOREM 4 · Let K be an algebraic extension field of k. Let $K_{\text{sep}} = \{a \in K \mid a \text{ is separable over } k\}$. Then the following assertions hold:

(a) K_{sep} is a subfield of k; in fact, it is the largest subfield of K which is separable over k.

(b) Let the ***characteristic exponent*** of k be p, that is, $p = \max(1, \chi(k))$. Let $K^p = \{a^p \mid a \in K\}$.

(1) The map that sends $a \in K$ onto a^p is a field isomorphism between K and the subfield K^p of K.

(2) $k[K^p] = \bigcap_{\delta \in \mathrm{Der}_k(K)} \ker \delta$.

(3) If K is separable over k, then $K = k[K^p]$.

Proof · Let L be the subfield of K generated by K_{sep} over k. We assert that L is separable over k. It is easy to see that the kernel of a derivation of a ring R is automatically a subring of R. Thus from the corollary to Theorem 1 we conclude that $\mathrm{Der}_k(L) = 0$. Suppose that $a \in L$ is inseparable over k. Then from the corollary to Theorem 3 and Lemma 3 we see that $\mathrm{Der}_k(k(a)) \neq 0$. Since $k(a)[K_{\text{sep}}] = L$, it follows from the corollary to Theorem 1 that $\mathrm{Der}_k(L) \neq 0$. Thus we have reached a contradiction; hence L must be separable over k as asserted. Consequently, $L = K_{\text{sep}}$. This proves (a).

(b) (1) follows from Frobenius' theorem when $p > 1$. From Lemma 3, we conclude that $k[K^p] \subset \bigcap_{\delta \in \mathrm{Der}_k(K)} \ker \delta$. Conversely, suppose that $a \in K - k[K^p]$. Since $\mathrm{Irr}(X, a, k[K^p]) \mid (X^p - a^p)$ in $k[K^p][X]$, we conclude that a is purely inseparable over $k[K^p]$ and that $\mathrm{Irr}(X, a, k[K^p]) = X^p - a^p$. From Lemma 3 we can find $\delta \in \mathrm{Der}_{k[K^p]}(k[K^p, a])$ such that $\delta(a) = 1$. Since $K^p \subset \ker \delta$, we can extend δ to a derivation of K by using Lemma 3 and Zorn's lemma.

Thus (2) must hold. Since each element in K_{sep} is both separable and purely inseparable over $k[K^p]$, we conclude from the corollary to Lemma 1 that (3) holds. «

Exercise 6 · Let K be an algebraic extension field of k. Show that K_{sep} is the intersection of all subfields L satisfying the following conditions:

(a) $k \subset L \subset K$,

(b) K is purely inseparable over L.

Show that, in particular, K is purely inseparable over K_{sep}.

THEOREM 5 · Let K be an extension field of k such that $[K : k]$ is finite. Then K is a separable extension of k if and only if $\text{Der}_k(K) = 0$.

Proof · From the preceding theorem we know that if K is separable over k then $\text{Der}_k(K) = 0$. Suppose that K is inseparable over k. Thus $K_{\text{sep}} \neq K$. Since $\text{Der}_{K_{\text{sep}}}(K) \subset \text{Der}_k(K)$, we may assume that $k = K_{\text{sep}}$. Since $[K : k]$ is finite, we may assume that $K = k[a_1, ..., a_t]$, where $a_1, ..., a_t$ is a minimal set of generators of K over k. Because $K \neq K_{\text{sep}} = k$, we may assume that $t \geqslant 1$. By choice we know that K is a purely inseparable simple extension of $k[a_1, ..., a_{t-1}]$ such that $[K : k[a_1, ..., a_{t-1}]] > 1$. It follows from Lemma 3 that $\text{Der}_k(K) \supset \text{Der}_{k[a_1,...,a_{t-1}]}(K) \neq 0$. «

Exercise 7 · Let $k = k_0(\pi)$ be a simple transcendental extension of k_0, $\chi(k_0) = p > 0$. Let k_i be the root field of $X^{p^i} - \pi$ over k in the algebraic closure $\bar{k}$ of k. Let $K = \bigcup_{i \in \mathbf{P}} k_i$. Verify the following assertions:

(a) k_i is purely inseparable over k and $[k_{i+1} : k_i] = p, \forall\, i \in \mathbf{P}^+$.

(b) K is purely inseparable over k and $k[K^p] = K$.

(c) $\text{Der}_k(K) = 0$.

We can now imitate the concept of algebraic closure and introduce the following definition:

DEFINITION 4 · Let K be an extension field of k.

(a) $K_{\text{sep}} = \{a \in K \mid a \text{ is separably algebraic over } k\}$ is called the ***separable algebraic closure*** of k in K.

(b) k is said to ***separably (algebraically) closed*** in K if and only if $k = K_{\text{sep}}$.

(c) k is said to be ***separably (algebraically) closed*** if and only if k is separably (algebraically) closed in every extension field.

(d) K is said to be a ***separable (algebraic) closure*** of k if and only if the following conditions hold:

(1) K is separably algebraic over k.

(2) K is separably (algebraically) closed.

Exercise 8 · Let $k \subset K \subset L$ be a field tower. Verify the following assertions:

(a) L is separably algebraic over k if and only if the following conditions are satisfied:

(1) K is separably algebraic over k,

(2) L is separably algebraic over K.

(b) K_{sep} is separably closed in K.

(c) Any algebraically closed field is separably closed.

(d) k has a separable closure $\bar{k}_{\text{sep}}$; $\bar{k}_{\text{sep}}$ is unique up to a k-isomorphism and has the following property:

(*) If K is a separably closed field extension of k, then there exists a k-monomorphism $\sigma : \bar{k}_{\text{sep}} \to K$.

(e) Let p be the characteristic exponent of k (see Theorem 4). Let $\bar{k}$ be an algebraic closure of k. Then $\bigcap_{i \in P} k[\bar{k}^{p^i}] = \bar{k}_{\text{sep}}$ is a separable closure of k.

We can also introduce the following definition:

DEFINITION 5 · Let K be an extension field of k.

(a) $K_{\text{per}} = \{a \in K \mid a \text{ is purely inseparably algebraic over } k\}$ is called the ***perfect closure of k in K***.

(b) k is said to be ***perfect in*** K if and only if $k = K_{\text{per}}$.

(c) k is said to be ***perfect*** if and only if k is perfect in every extension field.

(d) K is said to be a ***perfect closure of*** k if and only if the following conditions hold:

(1) K is purely inseparable over k.

(2) K is perfect.

Exercise 9 · Let $k \subset K \subset L$ be a field tower and let p be the characteristic exponent of k. Verify the following assertions:

(a) An element a of K is in K_{per} if and only if $a^{p^i} \in k$ for some $i \in \mathbf{P}$; $e = \min \{i \in \mathbf{P} \mid a^{p^i} \in k\}$ is the exponent of inseparability of $\operatorname{Irr}(X, a, k)$; in fact, $\deg \operatorname{Irr}(X, a, k) = p^e$ in the case that $a \in K_{\text{per}}$.

(b) L is purely inseparable over k if and only if the following conditions are satisfied:

(1) K is purely inseparable over k,

(2) L is purely inseparable over K.

(c) K_{per} is a subfield of K; in fact, K_{per} is the largest subfield of K that is purely inseparable over k,

(d) Any algebraically closed field is perfect. Any field of characteristic 0 is perfect.

(e) k has a perfect closure $\bar{k}_{\text{per}}$; $\bar{k}_{\text{per}}$ is unique up to a k-isomorphism and has the following property:

(*) If K is a perfect field extension of k, then there exists a k-monomorphism $\sigma : \bar{k}_{\text{per}} \to K$.

(f) Let $\bar{k}$ be an algebraic closure of k and let $k^{p^{-i}} = \{a \in \bar{k} \mid a^{p^i} \in k\}$. The $\bar{k}_{\text{per}} = \bigcup_{i \in \mathbf{P}} k^{p^{-i}}$ is a perfect closure of k.

Exercise 10 · Let $\bar{k}$ be an algebraic closure of the field k. Verify the following assertions:

(a) $\bar{k}_{\text{sep}}$ and $\bar{k}_{\text{per}}$ are subsets of $\bar{k}$ that are stable under every k-automorphism of $\bar{k}$.

(b) $\bar{k}$ is generated by $\bar{k}_{\text{sep}}$ and $\bar{k}_{\text{per}}$.

(c) If a_i, $1 \leqslant i \leqslant m$, are k-independent elements in $\bar{k}_{\text{sep}}$ and if b_j, $1 \leqslant j \leqslant n$, are k-independent elements in $\bar{k}_{\text{per}}$, then $\{a_i b_j \mid 1 \leqslant i \leqslant m, 1 \leqslant j \leqslant n\}$, is a k-independent set in $\bar{k}$. Equivalently, every k-independent subset of $\bar{k}_{\text{sep}}$ (respectively, $\bar{k}_{\text{per}}$) is $\bar{k}_{\text{per}}$-independent (respectively, $\bar{k}_{\text{sep}}$-

independent.). This property is usually termed "$\bar{k}_{\text{per}}$ and $\bar{k}_{\text{sep}}$ are linearly disjoint over k."

(d) The multiplication in $\bar{k}$ defines a k-isomorphism between $\bar{k}_{\text{sep}} \otimes_k \bar{k}_{\text{per}}$ and $\bar{k}$ as k-algebras, where $(a \otimes b)(c \otimes d)$ is defined as $ac \otimes bd$.

Example 3 · Let $k = k_0(u, v)$ be a purely transcendental extension of k_0, where k_0 is the field with two elements and u, v are algebraically independent over k_0. Let X be an indeterminate over k; k is the field of fractions of the UFD $k_0[u, v]$. Thus it follows from Eisenstein's criterion that $X^6 + uvX^2 + u$ is irreducible in $k[X]$. Let $K = k(a)$ be a simple algebraic extension of k such that $\text{Irr}(X, a, k) = X^6 + uvX^2 + u$. Then the following assertions can be verified:

(a) $\{a^i \mid 0 \leqslant i \leqslant 5\}$ is a k-basis for K.

(b) $\{1, u, v, uv\}$ is a k^2-basis for k and $k^2 = k_0(u^2, v^2)$.

(c) $K_{\text{sep}} = k(a^2)$, $\text{Irr}(X, a^2, k) = X^3 + uvX + u$.

(d) $K = K_{\text{sep}}(a)$, $\text{Irr}(X, a, K_{\text{sep}}) = X^2 - a^2 = X^2 + a^2$.

(e) $a^6 = u + uva^2$, $a^8 = ua^2 + uva^4$, $a^{10} = u^2v + u^2v^2a^2 + ua^4$.

Let $c_i \in k$, $0 \leqslant i \leqslant 5$. Then $(\sum_i c_i a^i)^2$ can be computed by (e). It is equal to $c_0^2 + c_3^2u + c_5^2u^2v + (c_1^2 + c_3^2uv + c_4^2u + c_5^2u^2v^2)a^2 + (c_2^2 + c_4^2uv + c_5^2u)a^4$. From (a) we see that the preceding element lies in k if and only if the coefficients of a^2 and a^4 are both zero. Applying (b) to the coefficient of a^4, we see that $c_2 = c_4 = c_5 = 0$. Applying (b) and the preceding result to the coefficient of a^2, we see that $c_1 = c_3 = 0$. Thus we may conclude that $w \in K$ is such that $w^2 \in k$ if and only if $w \in k$. This shows that $K_{\text{per}} = k$.

Using Theorem 2.1, we know that a subfield L of K which contains k must have degree 1, 2, 3, or 6 over k. Clearly, $[L : k] = 1$ if and only if $L = k$; $[L : k] = 6$ if and only if $L = K$. Suppose that $[L : k]$ is a prime; then, from Theorem 4, we know that L is either separable or purely inseparable over k. In the latter case $[L : k]$ is a power of $\chi(k) = 2$. Since $K_{\text{per}} = k$ and $[K_{\text{sep}} : k]$ is the prime 3, we see quickly that K_{sep} is the unique subfield strictly between k and K.

Exercise 11 · Let $\sigma : K \to K$ be a field monomorphism. Suppose there is a subfield k of K that satisfies the following conditions:

(a) $\sigma(k) = k$,

(b) K is algebraic over k,

(c) If L is any subfield of K containing k, then $\sigma(L) \subset L$.

Show that $\sigma(L) = L$ for every subfield L of K that contains k.

Hint. If $a \in K$, then $k[a]$ is finite-dimensional over k.

Exercise 12 · Let k be a field with characteristic exponent p. Show that k is perfect if and only if $k = k^p$. Use Exercise 11 to show that every *algebraic* extension field of a perfect field is again perfect.

Exercise 13 · Let $K = k(a_1, \ldots, a_n)$ be an extension field such that $a_1, \ldots, a_n$ are algebraically independent over k. Verify the following assertions:

(a) There exists a unique $\partial_i \in \mathrm{Der}_k(K)$ such that $\partial_i(a_j) = \delta_{ij}$, $1 \leqslant i, j \leqslant n$.

(b) $\mathrm{Der}_k(K)$ has a K-basis consisting of $\partial_1, \ldots, \partial_n$.

(c) $[\partial_i, \partial_j] = \partial_i \circ \partial_j - \partial_j \circ \partial_i = 0 \;\forall\, i, j$.

Exercise 14 · Let K be an algebraic extension field of k. Suppose that k has characteristic exponent p. Verify the following assertions:

(a) $[K : k[K^p]] = p^n$ for some n. (If $p = 1$, n is taken to be 0.)

(b) $\dim_K \mathrm{Der}_k(K) = n$, where n is defined in (a).

Exercise 15 · Let $k \subset K \subset L$ be a tower of fields such that $[L : k]$ is finite. Show that the following statements are equivalent:

(a) Every element of $\mathrm{Der}_k K$ has a unique extension to an element of $\mathrm{Der}_k L$.

(b) The zero element of $\mathrm{Der}_k K$ has a unique extension to an element of $\mathrm{Der}_k L$.

(c) L is separable over K.

We now consider the problem posed at the beginning of the section.

DEFINITION 4 · Let K be an extension field of k such that $[K : k]$ is finite. Then $[K : k]_s$ denotes the number of distinct k-monomorphisms of K into an algebraic closure $\bar{k}$ of k. $[K : k]_s$ is called the ***separable degree*** of K over k. $[K : k]_\iota = [K : k]/[K : k]_s$ is called the ***degree of inseparability*** of K over k.

We know from Lemma 1 that the two numbers above depend only on the k-isomorphism class of K. In particular, they do not depend on the choice of the algebraic closure $\bar{k}$ of k.

THEOREM 6 · Let $k \subset K \subset L$ be a tower of fields such that $[L : k]$ is finite. Let M be any algebraically closed field. Then the following assertions hold:

(a) If $\sigma : k \to M$ is a field monomorphism, then $[K : k]_s$ is the number of distinct extensions of σ to field monomorphisms of K into M.

(b) $[L : k]_s = [L : K]_s[K : k]_s$, $[L : k]_i = [L : K]_i[K : k]_i$.

(c) $1 \leqslant [L : k]_s \leqslant [L : k]$.

(d) L is separable over k if and only if $[L : k]_s = [L : k]$.

(e) L is purely inseparable over k if and only if $[L : k]_s = 1$.

(*f*) $[L : k]_s = [L_{\text{sep}} : k]$ and $[L : k]_i = [L : L_{\text{sep}}] = p^n$ for some $n \in \mathbf{P}^+$, where p is the characteristic exponent of k.

Proof · (a) ~~follows immediately from Lemma 1.~~

Let $\bar{L}$ be an algebraic closure of L. Thus from the hypothesis we see that $\bar{L}$ is also an algebraic closure of k and K. Hence $1 \leqslant [L : k]_s$, $[L : K]_s$, and $[K : k]_s$. Let $\{\rho_i \mid i \in I\}$ be the set of all k-monomorphisms of K into $\bar{L}$. Let $\{\sigma_j \mid j \in J\}$ be the set of all K-monomorphisms of L into $\bar{L}$. From (a) we see that each ρ_i may be extended to L in $[L : K]_s = |J|$ distinct ways. Thus let $\rho_{i,j}$, $j \in J$, be these extensions. We assert that $\{\rho_{i,j} \mid i \in I, j \in J\}$ is the set of all k-monomorphisms of L into $\bar{L}$ and $\rho_{i,j} = \rho_{s,t}$ if and only if $i = s$ and $j = t$.

Suppose that $\rho_{i,j} = \rho_{s,t}$. By restricting to elements of K, we see that $i = s$. Hence by definition $j = t$. This shows that the k-monomorphisms $\rho_{i,j}$ are all distinct. Conversely, suppose that $\tau : L \to \bar{L}$ is a k-monomorphism. By restricting τ to K, we see that τ must be an extension of ρ_i for some $i \in I$. Thus $\tau = \rho_{i,j}$ for some $i \in I, j \in J$. Hence (b) holds.

Since (c), (d), and (e) have all been verified for a simple extension, it is immediate that the general results follow from (b), Theorem 2.1(b) and an induction argument. (*f*) follows from (d), (e), and Exercise 6. «

» VII · 6 FINITE FIELDS: PRIMITIVE ELEMENT THEOREM

We now consider the structure of fields with a finite number of elements.

THEOREM 1 · Let $p \in \mathbf{P}^+$ be a prime. Let k_1 denote the prime field $\mathbf{Z}/(p)$ with p elements. Suppose that $\bar{k}_1$ is an algebraic closure of k_1. Then the following assertions hold:

(a) If k is a finite field, then $|k| = (\chi(k))^{[k:k_1]}$, where k_1 is the prime field of k. In particular, if $\chi(k) = p$, then $|k| = p^n$, where n is the field degree of k over the prime field of k.

(b) If k is a finite field with p^n elements, then $k^\star$ is a cyclic group with $p^n - 1$ elements.

(c) If k is a finite field and l is a subfield of k, then k is a simple extension field of l. In fact, a generator of $k^\star$ will generate k over l.

(d) If $n \in \mathbf{P}^+$, then $k_n = \{a \in \bar{k}_1 \mid a^{p^n} - a = 0\}$ is the unique subfield of $\bar{k}_1$ with p^n elements. Every finite field k with p^n elements is isomorphic to k_n.

(e) If k is a finite field with p^n elements and l is any subfield of k, then k is separable over l. In fact, if $a \in k$, then $\mathrm{Irr}(X, a, l)$ is a factor of $X^{p^n} - X$ in $l[X]$.

Proof · (a) is obvious.

We now recall that a polynomial $f \in K[X]$ can have at most $\deg f$ distinct zeros in the field K.

It is clear that $k^\star$ is a finite abelian group with $p^n - 1$ elements. Hence every element of $k^\star$ satisfies the equation $X^{p^n-1} - 1 = 0$. From the structure theorem for finite abelian groups we know that $k^\star$ is a direct product of cyclic groups C_i of order d_i, $1 \leqslant i \leqslant t$, where $d_i \mid d_{i+1}$, $1 \leqslant i \leqslant t - 1$, and $d_i > 1$. Thus $p^n - 1 = d_1 \cdots d_t$. (As usual, the empty product is taken to be 1.) It is clear that every element of $k^\star$ is also a zero of the polynomial $X^{d_t} = 1$. Thus $d_t \leqslant p^n - 1 \leqslant d_t$ holds when $t > 0$. It follows that $t \leqslant 1$ and that $k^\star$ is cyclic. This proves (b); (c) follows trivially from (b).

From the preceding paragraph, we know that every subfield of $\bar{k}_1$ which has p^n elements must be contained in k_n. From the universal property of an algebraic closure we know that every field with p^n elements must be isomorphic to a subfield of $\bar{k}_1$. Thus we only need to show that k_n is a subfield with p^n elements. We know that k_n is the set of zeros of the polynomial $X^{p^n} - X \in k_1[X]$ in $\bar{k}_1$. Since $D_X(X^{p^n} - X) = -1$, it follows from Exercise 5.3 that $X^{p^n} - X$ is a separable polynomial. Thus we know that $|k_n| = p^n$. Since $\bar{k}_1$ is a commutative ring, we know that k_n is closed under multiplication. Since $\chi(k)$ is equal to the prime p, we know from Frobenius' theorem that $(a + b)^{p^n} = a^{p^n} + b^{p^n} \ \forall\, a, b \in \bar{k}_1$. It is now easy to conclude that k_n is closed under addition. Since $0, 1 \in k_n$, it is clear that k_n is a finite

(margin note, middle): Let $k_1(a)$ be a simple ext of k, with $[k_1(a):k_1] = g$, with $\mathrm{Irr}(X, a, k_1) = a_0 + a_1 X \cdots + a_g X^g$. Then elts of $k_1(a)$ are uniquely represented as $a_0 + a_1 a + \cdots + a_{g-1} a^{g-1}$, each $a_i \in k_1$.

(margin note, right): Since the eqn $X^{d_t} = 1$ has at most d_t solns.

subring of $\bar{k}_1$ that contains k_1. Because $\bar{k}_1$ is a field, we deduce from Exercise 2.3 that k_n is a subfield. This proves (d).

(e) follows easily from Theorem 1.4(a) and the fact that $X^{p^n} - X$ is a separable polynomial. «

DEFINITION 1 · Let $p \in \mathbf{P}^+$ be a prime. If $n \in \mathbf{P}^+$, then $GF(p^n)$ denotes the field k_n defined in Theorem 1; $GF(p^n)$ is called a ***Galois field*** with p^n elements.

THEOREM 2 · Let $p \in \mathbf{P}^+$ be a prime. Let $F(p)$ be an algebraic closure of $GF(p)$. If L is an extension field of K, let $\mathcal{G}_K(L)$ be the group of all K-automorphisms of L. Then the following assertions hold:

(a) The Frobenius homomorphism $\theta : F(p) \to F(p)$ that sends each element onto its pth power has the following properties:

(1) If k is subfield of $F(p)$, then θ is a GF(p)-automorphism of k. Thus $\theta \in \mathcal{G}_{GF(p)}(k)$.

(2) $GF(p^n) = \{a \in F(p) \mid \theta^n(a) = a\}, \forall\, n \in \mathbf{P}^+$.

(3) The subgroup $\langle\theta\rangle$ in $\mathcal{G}_{GF(p)}(F(p))$ is an infinite cyclic group.

(4) There is a natural exact sequence of groups, $1 \to \langle\theta^n\rangle \to \langle\theta\rangle \xrightarrow{T} \mathcal{G}_{GF(p)}(GF(p^n)) \to 1, \forall\, n \in \mathbf{P}^+$. Thus $\mathcal{G}_{GF(p)}(GF(p^n))$ is a cyclic group of order n and it is generated by the Frobenius automorphism θ; moreover, $GF(p)$ is the set of fixed points of $\mathcal{G}_{GF(p)}(GF(p^n))$ on $GF(p^n)$.

(b) Let $\mathcal{F}(p)$ be the set of all finite subfields of $F(p)$. Then the map that sends $n \in \mathbf{P}^+$ onto $GF(p^n) \in \mathcal{F}(p)$ is a bijection such that $m \mid n$ in $\mathbf{P}^+$ if and only if $GF(p^m) \subset GF(p^n)$. The inverse of the preceding map is given by sending $GF(p^n)$ onto $[GF(p^n) : GF(p)] = n$.

Proof · (a)(1) follows from Frobenius' theorem and Exercise 5.11. (a)(2) follows from (d) of Theorem 1. (a)(3) follows from (a)(2) and the existence of $GF(p^n)\ \forall\, n \in \mathbf{P}^+$. Since $GF(p^n)$ is mapped onto itself under θ, therefore under $\theta^m\ \forall\, m \in \mathbf{Z}$, we see that the map which sends θ onto its restriction to $GF(p^n)$ is a group homomorphism of $\langle\theta\rangle$ into $\mathcal{G}_{GF(p)}(GF(p^n))$. From (a)(2) we see that $\langle\theta^n\rangle$ is in the kernel of this homomorphism. If $0 < i < n$, then from the evaluation of θ^i on a generator of the cyclic group $GF(p^n)^\star$ we conclude that θ^i is not in the kernel of this group homomorphism. Consequently, $\langle\theta^n\rangle$ is the kernel of the group homomorphism. From Theorem 5.6(c) we see that $|\ \mathcal{G}_{GF(p)}(GF(p^n))\ | \leqslant [GF(p^n) : GF(p)]_s \leqslant [GF(p^n) : GF(p)] = n$. It

since $\left|\langle\theta\rangle\big/\langle\theta^n\rangle\right| = n$ *and* $\langle\theta\rangle\big/\langle\theta^n\rangle \cong \operatorname{im} \tau$

follows from the first isomorphism theorem that our group homomorphism must be surjective. The remaining assertions of (a)(4) are now clear.

If $GF(p^m) \subset GF(p^n)$, then by counting we see that $p^n = (p^m)^{[GF(p^n):GF(p^m)]}$. Thus $m \mid n$.

Conversely, suppose that $m \mid n$ in $\mathbf{P}^+$. Let X be an indeterminate over $\mathbf{Z}$. Let $\rho : \mathbf{Z}[X] \to \mathbf{Z}[X^m]/\mathbf{Z}$ be the substitution homomorphism. Suppose that $md = n$, $d \in \mathbf{P}^+$. From the factor theorem we have $(X - 1)\mid(X^d - 1)$ in $\mathbf{Z}[X]$. If we apply ρ to this divisibility condition, we see that $(X^m - 1)\mid(X^n - 1)$. If we apply the substitution homomorphism $\mathbf{Z}[X] \to \mathbf{Z}[p]/\mathbf{Z}$ to the preceding divisibility condition, we see that $(p^m - 1)\mid(p^n - 1)$ in $\mathbf{Z}$. Repeating the argument with $p^m - 1$ and $p^n - 1$ in the places of m and n, we see that $(X^{p^m-1} - 1)\mid(X^{p^n-1} - 1)$ in $\mathbf{Z}[X]$. By multiplying each term by X and applying the ring homomorphism $\mathbf{Z} \to GF(p)$ we see that $(X^{p^m} - X)\mid(X^{p^n} - X)$ in $F(p)[X]$. *← Replace this line by this* Thus from (d) of Theorem 1 we deduce that $GF(p^m) \subset GF(p^n)$; (b) now follows.

map $\mathbf{Z}[X] \to \mathbf{Z}/(p)[X]$ *by* $\sum n_i x^i \to \sum [n_i] x^i$

to get $(x^{p^m}-x)\mid(x^{p^n}-x)$ *in* $\mathbf{Z}/(p)[X]$ *cong. mod p* $(\subseteq F(p)[X])$

COROLLARY · Every finite field is perfect.

Proof · Exercise 5.12 and Theorem 2.

By Thm 2(a)(2) the finite field $GF(p^m)$ satisfies $a^{p^m}=a$ $\forall a \in GF(p^m)$

∴ $GF(p^m) = (GF(p^m))^p$ and apply Ex 5.12.

Exercise 1 · Let $q = p^n$, where $p \in \mathbf{P}^+$ is a prime, and $n \in \mathbf{P}^+$. Prove that Theorem 2 holds with q in the place of p. Show that there is a natural exact sequence of groups:

$$1 \to \mathfrak{G}_{GF(q^s)}(GF(q^{st})) \to \mathfrak{G}_{GF(q)}(GF(q^{st})) \to \mathfrak{G}_{GF(q)}(GF(q^s)) \to 1.$$

Show that the preceding exact sequence corresponds to the sequence:

$$1 \to \frac{\langle \sigma^s \rangle}{\langle \sigma^{st} \rangle} \to \frac{\langle \sigma \rangle}{\langle \sigma^{st} \rangle} \to \frac{\langle \sigma \rangle}{\langle \sigma^s \rangle} \to 1,$$

where σ is the Frobenius automorphism of $F(q)$ which sends each element onto its qth power.

For comparison purposes, we have the following:

turn in

Exercise 2 · Let $p \in \mathbf{P}^+$ be a prime. Let $f = (X^p - 1)/(X - 1) = X^{p-1} + \cdots + X + 1 \in \mathbf{Q}[X]$. Suppose that ζ is a zero of f in the algebraic closure $\bar{\mathbf{Q}}$ of $\mathbf{Q}$. Verify the following assertions:

(a) f is irreducible in $\mathbf{Q}[X]$. *Hint*. Apply Eisenstein's criterion to $f\{X+1\}$.

(b) $\mathbf{Q}[\zeta] = \mathbf{Q}[\zeta^i]$, $1 \leqslant i \leqslant p-1$, is the root field of f over $\mathbf{Q}$. If $K = \mathbf{Q}[\zeta]$, then $[K : \mathbf{Q}] = p - 1$.

(c) There exists a unique element $\rho_i : \mathcal{G}_{\mathbf{Q}}(K)$ such that $\rho_i(\zeta) = \zeta^i$, $1 \leqslant i \leqslant p-1$. Moreover, $\mathcal{G}_{\mathbf{Q}}(K) = \{\rho_i \mid 1 \leqslant i \leqslant p-1\}$ is a group of order $p-1$ and $\mathbf{Q}$ is the set of fixed points of $\mathcal{G}_{\mathbf{Q}}(K)$.

(d) The map that sends $i + (p) \in \mathbf{Z}/(p) = GF(p)$, $1 \leqslant i \leqslant p-1$, onto ρ_i is an isomorphism between the cyclic group $GF(p)^\star$ and $\mathcal{G}_{\mathbf{Q}}(K)$.

Exercise 3 · Let p, q be distinct primes in $\mathbf{P}^+$. Suppose that n is the order of $q + (p)$ in $(\mathbf{Z}/(p))^\star$. Let $f = X^{p-1} + \cdots + X + 1$ be in $GF(q)[X]$. Verify the following assertions:

(a) f is the product of $(p-1)/n$ monic, irreducible polynomials, each of degree n, in $GF(q)[X]$.

(b) f is a product of linear factors in $GF(q^m)[X]$ if and only if $n \mid m$.

(c) Suppose that ζ is a zero of f in $GF(q^n)$. Then each monic, irreducible factor of f in $GF(q)[X]$ factors into $\prod_{0 \leqslant i \leqslant n-1}(X - \zeta^{eq^i})$ in $GF(q^n)[X]$ for a suitable $e \in \mathbf{P}^+$.

(d) With the notations of (c), there exists a unique $\sigma \in \mathcal{G}_{GF(q)}(GF(q^n))$ with $\sigma(\zeta) = \zeta^e$, $e \in \mathbf{P}^+$, if and only if $e \equiv q^i \bmod p$ for some $i \in \mathbf{P}$.

Carry out the detailed calculations in (a), (b), (c), and (d) for the case $p = 7$, $q = 2$.

Hints. (1) The set of zeros of f together with 1 in the algebraic closure of $GF(q)$ forms a group under multiplication. Since p is a prime, this group is of order 1 or p. Since $p \neq q$, the polynomial f is separable and the group has *prime* order p. Consequently, either f splits into a product of linear factors in $GF(q^m)$ or f has no linear factors in $GF(q^m)$.

(2) $GF(q^m)^\star$ is a cyclic group of order $q^m - 1$. Since each finite cyclic group of order t has a unique subgroup of order s for each divisor s of t in $\mathbf{P}^+$, we see that f has a zero in $GF(q^m)$ if and only if $p \mid (q^m - 1)$.

(3) We conclude from (2) that $GF(q^n)$ is the smallest subfield of the algebraic closure of $GF(q)$ that contains a zero of f; that is, $GF(q^n)$ is the root field of f in the algebraic closure of $GF(q)$. Thus $GF(q^n) = GF(q)[\zeta] = GF(q)[\zeta^i]$, $1 \leqslant i \leqslant p-1$; (b) follows from (1) and Theorem 2(b).

(4) From (3) we see that $[GF(q^n) : GF(q)] = \deg_X \mathrm{Irr}(X, \zeta^i, GF(q))$. Since $f = \prod_{1 \leqslant i \leqslant p-1}(X - \zeta^i)$ in $GF(q^n)[X]$, (a) follows rather easily.

(5) Let $1 \leqslant e \leqslant p - 1$. Suppose that $g = \text{Irr}(X, \zeta^e, GF(q)) \in GF(q)[X]$. Since $\rho g = g \;\forall\; \rho \in \mathcal{G}_{GF(q)}(GF(q^n))$, we deduce from Theorem 2 that ζ^{eq^i} is a zero of g in $GF(q^n)$ for $0 \leqslant i \leqslant n - 1$. From the choice of e and the definition of n we see that these are distinct zeros of g; (c) follows from the fact that $\deg g = n$, and (d) follows from (c).

Exercise 4 · Let $\mathcal{P}$ denote the set of all primes in $\mathbf{P}^+$. Define a ***supernatural number*** as a formal expression $\alpha = \prod_{p \in \mathcal{P}} p^{\alpha(p)}$, where $\alpha(p) \in \mathbf{P} \cup \{\infty\}$, $n < \infty \;\forall\; n \in \mathbf{P}$. Let Ψ denote the set of all supernatural numbers and define divisibility in Ψ by writing $\alpha \mid \beta$ if and only if $\alpha(p) \leqslant \beta(p) \;\forall\; p \in \mathcal{P}$. Verify the following assertions:

(a) The divisibility theory of Ψ extends the divisibility theory of $\mathbf{P}^+$.

(b) Let $F(q)$ be an algebraic closure of $GF(q)$. Let $\mathcal{F}(q)$ denote the set of all subfields of $F(q)$ that contains $GF(q)$. Then there is a unique map $\rho : \Psi \to \mathcal{F}(q)$ which satisfies the following condition:

$$(*) \quad \rho(\alpha) = \{a \in F(q) \mid a^{q^m} - a = 0,\ m \in \mathbf{P}^+, \quad \text{and} \quad m \mid \alpha\}.$$

(c) The map ρ of (b) is a bijection; moreover, $\alpha \mid \beta$ in Ψ if and only if $\rho(\alpha) \subset \rho(\beta)$. The restriction of ρ to $\mathbf{P}^+$ is the bijection described in Theorem 2(b) and Exercise 1.

In Theorem 1 we have seen that every extension field of finite degree over a finite field is a simple extension. For infinite fields the following result holds:

THEOREM 3 · (Primitive element theorem). Let k be an infinite field. Suppose $K = k[a_1, \ldots, a_t]$ is an extension field of finite degree over k, $t \in \mathbf{P}$. Then the following assertions hold:

(a) If $a_2, \ldots, a_t$ are separable over k, then K is a simple extension field of k.

(b) Suppose that $\bar{K}$ is an algebraic closure of K and that $\{a_{i,j} \mid 1 \leqslant j \leqslant n_i\}$ is the set of all distinct zeros of $f_i = \text{Irr}(X, a_i, k)$ in $\bar{K}$. Let $a_{i,1} = a_i$ in the preceding notation. Suppose that a_2 is separable over k and $n_2 > 1$:

(1) There exists $c \in k$ such that $a_{1,i} + a_{2,j}c \neq a_{1,1} + a_{2,1}c = a_1 + a_2 c$ for $1 \leqslant j \leqslant n_1$ and $2 \leqslant j \leqslant n_2$.

(2) If $c \in k$ satisfies (1), then $k[a_1 + a_2 c] = k[a_1, a_2]$.

Proof · By using induction on t we see that it is enough to verify (b).

Since $a_{2,j} \neq a_{2,1} = a_2$, the set $\{d \in k \mid a_{1,i} + a_{2,j}d = a_{1,i} + a_{2,1}d$

for some $j \neq 1$ and some $i\}$ is a finite set. Since k is infinite, we see that (b)(1) holds. Suppose $c \in k$ satisfies (1) of (b). Let $d = a_1 + a_2 c = a_{1,1} + a_{2,1}c$. It is clear that $k[a_1, a_2] \supset k[d]$. By the factor theorem, $f_1\{d - cX\}$, $f_2\{X\} \in k[d][X]$ have the common factor $X - a_2$ in $\bar{K}[X]$. Suppose that $X - e$ is an arbitrary common linear factor of $f_1\{d - cX\}$ and $f_2\{X\}$ in $\bar{K}[X]$. We assert that $e = a_2$.

Since $f_2\{e\} = 0$, we know that $e = a_{2,j}$ for some j. Similarly, $f_1\{d - ce\} = 0$ implies that $d - ce = a_{1,i}$ for some i. Thus $d = a_{1,i} + a_{2,j}c$ By the choice of c we see that $j = 1$. Thus $e = a_{2,1} = a_2$ as asserted.

Since f_2 is a separable polynomial, our preceding assertion implies that $X - a_2$ is a g.c.d. of $f_1\{d - cX\}$ and $f_2\{X\}$ in $\bar{K}[X]$. From Exercise 5.2 we see that $X - a_2$ must be the monic g.c.d. of $f_1\{d - cX\}$ and $f_2\{X\}$ in $k[d][X]$. This shows that $a_2 \in k[d]$. Since $a_1 = d - a_2 c$, we see that $a_1 \in k[d]$. Thus $k[d] \supset k[a_1, a_2]$. «

COROLLARY · Let K be a separable extension of finite degree over k. Then K is a simple extension of k.

Exercise 5 · Let $K = \mathbf{Q}[\sqrt{2}, \sqrt{3}, \sqrt{5}]$. Find an element $a \in K$ such that $K = \mathbf{Q}[a]$.

Exercise 6 · Let X, Y and Z be indeterminates over $GF(2)$. Let $K = GF(2)(X, Y, Z)$. Suppose that $k = GF(2)(X, Y^2, Z^2)$. Verify the following assertions:

(a) $K = k(Y, Z)$ is purely inseparable over k and $[K : k] = 4$.

(b) Let $f, g \in GF(2)[X]$. Set $M_{f,g} = k[fY + gZ]$. Then $M_{0,0} = k$ and $[M_{f,g} : k] = 2$ when $(f, g) \neq (0, 0)$.

(c) With the notation of (*b*), $M_{f,g} = M_{u,v}$ if and only if $fv = gu$, where $(f, g) \neq (0, 0) \neq (u, v)$ are elements of $GF(2)[X] \times GF(2)[X]$.

(d) Every subfield of K containing k and distinct from K and k has the form $M_{f,g}$ for some $(f, g) \neq (0, 0)$ in $GF(2)[X] \times GF(2)[X]$. In particular, there exists an infinite number of subfields between k and K.

(e) $K^2 \subset k$. Thus, K is not a simple extension of k.

THEOREM 4 · Let $K = k[a]$ be a simple algebraic extension of k. Suppose that M is a subfield of K containing k and that $\mathrm{Irr}(X, a, M) = X^m + a_{m-1}X^{m-1} + \cdots + a_0$. Then $M = k[a_0, \ldots, a_{m-1}]$.

Proof · Let $L = k[a_0, \ldots, a_{m-1}]$. It is clear that $L \subset M$. Moreover, $K = L[a] = M[a]$. Since $\mathrm{Irr}(X, a, M) \in L[X]$ is irreducible in

$M[X]$, it must also be irreducible in $L[X]$. It follows from Theorem 1.4 that $\operatorname{Irr}(X, a, M) = \operatorname{Irr}(X, a, L)$. Thus $[K : L] = \deg \operatorname{Irr}(X, a, L) = \deg \operatorname{Irr}(X, a, M) = [K : M]$. Hence from Theorem 2.1 we see that $[M : L] = 1$ or $M = L$. «

THEOREM 5 · Let K be an extension field of k. Then K is a simple algebraic extension field of k if and only if there exist only a finite number of subfields between k and K.

Proof · Suppose that $K = k[a]$. Let $f = \operatorname{Irr}(X, a, k)$. From Theorem 4 we know that each subfield M between k and K is uniquely determined by $g = \operatorname{Irr}(X, a, M)$. Since $f \in M[X]$ and $f\{a\} = 0$, it follows from Theorem 2.1 that $g \mid f$ in $M[X] \subset K[X]$. Since f has only a finite number of distinct monic factors in $K[X]$, it follows that there exist only a finite number of distinct subfields between k and K.

Conversely, assume that there exist only a finite number of subfields between k and K. Then the following assertions hold:

(a) K is algebraic over k. Suppose that K is not algebraic over k. Let $a \in K$ be transcendental over k; $k(a)$ then contains distinct subfields $k(a^n)$, $n \in \mathbf{P}$. This contradicts the given hypothesis.

(b) $[K : k]$ is finite. Suppose that $[K : k]$ is infinite. From (a) we can find a tower of subfields $k = K_0 \subset K_1 \subset \cdots$ such that $K_{i+1} = K_i[a_{i+1}]$, $a_{i+1} \notin K_i$. Since each K_i is an extension field of finite degree, we can form an infinite tower. Thus, again, we have reached a contradiction to the given hypothesis.

(c) K is a simple algebraic extension of k. From (b) we know that $K = k[a_1, \ldots, a_t]$. Since every subfield of K containing k has the same property as K, we may proceed by induction on t and assume that $t = 2$. From Theorem 1 we may assume that k is infinite. Let $M_c = k[a_1 + a_2 c]$, $c \in k$. Since k is infinite, it follows from the given hypothesis that $M_c = M_d$ for some $c \neq d$. Let $a = a_1 + a_2 c$. Thus $M_c = M_d = k[a]$. But $a_2 = (c - d)^{-1}(a_1 + a_2 c - (a_1 + a_2 d))$. Thus $a_2 \in k[a]$. Since $a_1 = a - a_2 c$, we see that $a_1 \in k[a]$. This shows that $K = k[a_1, a_2] = k[a]$. «

References

The reader may consult [6] and [8] for the uses of fields in algebraic geometry. For the uses of fields in the study of Diophantine equations and in algebraic number theory, the reader may consult [1], [2], [4] and [5]. For a detailed study of fields and commutative algebras, the reader may consult [9]. The reader may find the construction of the algebraic closure of a countable field by the "well-ordering" principle in [7].

1. E. Artin, *Theory of Algebraic Numbers*, Göttingen, Germany, 1959.
2. E. Artin, *Algebraic Numbers and Algebraic Functions*, New York University, 1951.
3. P. M. Cohn, Quadratic extensions of skew fields, *Proceedings of the London Mathematical Society*, (3), **11** (1961), 531–556.
4. D. Hilbert, *Gesammelte Abhandlungen*, Vol. 1, Springer, Berlin, 1932.
5. S. Lang, *Diophantine Geometry*, Interscience, New York, 1962.
6. S. Lang, *Introduction to Algebraic Geometry*, Interscience, New York, 1958.
7. B. L. van der Waerden, *Modern Algebra*, Vol. 1, Ungar, New York, 1949.
8. A. Weil, *Foundations of Algebraic Geometry*, revised and enlarged edition, American Mathematical Society, Providence, 1962.
9. O. Zariski and P. Samuel, *Commutative Algebras*, Vols. 1 and 2, Van Nostrand, Princeton, New Jersey, 1960.

CHAPTER VIII Galois Theory

In Chapter VII we saw that an algebraic extension of a prescribed field k can always be embedded into an algebraic closure of k. In this way the study of an arbitrary algebraic extension field of k is converted into the study of the subfield structure of an algebraic closure $\bar{k}$ of k.

In the special case of a finite field k we saw that the subfields of $\bar{k}$ that contain k are in bijective correspondence with the set of supernatural numbers. Moreover, the inclusion relation among such subfields corresponds to the divisibility theory in the set of supernatural numbers. If we restrict our attention to those subfields of $\bar{k}$ that are of finite field degree over k, we obtain a bijective correspondence between this set of subfields and the set $\mathbf{P}^+$. Again, the inclusion relation among such subfields corresponds to the divisibility theory in $\mathbf{P}^+$. Moreover, we were able to describe the group $\mathcal{G}_k(K)$ of all k-automorphisms of such subfields. In particular, we know how $\mathcal{G}_k(K)$ act on K. We also know that $\mathcal{G}_k(K)$ is a quotient group of a subgroup of $\mathcal{G}_k(\bar{k})$. Actually, it is very easy to see that $\mathcal{G}_k(K)$ is a quotient group of $\mathcal{G}_k(\bar{k})$.

The major feature of Galois theory is the investigation of the subfield structure of fields between a given field k and its algebraic closure $\bar{k}$. More specifically, this investigation includes a study of the subgroup structure of $\mathcal{G}_k(\bar{k})$ and a study of the action of $\mathcal{G}_k(\bar{k})$ on $\bar{k}$.

In general, both $\bar{k}$ and $\mathcal{G}_k(\bar{k})$ are very large. The investigation of $\bar{k}$ is broken up into two steps. The first step is the study of those subfields of $\bar{k}$ that are of finite field degrees over k. The second step involves the generalization of the results obtained in the first step through a "limiting" process. We have already seen a small part of this limiting process in the study of finite fields. However, we shall not go into a detailed study of the problems involved in the second step.

Instead, we shall content ourselves with the examination of the first step as well as a few applications. As particular applications, we consider such old favorites as "nonsolvability of general quintic equations by radicals," "impossibility of trisecting a general angle by ruler and compass," and "impossibility of doubling a cube by ruler and compass."

CONVENTIONS · The conventions and notations of Chapter VII remain in force. If k is a field, then $\bar{k}$ denotes an algebraic closure of k. An algebraic extension field K of k means a subfield of $\bar{k}$ that contains k. When L is an abstractly constructed extension field of k which happens to be algebraic over k, we know that there may be several ways of embedding L into $\bar{k}$. In particular, the images of L under these embeddings may be different subfields of $\bar{k}$. However, it is obvious that properties of L which depend only on the k-isomorphism class of L are independent of the particular embedding of L into $\bar{k}$.

In general, if M is a subfield between the field k and the extension field K of k, then M is called a subfield of K over k. Thus an algebraic extension field of k is simply a subfield of $\bar{k}$ over k. The multiplicative group $k - \{0\}$ of the field k is denoted by $k^{\star}$.

» VIII · 1 BASIC CONCEPTS

We begin this section with a few simple exercises.

Exercise 1 · Let G be a group of field automorphisms of the field K. Show that the fixed points of G form a subfield of K. (Recall that $a \in K$ is a fixed point of G if and only if $\sigma(a) = a \; \forall \; \sigma \in G$.) Sfd

Do for class

Exercise 2 · Let K be an extension field of k. Show that the set of all k-automorphisms of the field K is a subgroup of the symmetric group on the set K. Since each auto is a 1-1 map it belongs to sym. gp. Clear that it is a subgp, since contains iden. and if σ, τ auto, then $\sigma\tau^{-1}$ auto.

DEFINITION 1 · Let K be an extension field of k.

(a) The group of all k-automorphisms of the field K is denoted by $\mathcal{G}_k(K)$.

(b) If G is a group of field automorphisms of K, the set of all fixed points of G on K is called the ***fixed field*** of G.

(c) If k is the fixed field of $\mathcal{G}_k(K)$, then K is called a ***Galois extension*** of k, or simply, K ***is Galois over*** k; in this case we use

$\mathcal{G}(K/k)$ in place of $\mathcal{G}_k(K)$ and $\mathcal{G}(K/k)$ is called the ***Galois group*** of the Galois extension K of k.

Our main interest is centered on Galois extensions of finite field degrees over k. The following exercise is very easy and very useful in obtaining Galois extensions.

Exercise 3 · Let K be an extension field of k. Let G be a subgroup of $\mathcal{G}_k(K)$ with fixed field L. Verify the following assertions:

(a) k is contained in L.

(b) K is Galois over L and G is a subgroup of $\mathcal{G}(L/K)$.

Exercise 4 · Let K be an extension field of k. Let G be a subgroup of of $\mathcal{G}_k(K)$. Show that K_{per} is contained in the fixed field of G. In particular, show that a purely inseparable extension field K of k is Galois over k if and only if $K = k$.

Exercise 5 · Let $K = k(\pi)$ be a simple transcendental extension of k. If $\sigma = \left(\begin{smallmatrix} a & b \\ c & d \end{smallmatrix}\right) \in GL(2, k)$, then define $\rho_\sigma : K \to K$ as the k-monomorphism induced by the substitution homomorphism $k[\pi] \to k[(a\pi + b)/(c\pi + d)]$. Verify the following assertions:

(a) $\rho_\sigma \in \mathcal{G}_k(K)$; in fact, the map that sends $\sigma \in GL(2, k)$ onto ρ_σ is a group homomorphism of $GL(2, k)$ into $\mathcal{G}_k(K)$.

(b) The kernel of the preceding group homomorphism is the center of $GL(2, k)$; the center of $GL(2, k)$ is $\{\left(\begin{smallmatrix} a & 0 \\ 0 & a \end{smallmatrix}\right) \mid a \in k - \{0\}\}$. (It is known that this group homomorphism is surjective; see [9; p. 198].)

(c) If $k = \mathbf{Q}$, then k is the fixed field of $\mathcal{G}_k(K)$; in fact, k is even the fixed points of the single ρ_σ, $\sigma = \left(\begin{smallmatrix} 1 & 1 \\ 0 & 1 \end{smallmatrix}\right)$. (It is known that k is the fixed field of the image of $GL(2, k)$ if and only if k is infinite.)

Exercise 6 · Let $K = \mathbf{Q}[a]$ be a simple algebraic extension. Determine when K is Galois over $\mathbf{Q}$ in each of the following cases:

(a) $\text{Irr}(X, a, \mathbf{Q}) = X^2 - bX + c$.

(b) $\text{Irr}(X, a, \mathbf{Q}) = X^3 - d$.

(c) $\text{Irr}(X, a, \mathbf{Q}) = X^4 + 1$.

Exercise 7 · Let $k = GF(q)$. Let $\sigma \in \mathcal{G}_k(\bar{k})$ be the Frobenius automorphism of $\bar{k}$; that is, $\sigma(a) = a^q \; \forall \, a \in \bar{k}$. Verify the following assertions:

of Chap VII
By Thm 1.2(b) and Exercise 3.

(a) k is the fixed field of $G = \langle \sigma \rangle \leqslant \mathcal{G}_k(\bar{k})$; thus $\bar{k}$ is Galois over k.

Let K be an element of k.
Then $k \subseteq K \subseteq \bar{k}$. But
$\sigma|_K \in \mathcal{G}_k(K)$ so by part
(a) the result follows.

(b) Every algebraic extension of k is Galois over k.

(c) $\bar{k}$ is Galois over each of its subfields. ?

[Later we shall see that $G = \langle \sigma \rangle$ is a proper subgroup of $\mathcal{G}_k(\bar{k})$.]

Note: If a comment
on a multifield
of k into to be
intended to be
k-normal of finite deg
then by Thm VII 3.2
it belongs to the kit

DEFINITION 2 · Let $\bar{k}$ be an algebraic closure of k. $\mathcal{G}_k(\bar{k})$ is considered as a group of transformations on $\bar{k}$. (Since we are now using the functional notation, $\mathcal{G}_k(\bar{k})$ acts from the left.)

(a) Two elements (respectively, two subfields over k) in $\bar{k}$ are said to be k-**conjugate** if and only if there exists an element of $\mathcal{G}_k(\bar{k})$ that carries one onto the other.

Do for
class

(b) A subfield K of $\bar{k}$ over k is said to be a **normal** (algebraic) extension of k if and only if $\sigma(K) = K \; \forall \; \sigma \in \mathcal{G}_k(\bar{k})$. An abstract algebraic extension of k is said to be normal (algebraic) over k if and only if it is k-isomorphic to a normal extension of k in $\bar{k}$.

Restrict any $\sigma \in \mathcal{G}_k(\bar{k})$ to $\mathbb{Q}(\omega_1)$ in $(a) \times (c)$ of exercise 6 is clear from extendability, then that
$\sigma(\mathbb{Q}(\omega_1)) = \mathbb{Q}(\omega_1)$. Extend id map onto $\mathbb{Q}$ to non-iden auto on a splitting field of $X^3 - 2 \ni \alpha(\alpha) = \alpha_2$ (using notation of
But σ on L can be extended to σ by joining α_3 etc.

Exercise 8 · Show that the extension fields in (a) and (c) of Exercise 6 are normal extensions of **Q**. Show that the extension field in (b) of Exercise 6 is a non-normal extension of **Q**. Show that every algebraic extension field of a finite field is a normal extension.

Let k be a finite field and $\sigma \in E$
with $k \subseteq K \subseteq \bar{k}$, $\exists / a \in K$, then $k(a)$ is finite so $k(a) = \{b \mid b^{p^k} = b\}$. For $x \in k(a) \setminus \{0\}$, $\dim y \dots$

√ **Exercise 9** · Find the **Q**-conjugates of $\sqrt{2}$, $\sqrt[3]{2}$. Find the **Q**-conjugates of $\mathbf{Q}[\sqrt{2}, \sqrt{3}]$ and $\mathbf{Q}[\sqrt[3]{2}]$.

conj. of $\mathbb{Q}(\sqrt 2, \sqrt 3)$ is itself.
Q-conj. of $\sqrt 2$ are $\sqrt 2, -\sqrt 2$
" of $\sqrt[3]2$ are $\sqrt[3]2, \sqrt[3]2 e^{2\pi i/3}, \sqrt[3]2 e^{4\pi i/3}$
$\mathbb{Q}(\sqrt[3]2), \mathbb{Q}(\sqrt[3]2 e^{2\pi i/3}), \mathbb{Q}(\sqrt[3]2 e^{4\pi i/3})$

Exercise 10 · Let k be a field. Show that $\bar{k}$, $\bar{k}_{\text{sep}}$, and any subfield K of $\bar{k}_{\text{per}}$ are normal extension fields of k.

Clear $\bar{k}$ normal. To see $\bar{k}_{sep}$ normal let $\sigma \in \mathcal{G}_k(\bar{k})$, $a \in \bar{k}_{sep}$ and $f = \text{Irr}(x, a, k)$. Let $a, a_1, \dots, a_\ell$ be the roots of f. Then $\sigma a, \sigma a_1, \dots$ are roots of f and they are all in $\bar{k}_{sep}$. Hence $\sigma(\bar{k}_{sep}) = \bar{k}_{sep}$. Let K be a subfield of $\bar{k}_{per}$ and $b \in K$. Th
$\text{Irr}(x, b, k) = X^{p^e} - b^{p^e}$ so $\sigma(b) = b$. Hence $\sigma(K) = K$.

DEFINITION 3 · Let X be an indeterminate over a field k. Suppose that $\mathcal{I} = \{f_i \in k[X] \mid i \in I\}$ is an indexed set of polynomials. An extension field K of k is said to be a **splitting field** of $\mathcal{I}$ over k if and only if each f_i splits into a product of linear factors in $K[X]$, where X is an indeterminate over K. K is called the **root field** of $\mathcal{I}$ over k if and only if the following conditions are satisfied:

(a) K is a splitting field of $\mathcal{I}$ over k.

(b) If L is any splitting field of $\mathcal{I}$ over k, then there exists a k-monomorphism of K into L.

Either do for class or have them turn it in.

Let $\{a_i \mid i \in I\}$ be the zeros of polys. in $\mathcal{F}$ and let K be an ext of k in which each poly in $\mathcal{F}$ splits
Claim $k(a_i)_{i \in I}$ is root field. To see this apply Zorn. Define $(L, \sigma) \leq \mathcal{F}$ if L is subfield of $k(a_i)_{i \in I}$
Containing k and $\sigma : L \xrightarrow{k-mono} \bar{K}$. Order $\mathcal{F}$ as usual. Apply Zorn to get maximal elt. Show it is $k(a_i)_{i \in I}$

Exercise 11 · Let k be a field. Let $\mathcal{F}$ be a set of polynomials in $k[X]$. Show that, with the possible exception of the statement on field degree, all the assertions of Kronecker's theorem hold for a root field of $\mathcal{F}$ over k.

The following result is quite important.

THEOREM 1 · Let $k \subset K \subset L \subset \bar{k}$ be a field tower such that L is normal over k. Then the following assertions hold:

(a) If $\sigma : K \to \bar{k}$ is any k-monomorphism, then there exists $\rho \in \mathcal{G}_k(\bar{k})$ such that $\rho(a) = \sigma(a) \; \forall \, a \in K$.

(b) If ρ satisfies (a), then $\rho(L) = L$; hence the restriction of ρ to L is an element of $\mathcal{G}_k(L)$.

(c) There is a natural exact sequence of groups,

$$1 \to \mathcal{G}_K(L) \to I_{\mathcal{G}_k(L)}(K) \to \mathcal{G}_k(K) \to 1,$$

where $I_{\mathcal{G}_k(L)}(K)$ is the stabilizer of K in $\mathcal{G}_k(L)$; namely, $I_{\mathcal{G}_k(L)}(K) = \{\sigma \in \mathcal{G}_k(L) \mid \sigma(K) = K\}$; the first group homomorphism is the inclusion map, the second, the restriction map.

(d) If M is a normal extension of k such that M is k-isomorphic to L, then every k-monomorphism of M into $\bar{k}$ has image L.

(e) The root field of a set of polynomials in $k[X]$ is a normal extension field of k.

← Apply Zorn as in part (e)

Proof · From the proof of Theorem VII.3.2 we know that there is a k-monomorphism $\rho : \bar{k} \to \bar{k}$ such that $\rho(a) = \sigma(a) \; \forall \, a \in K$. From Theorem VII.2.2 we see that ρ is an k-automorphism of $\bar{k}$; (a) now holds; (b) follows from (a) and the definition of normality.

(a) and (b) together show that the restriction homomorphism is surjective. The exactness in (c) follows from the definition and the first isomorphism theorem. (d) follows from (a) and the observation that any image of M under a k-monomorphism of M into $\bar{k}$ is k-isomorphic to L. (e) follows from the fact that the zeros of $f \in k[X]$ in $\bar{k}$ are permuted under the action of any element of $\mathcal{G}_k(\bar{k})$ and from the generalization of Kronecker's theorem in Exercise 11. «

Let T map M k-mono. into $\bar{k}$ and let $H = TM$. Then H and L are k-isom., subfields of $\bar{k}$. Let σ be this isom., i.e. $\sigma : L \to H$. By part (a) it can be ext. to $\sigma \in \mathcal{G}_k(\bar{k})$. Then $\sigma(L) = L$. Since L normal, i.e. $L = TM$.

THEOREM 2 · Let k be a field. Then the following assertions hold for the tower $k \subset K \subset \bar{k}$:

(a) $a, b \in \bar{k}$ are k-conjugate if and only if $\mathrm{Irr}(X, a, k) = \mathrm{Irr}(X, b, k)$.

Proof of (a) ($\longrightarrow$) Let $a, b \in \bar{k}$ be k-conj., i.e. let $\sigma \in \mathcal{G}(\bar{k}) \ni \sigma(a) = b$. Then since $\sigma(\mathrm{Irr}(X, a, k)) = \mathrm{Irr}(X, a, k) \overset{\text{def}}{=} f$ we have $f(\sigma(a)) = 0 = f(b)$.
($\longleftarrow$) $k(a) \overset{k-\text{isom}}{\cong} k(b)$ so let $\sigma : k(a) \to \bar{k}$ be this isom. apply part (a) of Thm 1.

(b) The following conditions are equivalent:

(1) K is a normal extension of k.

(2) If $f \in k[X]$ is irreducible and has a linear factor in K, then f splits into a product of linear factors in $K[X]$.

(3) K is the root field of a set of polynomials in $k[X]$ over k.

Proof · (a) follows from Theorem 1 and Theorem VII.1.3. Assume that (b)(1) holds. If $X - a$ is a linear factor of f in $K[X]$, then a is a zero of f in K. From Theorem VII.1.4 we know that $f = u \cdot \mathrm{Irr}(X, a, k)$, where $u \in k - \{0\}$. (b)(2) follows from (a) and the normality of K. Assume that (b)(2) holds. It is then clear that K is the root field of $\{\mathrm{Irr}(X, a, k) \mid a \in K\}$ over k. Thus (b)(3) follows. From Theorem 1(e) we know that (b)(1) follows from (b)(3). «

COROLLARY · If the algebraic extension field K of k is a normal extension field, then K is a normal algebraic extension of every subfield M between k and K.

Since the concept of separability is quite important, we now give another characterization of a separable extension of finite field degree. This characterization is based on the concept of trace introduced in Definition VII.2.3. In passing, we should note that both the trace map and the norm map are important in the study of field extensions. Indeed, Definition VII.2.3 can be generalized to any finite dimensional algebra over the field k. However, we shall not concern ourselves with this particular generalization.

THEOREM 3 · Let $k \subset K \subset L \subset \bar{k}$ be a tower of fields such that $[L : k]$ is finite and such that $\bar{k}$ is the algebraic closure of k. Let $a \in L$ and let $\{\sigma_i \mid 1 \leqslant i \leqslant [L : k]_s\}$ be the distinct k-monomorphisms of L into $\bar{k}$. Then the following assertions hold:

(a) $N_{L/k}(a) = \{\prod_i \sigma_i(a)\}^{[L:k]_\iota}$.

(b) $\mathrm{Tr}_{L/k}(a) = [L : k]_\iota \cdot \sum_i \sigma_i(a)$.

(c) $N_{K/k}(N_{L/K}(a)) = N_{L/k}(a)$.

(d) $\mathrm{Tr}_{K/k}(\mathrm{Tr}_{L/K}(a)) = \mathrm{Tr}_{L/k}(a)$.

Proof · We first consider the special case of $L = k(a)$ in (a) and (b). From Definition VII.2.3 and Exercise VII.2.5 we know that $\mathrm{Irr}(X, a, k) = \chi(X, aI, k(a)/k) = X^l - \mathrm{Tr}_k(a)X^{l-1} + \cdots + (-1)^l N_k(a)$, $l = [k(a) : k] = [k(a) : k]_s[k(a) : k]_\iota$. From Theorems VII.1.3 and VII.5.3 we know that $\mathrm{Irr}(X, a, k) = \prod_i (X - \sigma_i(a))^{[k(a):k]_\iota}$. The main point is that σ_i is uniquely determined by the value $\sigma_i(a)$, where a generates $k(a) = L$ over k. If we multiply out the product and compare the coefficients, we find that (a) and (b) hold for $L = k(a)$.

We next consider the general case in (a) through (d). From Theorem VII.5.6 we know that each k-monomorphism of K into $\bar{k}$ can be extended in $[L : K]_s$ different ways to k-monomorphisms of L into $\bar{k}$. Moreover, the totality of these extensions is the set of σ_i's given. Thus we may assume that $\{\rho_{i,j} \mid 1 \leqslant i \leqslant [K : k]_s,\ 1 \leqslant j \leqslant [L : K]_s\} = \{\sigma_i \mid 1 \leqslant i \leqslant [L : k]_s = [L : K]_s[K : k]_s\}$, that $\{\rho_i \mid 1 \leqslant i \leqslant [K : k]_s\}$ is the set of distinct k-monomorphisms of K into $\bar{k}$, and that $\rho_{i,j}(b) = \rho_i(b)$ for $1 \leqslant j \leqslant [L : K]_s$ and for all $b \in K$.

From Exercise VII.2.5 we know that $N_{L/k}(a) = N_{k(a)/k}(a)^{[L:k(a)]}$ and that $\mathrm{Tr}_{L/k}(a) = [L : k(a)] \cdot \mathrm{Tr}_{k(a)/k}(a)$. We may now apply the special case considered at the beginning of the proof. By setting $K = k(a)$ we see that $N_{k(a)/k}(a)^{[L:k(a)]} = (\prod_i \rho_i(a))^{[k(a):k]_\iota[L:k(a)]}$. Since $[L : k(a)] = [L : k(a)]_s[L : k(a)]_\iota$ and $[L : k]_\iota = [L : k(a)]_\iota[k(a) : k]_\iota$, $N_{L/K}(a) = (\prod_i \rho_i(a))^{[L:k(a)]_s[L:k]_\iota} = (\prod_{i,j} \rho_{i,j}(a))^{[L:k]_\iota}$. Thus we prove (a). In a similar way we can verify (b).

We know that each ρ_i can be extended to an element of $\mathcal{G}_k(\bar{k})$. Let these extensions be denoted again by ρ_i. They are not unique; however, it will be seen that the result is independent of the choices of the extensions. Let ρ_1 be the identity map on K. It is clear that $\rho_i \circ \rho_{1,j}$, $1 \leqslant j \leqslant [L : K]_s$, must be the distinct k-monomorphisms of L into $\bar{k}$ that extend ρ_i on k. It follows that $\sum_{i,j} \rho_{i,j}(a) = \sum_i \rho_i(\sum_j \rho_{1,j}(a))$. Thus $\mathrm{Tr}_{L/k}(a) = [L : k]_\iota \sum_{i,j} \rho_{i,j}(a) = [K : k]_\iota \sum_i \rho_i([L : K] \sum_{j\iota} \rho_{1,j}(a))$. Since $\rho_{1,j}$ ranges over the distinct K-monomorphisms of L into $\bar{k}$, the inside sum is $\mathrm{Tr}_{L/K}(a)$. Since $\mathrm{Tr}_{L/K}(a)$ is in K, the choice of the extensions of ρ_i to elements of $\mathcal{G}_k(\bar{k})$ is immaterial; moreover, the outside sum give us $\mathrm{Tr}_{K/k}(\mathrm{Tr}_{L/K}(a))$ as desired. The reader should observe that we have used the fact that Tr is a linear map. Thus (d) holds. Similarly, we can verify (c) from (a). «

COROLLARY Suppose that K is an inseparable extension field of finite degree over k; then $\mathrm{Tr}_{K/k}(a) = 0$ for each $a \in K$.

THEOREM 4 · Let K be an extension field of k such that $[K : k]$ is finite. Then K is separable over k if and only if $\mathrm{Tr}_{K/k}(K) = k$. Equivalently, K is inseparable over k if and only if $\mathrm{Tr}_{K/k}(K) = 0$.

Proof · We know that $\mathrm{Tr}_{K/k} \in \mathrm{Hom}_k(K, k)$. Since $\dim_k k = 1$, it follows that $\mathrm{Tr}_{K/k}(K) = 0$ or k. Thus our two assertions are equivalent.

Suppose that K is inseparable over k. It follows from the preceding corollary that $\mathrm{Tr}_{K/k}(K) = 0$.

Suppose that K is separable over k. It follows that $[K:k]_s = [K:k]$ and that $K = k(a)$. Let σ_i, $1 \leqslant i \leqslant n = [K:k]$, be the distinct k-monomorphisms of K into the algebraic closure $\bar{k}$ of k. We know that all $\sigma_i(a)$ are distinct and that $f = \mathrm{Irr}(X, a, k)$ is equal to $\prod_i (X - \sigma_i(a))$ in $\bar{k}[X]$. From the Lagrange interpolation formula in Exercise IV.5.7 we know that

$$\sum_i \frac{f\{X\}}{(X - \sigma_i(a))\, D_X f\{\sigma_i(a)\}} = g$$

is the unique polynomial of degree less than n such that $g\{\sigma_i(a)\} = 1$. Since 1 is obviously such a polynomial, we conclude that $g = 1$. We may assume that $a \neq 0$, for otherwise $K = k$ and $\mathrm{Tr}_{K/k}$ is the identity map. By evaluating the left side at $X = 0$, we see that

$$\sum_i \frac{1}{\sigma_i(a)\, D_X f\{\sigma_i(a)\}} = \frac{-1}{f\{0\}}.$$

Thus

$$\mathrm{Tr}_{K/k}\left(\frac{1}{a \cdot D_X f\{a\}}\right) = \frac{-1}{f\{0\}} \neq 0.$$

Consequently, $\mathrm{Tr}_{K/k}(K) = k$. «

DEFINITION 4 · Let K be a field and let G be a group. Let $\mathrm{Map}(G, K)$ be the K-algebra of all K-valued maps of G into K. (See Definition IV.5.1) If $\sigma \in \mathrm{Map}(G, K)$ is a group homomorphism of G into $K^\star = K - \{0\}$, then σ is called a K-***character*** of G. A subset B of $\mathrm{Map}(G, K)$ is said to be K-***independent*** if and only if B is K-independent with respect to the K-vector space structure of $\mathrm{Map}(G, K)$, where elements of K are identified with the constant maps of $\mathrm{Map}(G, K)$ and where the K-vector space structure of $\mathrm{Map}(G, K)$ comes from the multiplication in the K-algebra $\mathrm{Map}(G, K)$.

The following result is very useful.

THEOREM 5 · (Independence of the K-characters of a group G). Let K be a field and let G be a group. Then the set of all K-characters on G is K-independent in Map(~~K, G~~ G, K).

Proof · Since K is a field, we know that a subset B of a K-vector space V is K-independent if and only if every finite subset of B is

K-independent. Thus it suffices to show that every finite set of K-characters $\sigma_1, \ldots, \sigma_n$ of G is K-independent.

If $n = 1$, then $\sigma_1(G) \subset K^\star$. Thus $\sigma_1 \neq 0$ and it must be K-independent. We now proceed by induction and assume that $n > 1$ and that every set of $n - 1$ distinct K-characters of G is K-independent. Suppose that $\sigma_1, \ldots, \sigma_n$ are n distinct K-characters of G that are K-dependent. From the induction hypothesis we see that there exist $a_1, \ldots, a_n \in K^\star$ such that $(\sum_i a_i\sigma_i)\{g\} = 0 \; \forall\, g \in G$.

Since $n > 1$ and $\sigma_n \neq \sigma_1$, there exists $h \in G$ such that $\sigma_1\{h\} \neq \sigma_n\{h\}$. Since each σ_i is a group homomorphism, we see that $0 = (\sum_i a_i\sigma_i)\{hg\} = \sum_i a_i\sigma_i\{h\}\sigma_i\{g\} \; \forall\, g \in G$. Hence we see that $0 = \sum_i a_i\sigma_i\{h\}\sigma_i\{g\} - \sigma_1\{h\} \sum_i a_i\sigma_i\{g\} = \sum_{i>1} a_i(\sigma_i\{h\} - \sigma_1\{h\})\sigma_i\{g\} \; \forall\, g \in G$. Since $a_n \neq 0$ and $\sigma_n\{h\} \neq \sigma_1\{h\}$, we see that $\sigma_2, \ldots, \sigma_n$ are K-dependent. This contradicts the induction hypothesis. «

Exercise 12 · Let G be a finite group. What is the relation between the subgroup of G generated by $\{g^2 \mid g \in G\}$ and the intersection of $\ker \sigma$, where σ ranges over all the $\mathbf{Q}$-characters of G?

We now derive a second proof of Theorem VII.6.6(c).

COROLLARY · Let L and K be extension fields of l and k, respectively. Suppose that $\sigma : k \to l$ is an isomorphism and that $\sigma_i : K \to L$, $1 \leqslant i \leqslant n$, are distinct extensions of σ to field monomorphisms of K. Then $n \leqslant [K : k]$. In particular, $[K : k]_s \leqslant [K : k]$.

Proof · Suppose, by way of contradiction, that $[K : k] < n$. Let v_i, $1 \leqslant i \leqslant [K : k]$, be a k-basis for the k-vector space K. Consider the system of $[K : k]$ linear homogeneous equations:

$$(*) \qquad \sum_j \sigma_j(v_i)x_j = 0, \; 1 \leqslant j \leqslant n,$$

where x_j is to be found in L.

Since the number of variables is more than the number of equations, we may deduce from Cramer's rule that the x_i's can be found so that at least one of them is nonzero.

Let $a_i \in k$. If we multiply the ith equation by $\sigma(a_i)$ and add these equations, then, from the hypothesis that each σ_j is an extension of σ, we obtain the result $\sum_j x_j\sigma_j\{\sum_i a_iv_i\} = 0$. Because v_i, $1 \leqslant i \leqslant [K : k]$, is a k-basis for K, it follows that $0 = \sum_j x_j\sigma_j \in \operatorname{Map}(K, L)$. Thus the L-characters, σ_j, $1 \leqslant j \leqslant n$, on the group $K^\star$ are L-dependent. This contradicts the preceding theorem. «

Exercise 13 · Let L be a field of characteristic 0. Describe the set of all L-characters on the group $\mathbf{Q}^\star$. *Hint.* $\mathbf{Q}^\star$ is the direct sum of a cyclic group of order 2 and a free abelian group with free $\mathbf{Z}$-basis consisting of the primes in $\mathbf{P}^+$.

VIII · 2 FUNDAMENTAL THEOREMS

Suppose that G is a group of automorphisms of the field K such that k is the fixed field of G. In exercise 1.5(c) we showed that G may well be a proper subgroup of $\mathcal{G}_k(K)$. However, we shall now show that when $\mathcal{G}$ is a finite group G must coincide with $\mathcal{G}_k(K)$. Moreover, according to our definition, K is Galois over k with Galois group $G = \mathcal{G}(K/k) = \mathcal{G}_k(K)$.

THEOREM 1 · Let G be a finite group of field automorphisms of the field K. Suppose that k is the fixed field of G. Then the following assertions hold:

(a) K is algebraic, normal, separable, and of finite field degree over every subfield M of K over k.

(b) $[K : k] = [K : k]_s = | G |$.

(c) K is Galois over k with $G = \mathcal{G}(K/k)$.

Proof · It is clear that we only have to verify (a) for $M = k$.

Suppose that $a \in K$. Let $f = \prod_{\sigma \in G} (X - \sigma(a)) \in K[X]$. Since G is a finite group, the preceding product is well-defined. Since G is a group. we know that $\rho G = G$. Thus $\rho f = \prod_{\sigma \in G} (X - \rho\sigma(a)) = f \; \forall \, \rho \in G$. Since k is the fixed field of G on K, we conclude that $f \in k[X]$. It is clear that $f\{a\} = 0$ and that K is the root field of all such polynomials as a ranges over K. Thus K is algebraic and normal over k. The remaining two assertions of (a) are consequences of (b).

Since each element of G is a k-monomorphism of K into K, we know that $| G | \leqslant [K : k]_s \leqslant [K : k]$. Let $G = \{\sigma_i \mid 1 \leqslant i \leqslant n\}$. Suppose, by way of contradiction, that $\{a_i \mid 1 \leqslant i \leqslant n + 1\}$ is a k-independent subset of K. Consider the following system of n linear homogeneous equations:

$$(*) \qquad \sum_i \sigma_j(a_i)x_i = 0, \ 1 \leqslant i \leqslant n + 1, \ 1 \leqslant j \leqslant n,$$

where $(x_1, \ldots, x_{n+1}) \in M_{1,n+1}(K)$.

Let V be the set of solutions of $(*)$ in $M_{1,n+1}(K)$. From Cramer's rule we know that V is a K-subspace of positive dimension.

Suppose that $\sigma_1 = 1$. Since $a_1, ..., a_{n+1}$ are k-independent, the first equation implies that $V \cap M_{1,n+1}(k) = 0$. Let G act on $M_{1,n+1}(K)$ by setting $\sigma(x_1, ..., x_{n+1}) = (\sigma(x_1), ..., \sigma(x_{n+1}))$. Since G is a group, we know that $\rho G = G \; \forall \; \rho \in G$. If we apply each $\rho \in G$ to the system (*), we see that $\rho V \subset V \; \forall \; \rho \in G$.

Among the elements of $V - \{(0, ..., 0)\}$, let v be selected so that it has the fewest number of nonzero components. Since $V \neq 0$, such an element can be found. We observe that $V - \{(0, ..., 0)\}$ is closed with respect to multiplication by elements of $K^\star = K - \{0\}$. After a suitable permutation of the indices, we may assume that $v = (1, c_2, ..., c_r, 0, ..., 0)$, where $c_i \neq 0 \; \forall \; i$. Since $V \cap M_{1,n+1}(k) = 0$, we may assume that $r > 1$ and $c_r \in K - k$. Since k is the fixed field of G, we may find $\sigma \in G$ such that $\sigma(c_r) \neq c_r$. Since V is a K-subspace which is stable under the action of G, we know that $\sigma(v) - v \in V$. From looking at the rth component of $\sigma(v) - v$, we know that $\sigma(v) - v \neq 0$. From looking at the 1st component of $\sigma(v) - v$, we know that $\sigma(v) - v$ has at most $r - 1$ nonzero components. This contradicts the choice of v. Thus $[K : k] \leqslant n = |G|$. From this we obtain (b) and (a).

[margin note: Stable means $\sigma V \leqslant V$.]

It is obvious that $G \leqslant \mathcal{G}_k(K)$. As we remarked before, K is Galois over k. We know that $|\mathcal{G}_k(K)| \leqslant [K : k]$ always holds. Thus (c) follows from (b). *[margin note: Since $|\mathcal{G}_k(K)| \leqslant [K : k]$, by definition]* **«**

COROLLARY · Let K be an extension field of k. Suppose that G is a finite subgroup of $\mathcal{G}_k(K)$. Then K is Galois over k with $G = \mathcal{G}(K/k)$ if and only if $|G| = [K : k]$.

Proof · If K is Galois over k with $G = \mathcal{G}(K/k)$, then from (b) of the preceding theorem we must have $|G| = [K : k]$.

Conversely, suppose that $|G| = [K : k]$. Suppose that L is the fixed field of G on K. It is obvious that $k \subset L$. Hence from the preceding theorem we know that $|G| = [K : L] \leqslant [K : k]$. Thus $L = k$ and G is Galois over k with $G = \mathcal{G}(K/k)$. **«**

We now give the following characterization of a Galois extension of finite degree over a prescribed field.

THEOREM 2 · Let K be an algebraic extension of finite degree over a field k. Then K is Galois over k if and only if the following conditions hold:

(a) K is separable over k.

(b) K is normal over k.

Proof · The necessity of (a) and (b) follows from Theorem 1(a). Conversely, assume that (a) and (b) hold. Let $\bar{K}$ be an algebraic closure of K. Since K is algebraic over k, we know that $\bar{K}$ may be viewed as an algebraic closure of k. From (a) we conclude that there exist exactly $[K : k]$ distinct k-monomorphisms of K into $\bar{K}$. From (b) we see that each of these k-monomorphisms is a k-automorphism of K. Since every k-automorphism of K is a k-monomorphism of K into $\bar{K}$, we conclude that $|\mathcal{G}_k(K)| = [K : k]$. From the preceding corollary we see that K is Galois over k. «

Exercise 1 · Show that every purely inseparable extension of k is a normal extension of k.

Exercise 2 · Show that $\mathbf{Q}[\sqrt[3]{2}]$ is a separable, non-normal extension of $\mathbf{Q}$.

Exercise 3 · Let K be the root field of $X^3 - 2$ over $\mathbf{Q}$. Show that K is Galois over $\mathbf{Q}$ and that $\mathcal{G}(K/\mathbf{Q})$ is isomorphic to $\mathbf{S}_3$. *Hint.* Consider $\mathcal{G}(K/\mathbf{Q})$ as a group of transformations on the zeros of $X^3 - 2$; use Exercise 2 and the Theorem of Kronecker.

Exercise 4 · Let $k = \mathbf{Q}$ and let K be the root field over k of (a) $X^2 - 2$ and (b) $X^3 - 2$ respectively. Find a generator of K over k by the primitive element theorem. Find all the subfields between k and K by the method indicated in Theorem VII.6.5. For each of these subfields M determine the subgroup $\mathcal{G}_M(K)$ of $\mathcal{G}(K/k)$.

COROLLARY · Let $k \subset K \subset L$ be a tower of fields such that L is Galois over k and such that $[L : k]$ is finite.

(a) L is Galois over K and $\mathcal{G}(L/K) = \{\sigma \in \mathcal{G}(L/k) \mid \sigma(a) = a \ \forall\, a \in K\}$. In particular, $|\mathcal{G}(L/K)| = [L : K]$.

(b) The following conditions are equivalent:

(1) K is Galois over k.

(2) K is normal over k.

Proof · Proof follows from Theorem 2 and the observations that (a) L is normal over K, (b) L is separable over K, and (c) K is separable over k.

DEFINITION 1 · Let $\mathcal{F}$ and $\mathcal{G}$ be sets partially ordered by $\subset$ and $\leqslant$, respectively. Let $f : \mathcal{G} \to \mathcal{F}$ and $g : \mathcal{F} \to \mathcal{G}$ be maps satisfying the following conditions:

(a) $f \circ g$ and $g \circ f$ are identity maps on $\mathcal{F}$ and $\mathcal{G}$, respectively.

(b) If G_1, $G_2 \in \mathcal{G}$ and F_1, $F_2 \in \mathcal{F}$ are corresponding elements under f and g, then $G_1 \leqslant G_2$ holds if and only if $F_2 \subset F_1$.

We then say that f and g form a ***Galois correspondence*** between $\mathcal{F}$ and $\mathcal{G}$.

Exercise 5 · Let $\mathcal{G}$ denote the set of all subgroups of $\mathbf{Z}, +$. Let $\mathcal{G}$ be partially order by the inclusion relation $\subset$. Let $\mathbf{P}$ be partially ordered by $|$. Define $f : \mathcal{G} \to \mathbf{P}$ as the map that sends $\langle m \rangle$ onto $| m |$. Define $g : \mathbf{P} \to \mathcal{G}$ as the map that sends n onto $\langle n \rangle$. Show that f and g form a Galois correspondence.

THEOREM 3 · Let $\mathcal{F}$ and $\mathcal{G}$ be sets partially ordered by $\subset$ and $\leqslant$, respectively. Suppose that $f : \mathcal{G} \to \mathcal{F}$ and $g : \mathcal{F} \to \mathcal{G}$ are maps satisfying the following conditions:

(a) If $s \leqslant t$ in $\mathcal{G}$, then $f(t) \subset f(s)$ in $\mathcal{F}$.

(b) If $u \subset v$ in $\mathcal{F}$, then $g(v) \leqslant g(u)$ in $\mathcal{G}$.

(c) If $s \in \mathcal{G}$, then $s \leqslant g(f(s))$ in $\mathcal{G}$.

(d) If $u \in \mathcal{F}$, then $u \subset f(g(u))$ in $\mathcal{F}$.

Then the following assertions hold:

(1) $f(g(f(s))) = f(s) \ \forall \ s \in \mathcal{G}$.

(2) $g(f(g(u))) = g(u) \ \forall \ u \in \mathcal{F}$.

(3) The restrictions of f and g form a Galois correspondence between $g(\mathcal{F})$ and $f(\mathcal{G})$.

Proof · It is clear that (3) is a consequence of (1) and (2). Since the situation is symmetric, it suffices to verify (1). If we combine (a) and (c), we obtain $f(g(f(s))) \subset f(s)$. If we set u to be $f(s)$ in (*d*), we obtain $f(s) \subset f(g(f(s)))$. Thus (1) holds. «

Exercise 6 · Let A be a set partially ordered by $\leqslant$. Define the relation $\subset$ on A by setting $a \subset b$ if and only if $b \leqslant a$. Show that the identity maps form a Galois correspondence between $A, \leqslant$, and $A, \subset$.

Exercise 7 · Let M be a torsion module of finite type over the PID R. Suppose that $d \in R - \{0\}$ such that $dM = 0$. Let $M^{\#} = \mathrm{Hom}_R(M, R/Rd)$. Show that the maps ! and § form a Galois correspondence between the R-submodules of M and those of $M^{\#}$, where the sets of R-submodules are partially ordered by inclusion. Show that the case of a finite dimension vector space over a field k can be considered as a special case by taking R to be $k[X]$ and d to be X.

Exercise 8 · Let K be a separable extension of finite degree over the field k. Show that $\mathrm{Tr}_{K/k} : K \times K \to k$, given by $\mathrm{Tr}_{K/k}(x, y) = \mathrm{Tr}_{K/k}(xy)$, is a dual pairing. Find a natural Galois correspondence between the partially ordered (by inclusion) set of all k-subspaces of K and itself.

Exercise 9 · Let A, B, and C be three partially ordered sets. Suppose that f, g and F, G form Galois correspondences between A, B and B, C, respectively. Show that $F \circ f$ is an order-preserving bijection between A and C. and that the inverse map is $g \circ G$.

THEOREM 4 (Galois) · Let K be Galois over k of finite degree with $G = \mathcal{G}(K/k)$. Let $\mathcal{G}$ be the set of all subgroups of G and let $\mathcal{F}$ be the set of all subfields between k and K. Suppose that $f : \mathcal{G} \to \mathcal{F}$ is given by $f(H)$ = fixed field of H in K. Suppose that $g : \mathcal{F} \to \mathcal{G}$ is given by $g(M) = \mathcal{G}(K/M)$. Then the following assertions hold:

(a) f and g form a Galois correspondence with respect to the inclusion relation.

(b) f and g preserve the relation of conjugation; in fact, if $\sigma \in G$, then $\sigma(f(H)) = f(\sigma H \sigma^{-1})$ and $\sigma g(M) \sigma^{-1} = g(\sigma(M))$, where $H \in \mathcal{G}$, $M \in \mathcal{F}$.

(c) If $H_1 \leqslant H_2 \leqslant G$, then $|H_2 : H_1| = [f(H_1) : f(H_2)]$. Similarly, if $k \subset M_1 \subset M_2 \subset K$, then $[M_2 : M_1] = |g(M_1) : g(M_2)|$.

(d) f and g preserve the relation of normality; that is, H_1 is a normal subgroup of H_2 if and only if $f(H_1)$ is a normal extension of $f(H_2)$ and M_2 is a normal extension of M_1 if and only if $g(M_2)$ is a normal extension of $g(M_1)$.

(e) Suppose that M is a normal extension of k in K. Then M is Galois over k and there is a natural exact sequence of groups:

$$1 \to \mathcal{G}(K/M) \xrightarrow{\iota} \mathcal{G}(K/k) \xrightarrow{\eta} \mathcal{G}(M/k) \to 1,$$

where ι is the inclusion map and η is the restriction map.

Proof · It is trivial to verify that (a), (b), (c), and (d) of

Theorem 3 are satisfied. We need only verify that f and g are both surjective. Suppose that $M \in \mathfrak{F}$. From the Corollary of Theorem 2 it is clear that $M = f(\mathfrak{G}(K/M))$. Thus f is surjective. Suppose that $H \in \mathfrak{G}$. Since H is a finite group, it follows from Theorem 1 that $H = g(f(H))$. Thus g is also surjective. This proves (a).

(b) follows easily from the definition. (c) follows easily from Theorem 1. (d) is an immediate consequence of (b) and the observation that every k-monomorphism of a subfield of K over k must have an image lying in K. (e) is a special case of Theorem 1.1(c). «

The main point of the preceding theorem is that a Galois correspondence exists between the set of subfields of the Galois extension K over k and the set of subgroups of the Galois group $\mathfrak{G}(K/k)$. Moreover, the Galois correspondence is given in a completely natural way and has the additional properties described in (b), (c), (d), and (e).

Exercise 10 · Let K be a normal extension of finite degree over k. Verify the following assertions:

(a) K_{sep} is Galois over k and the restriction homomorphism $\eta : \mathfrak{G}_k(K) \rightarrow \mathfrak{G}(K_{\text{sep}}/k)$ is an isomorphism.

(b) K is Galois over K_{per} and $\mathfrak{G}(K/K_{\text{per}}) = \mathfrak{G}_k(K)$.

(c) Multiplication in K defines a k-isomorphism between $K_{\text{per}} \otimes_k K_{\text{sep}}$ and K. *Hint*. Show that K is generated by K_{per} and K_{sep} so that the map from $K_{\text{per}} \otimes_k K_{\text{sep}}$ to K defined by multiplication in K is surjective. Compute the dimensions of the two k-vector spaces to conclude that the preceding surjective map must be an isomorphism. The reader should observe that this is the finite analog of Exercise VII.5.10.

Exercise 11 · Find all the subfields and establish the Galois correspondences according to Galois' theorem for the root field over **Q** for each of the following polynomials:

(a) $X^3 - 2$.

(b) $X^4 + X^3 + X^2 + X + 1$.

(c) $X^4 - 5X^2 + 6$.

Exercise 12 · Translate the theorems on finite fields in terms of Galois' theorem. In particular, verify the following assertions:

(a) If K is a finite field, then K is Galois over each of its subfield.

(b) Let K be a finite field of degree n over the field $GF(q)$. Then $N_{K/GF(q)}(a) = a^{(q^n-1)/(q-1)}$. Thus $N_{K/GF(q)}(K) = GF(q)$.

Exercise 13 · Let k be a field. Verify the following assertions for $\bar{k}$:

(a) Every extension field of degree at most 2 over k is normal.

(b) Every separable extension of degree 2 over k is Galois.

(c) If $\chi(k) \neq 2$, there is a natural bijection between the set of all extensions of degree at most 2 and the group $k^\star/(k^\star)^2$, where K_a = root field of $X^2 - a$, $a \in k^\star$, is associated to the coset of a in $k^\star/(k^\star)^2$.

(d) If $\chi(k) = 2$:

(1) The map $\mathfrak{T} : k \to k$ defined by $\mathfrak{T}(x) = x^2 - x$ is a group homomorphism with respect to addition.

(2) There is a natural bijection between the set of all separable extensions of degree at most 2 and the group $k/\mathfrak{T}(k)$, where K_a = root field of $X^2 - X - a$, $a \in k$, is associated to the coset of a in $k/\mathfrak{T}(k)$.

Exercise 14 · Let K_1, K_2 denote subfields of the extension field K over k. Let K_1K_2 denote the subfield generated by K_1 and K_2 over k. Verify the following assertions:

(a) If K_1 is normal (respectively, separable, purely inseparable) over k, then K_1K_2 is normal (respectively, separable, purely inseparable) over K_2.

(b) If K_1 is Galois over k of finite degree, then K_1K_2 is Galois over K_2 of finite degree and there is a natural isomorphism between $\mathcal{G}(K_1K_2/K_2)$ and $\mathcal{G}(K_1/(K_1 \cap K_2))$.

(c) If K_1 and K_2 are Galois over k and of finite degree, then both K_1K_2 and $K_1 \cap K_2$ are Galois and of finite degree over k. Moreover, there is a natural isomorphism between $\mathcal{G}(K_1K_2/(K_1 \cap K_2))$ and the external direct product of $\mathcal{G}(K_1/(K_1 \cap K_2))$ and $\mathcal{G}(K_2/(K_1 \cap K_2))$.

Hint. In (b) assign to $\sigma \in \mathcal{G}(K_1K_2/K_2)$ its restriction to K_1. Show that this is a monomorphism from $\mathcal{G}(K_1K_2/K_2)$ to $\mathcal{G}(K_1/(K_1 \cap K_2))$. Verify that $[K_1K_2 : K_2] \geqslant [K_1 : (K_1 \cap K_2)]$ and conclude that the map defined is an isomorphism; (c) can be verified from (b).

DEFINITION 2 · Let $k \subset K \subset \bar{k}$ be a field tower such that $\bar{k}$ is the algebraic closure of k; $\cap L$, where L ranges over normal extensions of k in $\bar{k}$ satisfying the condition that $K \subset L$, is called the ***normal closure*** of K over k in $\bar{k}$.

THEOREM 5 · Let $k \subset K \subset \bar{k}$ be a tower of fields such that $\bar{k}$ is the algebraic closure of k. Let L be the normal closure of K over k in $\bar{k}$. Then the following assertions hold:

(a) L is the root field of $\{\mathrm{Irr}(X, a, k) \mid a \in K\}$; L is also the subfield of $\bar{k}$ generated by the k-conjugates of K. Thus the k-isomorphism class of L depends only on the k-isomorphism class of K over k.

(b) $L = K$ if and only if K is normal over k.

(c) L is separable over k if and only if K is separable over k.

(d) $[L : k]$ is finite if and only if $[K : k]$ is finite.

Proof · (a) is an easy consequence of the proof of Theorem 1.2(b). The remaining assertions may be deduced quickly from (a). We leave the details to the reader as an exercise.

THEOREM 6 · Let $k \subset K \subset \bar{k}$ be a tower of fields such that $\bar{k}$ is the algebraic closure of k. Let L be the normal closure of K over k in $\bar{k}$. Then the following assertions hold:

(a) $\mathcal{G}_k(\bar{k})$ is a transitive group of transformations on the set of all k-conjugates of K. If $I_{\mathcal{G}_k(\bar{k})}(K)$ is the stabilizer of K in $\mathcal{G}_k(\bar{k})$, there is a natural exact sequence of groups:

$$1 \to N \to \mathcal{G}_k(\bar{k}) \to \mathbf{S}_E\,,$$

where E is the set of all k-conjugates of K and N is the intersection of all $\mathcal{G}_k(\bar{k})$-conjugates of $I_{\mathcal{G}_k(\bar{k})}(K)$; moreover, there is a natural exact sequence of groups:

$$1 \to \mathcal{G}_L(\bar{k}) \to \mathcal{G}_k(\bar{k}) \to \mathcal{G}_k(L) \to 1.$$

(b) If $K = k(a)$ is a simple extension of degree n, there is a natural exact sequence of groups:

$$1 \to \mathcal{G}_L(\bar{k}) \to \mathcal{G}_k(\bar{k}) \to \mathbf{S}_F\,,$$

where F is the set of all k-conjugates of a in $\bar{k}$. In particular, $|F|$ is the reduced degree of $\mathrm{Irr}(X, a, k)$ and there is a monomorphism of $\mathcal{G}_k(L)$ into $\mathbf{S}_F$.

Proof · We observe that $\mathcal{G}_k(\bar{k})$ is a transitive group of transformations on the set of k-conjugates of K as well as on the set of k-conjugates of a. Our assertions can be derived easily from the fundamental theorem on transformation groups and Theorem 1.1. The details are left to the reader.

COROLLARY · Let L be the normal closure of $K = k(a)$ in the algebraic closure $\bar{k}$ of k such that $a \in \bar{k}$. Suppose that $\operatorname{Irr}(X, a, k)$ is separable and of degree n. Then the following assertions hold:

(a) 1 is the largest normal subgroup of $\mathcal{G}(L/k)$ contained in $\mathcal{G}(L/K)$. The transitive representation of $\mathcal{G}(L/k)$ on the set of all left cosets of $\mathcal{G}(L/K)$ is a monomorphism of $\mathcal{G}(L/k)$ into $\mathbf{S}_n$.

(b) $\mathcal{G}(L/K)$ is a maximal subgroup of $\mathcal{G}(L/k)$ if and only if every element of $K - k$ generates K over k.

Proof · (a) follows easily from Theorem 6(b). From the Galois correspondence between the subfields of L over k and the subgroups of $\mathcal{G}(L/k)$ we see that $\mathcal{G}(L/K)$ is a maximal subgroup of $\mathcal{G}(L/k)$ if and only if k and K are the only subfields of L between k and K; (b) now follows immediately. «

Theorem 4 tells us that problems involving the knowledge of subfields between a prescribed field k and a Galois extension K of finite degree over k can be converted into problems involving the knowledge of subgroups of the Galois group $\mathcal{G}(K/k)$. The corollary above tells us that the Galois group $\mathcal{G}(L/k)$ is representable as a transitive permutation group on a finite set. Consequently, we may utilize results from the theory of permutation groups in the study of Galois extensions of finite degree.

Excursion IX

We now consider the generalization of some of the preceding results to infinite but algebraic extension fields.

THEOREM 1 · Let K be an algebraic extension field of k. Then K is Galois over k if and only if the following conditions hold:

(a) K is normal over k.

(b) K is separable over k.

Proof · Suppose that K is Galois over k. Thus k is the fixed field of $\mathcal{G}_k(K) = \mathcal{G}(K/k)$. Let $a \in K$ and let $f = \operatorname{Irr}(X, a, k)$. Since K is algebraic over k, $\operatorname{Irr}(X, a, k)$ is of positive degree. Moreover, $\mathcal{G}(K/k)$

is a group of transformations on the finite set of zeros of f in K. Hence the kernel N of the group homomorphism of $\mathcal{G}(K/k)$ into the symmetric group on the set of zeros of f in K must be of finite index in $\mathcal{G}(K/k)$. Let $\sigma_i \in \mathcal{G}(K/k)$, $1 \leqslant i \leqslant n$, be a complete set of representatives of the left cosets of $\mathcal{G}(K/k)/N$. Consider the polynomial $g = \prod_i (X - \sigma_i(a))$. Since $\sigma(a) = a \;\forall\; \sigma \in N$ and $\{\rho\sigma_i \mid 1 \leqslant i \leqslant n\}$ is another complete set of representatives for each $\rho \in \mathcal{G}(K/k)$, we conclude that $\rho g = g \;\forall\; \rho \in \mathcal{G}(K/k)$. Thus $g \in k[X]$. It is clear that K is the root field of these g's over k and (a) must hold. Let L be the normal closure of $k(a)$ over k in the algebraic closure $\bar{k}$ of K (hence of k). Since K is normal over k, we know that $L \subset K$. Since K is Galois over k, it is clear that L is stable under $\mathcal{G}(K/k)$ and that k is the fixed field of the group of k-automorphisms of L induced by elements of $\mathcal{G}(L/k)$. Thus L is also Galois over k. Since $k(a)$ has finite degree over k, we know that L is of finite degree over k. Hence L is separable over k, and, since $a \in K$ is arbitrary, we see that (b) must hold.

Conversely, suppose that (a) and (b) hold for K. Let $a \in K$ and suppose that L is the normal closure of $k(a)$ in the algebraic closure $\bar{k}$ of K (hence of k). Since K is normal over k, we know that $L \subset K$. It follows from (b) and Theorem 5 that L is Galois over k of finite degree. Thus, if a is not in k, then there exists $\sigma \in \mathcal{G}(L/k)$ such that $\sigma(a) \neq a$. From Theorem 1.1 we know that there exists $\rho \in \mathcal{G}_k(K)$ such that ρ extends σ on L. Hence we may conclude that $a \in K - k$ implies that a is not in the fixed field of $\mathcal{G}_k(K)$. Since k is obviously contained in the fixed field of $\mathcal{G}_k(K)$, we conclude that k is precisely the fixed field of $\mathcal{G}_k(K)$; that is, K is Galois over k. «

Exercise 1 · Show that Exercise VIII.2.10 holds without the finiteness hypothesis.

Exercise 2 · Let K be an algebraic and Galois extension over k. Let $\mathcal{F}$ be the set of *all* subfields between k and K and let $\mathcal{G}_c$ be the set $\{\mathcal{G}(K/M) \mid M$ ranges over the subfields of K over $k\}$. Show that there is a Galois correspondence between $\mathcal{F}$ and $\mathcal{G}_c$. Generalize Galois' theorem to the set $\mathcal{F}$ and $\mathcal{G}_c$.

Hint. The reader should observe that the maps f and g may be defined as in Galois' theorem; $\mathcal{G}_c$ is the image of g and $\mathcal{F}$ is the image of f. The difference between the finite and the infinite Galois extension lies in the fact that $\mathcal{G}_c$ is the set of all subgroups of $\mathcal{G}(K/k)$ when and only when K is of finite degree over k. The details of infinite Galois theory may be found in the references at the end of this chapter.

Excursion X

Let K be an extension field of k. The map that sends each $a \in K$ onto $aI \in \operatorname{Hom}_k(K, K)$ is a k-algebra monomorphism of K into $\operatorname{Hom}_k(K, K)$. Suppose that $\rho : G \to \mathcal{G}_k(K)$ is a group homomorphism. Then, through the consideration of $\mathcal{G}_k(K)$ as a subgroup of $GL_k(K)$, we may raise the question, "What is the k-subalgebra generated by KI and $\rho(G)$ in $\operatorname{Hom}_k(K, K)$?"

We observe that the fields K and k in the preceding paragraph can be replaced by a commutative ring S and a subring R of S, respectively. The same question may be raised in this general situation in which $\mathcal{G}_R(S)$ is the group of R-algebra automorphisms of S. In any event, Theorem VIII.1.5 has the following interpretation:

THEOREM 1 · Let G be a finite subgroup of $\mathcal{G}_k(K)$, where K is a field extension of k. Then the following conditions are equivalent:

(a) K is Galois over k with $G = \mathcal{G}_k(K)$.

(b) $\operatorname{Hom}_k(K, K)$ is generated by K and G as a k-algebra.

Proof · Let L be the k-subalgebra generated by K and G in $\operatorname{Hom}_k(K, K)$. Since K is a field, we may consider L as a left K-vector space with respect to left multiplication by elements of K. We assert that L has G as a K-basis. From Theorem VIII.1.5 we know that G is K-independent. Suppose that $a \in K$ and that $\sigma \in G$. Then the action of $\sigma \circ aI$ on K is given by $(\sigma \circ aI)(v) = \sigma(av) = \sigma(a)\sigma(v) = (\sigma(a)I \circ \sigma)(v)$. Thus $\sigma \circ aI = \sigma(a)I \circ \sigma$. Since the identity element of G is the identity element of $\operatorname{Hom}_k(K, K)$, we see that the K-subspace generated by G in $\operatorname{Hom}_k(K, K)$ is already a k-subalgebra. Thus L has G as a K-basis. Consequently, $\dim_K L = |G|$.

We now assert that the following statement holds:

(*) $\dim_K \operatorname{Hom}_k(K, K)$ is finite if and only if $[K : k]$ is finite.

First of all, if $[K : k]$ is finite, then $\dim_k \operatorname{Hom}_k(K, K) = [K : k]^2$ via the identification of $\operatorname{Hom}_k(K, K)$ with the matrix ring $M_{[K:k]}(k)$. Conversely, assume that $[K : k]$ is infinite. Let $v_i \in I$ be a k-basis for K. Define $v_i^* \in \operatorname{Hom}_k(K, K)$ by setting $v_i^*(v_j) = \delta_{ij}$. Suppose that J is a finite subset of I and $a_j \in K$; then $\sum_j a_j v_j^*(v_i) = a_i$. Thus $\sum_j a_j v_j^* = 0$ implies that $a_j = 0 \; \forall j \in J$. This shows that the v_i^*'s are K-independent. Hence $\dim_K \operatorname{Hom}_k(K, K) \geqslant |I|$ and (*) is proved.

As a consequence of (*), we see that (b) is equivalent to the following conditions: (a) $[K : k]$ is finite and (b) $|G| = [K : k]$. Thus our Theorem 1 is equivalent to Theorem VIII.2.1. «

The content of Theorem 1 is the starting point of a Galois theory of commutative R-algebras, in which R is a commutative ring. The special case in which R is a field has been studied under the title of Galois algebras in [11]. In the general situation the group $\mathcal{G}_R(S)$ does not have to coincide with G. Indeed, $\mathcal{G}_R(S)$ may be infinite, and there may be many possible choices of G in $\mathcal{G}_R(S)$.

In the proof of Theorem 1 the multiplication in L has been shown to be determined by the multiplication of K and the action of G on K. This procedure may be used to construct an abstract k-algebra. The end result is a special case of what is known as a crossed product of K by G. This construction is very important in the study of simple k-algebras of finite dimension. Interested reader may consult [3].

» VIII · 3 SOLVABILITY OF POLYNOMIAL EQUATIONS BY RADICALS

DEFINITION 1 · Let K be an extension field of k of finite degree. K is called a ***radical extension*** if and only if there is a tower of fields $k = K_0 \subset K_1 \cdots \subset K_n = K$ such that $K_i = K_{i-1}[a_i]$ with $a_i^{t(i)} \in K_{i-1}$ for some $t(i) \in \mathbf{P}^+$ and $1 \leqslant i \leqslant n$.

Let $f(X) \in k[X]$. The equation $f(X) = 0$ is said to be ***solvable by radicals*** if and only if the root field of f over k is contained in a radical extension of k. Thus the zeros of f in an algebraic closure $\bar{k}$ of k may be obtained from elements of k by an iteration of the processes of addition, subtraction, multiplication, division, and extraction of roots a finite number of times.

Exercise 1 · Let k be a field with a characteristic different from 2. Show that every polynomial equation of degree 2 is solvable by radicals.

Exercise 2 · Let k be a finite field. Show that every polynomial equation over k is solvable by radicals.

DEFINITION 2 · Let G be a group. Let $G = G^{(0)}$ and define inductively $G^{(i+1)} = [G^{(i)}, G^{(i)}]$—the commutator subgroup of $G^{(i)}$; G is said to be ***solvable*** if and only if $G^{(n)} = 1$ for some $n \in \mathbf{P}$.

Proof that $G^{(2)} \triangleleft G$. Let $a', b' \in G^{(1)}$. Need only show $x^{-1} a'^{-1} b'^{-1} a' b' x \in G^{(2)} \forall x \in G$. Can insert $x x^{-1}$ between all commutators. But $x^{-1} a' x \in G^{(1)}$ as done on p80 so result follows. Proof th...

Exercise 3 · Let G be a group. Show that the following hold:

Do for class →

(a) $G^{(i)}$ is a normal subgroup of $G \forall i \in \mathbf{P}$.   ← *similarly inductively prov...*

(b) If G is solvable, every subgroup and every quotient group of G is solvable. *Let $H \leq G$. Surely $H^{(i)} \subseteq G^{(i)} \forall i$, hence H is solv. Next let $N \triangleleft G$, G solv. hence for $aN, bN \in G/H$, $(aN)^{-1}... aN bN = a^{-1}... a b N$ and since $\exists i \ni G^{(i)} = 1 \exists i \ni (G/H)^{(i)} = \{1\}H =$*

(c) Let H be a normal subgroup such that H and G/H are solvable; then G is solvable. *Since G/H is solvable $\exists i \ni G^{(i)} \subseteq H$. But H solv $\Rightarrow \exists j \ni H^{(j)} = 1$. Hence $(G^{(i)})^{(j)} = 1$*

(d) G is solvable if and only if there is a chain of subgroups $G = G_0 \geqslant G_1 \geqslant \cdots \geqslant G_n = 1$ such that G_{i+1} is normal in G_i and G_i/G_{i+1} is abelian $\forall i$. When G is a finite group, the word "abelian" may be replaced by "cyclic." *For cyclic part note if G_{i-1}/G_i is not prime map $G_{i-1} \to G_{i-1}/G_i$ and let H/G_i*

see Herstein *$\ni G_{i-1} : H$ is prime. Since G_{i-1}/G_i is abel $H \triangleleft G_{i-1}$, by 1st isom. thm. also $G_{i-1}/H \cong G_{i-1}/G_i \big/ H/G_i$; H/G_i is prime order with G_i $G_{i-1} \trianglerighteq H \trianglerighteq G_i$*   *$\ni \frac{G_{i-1}}{G_i} : \frac{H}{G_i}$ in prime.*

(e) If G is a finite p-group, then G is solvable. *Use exercise 8 on p 77*

(f) S_n is solvable if and only if $n < 5$. *See Herstein.*

(g) If $H \leqslant G$ such that $| G : H | \leqslant 4$, then G/N is solvable where N denotes the largest normal subgroup of G contained in H. *Note as in proof of 6 x 5 on p 77 $G/N \leq S_4$ so result follows.*

✓ **Exercise 4** · Let K and L be subfields of $\bar{k}$ over k. Show that the following hold:

(a) If K is a radical extension field of k, then KL is a radical extension of L. *If $K \supseteq K_{m-1} \supseteq K_{m-2} \supseteq \cdots \supseteq K_0 = k$ with $K = K_{m-1}[a_i]$ and $a_i^{t(i)} \in K_{i-1}$ t(i)... then letting $G_i = G_{i-1}[a_i]$ and $L = G_0$ get KL is rad. ext. of L.*

(b) If K is a radical extension field of k, then K is a radical extension field of every subfield between K and k. *Use same a's used in forming tower from k*

(c) If K and L are radical extensions of k, then KL is a radical extension of k. *Use a's that used in forming towers from k to L and k to K.*

(d) If $[K : k]$ is finite, then K has only a finite number of k-conjugates in $\bar{k}$. Thus the normal closure of K over k in $\bar{k}$ is the subfield generated by these finite number of conjugates in $\bar{k}$. *The finite number of k-conjugates follows from La... $\sigma \in G(\bar{k})$ orders a k-isomo of K into $\bar{k}$ and there are on...*

(e) If K is a radical extension of k, then the normal closure of K in $\bar{k}$ is a radical extension of k. *K rad ext of k $\Rightarrow [K : k]$ is finite. Then top by...*
K and a_i; are as in part (a) and $\{\sigma(K) \mid \sigma \in L\}$ are the k-conj.; adjoin $\{a_i | (\sigma a) \} \cup \{\sigma(a_i)\}$...

(f) If K is purely inseparable of finite type over k, then K is a radical extension of k. *Clear: Let $K = k(A)$, A finite. Then $x \in A \Rightarrow x^{p^e} \in k$, take q...*

DEFINITION 3 · Let K be a Galois extension field of k; K is called a **solvable**, **abelian**, respectively **cyclic**, extension of k if and only if $\mathfrak{G}(K/k)$ is solvable, abelian (commutative), respectively cyclic.

LEMMA 1 · Let k be a field and let $m \in \mathbf{P}^+$. Then the root field of $X^m - 1$ over k is an abelian extension of k.

Proof · Let K be the root field of $X^m - 1$ over k. From Theorem 1.2 we see that K is a normal extension of k. If $p = \chi(k)$ and $m = np$, $n \in \mathbf{P}^+$, then $X^m - 1 = (X^n - 1)^p$; hence K is also the root field of $X^n - 1$. It follows that we may assume that $p \nmid m$. Thus $D_X(X^m - 1) = mX^{m-1}$ and $X^m - 1$ have 1 as a g.c.d. in $k[X]$. From Exercise VII.5.3 we conclude that $X^m - 1$ is separable. Thus K is separable over k; and $K = k[\Gamma]$, where Γ is the set of all the zeros of $X^m - 1$ in K. Since $X^m - 1$ is separable, it is clear that Γ is a subgroup of order m in $K^\star$. As in a finite field, any finite subgroup of $K^\star$ must be cyclic. Thus Γ is a cyclic group of order m. From Theorem 2.2 we know that K is Galois over k. It is clear that $\sigma \in \mathcal{G}(K/k)$ is uniquely determined by its effect on Γ. Thus we have a monomorphism of $\mathcal{G}(K/k)$ into $\operatorname{Aut}(\Gamma)$. Since Γ is cyclic of order m, it follows from Exercise III.3.4 that $\mathcal{G}(K/k)$ is isomorphic to a subgroup of $U(\mathbf{Z}/(m))$. Thus K is abelian over k. «

LEMMA 2 · Let k be a field such that $X^m - 1$ splits into a product of linear factors in $k[X]$, where $m \in \mathbf{P}^+$ and $p \nmid m$, $p = \chi(k)$. Let $K = k[a]$ such that $a^m \in k$. Then K is cyclic over k.

Proof · Let Γ be the cyclic group of all the mth roots of 1 in k. Evidently, K is the root field of $X^m - a^m = \prod_{\zeta \in \Gamma} (X - a\zeta)$ over k. We may assume that $a \neq 0$. Thus $X^m - a^m$ is separable over k. By Theorem 2.2 K is Galois over k. It is clear that $\sigma \in \mathcal{G}(K/k)$ is uniquely determined by its effect on a. It is also clear that $\sigma(a) = a\zeta$ for a unique $\zeta \in \Gamma$. Since Γ is contained in the fixed field of $\mathcal{G}(K/k)$, we see that $a^{-1} \cdot \rho(\sigma(a)) = a^{-1}\rho(a \cdot a^{-1}\sigma(a)) = a^{-1}\rho(a) \cdot a^{-1}\sigma(a)$. Thus the map that sends $\sigma \in \mathcal{G}(K/k)$ onto $a^{-1}\sigma(a) \in \Gamma$ is a monomorphism of $\mathcal{G}(K/k)$ into the cyclic group Γ. Since a subgroup of a cyclic group is again cyclic, we see that K is cyclic over k. «

Exercise 5 · Let K and L be extensions of k in $\bar{k}$. Show that the following hold:

(a) If K and L are normal over k, then KL is normal over k.

(b) If K is solvable, abelian, respectively cyclic, over k, then KL is solvable, abelian, respectively cyclic, over L. This applies in particular to the case when L is contained in K.

(c) If K is solvable, abelian, respectively cyclic, over k and L is a normal extension of k contained in K, then L is solvable, abelian, respectively cyclic, over k.

(d) If K is Galois over k and L is a normal extension of k contained in K, then K is solvable over k if and only if (1) K is solvable over L and (2) L is solvable over k.

LEMMA 3 · Let $k \subset K \subset L$ be a tower of fields such that $[L : k]$ is finite. If K is solvable over k and L is solvable over K, the normal closure M of L over k is solvable over k.

Proof · The whole point of Lemma 3 is centered around the difficulty that a normal extension of a normal extension of k is not necessarily a normal extension of k.

Since $[L : k]$ is finite and L is separable over k, it follows from Theorem 2.5 that M is Galois and of finite degree over k. Moreover, M is generated by the finite number of k-conjugates of L, say $L(i)$, $1 \leqslant i \leqslant t$. Since K is a normal extension of k contained in L, we see that K is contained in each $L(i)$. Since L is solvable over K, we see that $L(i)$ is solvable over K for each i. By repeated applications of Exercise 5 to the pair K and M we see that M is solvable over K and by using Exercise 5(d) we may conclude that M is solvable over k. «

THEOREM 1 · Let K be a radical extension of k and let M be the normal closure of K over k in $\bar{k}$. Then $\mathcal{G}_k(M)$ is solvable.

Proof · Let k' be the fixed field of $\mathcal{G}_k(M)$. From Theorem 2.5 we see that M is of finite degree over k. Thus M is a finite Galois extension of k' with $\mathcal{G}(M/k') = \mathcal{G}_k(M)$. Since k' is fixed under every k-automorphism of $\mathcal{G}_k(\bar{k})$, we see that M is the normal closure of Kk' over k'. From Exercise 5 we see that Kk' is a radical extension of k'. It follows that we may assume that $k' = k$, that is, M is Galois over k.

Let $k = K_0 \subset K_1 \subset \cdots \subset K_t = K$ such that $K_i = K_{i-1}[a_i]$, $a_i^{n(i)} \in K_{i-1}$, $n(i) \in \mathbf{P}^+$, $1 \leqslant i \leqslant t$. Let M_i be the normal closure of K_i over k, $1 \leqslant i \leqslant t$. Thus $k = M_0 \subset M_1 \subset \cdots \subset M_t = M$. Since M is Galois over k, it follows from Theorem 2.4 that each M_i is Galois over k and that M is Galois over each M_i.

We now proceed by induction on t. If $t = 0$, then $M = M_0 = k$ and the result is obvious. Thus we may assume that M_{t-1} is solvable over k. Since $K_{t-1} \subset M_{t-1}$, we see that $M = M_t$ is the normal closure of $M_{t-1}[a_t]$ over k. From Lemma 3 it suffices to show that the normal closure L of $M_{t-1}[a_t]$ over M_{t-1} is solvable over M_{t-1}. Since M is Galois over M_{t-1}, we see that Theorem 2.4 implies that L is Galois over M_{t-1}. Thus we are reduced to proving the following:

(*) Let $K = k[a]$ be a separable extension of k such that $a^m \in k$, $m \in \mathbf{P}^+$. Then the normal closure L of K over k is solvable over k.

Let $p = \chi(k)$. If $m = np$, $n \in \mathbf{P}^+$, then $a^n \in K$ is both separable and purely inseparable over k. Hence $a^n \in k$ and we may assume that $p \nmid m$.

Let l be the root field of $X^m - 1$ over k. From Lemma 1 we see that l is an abelian extension of k. From Lemma 2 we see that $Kl = l[a]$ is a cyclic extension of l. Thus from Lemma 3 we see that the normal closure of Kl over k is a solvable extension of k. It is clear that L is contained in the normal closure of Kl over k. It follows from Exercise 5(c) that L is solvable over k. «

In the last paragraph of the proof of Theorem 1 it would be a mistake to assert that l is already contained in L. If L were the root field of $X^m - a^m$ over k, this would indeed have been the case. But L is only the normal closure of $k[a]$ over k; that is, L is the root field of $\mathrm{Irr}(X, a, k)$. However, the field Kl is the root field of $X^m - a^m$ over k. Thus it was not necessary to consider the process of taking the normal closure of Kl over k.

The converse of Theorem 1 is valid under the assumption that $\chi(k) \nmid |G_k(M)|$; that is, if M is a normal extension of k such that $\mathcal{G}_k(M)$ is a solvable finite group of order not divisible by the characteristic of k. then M is contained in a radical extension of k. We shall not go into the details of the proof of this converse of Theorem 1. The interested reader may consult [1].

In connection with the solutions of equations, Theorem 1 has the following corollary.

COROLLARY · Let k be a field and let $f(X) \in k[X]$ be monic and irreducible. Suppose that $f(X) = 0$ is solvable by radicals. Then $\mathcal{G}_k(K)$ is a solvable finite group, where K is the root field of $f(X)$ over k.

Proof · By hypothesis K is contained in a radical extension M of k. It follows that K is contained in the normal closure of M over k. From Lemma 1.1 we see that $\mathcal{G}_k(K)$ is a homomorphic image of $\mathcal{G}_k(M)$. From Theorem 1 and Exercise 3 we see that $\mathcal{G}_k(K)$ is a solvable finite group. «

THEOREM 2 · Let G be a finite group. Then there exist fields K and k such that K is Galois over k with $\mathcal{G}(K/k) \simeq G$.

Proof · By Cayley's theorem G may be considered as a subgroup of $\mathbf{S}_n$, for a suitable $n \in \mathbf{P}^+$. Let F be any field and let $X_1, \ldots, X_n$ be a set of n indeterminates over F. Let $K = F(X_1, \ldots, X_n)$ and consider $\mathbf{S}_n$ as the permutation group on the set $\{X_1, \ldots, X_n\}$. Thus each element of $\mathbf{S}_n$ may be extended uniquely to an F-automorphism of K. Hence G may be considered as a finite subgroup of $\mathcal{G}_F(K)$. If we let k be the fixed field of G on K, our assertion follows from Theorem 2.1. «

DEFINITION 4 · Let $X_1, \ldots, X_n, T$ be $n + 1$ indeterminates over the field k, where $n \in \mathbf{P}^+$. Then $T^n + X_1 T^{n-1} + \cdots + X_n$ is called the ***generic polynomial of degree n*** over k.

The point of Definition 4 is that any monic polynomial in $k[T]$ of degree n is the image of the generic polynomial under a substitution homomorphism over $k[T]$; namely, under $k[X_1, \ldots, X_n, T] \to k[a_1, \ldots, a_n, T]/k[T]$ where $a_1, \ldots, a_n \in k$ are the corresponding coefficients.

DEFINITION 5 · Let k be a field. Then the root field of the generic polynomial over $k(X_1, \ldots, X_n)$ is called a ***generic root field*** for polynomials of degree n over k.

DEFINITION 6 · Let $X_1, \ldots, X_n, T$ be $n + 1$ indeterminates over the field k. Let $f(T, X_1, \ldots, X_n) = \prod_{1 \leqslant i \leqslant n} (T + X_i) = T^n + p_1 T^{n-1} + \cdots + p_n \in k[T, X_1, \ldots, X_n]$, where $p_i \in k[X_1, \ldots, X_n]$, $1 \leqslant i \leqslant n$. Then p_i is called the ***elementary symmetric polynomial of degree*** i in $X_1, \ldots, X_n$.

✓ ***Exercise 6*** · Let k be a field. Show that there exist exactly $\binom{n}{i}$ monomials in the indeterminates $X_1, \ldots, X_n$ over k of the form $\prod_j X_j^{n(j)}$, $0 \leqslant n(j) \leqslant 1$ and $\Sigma_j n(j) = i$. Show that p_i is the sum of these monomials. stfd

THEOREM 3 · Let $X_1, \ldots, X_n, Y_1, \ldots, Y_n, T$ be indeterminates over the field k. Let $\mathbf{S}_n$ be the subgroup of $\mathcal{G}_k(K)$, $K = k(Y_1, \ldots, Y_n)$, defined by all permutations of the set $\{Y_1, \ldots, Y_n\}$. Then the following hold:

By Thm 2.1 this says $\mathcal{G}(K/k(p_1, \ldots, p_n)) = S_n$

(a) $k(p_1, \ldots, p_n)$ is the fixed field of $\mathbf{S}_n$, where the p_i's are the elementary symmetric polynomials in $Y_1, \ldots, Y_n$.

(b) $p_1, \ldots, p_n$ form a transcendence base for K over k.

(c) K is k-isomorphic to the root field of $T^n + X_1 T^{n-1} + \cdots + X_n$ under the k-isomorphism $k(X_1, \ldots, X_n) \to k(p_1, \ldots, p_n)/k$.

By (b) $k(X_1, \ldots, X_n)$ is naturally k-isom to $k(p_1, \ldots, p_n)$. Let σ denote this isom. Then under σ, the poly $f = T^n + X_1 T^{n-1} + \cdots + X_n$ maps to $g = T^n + p_1 T^{n-1} + \cdots + p_n$ so root field of f over $k(X_1, \ldots, X_n)$ is k-isom to root field of g over $k(p_1, \ldots, p_n)$. But from Def. 6, K is the root field of g over k(p ...

η Pte that $p_i = \sum_{1 \leq j_1 i_2 \cdots 1 \leq m}^{} Y_{i_1} Y_{i_2} \cdots Y_{i_i}$ so σ $p_i = p_i$ ∀ i , σ ∈ S_m ✓

Proof · (a) It is clear that $k(p_1, ..., p_n)$ is contained in the fixed field k' of $\boldsymbol{S}_n$ in K.

Because $-Y_i$ is a zero of

— Note that this numerator is $T^m + p_i T^{m-1} + \cdots + p_m$

$$(T + Y_1) \cdot \cdots \cdot (T + Y_i) = \prod_{1 \leq j \leq n} (T + Y_j) \Big/ \prod_{i+1 \leq j \leq n} (T + Y_j),$$

it follows that

$$[k(p_1, ..., p_n, Y_i, ..., Y_n) : k(p_1, ..., p_n, Y_{i+1}, ..., Y_n)] \leqslant i.$$

Hence by forming the product of these inequalities we see that $[K : k(p_1, ..., p_n)] \leqslant n!$. However, we know from Theorem 2.1 that $[K : k'] = |\boldsymbol{S}_n| = n!$. From $k(p_1, ..., p_n) \subset k'$ we conclude (a).

(b) From the definition we have tr. deg.$_k K = n$. Thus (b) follows from (a) and Exercise VII.4.2; (c) follows from (b) and Definition 4. «

Margin notes: since $[K : k(p_1, \cdots p_n)] \leq n!$ $= [K : k'][k' : k(p_1 \cdots)]$ so $[k' : k(p_1, \cdots p_n)] = 1$

COROLLARY · The generic polynomial of degree greater than 4 is not solvable by radicals. *Proof:* Since in Thm 3 $[K : k(p_1, \cdots p_n)] = n!$, $f = T^n + p_1 T^{n-1} \cdots + p_n$ is irred. over $k(p_1, \cdots p_n)$ and hence $T^m + x, T^{m-1} \cdots + x_m$ is irred. over $k(x_1, \cdots x_m)$. If g is solv. by rad. then by Cor. to Thm 1 ...

We observe that the Corollary does *not* assert that every polynomial equation of degree greater than 4 is not solvable by radicals. If $f(T)$ is a monic, irreducible polynomial of degree n over the field k, then $f(T)$ is the image of the generic polynomial under a substitution homomorphism. The corollary *does* assert that if we consider all possible fields and all possible polynomials of degree greater than 4 it is not possible to give a "universal" procedure for solving such an equation by radicals.

Margin notes: $g(x_1, \cdots)$ $\rho(k_1, \cdots k_n)$ is Since a sol. in ... But this is not true for n > 4 by Exercise 5.

At the end of Chapter IX we show that $X^3(X^2 - 4) - 2 = 0$ is not solvable by radicals over the field of rational numbers.

Explicit calculation of the Galois group of the root field of a separable, irreducible polynomial over a given field k is not an easy matter. We mention briefly one approach to the problem.

Let k be the quotient field of a UFD R. Assume that $f(X) \in R[X]$ is a monic, irreducible, separable polynomial in $k[X]$. Let p be a nonzero prime in R. It is then possible to consider $f(X)$ as a polynomial in $R/Rp[X]$ by reducing its coefficients mod Rp. Occasionally, explicit knowledge of the ideal theory in R allows us to extract some information concerning the Galois group of the root field of $f(X)$ over k from the factorization of $f(X)$ in $R/Rp[X]$. For example, when R is a "Dedekind domain" (it includes all PID), R/Rp is a field. There is then a well-developed theory connecting the Galois group of the root field of $f(X)$ over k and the Galois group of the root field of an irreducible separable factor of $f(X)$ over R/Rp. By choosing p judiciously, we may find it possible to obtain enough information on the Galois group of the splitting field of $f(X)$ over k to decide whether $f(X)$ is, or is not, solvable by radicals. To carry out such a procedure successfully we also need some results concerning subgroups of $\mathbf{S}_n$, $n = \deg_X f(X)$. Readers interested in Dedekind domains and its Galois theory may consult [12].

A method for showing the existence of polynomial equations over specific fields (for example, over $\mathbf{Q}$) with a prescribed Galois group (for example, $\mathbf{S}_n$) utilizes the Hilbert irreducibility theorem; namely, suppose that K is Galois over $k = \mathbf{Q}(X_1, ..., X_n)$ with a finite Galois group $G = \mathcal{G}(K/k)$, where $X_1, ..., X_n$ are indeterminates over $\mathbf{Q}$. According to the primitive element theorem, $K = k(a)$. It is very easy to show that for a suitable $d \in \mathbf{Q}[X_1, ..., X_n]$, $d \neq 0$, $\mathrm{Irr}(X, da, k) \in \mathbf{Q}[X_1, ..., X_n][X]$. By replacing a with da we may assume that $\mathrm{Irr}(X, a, k) \in \mathbf{Q}[X_1, ..., X_n][X]$. Hilbert's theorem then asserts that it is possible to find $a_1, ..., a_n \in \mathbf{Q}$ which satisfies the following conditions:

(a) The polynomial $\mathrm{Irr}(X, a, k)$ is sent onto an irreducible polynomial $f \in \mathbf{Q}[X]$ under the substitution homomorphism $\mathbf{Q}[X_1, ..., X_n] \to \mathbf{Q}[a_1, ..., a_n]/\mathbf{Q}$.

(b) The root field of f over $\mathbf{Q}$ has a Galois group isomorphic to G.

Unfortunately, the irreducibility theorem is only an existence theorem. It does not tell us how to find $a_1, ..., a_n$ explicitly.

In any event, there are now two problems. First, we need to determine those fields that may be used in place of $\mathbf{Q}$ in the irreducibility theorem: for example, we know that finite fields cannot be used, since Galois groups of finite extensions of finite fields are always cyclic. Similarly, algebraically closed fields cannot be used. Second, we need to know how to construct a Galois extension K of $k(X_1, ..., X_n)$ with a prescribed Galois group G. It is very tempting for us to try to do this backward; namely, let $K = k(Y_1, ..., Y_n)$, where $Y_1, ..., Y_n$ are indeterminates; let G be a subgroup of $\mathbf{S}_n$; finally, let G act on K by permuting $Y_1, ..., Y_n$. Then we might hope to prove that the fixed field k' of G is k-isomorphic to $k(X_1, ..., X_n)$. Unfortunately, except in a few very special cases, it is difficult to determine k'. We may be tempted to make the sweeping general assertion that "if L is a subfield of $K = k(Y_1, ..., Y_n)$ over k such that $[K : L]$ is finite then L is k-isomorphic to $k(X_1, ..., X_n)$" but this is generally false.

The reader interested in results connected with Hilbert's irreducibility theorem may consult [6].

Historically, another problem is often mentioned at the same time as the problem of nonsolvability of generic quintic equations by radicals. This problem is "the impossibility of trisecting a generic angle by ruler and compass." We shall not carry out the proof in detail. We need the theorem which asserts that it is possible to "coordinatize" the plane. It is then possible to translate "construction by ruler and compass" into the statement "formation of extension fields of degree a power of 2." Trisection of a generic angle, or even of a 60° angle, will involve the solution of an irreducible cubic equation. (In the case of a 60° angle the equation in question may be chosen to be $8X^3 - 6X - 1 = 0$ over **Q**.) Thus we must form an extension field of degree 3. From Theorem VII.2.1 it is immediately obvious that a cubic extension field cannot be contained in an extension field of degree a power of 2. Granting the result on coordinatizing the plane, the reader may consult [1; *p.* 80] for a somewhat amplified explanation of the assertions we have just made.

Sometimes, the problem of "doubling the cube" is also mentioned. This corresponds to the construction of the cube root of 2 by ruler and compass, that is, solving the equation $X^3 - 2 = 0$ over **Q** by "ruler and compass construction, starting with points in the plane with coordinates in **Q**." The preceding argument may be adapted to show that this is also impossible.

As for solving equations of degree less that 5 by means of radicals, methods have been known for a long time. The interested reader may consult [10, p. 179].

» VIII · 4 CYCLOTOMIC POLYNOMIALS OVER Q: KUMMER EXTENSIONS

Having discussed some of the difficulties involved in the determination of Galois groups of Galois extensions, we now examine some special cases in which it is possible to determine the Galois groups "explicitly."

DEFINITION 1 · Let $\mathbf{Q}_m$ be the root field of $X^m - 1$ over **Q**, $m \in \mathbf{P}^+$. Let ζ be a generator of the cyclic group Γ of all the zeros of $X^m - 1$ in $\mathbf{Q}_m$. [We already know that ζ^n generates Γ if and only if $(m, n) = (1)$.] The polynomial $\Phi_m(X) = \prod_i (X - \zeta^i)$, $0 \leqslant i < m$, $(i, m) = (1)$, is called the ***cyclotomic polynomial of primitive mth roots of 1***.

From the proof of Lemma 3.1 we see that $\mathbf{Q}_m$ is Galois over $\mathbf{Q}$ with $\mathcal{G}(\mathbf{Q}_m/\mathbf{Q})$ isomorphic to a subgroup of $U(\mathbf{Z}/(m))$.

THEOREM 1 · In the notation of Definition 1 the following hold:

(a) $\Phi_m(X)$ is a monic, irreducible polynomial in $\mathbf{Q}[X]$. In fact, $\Phi_m(X) \in \mathbf{Z}[X]$ and $\mathbf{Q}_m$ is the root field of $\Phi_m(X)$ over $\mathbf{Q}$.

(b) $\mathbf{Q}_m$ is an abelian extension of $\mathbf{Q}$ such that $\mathcal{G}(\mathbf{Q}_m/\mathbf{Q})$ is isomorphic to $U(\mathbf{Z}/(m))$; hence $[\mathbf{Q}_m : \mathbf{Q}] = |\,U(\mathbf{Z}/(m))| = \varphi(m) = \deg_X \Phi_m(X)$, where φ is the Euler φ-function.

Proof · Let $\sigma \in \mathcal{G}(\mathbf{Q}_m/\mathbf{Q})$. As before, σ induces an automorphism of Γ. In particular, σ must permute the generators of Γ. Thus $\sigma(\Phi_m)(X) = \Phi_m(X)\ \forall\ \sigma \in \mathcal{G}(\mathbf{Q}_m/\mathbf{Q})$; therefore $\Phi_m(X) \in \mathbf{Q}[X]$. Since Γ is generated by ζ and since $\mathbf{Q}_m = \mathbf{Q}[\zeta]$, it follows that $\mathbf{Q}_m$ is the root field of $\Phi_m(X)$ over $\mathbf{Q}$. It is obvious that $\Phi_m(X)$ is monic.

Now $\mathbf{Q}$ is the quotient field of the UFD $\mathbf{Z}$; thus from Theorem IV.1.7 we may conclude that the irreducible factors of the monic polynomial $X^m - 1$ in $\mathbf{Z}[X]$ can be assumed to be monic (if necessary, multiply the factor by -1) and therefore irreducible in $\mathbf{Q}[X]$.

Since $\Phi_m(X) \in \mathbf{Q}[X]$ and since $\Phi_m(X) | (X^m - 1)$ in $\mathbf{Q}_m[X]$, it follows from Exercise VII.5.2 that $\Phi_m(X) | (X^m - 1)$ in $\mathbf{Q}[X]$. According to Theorem IV.1.8, $\mathbf{Z}[X]$ is a UFD. It follows from the preceding paragraph that $\Phi_m(X)$ is a product of monic, irreducible polynomials in $\mathbf{Z}[X]$. Thus $\Phi_m(X) \in \mathbf{Z}[X]$.

Let $f(X) = \operatorname{Irr}(X, \zeta, \mathbf{Q})$. As in the preceding argument, we can conclude that $f(X) \in \mathbf{Z}[X]$ and that $f(X) \mid \Phi_m(X)$ in $\mathbf{Z}[X]$. Putting them together, we have $X^m - 1 = f(X)g(X)h(X)$, $\Phi_m(X) = f(X)g(X)$, and $f(X)$, $g(X)$, and $h(X)$ are monic in $\mathbf{Z}[X]$. The irreducibility of $f(X)$ is equivalent to $g(X) = 1$. Suppose, by way of contradiction, that $g(X) \neq 1$. Since $g(X)$ in monic in $\mathbf{Z}[X]$, it follows that $\deg_X g(X) > 0$. We now make the following assertion:

(*) If p is a prime in $\mathbf{P}^+$ such that $p \nmid m$, then ζ^p is a zero of $f(X)$ in $\mathbf{Q}_m$.

If (*) is false, then, from the fact that ζ^p is a zero of $\Phi_m(X)$ in $\mathbf{Q}_m$, we see that ζ^p is a zero of $g(X)$ in $\mathbf{Q}_m$. Thus ζ is a zero of $g(X^p)$ in $\mathbf{Q}_m$. It is clear that $g(X^p) \in \mathbf{Z}[X]$. From Theorem VII.1.4 we have $f(X) \mid g(X^p)$ in $\mathbf{Q}[X]$. As before, it follows that $f(X) \mid g(X^p)$ in $\mathbf{Z}[X]$. Hence $g(X^p) = f(X)\, d(X)$ with $d(X) \in \mathbf{Z}[X]$.

We now consider the homomorphism $\mathbf{Z}[X] \to (\mathbf{Z}/(p))[X] = R$ which reduces the coefficients of polynomials in $\mathbf{Z}[X]$ mod p. We denote the equality of the images of $a(X)$, $b(X) \in \mathbf{Z}[X]$ in R by writing $a(X) \equiv b(X) \bmod p$. From the Frobenius' theorem and the little Fermat theorem we have $g(X^p) \equiv g(X)^p \bmod p$. Hence we have $g(X)^p \equiv f(X)\,d(X) \bmod p$. Since $R = (\mathbf{Z}/(p))[X]$ is a UFD, it follows that an irreducible factor $\alpha(X)$ of the image of $f(X)$ in R must divide the image of $g(X)^p$ in R, hence the image of $g(X)$ in R. Consequently, $\alpha(X)^2$ must divide the image of $X^m - 1 = f(X)\,g(X)\,h(X)$ in R, and $X^m - 1$ is inseparable in R. However, since $p \nmid m$, $D_X(X^m - 1) = mX^{m-1}$ and $X^m - 1$ are relatively prime in the PID R. Thus $X^m - 1$ is separable in R. This contradiction shows that (*) must hold.

Now let $0 \leqslant i < m$ such that $(i, m) = (1)$. We write $i = p_1 \cdots p_t$, where $p_j \in \mathbf{P}^+$ is a prime, $p_j = p_l$ for $j \neq l$ is allowed. Thus $p_j \nmid m \;\forall j$. We conclude from (*) that ζ^{p_1} is a zero of $f(X)$. Since $f(X) = \operatorname{Irr}(X, \zeta, \mathbf{Q})$, we can find $\sigma \in \mathcal{G}(\mathbf{Q}_m/\mathbf{Q})$ such that $\sigma(\zeta) = \zeta^{p_1}$. Thus ζ^{p_1} may be used in place of ζ. By induction on t we see that ζ^i is a zero of $f(X)$. Since $\Phi_m(X)$ is a separable polynomial in $\mathbf{Q}[X]$, we see that $\Phi_m(X) \mid f(X)$ in $\mathbf{Q}_m[X]$. Thus $g(X)$ must be equal to 1 and $\Phi_m(X)$ is irreducible in $\mathbf{Q}[X]$.

(b) is now an easy consequence of (a) and the proof of Lemma 3.1. «

Before we consider Kummer extensions, we need some preliminary results.

DEFINITION 2 · Let G be a subgroup of $\mathcal{G}_k(K)$, where K is an extension field of k. An indexed set of elements $\{a_\sigma \in K^\star \mid \sigma \in G\}$ is called a solution of ***Noether's equation*** if and only if the following holds:

$$(*) \qquad a_\rho \rho(a_\sigma) = a_{\rho\sigma}\,, \;\forall\, \rho, \sigma \in G.$$

We note that (*) always has the trivial solution, $a_\sigma = 0 \;\forall\, \sigma \in G$. Moreover, if $a_\sigma = 0$ for one $\sigma \in G$, the fact that G is a group implies that $a_\rho = 0 \;\forall\, \rho \in G$. For this reason we exclude the trivial solution in our definition.

LEMMA 1 · Let G be a *finite* subgroup of $\mathcal{G}_k(K)$, where K is an extension field of k. Let l be the fixed field of G. Then the following hold:

(a) $\{a_\sigma \in K^\star \mid \sigma \in G\}$ is a solution of Noether's equation if and only if there exists $d \in K^\star$ such that $a_\sigma = d^{-1}\sigma(d) \;\forall\, \sigma \in G$.

(b) If $\theta : G \to l^\star$ is a character, that is, a group homomorphism, there exists $d \in K^\star$ such that $\theta(\sigma) = d^{-1}\sigma(d)\ \forall\ \sigma \in G$.

(c) If $d \in K^\star$ is such that $d^{-1}\sigma(d) \in l\ \forall\ \sigma \in G$, then $\theta : G \to l^\star$ given by $\theta(\sigma) = d^{-1}\sigma(d)\ \forall\ \sigma \in G$ is a character of G.

Proof · (a) Let $a_\sigma = d^{-1}\sigma(d)\ \forall\ \sigma \in G$, where $d \in K^\star$. It follows that $a_\rho\rho(a_\sigma) = d^{-1}\rho(d)\ \rho(d^{-1}\sigma(d)) = d^{-1}\ \rho\sigma(d) = a_{\rho\sigma}$. Thus $\{a_\sigma \in K^\star \mid \sigma \in G\}$ is a solution of Noether's equations.

Conversely, let $\{a_\sigma \in K^\star \mid \sigma \in G\}$ be a solution of Noether's equation. Since elements of G are distinct K-characters of $K^\star$, it follows from Theorem 1.5 that there exists $c \in K^\star$ such that $\sum_{\sigma\in G} a_\sigma\sigma(c) = e \neq 0$. Now $\rho(e) = \sum_{\sigma\in G} \rho(a_\sigma)\rho\sigma(c)$. Thus from Noether's equation we have $a_\rho\rho(e) = \sum_{\sigma\in G} a_\rho\ \rho(a_\sigma)\rho\sigma(c) = \sum_{\sigma\in G} a_{\rho\sigma}\rho\sigma(c) = e$. If we set $d = e^{-1}$, we see that $a_\rho = d^{-1}\rho(d)\ \forall\ \rho \in G$, as asserted.

(b) Suppose that $\theta : G \to l^\star$ is a character. Then it is clear that $\theta(\rho)\ \rho(\theta(\sigma)) = \theta(\rho)\ \theta(\sigma) = \theta(\rho\sigma)\ \forall\ \rho,\ \sigma \in G$. Thus (b) follows from (a).

(c) Suppose that $d \in K^\star$ is such that $d^{-1}\rho(d) \in l\ \forall\ \rho \in G$. Then it is clear that $(d^{-1}\rho(d))(d^{-1}\sigma(d)) = (d^{-1}\rho(d))\rho(d^{-1}\sigma(d)) = d^{-1}\rho\sigma(d)$. Hence (c) holds. «

DEFINITION 3 · Let k be a field. Suppose that $m \in \mathbf{P}^+$ is such that $k^\star$ contains a cyclic group Γ of order m; thus $\chi(k) \nmid m$ and $X^m - 1$ splits into a product of linear factors in $k[X]$. An extension field K of k is called a ***Kummer extension*** of exponent m over k if and only if K is the root field of $f = \prod_{1\leqslant i\leqslant t}(X^m - a_i)$, $a_i \in k^\star$, over k for a suitable f.

THEOREM 2 · Let K be a Kummer extension of exponent m over the field k. Then the following assertions hold:

(a) K is an abelian extension of k.

(b) $\mathcal{G}(K/k)$ has an exponent dividing m, that is, each element of $\mathcal{G}(K/k)$ has an order dividing m.

Proof · Let Γ be as in Definition 3. Since $\chi(k) \nmid m$, each $X^m - a_i$ is separable. It follows that K is separable and normal over k. Hence K is Galois over k.

Let $b_i \in K$ be a zero of $X^m - a_i$. If $\sigma \in \mathcal{G}(K/k)$, then there exists $\zeta_i \in \Gamma$ such that $\sigma(b_i) = \zeta_i b_i$. Since Γ is contained in the fixed field of $\mathcal{G}(K/k)$, we have $\sigma^m(b_i) = \zeta_i^m b_i = b_i\ \forall\ i$. Since K is generated by these b_i's, we see that $\sigma^m = 1\ \forall\ \sigma \in \mathcal{G}(K/k)$. This shows that every element of $\mathcal{G}(K/m)$ has order dividing m; hence (b) holds. Similarly, we may attach to each $\sigma \in \mathcal{G}(K/k)$ the set of ζ_i's, where b_i ranges over the distinct zeros of $X^m - a_i$ in K and $1 \leqslant i \leqslant t$; that is, with each σ we associate an element of the direct product of Γ with itself mt times. Using the fact that Γ is contained in the fixed field, we find that this is a monomorphism of $\mathcal{G}(K/k)$ into the direct product of Γ with itself mt times. Thus (a) holds. «

We now prove the converse of Theorem 2.

THEOREM 3 · Let k be a field such that $k^\star$ contains a cyclic subgroup Γ of order m, $m \in \mathbf{P}^+$. Let K be an extension field of k such that the following hold:

(a) K is an abelian extension of k.

(b) $\mathcal{G}(K/k)$ is a finite group of exponent dividing m.

Then K is a Kummer extension of exponent m over k.

Proof · Let $G = \mathcal{G}(K/k)$. From Theorem V.6.6 we know that $\text{Hom}(G, \Gamma)$ is isomorphic to G and that for each $\sigma \in G$, $\sigma \neq 1$, there exists $\theta \in \text{Hom}(G, \Gamma)$ such that $\theta(\sigma) \neq 1$.

Let $\Delta = \{d \in K^\star \mid d^m \in k^\star\}$ and $\Delta^m = \{d^m \mid d \in \Delta\} \subset k^*$. By using the first isomorphism theorem and the fact that Γ is contained in the field k we see that $\Delta/k^\star \cong \Delta^m/k^{\star m}$.

Let $d \in \Delta$. It follows that for $\sigma \in \mathcal{G}(K/k)$, $(d^{-1}\sigma(d))^m = (d^m)^{-1}\sigma(d^m) = 1$. Thus $d^{-1}\sigma(d) \in \Gamma\ \forall\ \sigma \in G$. From Lemma 1(c) we obtain a map of Δ into $\text{Hom}(G, \Gamma)$. We note from hypothesis (b) that every character of G in K is an element of $\text{Hom}(G, \Gamma)$. It is clear that our map is a homomorphism from Δ to $\text{Hom}(G, \Gamma)$. From Lemma 1(b) we see that for each character $\theta \in \text{Hom}(G, \Gamma)$ there is a $d \in K^\star$ such that $\theta(\sigma) = d^{-1}\sigma(d)\ \forall\ \sigma \in G$. Since $\theta(\sigma) \in \Gamma$, we see that $1 = (d^{-1}\sigma(d))^m = (d^m)^{-1}\sigma(d^m)\ \forall\ \sigma \in G$. Thus $d^m \in k^\star$ and d must lie in Δ. It follows that the map is an epimorphism from Δ to $\text{Hom}(G, \Gamma)$ and it is clear that the kernel of this epimorphism is $k^\star$. Thus from the first isomorphism theorem we have $\Delta/k^\star \cong \text{Hom}(G, \Gamma) \cong G = \mathcal{G}(K/k)$.

Since G is a finite group. we may take $b_1k^\star, \ldots, b_tk^\star$ to be the distinct elements of $\Delta/k^\star$, where $b_i \in \Delta$. Thus from the definition, we have $a_i = b_i^m \in k^\star$. It follows that $f(X) = \prod_{1 \leqslant i \leqslant t} (X^m - a_i)$ splits into a product of linear factors in $K[X]$. Let L be the root field of $f(X)$ over k in K. We must show that $L = K$.

Suppose that L is not K. From Theorem 2.2 we can find $\sigma \in \mathcal{G}(K/L) \leqslant G$ such that $\sigma \neq 1$; hence we can find a character $\theta \in \text{Hom}(G, \Gamma)$ such that $\theta(\sigma) \neq 1$. From earlier remarks we can find

Since $\Delta \to \text{Hom}(G,\Gamma)$ *given by* $d \to \theta$ *is surjective*

If $c \in \Delta$ *then* $\exists\, b_i^m \subseteq k = b_i^m$ $\ne\! c^{-1} b_i \in k^\star \subseteq L$, *But* b_i *so* $c^{-1} \cdot$ *and then* $c \in L$

$d \in \Delta$ such that $\theta(\sigma) = d^{-1}\sigma(d) \neq 1$. However, since $\Delta \subset L$ and $\sigma \in \mathcal{G}(K/L)$, we see that $\theta(\sigma) = 1$. This contradiction shows that $L = K$. Hence K is a Kummer extension of k for the exponent m. **«**

The proof of Theorem 2 actually shows more; namely, it shows that the Galois group $\mathcal{G}(K/k)$ is isomorphic to a suitable finite subgroup of $k^\star/k^{\star m}$. This isomorphism is not natural. What is natural is the existence of a bi-homomorphism from $\Delta/k^\star \times \mathcal{G}(K/k)$ to Γ such that each is the "dual" of the other. If we represent Γ as the additive group of $\mathbf{Z}/(m)$ and consider $\Delta/k^\star$ and $\mathcal{G}(K/k)$ as $\mathbf{Z}/(m)$-modules, then each is isomorphic to the dual of the other in a natural way through the bi-homomorphism. The bi-homomorphism sends the pair $(dk^\star, \sigma)$ onto the element $d^{-1}\sigma(d) \in \Gamma$.

Using the natural isomorphism between $\Delta/k^\star$ and $\Delta^m/k^{\star m}$, we can conclude that all Kummer extensions of k are "classified" by the distinct finite subgroups of $k^\star/k^{\star m}$. Exercise 2.13(c) is a special case of our assertion.

In the case in which $\chi(k) = p > 0$ we can raise the same question about abelian extensions of exponent p or even a power of p. In such a case the Kummer theory does not work, for 1 is the only pth root of 1. Kummer extensions must lead to purely inseparable extensions. As in Exercise 2.13, it can be shown without much difficulty that the finite subgroups of $k^\star/k^{\star p}$ still "classify" the Kummer extensions of exponent p. However, these are not abelian extensions. In order to obtain abelian extensions of exponent p, we must consider Artin-Schreier extensions of exponent p, that is, root fields of polynomials of the form $X^p - X - a \in k[X]$. The pth power map is replaced by the map $\mathcal{S}$ which sends an element $d \in K$ onto $d^p - d$. The end result is that the finite subgroups of $k/\mathcal{S}(k), +$ "classify" the abelian extensions of k of exponent p. For exponent p^n, $n > 1$, more complicated groups arising from k must be constructed to obtain a "classification." We shall not go into these topics in detail. Interested readers may consult [5; Chapter 3.]

References

A basic reference to Galois theory is Artin's little pamphlet [1]; a more detailed treatment can be found in [5]. For a study of infinite Galois extension the reader may consult [7]. We made no mention of Galois cohomology and only briefly alluded to the topic of simple algebras. The interested reader may consult

[8] and [9]. For a classical treatment of cyclotomic fields the reader may consult [4]. Galois extensions of fields of characteristic $p > 0$ and with abelian Galois groups of order a power of p come under the heading of Artin-Schreier theory. The reader may consult [5; Chapter 3.].

1. E. Artin, *Galois Theory*, Notre Dame, Indiana, 1955.
2. E. Artin, *Algebraic Numbers and Algebraic Functions*, New York University, New York, 1951.
3. M. Auslander and O. Goldman, The Brauer group of a commutative ring, *Transactions of the American Mathematical Society*, **11** (1960), 367–409.
4. D. Hilbert, *Gesammelte Abhandlungen*, Vol. 1, Springer, Berlin, 1932.
5. N. Jacobson, *Lectures in Abstract Algebra*, Vol. 3, Van Nostrand, Princeton, N.J., 1964.
6. S. Lang, *Diophantine Geometry*, Interscience, New York, 1962.
7. O. F. G. Schilling, *The Theory of Valuations*, American Mathematical Society, New York, 1950.
8. J. P. Serre, *Applications algèbriques de la cohomologie des groupes*, Seminaire Henri Cartan, Vol. 3, Ecole Normale Supericure, Paris, 1950–1951.
9. J. P. Serre, *Corps locaux*, Hermann, Paris, 1962.
10. B. L. van der Waerden, *Modern Algebra*, Vol. 1, 2nd ed., Ungar, New York, 1949.
11. P. Wolf, *Algebraische Theorie der Galoisschen Algebren*, Deutscher Verlag der Wissenshaften, Berlin, 1956.
12. O. Zariski and P. Samuel, *Commutative Algebras*, Vol. 1, Van Nostrand, Princeton, 1960.

CHAPTER IX Real and Complex Numbers

We now give a proof of the "fundamental theorem of algebra," which asserts that the "complex number field" is algebraically closed. We already know that algebraically closed fields exist. What is of interest at this point is that the complex number field is "explicitly" constructed from **Q** in a particular way.

The usual proofs of the "fundamental theorem of algebra" involve techniques outside the realm of algebra. We present a proof that is almost completely algebraic in nature. However, it is also necessary to use the "intermediate value theorem" from elementary analysis. In a sense this is unavoidable, for the particular construction of the real numbers depends on a process of taking "limits" and we must obtain some algebraic consequences of this "limiting" procedure.

» IX · 1 CONSTRUCTION OF REAL AND COMPLEX NUMBERS

There are many procedures available for constructing real numbers. The one we chose works in several other situations. In fact, it leads to the construction of some interesting fields that are useful in the study of number theory. Moreover, after we have constructed the real numbers the procedure may then be repeated to construct fields by using the real numbers in place of **Q**.

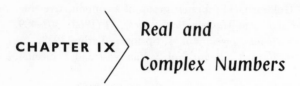

DEFINITION 1 · Let k be a field. The set of all maps from $\mathbf{P}$ to k is denoted by $k^{\mathbf{P}}$. Each such map is called a ***sequence*** in k. Since a map

is uniquely determined by its set of values, we denote a sequence in k by $[a_i]$, where $a_i \in k$ and $i \in \mathbf{P}$. By the componentwise addition and multiplication, and by the identification of $a \in k$ with the constant sequence $[a] \in k^{\mathbf{P}}$, we see that $k^{\mathbf{P}}$ is a commutative k-algebra.

DEFINITION 2 · Let k be a field. A map $| \quad | : k \to \mathbf{Q}$ is called a ***Q-absolute value*** if and only if the following hold:

(a) $| a | \geqslant 0 \; \forall \, a \in k$; $| a | = 0$ if and only if $a = 0$.

(b) $| ab | = | a | \cdot | b | \; \forall \, a, b \in k$.

(c) $| a + b | \leqslant | a | + | b |$ (triangle inequality).

The field k together with $| \quad |$ is then called a **Q**-valued field.

Exercise 1 · Let R be an integral domain and let $| \quad | : R \to \mathbf{Q}$ be a map satisfying (a), (b), and (c) of Definition 2. Show that $| \quad |$ admits a unique extension to the field of fractions k of R such that k together with this extension becomes a **Q**-valued field.

Exercise 2 · Let k be any field and define $| a | = 1 \; \forall \, a \in k^{\star}$ and $| 0 | = 0$. Show that $k, | \quad |$ is a **Q**-valued field. This map is called the ***trivial Q-absolute value*** on k.

Exercise 3 · Let $| \quad |$ be a **Q**-absolute value on k. Let $a \in k$ such that $a^n = 1$ for some $n \in \mathbf{P}^+$. Show that $| a | = 1$. Thus show that finite fields admit only the trivial **Q**-absolute value.

Exercise 4 · Show that the following are **Q**-absolute values on the field **Q**:

(a) $| a |_\infty = a$ when $a \geqslant 0$ and $| a |_\infty = -a$ when $a < 0$.

(b) Let $p \in \mathbf{P}^+$ be a prime. If $a \in \mathbf{Z}$, then let $\operatorname{ord}_p(a) = \max\{n \in \mathbf{P} \mid p^n$ divides a in $\mathbf{Z}\}$ with the agreement that $\operatorname{ord}_p(0) = \infty$. Define $| a |_p$ to be $p^{-\operatorname{ord}_p(a)}$, where $p^{-\infty} = 0$; $| \quad |_p$ is then extended to **Q** according to Exercise 1.

We may generalize Exercise 4 (b) to the following,

Exercise 5 · Let k be field of fractions of the integral domain R. Let p be a prime in R. Let $e \in \mathbf{Q}$ such that $0 < e < 1$. If $a \in R$, then let $\operatorname{ord}_p(a) = \max\{n \in \mathbf{P} \mid a \in Rp^n\}$ with the agreements that $\operatorname{ord}_p(0) = \infty$, $Rp^0 = R$. Show that $| a |_p = e^{\operatorname{ord}_p(a)}$ is a **Q**-absolute value on R. Thus $k, | \quad |_p$ is a **Q**-valued field. Show that $| \quad |_0$ is the trivial **Q**-absolute value. Show that the procedure fails when p is not a prime in R; in particular, (b) of Definition 2 fails.

Exercise 6 · Let X be an indeterminate over the field k. Let $n > 1$, $n \in \mathbf{Q}$. Define $|\ \ | : k[X] \to \mathbf{Q}$ by $|f(X)| = n^{\deg f}$, where $n^{-\infty} = 0$. Show that $|\ \ |$ is a $\mathbf{Q}$-absolute value on $k[X]$.

DEFINITION 3 · Let $k, |\ \ |$ be a $\mathbf{Q}$-valued field and $[a_i] \in \mathbf{Q}^{\mathbf{P}}$. Then $[a_i]$ is called a ***Cauchy sequence*** in k if and only if

(*) For each $n \in \mathbf{P}^+$ there exists $M(n) \in \mathbf{P}$ such that $|a_i - a_j| < 1/n$ whenever $i, j > M(n)$;

$[a_i]$ is called a ***null sequence*** in k if and only if

(**) For each $n \in \mathbf{P}^+$ there exists $M(n) \in \mathbf{P}$ such that $|a_i| < 1/n$ whenever $i > M(n)$.

The set of Cauchy sequences respectively, null sequences in $k, |\ \ |$, is denoted by $C(k)$, respectively, $N(k)$.

Exercise 7 · Let $k, |\ \ |$, be a $\mathbf{Q}$-valued field; $[a_i] \in k^{\mathbf{P}}$ is said to be ***eventually constant*** if and only if there exists $M \in \mathbf{P}$ such that $a_i = a \in k\ \forall\, i > M$. Show that an eventually constant sequence is in $C(k)$ and an eventually zero sequence lies in $N(k)$.

Exercise 8 · Let $k, |\ \ |$, be a $\mathbf{Q}$-valued field satisfying

(c*) $|a + b| \leqslant \max(|a|, |b|)\ \forall\, a, b \in k$ (strong triangle inequality).

Show that the following hold:

(a) If $|a| < |b|$, then $|a + b| = |b|$.

(b) $[a_i] \in C(k)$ if and only if $[|a_{i+1} - a_i|]$ is a null sequence in $\mathbf{Q}, |\ \ |_\infty$, where $|\ \ |_\infty$ is defined according to Exercise 4.

(c) The $\mathbf{Q}$-absolute values of Exercises 4(b), 5, and 6 all satisfy the strong triangle inequality.

(d) In Exercises 5 and 6 the sets $C(k)$ and $N(k)$ are independent of the choices of e and n, respectively. *Hint*. Use (b).

LEMMA 1 · Let $k, |\ \ |$, be a $\mathbf{Q}$-valued field.

(a) If $[a_i] \in C(k)$, then there exists $B \in \mathbf{P}^+$ such that $0 \leqslant |a_i| \leqslant B\ \forall\, i \in \mathbf{P}$.

(b) $C(k)$ is a k-subalgebra of $k^{\mathbf{P}}$.

Proof · (a) Let $M(1) \in \mathbf{P}$ such that $| a_i - a_j | < 1$ whenever $i, j > M(1)$. Since $| a_i | \in \mathbf{Q}$, we can find $B \in \mathbf{P}^+$ such that $B > \max(| a_0 |, \ldots, | a_{M(1)+1} |) + 1$. If $i > M(1)$, we have $| a_i | \leqslant | a_i - a_{M(1)+1} | + | a_{M(1)+1} | \leqslant 1 + | a_{M(1)+1} | < B$. Hence (a) holds.

(b) From the definition it is easy to see that $C(k)$ is closed under addition. By use of (a) it is easy to see that $C(k)$ is closed under multiplication. Since constant sequences lie in $C(k)$, we see that (b) follows. We leave further details to the interested reader. «

THEOREM 1 · Let $k, |\ \ |$, be a $\mathbf{Q}$-valued field. Then $\tilde{k} = C(k)/N(k)$ is an extension field of k under the natural identification of elements of k with the cosets determined by the constant sequences.

Proof · It follows from Lemma 1(a) that $N(k)$ is an ideal of $C(k)$. Since the constant 1 sequence is in $C(k) - N(k)$, we know that $\tilde{k}$ is not the zero k-algebra. Let $[a_i] \in C(k) - N(k)$. We assert that

(*) There exists $T, t \in \mathbf{P}^+$ such that $| a_i | > 1/t \ \forall\, i > T$.

Suppose that (*) were false; then, for any $n \in \mathbf{P}^+$ and any $m \in \mathbf{P}^+$ there exists $s(n, m) \in \mathbf{P}$, $s(n, m) > m$, such that $| a_{s(n,m)}| < 1/n$. Let $M(2n) \in \mathbf{P}$ such that $| a_i - a_j | < 1/(2n) \ \forall\, i, j > M(2n)$. Thus, if $i > M(2n)$, then $| a_i | \leqslant | a_i - a_{s(2n,M(2n))}| + | a_{s(2n,M(2n))}| \leqslant 1/(2n) + 1/(2n) = 1/n$. Hence $[a_i] \in N(k)$, a contradiction.

We now define $[b_i] \in k^{\mathbf{P}}$ so that $b_i = 0$ for $i \leqslant T$ and $b_i = a_i^{-1}$ for $i > T$. We assert that $[b_i] \in C(k)$. To see this, we let $n \in \mathbf{P}^+$ and select $M(n) \in \mathbf{P}^+$ such that $| a_i - a_j | < 1/n \ \forall\, i, j > M(n)$. Thus, when $i, j > \max(M(t^2 n), T)$, then $| b_i - b_j | = | a_i^{-1} a_j^{-1} | \cdot | a_i - a_j | < t^2/(t^2 n) = 1/n$. Hence $[b_i] \in C(k)$, as asserted. We note that the last calculation depends on (b) of Definition 2.

By using Exercise 7 it is clear that $([a_i] + N(k))([b_i] + N(k)) = [1] + N(k)$. Thus $\tilde{k}$ is a field. Since $\tilde{k}$ is a k-algebra under the natural identification mentioned, we see that $\tilde{k}$ is an extension field of k. «

We now examine the special case of the $\mathbf{Q}$-valued field $\mathbf{Q}, |\ \ |_\infty$.

LEMMA 2 · Let $|\ \ |$ be the $\mathbf{Q}$-absolute value $|\ \ |_\infty$ on $\mathbf{Q}$ defined in Exercise 4(a). Let $[a_i] \in C(\mathbf{Q}) - N(\mathbf{Q})$; then there exists $B, b \in \mathbf{P}^+$ such that exactly one of the following holds:

(a) $i > B$ implies that $a_i > 1/b$.

(b) $i > B$ implies that $a_i < -1/b$.

Proof · From (*) of the proof of Theorem 1 we can find $T, b \in \mathbf{P}^+$ such that $|a_i| > 1/b$ whenever $i > T$. Thus we may choose $B > T$ such that $|a_i - a_j| < 1/b$ whenever $i, j > B$. It follows that $|a_i| > 1/b$ whenever $i > B$. Thus, when $i > B$, we must have either $a_i > 1/b$ or $a_i < -1/b$. Suppose that there exist $i, j > B$ such that $a_i > 1/b$ and $a_j < -1/b$; then it would follow that $|a_i - a_j| = a_i - a_j > 2/b > 1/b$, a contradiction. Hence exactly one of (a) and (b) holds. «

DEFINITION 4 · Let $[a_i] \in C(\mathbf{Q}) \dot{-} N(\mathbf{Q})$. Then $[a_i]$ is called ***positive*** (respectively ***negative***) if and only if (a) [respectively (b)] of Lemma 2 holds, where $\mathbf{Q}$ is equipped with the $\mathbf{Q}$-absolute value $|\ \ |_\infty$.

We observe that B, b of Lemma 2 are not unique. Indeed, we may replace them by B' and b' with $B' > B$ and $b' > b$.

LEMMA 3 · Continuing with the notation of Lemma 2, we let $[a_i] \in C(\mathbf{Q})$ be positive (respectively, negative) and let $[b_i] \in N(\mathbf{Q})$. Then $[a_i] + [b_i]$ is positive (respectively, negative). Moreover, the following assertions hold:

(a) $[a_i]$ is positive if and only if $-[a_i] = [-a_i]$ is negative.

(b) $[a]$ is positive (respectively, negative) if and only if $a > 0$ (respectively, $a < 0$).

(c) The set of positive Cauchy sequences is closed under addition and multiplication.

Proof · All of these assertions are left to the reader as exercises.

DEFINITION 5 · Let $|\ \ |$ be the $\mathbf{Q}$-absolute value $|\ \ |_\infty$ on $\mathbf{Q}$. The field $\tilde{\mathbf{Q}}$ is called the field of ***real numbers*** and is denoted by $\mathbf{R}$ or by $\mathbf{Q}_\infty$. An element of $\mathbf{R}$ is called ***positive*** (respectively, ***negative***) if and only if it is the coset of a positive (respectively, a negative) Cauchy sequence of $C(\mathbf{Q})$. We write $r > 0$ (respectively, $r < 0$ to indicate that r is positive respectively, negative) in $\mathbf{R}$. We write $r > s$ to mean that $r - s > 0$.

THEOREM 2 · $\mathbf{R}$ is an extension field of $\mathbf{Q}$ which satisfies the following conditions:

(a) $<$ is a linear ordering on $\mathbf{R}$ extending the linear ordering $<$ on $\mathbf{Q}$.

(b) The set $\{r \in \mathbf{R} \mid r > 0\}$ is closed under addition and multiplication.

Theorem 2 is nothing more than a summary of Lemma 3.

DEFINITION 6 · Let $| \quad | : \mathbf{R} \to \mathbf{R}$ be the map given by $| r | = r$ for $r \geqslant 0$ and $| r | = -r$ for $r < 0$. This map is called the ***absolute value map*** on **R**.

LEMMA 4 · The field **R** of real numbers has the following properties:

(a) **Q** is dense in **R** with respect to $| \quad |$; that is, for each $r \in \mathbf{R}$ and each $n \in \mathbf{P}^+$, there exists $a(r, n) \in \mathbf{Q}$ with $| r - a(r, n)| < 1/n$.

(b) If $a, b \in \mathbf{R}$:

(1) $| a | \geqslant 0$; and $| a | = 0$ if and only if $a = 0$.
(2) $| ab | = | a | \cdot | b |$.
(3) $| a + b | \leqslant | a | + | b |$.

Proof · (a) Let $r = [a_i] + N(\mathbf{Q}) \in \mathbf{R}$. Let $M(n) \in \mathbf{P}$ be chosen such that $| a_i - a_j | < 1/n$ whenever $i, j > M(n)$. Finally, let $a(r, n)$ be the constant sequence determined by $a_{M(n)+1} \in \mathbf{Q}$. It is immediate that (a) holds.

(b) (1) holds from the definition; (2) follows easily from the definition and Theorem 2(b); and (3) follows from (a) and the triangle inequality of $| \quad |_\infty$ in **Q**. «

DEFINITION 7 · Using **R** in place of **Q** in Definition 2, we may define an ***R-valued field*** in a similar manner. Using Lemma 4(a) and (*), (**) of Definition 3, we may define a Cauchy sequence and a null sequence in any **R**-valued field. Let r_i, $i \in \mathbf{P}$, be a sequence of elements of an **R**-valued field k, $| \quad |$; then $s \in k$ is called a ***limit*** for $\{r_i \in k \mid i \in \mathbf{P}\}$ if and only if $[r_i - s]$ is a null sequence in k.

THEOREM 3 · In the field **R** of real numbers the following hold:

(a) (Archimedean property). Let $r, s \in \mathbf{R}$, and $r > 0$; then there exists $M \in \mathbf{P}^+$ such that $Mr > s$.

(b) (Completeness property). Every Cauchy sequence in $\mathbf{R}, | \quad |$ has a unique limit in **R**.

(c) (Least upper bound property). Let S be a nonempty subset of **R** such that there exists $B \in \mathbf{P}$ with $s \leqslant B \; \forall \, s \in S$. Then there exists a unique $b \in \mathbf{R}$ such that

(1) $s \leqslant b \; \forall \, s \in S$.
(2) If $t \in \mathbf{R}$ such that $s \leqslant t \; \forall \, s \in S$, then $b \leqslant t$.

Proof · (a) follows easily from Lemma 1(a) and Lemma 2(a).

(b) The uniqueness of the limit follows easily from the definition of a Cauchy sequence. Let t_i, $i \in \mathbf{P}$, be a Cauchy sequence in **R**. From Lemma 4(a) we select $a_i \in \mathbf{Q}$ such that $| t_i - a_i | < 1/2^i \; \forall \, i \in \mathbf{P}$. It is easy to see that $[a_i] \in C(\mathbf{Q})$. Let $r = [a_i] + N(\mathbf{Q}) \in \mathbf{R}$. It then follows easily that $[r - a_i]$ and $[r - t_i]$ are both null sequences in **R**. Hence r is the limit of t_i.

(c) The uniqueness follows from the fact that $<$ is a linear ordering in **R**. To show the existence we proceed as follows:

Let $T = \{r \in \mathbf{R} \mid s \leqslant r \; \forall \, s \in S\}$. By the hypothesis, $B \in T$; thus T is nonempty. Moreover, if $b \in T$ and $c \geqslant b$, then $c \in T$.

If $S \cap T \neq \emptyset$, it is clear that $S \cap T$ must consist of a single element $b \in \mathbf{R}$. This element must be the least element of T and the greatest element of S; hence it satisfies (1) and (2).

We now assume that $S \cap T = \emptyset$; hence $s < t \; \forall \, s \in S, \; t \in T$. Moreover, if $a \in \mathbf{R} - T$, then there exists $s(a) \in S$ such that $a \leqslant s(a)$.

Let $s_0 \in S$ and $t_0 \in T$. Suppose that $s_n \in S$ and $t_n \in T$ have been chosen such that $0 \leqslant t_n - s_n \leqslant (t_0 - s_0)/2^n$. Then we select $s_{n+1} \in S$ and $t_{n+1} \in T$ as follows:

If $(s_n + t_n)/2 \in T$, let $s_{n+1} = s_n$, $t_{n+1} = (s_n + t_n)/2$.

If $(s_n + t_n)/2 \notin T$, select $s_{n+1} \in S$ such that $(s_n + t_n)/2 \leqslant s_{n+1}$ and let $t_{n+1} = t_n$.

It is now clear that $0 < t_{n+1} - s_{n+1} \leqslant (t_0 - s_0)/2^{n+1}$ and that $s_0 \leqslant s_1 \leqslant \cdots \leqslant \cdots < \cdots \leqslant \cdots \leqslant t_1 \leqslant t_0$. From the binomial theorem we see that $2^n > n \; \forall \, n \in \mathbf{P}^+$. By using (b) we see that $[s_i]$ and $[t_i]$ are Cauchy sequences in **R** with the same limit b; (1) now follows from the fact that b is a limit of elements of T; (2) then follows from the fact that b is a limit of elements of S. «

DEFINITION 8 · Let $f : \mathbf{R} \to \mathbf{R}$ be a map; f is said to be ***continuous*** at $t \in \mathbf{R}$ if and only if the following holds:

(*) If $[x_i] \in \mathbf{R}^{\mathbf{P}}$ is a sequence with limit t in **R**, then $[f(x_i)]$ is a sequence with limit $f(t)$ in **R**; f is said to be ***continuous*** if and only if it is continuous at t $\forall\, t \in \mathbf{R}$. $C^0(\mathbf{R})$ denotes the set of all continuous maps from $\mathbf{R}$ to $\mathbf{R}$.

Exercise 9 · Show that the following hold for $\mathbf{R}$:

(a) Let $\mathbf{R}^{\mathbf{R}}$ be the set of all maps from $\mathbf{R}$ to $\mathbf{R}$. If $f, g \in \mathbf{R}^{\mathbf{R}}$, then let $(f \# g)(x) = f(x) \# g(x)$ $\forall\, x \in \mathbf{R}$, where $\#$ stands for $+$ or for $\cdot$. $C^0(\mathbf{R})$ is a commutative $\mathbf{R}$-subalgebra of the commutative $\mathbf{R}$-algebra $\mathbf{R}^{\mathbf{R}}$.

(b) Every polynomial function on $\mathbf{R}$ is in $C^0(\mathbf{R})$.

(c) If $f, g \in C^0(\mathbf{R})$, then $f \circ g \in C^0(\mathbf{R})$.

(d) Let $f \in C^0(\mathbf{R})$ and let $a \in \mathbf{R}$. Suppose that $f(a) > 0$, respectively, < 0. Then there exists $n \in \mathbf{P}^+$ such that $f(x) > 0$, respectively, < 0, whenever $|x - a| < 1/n$.

THEOREM 4 · (Weierstrass nullstellensatz, or intermediate value theorem) Let $f \in C^0(\mathbf{R})$. Suppose that $a, b \in \mathbf{R}$ such that

(a) $a < b$.

(b) $f(a) < 0 < f(b)$.

Then there exists $c \in \mathbf{R}$ such that $f(c) = 0$ and $a < c < b$.

Proof · Let $S = \{r \in \mathbf{R} \mid a \leqslant r \text{ and } f(t) < 0 \;\forall\, t \text{ with } a \leqslant t \leqslant r\}$. It is clear that $s \in S$ and that $s < b$ $\forall\, s \in S$. Hence from the least upper bound property we can find a least upper bound c for S. Using Exercise 9(d), we see that $f(c) = 0$. It is clear that $a \leqslant c \leqslant b$. Thus from the hypothesis (b) we see that $a < c < b$. «

THEOREM 5 · Let X be an indeterminate over $\mathbf{R}$. Let $f(X) \in \mathbf{R}[X]$. If either $\deg_X f(X)$ is odd or $f(X) = X^2 - r$, $r \geqslant 0$, then $f(X)$ has a zero in $\mathbf{R}$. If $f(X) = X^2 + 1$, then $f(X)$ has no zero in $\mathbf{R}$.

Proof · We may assume that $f(X)$ is monic. It is easy to see that when $\deg_X f(X)$ is odd, or when $f(X) = X^2 - r$, $r \geqslant 0$, $f(a) > 0$ for $a > 0$ and a large. Moreover, when $\deg_X f(X)$ is odd, $f(a) < 0$ for $a < 0$ and $|a|$ large; when $f(X) = X^2 - r$, $f(0) = -r \leqslant 0$. Thus from Theorem 4 $f(X)$ has a zero in $\mathbf{R}$. The last assertion follows from the fact that $f(a) = a^2 + 1 \geqslant 1$ $\forall\, a \in \mathbf{R}$. «

DEFINITION 9 · From Theorem 5 $\mathbf{C} = \mathbf{R}[X]/(X^2 + 1)$ is a field. $\mathbf{C}$ is called the field of ***complex numbers***. The coset determined by $a + bX$, $a, b \in \mathbf{R}$ is denoted by $a + bi$. Thus $i^2 = -1$.

Exercise 10 · Show that the following hold:

(a) $\mathbf{C}$ is Galois over $\mathbf{R}$ and $\mathcal{G}(\mathbf{C}/\mathbf{R})$ is cyclic of order 2.

(b) The map that sends $a + bi$, $a, b \in \mathbf{R}$ onto $a - bi$ is the nonidentity element of $\mathcal{G}(\mathbf{C}/\mathbf{R})$. This map is called the **complex conjugation**. If $c \in \mathbf{C}$, then $\bar{c}$ denotes the complex conjugate of c in $\mathbf{C}$.

(c) $c\bar{c} \geqslant 0 \ \forall c \in \mathbf{C}$; $c\bar{c} = 0$ if and only if $c = 0$.

(d) Let $| \ | : \mathbf{C} \to \mathbf{R}$ be defined such that $|c| \geqslant 0$ and $|c|^2 = c\bar{c} \ \forall c \in \mathbf{C}$. Then $\mathbf{C}, | \ |$ is an $\mathbf{R}$-valued field.

Exercise 11 · If X is an indeterminate over $\mathbf{C}$ and $c \in \mathbf{C}$, then $X^2 - c$ has a zero in $\mathbf{C}$. *Hint*. Let $c = a + bi$, $a, b \in \mathbf{R}$. It is necessary to find $x, y \in \mathbf{R}$ such that $(x + yi)^2 = a + bi$; that is, $x^2 - y^2 = a$ and $2xy = b$. By squaring these equations and adding we obtain $(x^2 + y^2)^2 = a^2 + b^2 \geqslant a^2$. From Theorem 4 find $r \in \mathbf{R}$ such that $r \geqslant |a|$, $r^2 = a^2 + b^2$. Now solve the equations $x^2 + y^2 = r$ and $x^2 - y^2 = a$ to get $x^2 = (r + a)/2$ and $y^2 = (r - a)/2$. Since $r \geqslant |a|$, x and y may be solved from these equations. For these values of x and y, we have $x^2y^2 = (r^2 - a^2)/4 = b^2/4$. Hence by selecting the positivity of x and y correctly we can also satisfy $2xy = b$.

» IX · 2 FUNDAMENTAL THEOREM OF ALGEBRA

THEOREM 1 (Fundamental theorem of algebra) · $\mathbf{C}$ is an algebraic closure of $\mathbf{R}$. $\mathcal{G}(\mathbf{C}/\mathbf{R})$ is a cyclic group of order 2 generated by the complex conjugation map.

Proof · From the definition of $\mathbf{C}$ we know that $\mathbf{C}$ is algebraic over $\mathbf{R}$; in fact, $\mathbf{C}$ is Galois over $\mathbf{R}$ with $\mathcal{G}(\mathbf{C}/\mathbf{R})$ equal to the cyclic group of order 2 generated by the complex conjugation map. We must show that $\mathbf{C}$ is algebraically closed.

Let $b \in \bar{\mathbf{C}}$, where $\bar{\mathbf{C}}$ is an algebraic closure of $\mathbf{C}$. Let K be the root field of $(X^2 + 1) \cdot \operatorname{Irr}(X, b, \mathbf{R})$ in $\bar{\mathbf{C}}$ over $\mathbf{R}$. Thus $\mathbf{C} \subset K$, and K is normal of finite degree over $\mathbf{R}$. Since $\mathbf{R}$ has characteristic 0, we know that K is Galois over $\mathbf{R}$. It follows that $\mathcal{G}(K/\mathbf{R})$ is a finite group of order $[K : \mathbf{R}]$.

Let T be a 2-Sylow subgroup of $\mathcal{G}(K/\mathbf{R})$ and assume that L is the fixed field of T in K. It follows that $[L : \mathbf{R}] = |\mathcal{G}(K/\mathbf{R}) : T|$ is odd. If $a \in L$, then $\deg_X \operatorname{Irr}(X, a, \mathbf{R}) = [\mathbf{R}(a) : \mathbf{R}]$ is a divisor of $[L : \mathbf{R}]$. From theorem 5 we conclude that $\operatorname{Irr}(X, a, \mathbf{R})$ has a zero in $\mathbf{R}$. Thus $\operatorname{Irr}(X, a, \mathbf{R})$ must have degree 1 and $a \in \mathbf{R}$. This shows that $L = \mathbf{R}$ and that $\mathcal{G}(K/\mathbf{R}) = T$ is a 2-group.

Let $H = \mathcal{G}(K/\mathbf{C})$. From the preceding paragraph we know that H is also a 2-group. Suppose that $H \neq 1$. From Exercise III.3.8 we know that H has at least one normal subgroup N of index 2. Let L be the fixed field of N in K. From Galois' theorem we know that $L \supset \mathbf{C}$ and $[L : \mathbf{C}] = |H : N| = 2$. If $a \in L - \mathbf{C}$, then $L = \mathbf{C}(a)$ and $\deg_X \operatorname{Irr}(X, a, \mathbf{C}) = 2$. This contradicts Exercise 11. Thus $H = 1$ and $K = \mathbf{C}$.

Since $b \in \bar{\mathbf{C}}$ is an arbitrary element, we see $\mathbf{C} = \bar{\mathbf{C}}$. «

COROLLARY · Every monic, irreducible polynomial in $\mathbf{R}[X]$ has degree at most 2; $X^2 + bX + c \in \mathbf{R}[X]$ is irreducible if and only if $b^2 - 4c < 0$.

Proof · This is left as an exercise for the reader.

Excursion XI

In the form presented the fundamental theorem of algebra may be generalized.

DEFINITION 1 · A field k is called an ***ordered field*** under a partial ordering $<$ if and only if the following hold:

(a) $<$ is a linear ordering; that is, exactly one of the relations, $a < b$, $a = b$, or $b < a$ holds for any pair of elements $a, b \in k$.

(b) $a < b$ if and only if $0 < b - a$.

(c) The set $\{a \in k \mid 0 < a\}$ is closed under addition and multiplication. It is called the set of positive elements.

Exercise 1 · Let k, $<$ be an ordered field; then the following hold:

(a) $\chi(k) = 0$.

(b) If $a \in k^\star$, then $0 < a^2$. Hence any finite sum of squares of nonzero elements is positive. In particular, -1 is not a sum of squares.

Exercise 2 · Show that $\mathbf{R}$, $<$ is an ordered field. Furthermore, show that $\mathbf{R}$ can be an ordered field in exactly one way.

Exercise 3 · Show that $k = \mathbf{Q}[X]/(X^2 + r)$, $r > 0$, can be ordered in (exactly) two different ways. *Hint*. Consider monomorphisms of k into $\mathbf{C}$ and show that the images always lie in $\mathbf{R}$.

The last statement of Exercise 1(b) may be used as the definition of a "formally real field." A field is said to be ***real closed*** if and only if it is formally real and no proper algebraic extension of it is formally real; for example, $\mathbf{R}$ is real closed. Indeed, Theorem 1.5 is a characterization of a real closed field. The fundamental theorem of algebra then holds with any real closed field k playing the role of $\mathbf{R}$ and with $k[X]/(X^2 + 1)$ playing the role of $\mathbf{C}$. Finally, by use of the Galois theory it is possible to prove the following amazing result.

THEOREM · Let K be an algebraically closed field. Suppose that k is a subfield of K such that $[K : k]$ is finite and distinct from 1. Then k is a real closed field and $K = k[i]$, where $\text{Irr}(X, i, k) = X^2 + 1$.

The interested reader may consult [1].

Excursion XII

We now present a sequence of exercises to indicate some of the properties of $\tilde{k}$ for an $\mathbf{R}$-valued field k.

Exercise 1 · Let $k\,|\ \ |$ be an $\mathbf{R}$-valued field such that the strong triangle inequality holds,

(c*) $|a + b| \leqslant \max(|a|, |b|)$.

Then the following hold:

(a) The set $\mathcal{O} = \{a \in k \mid |a| \leqslant 1\}$ is an integral domain.

(b) The set $\mathcal{I} = \{a \in k \mid |a| < 1\}$ is the unique maximal ideal of $\mathcal{O}$.

(c) k is the quotient field of $\mathcal{O}$ and $U(\mathcal{O}) = \mathcal{O} - \mathcal{I}$. $\mathcal{O}$ is called the ***ring of*** $|\ \ |$***-integers*** and $\mathcal{F} = \mathcal{O}/\mathcal{I}$ is called the ***residue class field*** of $k, |\ \ |$.

(d) If $[a_i]$ is a Cauchy sequence of $k, |\ \ |$, then there exists $N \in \mathbf{P}$ such that $|a_i| = |a_j|\ \forall\, i, j \geqslant N$.

(e) $\{|a| \mid a \in k^\star\}$ is a subgroup of $\mathbf{R}^\star, \cdot$. This group is called the ***value group*** of k.

Exercise 2 · Let $k, | \ |$ be an **R**-valued field. Show that $| \ |$ may be extended uniquely to $\tilde{k} = C(k)/N(k)$ such that the following hold:

(a) $\tilde{k}$ is an **R**-valued field under the extended $| \ |$.

(b) k is dense in $\tilde{k}$ in the sense that for each $r \in \tilde{k}$ and each $n \in \mathbf{P}^+$ there exists $a(r, n) \in k$ such that $|r - a(r, n)| < 1/n$.

(c) $\tilde{k}$ is complete with respect to $| \ |$ in the sense that every Cauchy sequence in $\tilde{k}, | \ |$ has a limit in $\tilde{k}$.

Hint. In order to define $| \ |$ on $\tilde{k}$, it is necessary to use Theorem 3 (b); namely, if $[a_i]$ is a Cauchy sequence in k, then $[| a_i |]$ is a Cauchy sequence in **R**. This may be verified by using $|\,| a | - | b |\,| \leqslant | a - b | \ \forall\, a, b \in k$. The quantity $|[a_i] + N(k)|$ is then defined as the limit of $[| a_i |]$ in **R**.

Exercise 3 · Let $k, | \ |$ be an **R**-valued field such that the strong triangle inequality holds. Show that the following hold:

(a) $\tilde{k}, | \ |$ satisfies the strong triangle inequality.

(b) $\mathcal{O}$ is dense in the ring of integers in $\tilde{k}$; the latter is denoted by $\tilde{\mathcal{O}}$. Similarly, $\mathfrak{I}$ is dense in the maximal ideal of $\tilde{\mathcal{O}}$; the latter is denoted by $\tilde{\mathfrak{I}}$.

(c) $\mathfrak{I} = \mathcal{O} \cap \tilde{\mathfrak{I}}$ and $\tilde{\mathcal{O}}/\tilde{\mathfrak{I}}$ is naturally isomorphic to $\mathcal{F} = \mathcal{O}/\mathfrak{I}$.

(d) The value group of $\tilde{k}$ coincides with the value group of k.

DEFINITION 1 · Let $k, | \ |$ be an **R**-valued field. The field $\tilde{k}$ is called the ***completion of k*** with respect to $| \ |$. If $k = \mathbf{Q}$ and $| \ | = | \ |_p$ of Exercise 1.5, where $p = \infty$ or p is a prime in $\mathbf{P}^+$, then $\tilde{k}$ is denoted by $\tilde{\mathbf{Q}}_p$ or simply $\mathbf{Q}_p$. These are called the ***field of real numbers*** and the ***field of rational p-adic numbers***. In general, if k is the field of fractions of a UFD R and $p \in R$ is a nonzero prime, then $\tilde{k}, | \ |_p$ as defined in Exercise 1.6, is called the ***Rp-completion*** of k.

As the reader can convince himself rather easily, the relevant objects in an **R**-valued field $k, | \ |$, which arise from an UFD and a nonzero prime in the UFD, are the ring $\mathcal{O}$ and its unique maximal ideal $p\mathcal{O} = \mathfrak{I}$. These objects then lead to the concept of a ***rank one discrete valuation ring***. The interested reader may consult [6] for further details.

Exercise 4 · Let k be a finite field with q elements. Let $p \in \mathbf{P}^+$ be a prime. Let $k(p, n)$ be the unique extension of k of degree p^n over k in a fixed algebraic closure $\bar{k}$ of k. Thus $k(p, n) \subset k(p, n + 1)$. Let $k(p, \infty) = \bigcup_{n \in \mathbf{P}} k(p, n)$.

Let $\sigma \in \mathcal{G}(\bar{k}/k)$ be the map that sends $a \in \bar{k}$ onto $a^q \; \forall \, a \in \bar{k}$. Let $\tilde{\mathbf{Z}}_p$ be the $| \;\; |_p$ — integers in $\tilde{\mathbf{Z}}_p$. If $s \in \tilde{\mathbf{Z}}_p$ and $a \in k(p, n)$, take $m \in \mathbf{Z}$ such that $| s - m |_p < 1/p^n$. Set $\sigma^s(a) = a^{q^m}$. Show that the following hold:

(a) $\sigma^s(a)$ is well-defined, independent of the choice of m in $\mathbf{Z}$.

(b) The map that sends $s \in \tilde{\mathbf{Z}}_p$ onto σ^s is a monomorphism of $\tilde{\mathbf{Z}}_p , +$ into $\mathcal{G}(k(p, \infty)/k)$. Indeed, it is known that this is a group isomorphism.

(c) $\tilde{\mathbf{Z}}_p , +$ is not an infinite cyclic group. Hence $\mathcal{G}(\bar{k}/k)$ is not generated by σ. Nevertheless, k is the fixed field of σ on $\bar{k}$.

In actual fact $\mathcal{G}(\bar{k}/k)$ is isomorphic to the direct product of the groups $\tilde{\mathbf{Z}}_p$, where p ranges over the primes of $\mathbf{P}^+$.

Exercise 5 · Let p be a prime in $\mathbf{P}^+$. Let $\mathbf{Q}(p, n)$ be the root field of $X^{p^n} - 1$ over $\mathbf{Q}$ in $\mathbf{C}$. Let $\mathbf{Q}(p, \infty) = \bigcup_{n \in \mathbf{P}} \mathbf{Q}(p, n)$. Let $\zeta(p, n)$ be a generator of the cyclic group of p^n-th roots of 1 in $\mathbf{Q}(p, \infty)$. Thus $\mathbf{Q}(p, n) = \mathbf{Q}[\zeta(p, n)]$. Let $u \in U(\tilde{\mathbf{Z}}_p)$. For each $n \in \mathbf{P}$ select $m \in \mathbf{Z}$ such that $| m - u |_p < 1/p^n$. Set $u(\zeta(p, n)) = \zeta(p, n)^m$. Show that the following hold:

(a) $u(\zeta(p, n))$ is well-defined, independent of the choice of m.

(b) $f_{p.n}(X) = \prod_i (X - \zeta(p, n)^i)$ is irreducible in $\mathbf{Q}[X]$, where $0 \leqslant i < p^n$ and $p \nmid i$.

(c) The definition of u on each $\zeta(p, n)$ may be extended to an element of $\mathcal{G}(\mathbf{Q}(p, \infty)/\mathbf{Q})$. This is a monomorphism of $U(\tilde{\mathbf{Z}}_p)$ into $\mathcal{G}(\mathbf{Q}(p, \infty)/\mathbf{Q})$. This map is again known to be an isomorphism of groups.

In both Exercises 4 and 5, the extensions are Galois (see Excursion IX). Moreover, the Galois groups are abelian.

The fields $\tilde{\mathbf{Q}}_p$ are important in the study of algebraic number theory. Historically, $\tilde{\mathbf{Q}}_\infty$, the real numbers came first and had been given a distinguished role, especially in analysis. More recently, however, the p-adic numbers have played an increasingly important role in number theory and other fields of mathematics.

In the following sequence of exercises, we will show that the equation $X^3(X^2 - 4) - 2 = 0$ over $\mathbf{Q}$ is not solvable by radicals.

Exercise 6 · Let H be a subgroup of $\mathbf{S}_p$, where p is a prime in $\mathbf{P}^+$. Show that $H = \mathbf{S}_p$ if and only if H contains a p-cycle ρ and a 2-cycle σ. *Hint.* Let $\sigma = (12)$. Using the fact that p is a prime, verify that a suitable power of ρ may be assumed to be of the form $(12 \ldots p)$. Thus, $\rho^{-i}\sigma\rho^i = (i + 1, i + 2) \in H$, $1 \leqslant i \leqslant p - 2$. Conjugating σ by (23), then by (34), etc, we see that $(1i) \in H$ for $i = 2,\ldots, p$. Since $(ij) = (1i)(1j)(1i)$ for $1 < i < j$, we see that H contains all 2-cycles. Thus, $H = \mathbf{S}_p$.

Exercise 7 · Show that $X^3(X^2 - 4) - 2$ is irreducible in $\mathbf{Q}[X]$ and has exactly three real zeroes in $\mathbf{R}$. *Hint.* $X^3(X^2 - 4) - 2$ has the form $X^5 - 4X^3 - 2$. Thus Eisenstein's criterion is applicable. Let $f = X^3(X^2 - 4) - 2$. Consider f as a continuous function on $\mathbf{R}$. Use the fact that $D_X f = X^2(5X^2 - 12)$ to show that f has exactly three distinct zeros in $\mathbf{R}$.

Exercise 8 · Let K be the root field of $X^3(X^2 - 4) - 2$ over $\mathbf{Q}$ in $\mathbf{C}$. Show that $\mathcal{G}(K/\mathbf{Q})$ is $\mathbf{S}_5$. Thus $X^3(X^2 - 4) - 2$ is not solvable by radicals over $\mathbf{Q}$.

Hint. Since the given polynomial is irreducible of degree 5 over $\mathbf{Q}$. $\mathcal{G}(K/\mathbf{Q})$ must be a subgroup of $\mathbf{S}_5$ which is transitive on the zeros of the given polynomial. Thus $\mathcal{G}(K/\mathbf{Q})$ has an order which is divisible by 5. Since 5 is a prime, we know that $\mathcal{G}(K/\mathbf{Q})$ must contain an element of order 5. Such an element in $\mathbf{S}_5$ must be a 5-cycle. Next, we consider the complex conjugation map in $\mathcal{G}(\mathbf{C}/\mathbf{R})$. This map is the identity map on $\mathbf{Q}$. Thus it must induce a $\mathbf{Q}$-automorphism of the algebraic closure $\bar{\mathbf{Q}}$ of $\mathbf{Q}$ in $\mathbf{C}$. Since K is normal over $\mathbf{Q}$, the complex conjugation map must induce an element σ of $\mathcal{G}(K/\mathbf{Q})$. Since the complex conjugation map is the identity map on $\mathbf{R}$, we see that σ must leave the three zeros of $X^3(X^2 - 4) - 2$ in $\mathbf{R}$ fixed; moreover, σ must interchange the remaining zeros of $X^3(X^2 - 4) - 2$ in $\mathbf{C} - \mathbf{R}$. It follows that σ is a 2-cycle in $\mathcal{G}(K/\mathbf{Q})$. Exercise 6 now implies that $\mathcal{G}(K/\mathbf{Q}) = \mathbf{S}_5$. The reader should observe that the algebraic closure of $\mathbf{Q}$ in $\mathbf{C}$ is $\mathbf{Q}$-isomorphic to the algebraic closure of $\mathbf{Q}$. In particular, the root field K may be assumed to be a subfield of $\mathbf{C}$.

References

Our development of the real and complex numbers follows that of Artin and Schreier. The reader may consult [1] and [5] for details. The results in Excursion XII are useful in algebraic number theory. The reader may consult [2]. For a more detailed study of the "p-adic" fields $\tilde{\mathbf{Q}}_p$, the reader may consult [4]. The method indicated in Exercises 6, 7, and 8 for the construction of an irreducible polynomial of degree p whose root field has Galois group $\mathbf{S}_p$ over $\mathbf{Q}$ is due to R. Brauer. A more detailed discussion may be found in [3].

1. E. Artin, *The Collected Papers of Emil Artin*, Addison-Wesley, Reading, Mass., 1965.
2. E. Artin, *Theory of Algebraic Numbers*, Gottingen, Germany, 1959.
3. N. Jacobson, *Lectures on Abstract Algebra*, Vol. III, Van Nostrand, Princeton, 1964.
4. J. P. Serre, *Corps locaux*, Hermann, Paris, 1962.
5. B. L. van der Waerden, *Modern Algebra*, Vol. 1, 2nd ed., Ungar, New York, 1949.

INDEX

SYMBOLS AND NOTATIONS

$\varnothing$	the empty set,	1
$\{x \mid P\}$	the set of all x for which P holds,	1
$x \in A$	x is a member of the set A,	1
$x \notin A$	x is not a member of the set A,	1
$A \subset B$, $B \supset A$	the set A is a subset of the set B,	1
$A = B$	the sets A and B coincide,	1
$A - B$	$\{x \mid x \in A \text{ and } x \notin B\}$,	1
$A \cup B$, $\bigcup_{i \in I} A_i$	the union of the sets A, B; the union of the sets A_i,	2
$A \cap B$, $\bigcap_{i \in I} A_i$	the intersection of the sets A, B; the intersection of the sets A_i,	2
$A \times B$	the cartesian product of the sets A and B,	2
$\prod_{i \in I} A_i$	the cartesian product of the sets A_i,	8
$G \circ F$	the composition of the maps F and G,	4
$F : A \to B$	F is a map from the set A to the set B,	4
$\coprod_{i \in I} A_i$	disjoint union of the sets A_i (seldom used),	10
$\coprod_{i \in I} A_i$	direct sum of the modules A_i,	128
$\mathbf{P}$	the set of all natural numbers,	21
$\mathbf{Z}$	the set of all integers,	28
$\mathbf{Q}$	the set of all rational numbers,	38
$\mathbf{R}$	the set of all real numbers,	45, 324
$\mathbf{C}$	the set of all complex numbers,	327
$\mathbf{S}_n$	the symmetric group of degree n,	80
$\mathbf{A}_n$	the alternating group of degree n,	84
G/H	the set of all left cosets of the group G with respect to H,	66
$\mid G : H \mid$	the index of the subgroup H in the group G,	67
$N_G(S)$	the normalizer of the set S in the group G,	71
$C_G(S)$	the centralizer of the set S in the group G,	71
R^o	the opposite of the ring R,	103
δ_{ij}	Kronecker deltas,	135

$A \otimes_R B$	the tensor product of the R-modules A and B,	144
$GL(n, R)$, $GL_R(M)$	the general linear group,	157
$U(R)$	the units of the ring R,	160
$k[B]$	the subring generated by k and B,	240
$k(B)$	the subfield generated by k and B,	240
$\chi(k)$	the characteristic of a field k,	241
$\mathrm{Irr}(X, a, k)$	the irreducible polynomial of the element a over the field k,	242
$\mathcal{G}_k(K)$	the group of all k-automorphisms of the field K,	285
$\mathcal{G}(K/k)$	the Galois group of the Galois extension K of k,	287